D0894906

Reference Book of
Inorganic Chemistry

THE MACMILLAN COMPANY
NEW YORK · CHICAGO
DALLAS · ATLANTA · SAN FRANCISCO
LONDON · MANILA
BRETT-MACMILLAN LTD.
TORONTO

REFERENCE BOOK
of Inorganic Chemistry

BY WENDELL M. LATIMER

Professor of Chemistry in the University of California

AND JOEL H. HILDEBRAND

Professor of Chemistry in the University of California

THIRD EDITION · NEW YORK

The Macmillan Company

PREFACE TO THE THIRD EDITION

In preparing this third edition, we have kept constantly in mind our original objective, a single convenient volume to which the chemist may turn to find the facts or data relevant to the majority of problems which he may encounter. Increased emphasis has been placed upon thermodynamical data, such as oxidation potentials, equilibrium constants and free energies, since they may be used to express so concisely the tendency of a reaction to go, and the nature of the equilibrium state. Oxidation-reduction potential diagrams have now been given for almost every element.

Actinium and the heavier elements have been treated in a new chapter with the title, "The Actinide Elements," and considerable attention has been given to the chemistry of plutonium and the other new transuranium elements. The chapter on the atomic nucleus has been completely rewritten to include all the general types of nuclear reactions. A discussion of nuclear fission and various pile reactors has been added. At the end of this chapter, the table of nuclear properties has been extended to include all known isotopes.

New investigations have been noted in the general field of inorganic chemistry and additions have been made to most chapters, especially those dealing with boron, phosphorus, and silicon. Sections on the chemical industries have been brought up to date, and in many cases, greatly expanded.

The text has not been "written down" to the level of elementary students. A foreign language may be mastered either by starting with a primer or by hearing the language spoken and used in every day life. In the first year chemistry course at the University of California, both methods of teaching the language of chemistry are employed. We believe that, by the end of the year, the students can acquire the facility to read and understand the literature of inorganic chemistry, and that the ability to use the *Reference Book* will be of great value to them in their subsequent professional work.

W. M. L.

BERKELEY, CALIFORNIA
March, 1951

PREFACE TO THE FIRST EDITION

This book represents the fulfillment of a plan, long cherished, of providing a volume of descriptive chemistry to complete the series begun with "Principles of Chemistry" by Hildebrand, which adheres strictly to its title, and continued with the "Course in General Chemistry" by Bray and Latimer, which presents a laboratory course. The rather radical experiment in teaching general chemistry, begun in the University of California in 1912, has been somewhat hampered by the lack of a reference book on descriptive chemistry employing the language and the point of view adopted for our instructional scheme.

This "Reference Book of Inorganic Chemistry" has been written as a reference book rather than a text. The authors have sought to present essential chemical facts briefly, clearly, and in due relation to other facts and principles. The instructor using it will have to map out his own course, following whatever order of arrangement appeals to him. The numbering of paragraphs will make it possible for him to assign for study material selected from any desired portion of the book. We feel that many teachers will welcome the greater freedom thus afforded of developing their own pedagogical methods.

Chemical properties have been widely related to atomic structures and sizes. These ideas, although new, and subject to revision, are so illuminating that they appeal strongly to the imagination. Moreover, they are not difficult to grasp; many concepts traditionally introduced into freshman courses are far more elusive.

The formulas of many compounds have been given in terms of the Lewis theory of valence, not with the idea that these formulas represent the definite locations of the

vii

electrons, but rather to call attention to the importance of considering the total number of electrons or electron pairs in a molecule.

The extensive tabulation of "half reaction" potentials, equivalent to free energy values, will enable one to predict the direction and driving force of an immense number of reactions. Many of these potentials have been calculated for this book from reaction heats and entropy values, and have not heretofore been published.

We have treated industrial processes with emphasis upon their chemistry, relation to other industries, and economic magnitude, rather than upon their mechanical features. Illustrations of industrial processes, of the sort extensively used in some texts, have been left to the instructor to provide, as he can do so far more adequately, by the use of lantern slides and motion pictures. Many excellent films are now available at a nominal expense.

The book contains much more material than the average student, or even the average chemist, can assimilate. We believe, however, that students should be "exposed" to a far greater range of subject matter than is usually presented. We have found the appetite and assimilative capacity of the superior students to be almost unlimited, and we see no value in an intellectual diet list. For the average student, the presence of this extra material in the book does no more damage than the unordered articles listed on a restaurant menu.

We anticipate that this kind of a book will prove useful, not only to the freshman student, but also to the student who desires a reference book in advanced courses in chemistry and allied subjects; and further that teachers and industrial chemists will also find in it answers to many of their questions. To increase its usefulness, a large mass of data has been included in the form of tables, both in the text and in the various appendices.

In the endeavor to keep the size and cost of the book at

a low figure, it was decided to omit references to the original sources of material, although in many instances such references would be of historical and scientific value. Frequent use has been made of the more comprehensive treatises, especially: Gmelin-Kraut's Handbuch der anorganischen Chemie; Abegg and Auerbach Handbuch der anorganischen Chemie; A Text-Book of Inorganic Chemistry, Edited by Friend; A Comprehensive Treatise on Inorganic and Theoretical Chemistry by Mellor; Lexikon der anorganischen Verbindungen by Hoffman; Landolt-Börnstein Tabellen; and The International Critical Tables.

The authors are much indebted to their colleagues in the Department of Chemistry of the University of California, especially to Professors G. N. Lewis and W. C. Bray, not only for specific criticisms and suggestions, but for many of the general ideas upon which our interpretation of the facts of inorganic chemistry has been constructed.

WENDELL M. LATIMER
JOEL H. HILDEBRAND

BERKELEY, CALIFORNIA
December, 1928.

CONTENTS

Appendices

Reference Book of
Inorganic Chemistry

Chapter I

HYDROGEN

1. Structure of Hydrogen Atom.—The element, hydrogen, has three **isotopes,** their mass numbers being one, two, and three. The isotope of mass one is by far the most abundant; the hydrogen of ordinary water contains 0.0156 per cent of the isotope with mass two, and practically none of the isotope with mass three. The latter is formed in certain nuclear reactions but undergoes radioactive decomposition. The mass two isotope is called **deuterium** and the mass three isotope is called **tritium.** It is not customary to designate isotopes by special names, but in this case the percentage difference in the masses greatly exceeds that of any two isotopes of the other elements and there is a correspondingly greater divergence in their physical and chemical properties.

The hydrogen atom (mass one isotope) is composed of two corpuscles; one, the **proton,** is positively charged and the other, the **electron,** is negatively charged. The mass of the proton is about 1,850 times that of the electron but the electrical charges, though opposite in sign, are equal in magnitude.

The atom has a large number of energy states representing different configurations of the electron and proton. The values for the energy of the atom in these different states may be expressed as a close approximation by the very simple relation $E = \dfrac{-13.54Z^2}{N^2}$ volts per unit charge, where

1

Z is the charge on the proton (equal to unity) and N, called the **quantum number,** is any integer from 1 to ∞. The normal atom is in the first quantum state ($N = 1$) and the energy in volts required to move the electron to the 2, 3, 4, 5, $\cdots \infty$ quantum states is shown in Fig. 1. When $N = \infty$ the energy is zero. This corresponds to the complete separation of the electron and proton, and the total energy required per unit charge is given as 13.54 volts.

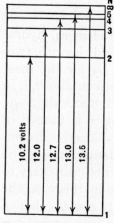

FIG. 1. Energy levels in the hydrogen atom.

When the electron moves from a higher quantum level to a lower, the energy difference is emitted in the form of light, whose frequency, ν, is related to the energy difference, ΔE, by the equation, $\Delta E = h\nu$, where h is a constant ("Planck constant"). Likewise the atom in a lower quantum state may absorb energy in the form of light of a given frequency and the electron thereby move to a quantum level of correspondingly higher energy. The spectral lines arising from electrons falling from outer levels to the first quantum level are far out in the ultraviolet, but transitions from outer levels to the second quantum state give rise to the Balmer series which is in the visible spectrum. The highest frequency in the hydrogen spectrum is, of course, that corresponding to the electron falling from the infinite quantum state.

Bohr has sought to account for these quantum states by picturing the electron as revolving about the proton in some one of a number of possible orbits, which are circles or ellipses. These orbits are defined by the restriction that the momentum of the system must always be some multiple, i.e. the quantum number, of a single fundamental quantity. The total quantum number was considered to be the sum of two other numbers, one giving the units of angular mo-

mentum and the other the units of radial momentum, that
is, momentum in the direction of the radius. These numbers
fix the size and shape of the orbits. Figure 2 represents these
orbits for the total quantum number, $N = 1$, 2, and 3, and
the angular momentum as
given by the subscripts. The
radius of the 1_1 orbit is
0.529×10^{-8} cm.

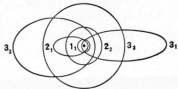

While the existence of discrete energy states rests upon

FIG. 2. Electron orbits of hydrogen as pictured by Bohr.

experimental facts, the Bohr
theory has had to be modified
so that the orbits no longer have their former clear-cut
meaning. The changes are due to the discovery that some
sort of wave motion is associated with a moving particle.
This has led to modifications in the equations of motion
to give probabilities rather than precise answers. The
orbits are now generally referred to as eigen functions, or
orbitals, from which the probability of finding the electron
in a given region may be determined. Figure 3 is a schematic
representation of the wave mechanic picture and may be
considered as a composite of the electron in many positions
to give an average electron density. The electrons are
designated as $s, p, d, f, g \cdots$ corresponding to 0, 1, 2, 3, 4 $\cdots$
units of angular momentum.

2. The same general quantum relations as outlined above
hold for the other elements, complicated, however, by the
facts: (1) that the positive center is no longer a simple unit
charge but a complex structure with a net positive charge
equal to the atomic number, and (2) that the number of
electrons is not one, but a number equal to the atomic number. It is the distribution of these electrons among the
various quantum states that determines the grouping of the
elements into the so-called "chemical families." The maximum number of electrons in any atom that can have the
same total quantum number N is $2N^2$, e.g. for $N = 1$, the

maximum number of electrons is 2; for $N = 2$, it is 8. Hence when the first quantum level is complete with the second element, helium, the three electrons of the third element, lithium, cannot all remain in the first level, but one of them is forced into the second. With each succeeding element of higher atomic number, the number of electrons in the second level increases until it is filled with eight electrons, i.e. in neon. Each alkali metal marks the beginning of a

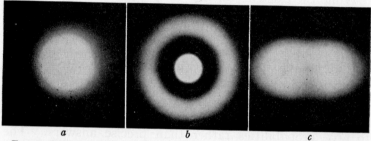

FIG. 3. Different states of the hydrogen atom (after H. E. White): a, the atom with a 1 s electron; b, 2 s electron; c, one of the states with a 2 p electron in a magnetic field.

new quantum group and each noble gas the completion of a group.

Each orbital (Par. 1) contains a maximum of two electrons and the total number of electrons for any one value of the total quantum number, N, and radial quantum number l is $2(2l + 1)$. Thus for the first shell there are two s electrons, for the second two s and six p, for the third, two s, six p, and ten d, and so on. A complete table of the distribution of the electrons in the various atoms is given in Appendix XVIII. The magnetic properties of the electron indicate that it has a quantized spin motion. However when an orbital contains two electrons, the resultant magnetic spin moment is zero, that is, the two spins are in opposite directions.

3. Occurrence of Hydrogen.—Only about one per cent by weight of the earth's crust (outer 10 miles) is hydrogen.

However, if the composition is expressed in terms of the number of atoms, it may be stated that about sixteen per cent of all the atoms on the earth's surface are hydrogen, being second in abundance to oxygen. The major portion of the earth's hydrogen is combined with oxygen in water. It also frequently occurs combined with sulfur, carbon, nitrogen, and chlorine, and less frequently with the other halogens and phosphorus. Hydrogen is a constituent of all acids, and of all animal and vegetable tissue. Only a trace of free hydrogen is found in the atmosphere, but larger quantities are sometimes found in volcanic and other natural gases. Hydrogen appears to constitute 30 per cent of the mass of the sun and spectral analysis of light from the stars indicates that hydrogen is by far the most abundant element in the universe (cf. Append. XIX).

4. Molecular Hydrogen.—Atomic hydrogen combines to form the molecule H_2. Representing the proton by **H,** and the electron by a dot, we may write **H:H** as the electronic formula of the molecule, indicating that the two electrons constitute a bond holding the protons together. Due to the spin of the protons, two forms of the molecule exist: para- with spin directions opposed and ortho- with the spins the same. At room temperature the gas is $\frac{1}{4}$ para- and $\frac{3}{4}$ ortho- in an equilibrium mixture. Equilibrium at the boiling point gives almost pure para- but the change from the high temperature mixture is slow. It is however catalyzed by charcoal and other surfaces. The boiling point of pure para-hydrogen is 20.25° K.

Hydrogen has the lowest molecular weight and hence the smallest density of any substance, and, with the exception of helium, the lowest melting point and the lowest boiling point. The gas is odorless, tasteless, and colorless. The most important physical constants are collected in Table I.

Hydrogen was first liquefied by Dewar (1898). The gas in expanding from high pressure to low pressure is

TABLE I

PHYSICAL CONSTANTS OF HYDROGEN

Melting point, ° C........	− 259.2	Density g./liter at 0° and	
° A........	13.9	760 mm...............	0.08985
Heat of fusion, cals. per		Density of liquid g./cc......	0.071
mole................	28		
		Solubility in water at 25°	
Boiling point, ° C........	− 252.7	vol. per 100 vol. of H_2O...	1.8
° A........	20.4		
		Heat of dissociation, $H_2 =$	
Heat of vaporization, cals.		2H cal. per mole........	103,730
per mole.............	218		
		Per cent H_2 dissociated at	
Critical temperature, ° C..	− 241	1 atm. total pressure	
° A..	32	At 2,500° A.............	1.3
		3,500° A.............	29.7
Critical pressure, atmos...	20		

heated at ordinary temperatures, but if cooled in liquid air (− 185° C.), the sign of this heat is reversed. Advantage is taken of this fact in the liquefaction process. (For further discussion of liquefaction process cf. III—6.) The metals of the nickel, palladium, platinum groups occlude or dissolve hydrogen to a remarkable degree. Under certain conditions one volume of palladium will take up almost 900 volumes of hydrogen at 20° and 1 atmosphere. (Cf. Palladium, XX—27.) Molecular hydrogen has a very high relative rate of diffusion since this property is inversely proportional to the square root of the density. Thus the densities of hydrogen and oxygen are in the ratio of 1/16 and hydrogen diffuses four times as fast as oxygen.

5. Reactions of Hydrogen.—Hydrogen combines directly with most of the lighter elements, accompanied in the case of the more electronegative elements with the evolution of large amounts of energy; e.g. a jet of hydrogen burns readily in an atmosphere of oxygen or chlorine, and its mixtures with these gases are highly explosive.

The electron formulas of the compounds with the elements from lithium to fluorine are as follows:

Element

  Li·   Be: ·B: :C: :N: :Ö: :F̈:

Compound

                  H   H   H

Li:H H:Be:H H:B̈:H H:C̈:H H:N̈:H H:Ö:H H:F̈:

                             H

From CH_4 to H_2O the four pairs of electrons have tetrahedral symmetry. Thus in H_2O the molecule is not linear as indicated in the electron formula given above, but the hydrogens are located approximately at corners of a tetrahedron. BH_3 exists only as the dimer, B_2H_6 (cf. VI—11).

The more negative the element, the more completely does it tend to acquire the electrons of hydrogen, thus leaving the hydrogen with a charge of + 1. The more positive elements, on the other hand, tend to lose their electrons to hydrogen, giving it a charge of − 1, since, as mentioned in Paragraph 2, there is room for two electrons in the first quantum state of the hydrogen atom. In this respect hydrogen resembles the halogen family, all members of which lack one electron of completing the noble gas structure.

Hydrogen in the − 1 state is known as hydride. The ion in water solutions is unstable with respect to the reaction

$$H^- + H_2O = H_2 + OH^-$$

For the hydride potential see Appendix II. The details of the reactions of hydrogen will be discussed under the various elements, although the general reaction of hydrogen to hydrogen ion is to be considered under the following topic.

6. Properties of the Hydrogen Ion.—Hydrogen ion is the substance present in all solutions of strong acids and its properties are the familiar properties common to all acids, such as sour taste, characteristic color changes with organic indicators, e.g. the change of blue litmus to red, the neutralization of bases, and the solution of base metals. A complete statement of the properties of hydrogen ion would include values for the degree of dissociation, volatility, and solubility of all of its compounds, since these quantities determine the extent to which hydrogen ion will unite with negative ions. For example, the statement that the concentrations of hydrogen ion and hydroxide ion in pure water are 10^{-7} moles per liter is equivalent to saying that the reaction, $H^+ + OH^- = H_2O$, takes place until the concentrations of the ions reach this value. Likewise the statement that the volatility of hydrogen chloride from its water solution is high at $100°$ C. is equivalent to saying that the reaction, $H^+ + Cl^- = HCl$ (gas), has a strong tendency to take place at this temperature.

7. Many of the most important reactions of hydrogen ion and hydrogen gas may be summarized in terms of the oxidation-reduction couple, $\frac{1}{2}H_2 = H^+ + e^-$. (The electron will be denoted by a dot in certain structural formulas, as in Paragraph **5,** but in writing ordinary equations, we will use the symbol e^-.) For example, zinc will displace or liberate hydrogen from acids because the reaction, $Zn = Zn^{++} + 2e^-$, gives a higher "pressure" (voltage) of electrons. The total reaction, $Zn + 2H^+ = Zn^{++} + H_2$, is the result of the transfer of the electrons from the zinc to the hydrogen ion. On the other hand, the reaction $Ag = Ag^+ + e^-$ has a lower voltage than hydrogen; and hydrogen reduces silver ion, $2Ag^+ + H_2 = 2Ag + 2H^+$, by the transfer of electrons from the hydrogen to the silver ion. Reference may be made to the table of oxidation-reduction potentials (Append. II) for the position of hydrogen in respect to a large number of oxidation-reduction couples. Mention should be made of the fact that the oxidation of metals by hydrogen ion is often a slow reaction, and that the speed depends greatly upon the nature of the surface upon which the gas deposits. Thus the action of acid upon zinc proceeds very slowly if the zinc is pure, and rapidly only when impurities are present. The power of nydrogen ion as an oxidizing agent depends, of course, upon its concentration. In normal alkaline solution, a stronger reducing agent is required to liberate hydrogen than in acid since the potential of the reaction, $\frac{1}{2}H_2 + OH^- = H_2O + e^-$, is 0.83 volt more positive than the potential of the acid couple.

Although the formula of hydrogen ion in water solution is written as H^+, the ion exerts such a strong attraction upon the water molecules that it might be written $H(H_2O)_n^+$. The energy of hydration of the hydrogen ion, approximately 250,000 cal., is larger than that of any other singly charged ion.

8. Preparation.—Although hydrogen is liberated by the action of the electropositive metals, such as sodium, potassium, and calcium upon water, these metals are too expensive for its practical preparation. Hydrogen is sometimes prepared by passing steam over finely divided iron heated to redness. $3Fe + 4H_2O = Fe_3O_4 + 4H_2$. The gas is conveniently prepared in the laboratory by the action of dilute sulfuric or hydrochloric acid upon zinc or aluminum. Hydrogen so prepared usually contains small quantities of volatile hydrogen compounds resulting from the presence of impurities in the metals. These may be removed by bubbling the gas through a permanganate solution. Water vapor is conveniently removed by contact with concentrated sulfuric acid.

There are four principal sources of commercial hydrogen: the reduction of water by carbon, the destructive distillation of coal, the cracking of methane, CH_4, and the electrolysis of aqueous solutions. The reduction of water by carbon involves the water gas reaction: $H_2O + C = CO + H_2$, and the further reaction, $H_2O + CO = H_2 + CO_2$ (cf. **XIII—6**). Coke-oven hydrogen is a by-product of the destructive distillation of coal and contains large quantities of methane, which may be removed by liquefaction. Electrolytic hydrogen is now usually prepared by the electrolysis of concentrated sodium hydroxide solutions with iron or nickel electrodes. Hydrogen is liberated at the cathode and oxygen at the anode. The gas is quite pure except for a small quantity of oxygen which is present by diffusion from the anode. This may be removed by passing the gas over a catalyst, e.g. finely divided nickel at 250° C., which accelerates the combinations of hydrogen and oxygen. Large quantities of hydrogen are also formed as a by-product in the manufacture of sodium hydroxide (cf. **IV—12**) by the electrolysis of salt brine.

9. Commercial Uses.—The oxy-hydrogen flame is used in cutting and welding metals. The temperature of the flame is approximately 2,500° C. A special burner is employed which prevents the explosion of the gases by mixing them just before they reach the orifice. The atomic hydrogen torch, recently developed, has many advantages in welding under reducing conditions. The atomic hydrogen is formed by blowing hydrogen through a very hot electric arc. The metal surface acts as a catalyst for the union of the atomic hydrogen and is heated to a high temperature, estimated between 4,000 and 5,000° C., by the heat liberated through the formation of the H_2 molecule.

Large quantities of hydrogen are consumed in the manufacture of synthetic ammonia by the direct union of the elements. The synthetic production of methanol, CH_3OH, and other liquid fuels by the reaction of hydrogen and carbon monoxide in the presence of catalysts promises to become of great industrial significance. Another important use is in the hydrogenation of many oils, such as cottonseed oil, to form solid fats.

Hydrogen is also employed as a lifting medium in balloons. Its efficiency depends upon the difference in weight of equal volumes of hydrogen and air. This is 1.2 grams per liter at 0° C. and 1 atmosphere.

10. Analytical.—Hydrogen is often determined by mixing with an excess of oxygen and passing the mixture over a glowing filament electrically heated. The per cent of hydrogen is calculated by the contraction in volume due to the formation of water. Hydrogen is also determined by passing the gas over hot copper oxide, $CuO + H_2 = Cu + H_2O$, and absorbing the water in a weighed tube of calcium chloride.

11. Deuterium.—Since the mass of deuterium is approximately double that of ordinary hydrogen, its **nucleus** may be considered to be composed of one proton and one **neutron**. The resulting charge is one positive so the atom has but one "orbital" electron. The electron energy levels are almost identical with those of the mass one isotope and the principal differences in the physical and chemical properties of the two isotopes are due to the difference in the energy of vibration of the two atoms in their various molecules. For example, the energy of dissociation of D_2 is 1.8 kcal. larger than that of H_2 because of the difference in energy of the vibrational states. Similar differences in the energies of the bonds of hydrogen and deuterium to oxygen exist in the oxides H_2O and D_2O. The heat of vaporization of D_2O is about 260 cal. per mole greater than that of H_2O.

TABLE II

PHYSICAL CONSTANTS OF DEUTERIUM AND HEAVY WATER

Atomic weight D.........	2.00147	Density D_2O 25° C.	1.1066
Boiling point D_2, ° A......	23.5	Melting point D_2O ° C...	3.82
Freezing point D_2, ° A.....	18.7	Boiling point D_2O ° C...	101.42
$D_2 = 2D^+$ (in pure D_2O)		Temperature of maximum	
$+ 2e^-$ E° (volts).......	0.0046	density, ° C..........	11.6
		$D_2O = OD^- + D^+$ $K_{25°}$.	0.3×10^{-14}

The preparation of pure deuterium was first carried out by the fractional electrolysis of a sodium hydroxide solution with nickel electrodes; the hydrogen evolved at the cathode is 5 to 8 times poorer in deuterium than the water and the heavier isotope thus accumulates in the residues.

Concentration of DH and D_2 in liquid hydrogen may also be effected in an efficient distilling column.

The replacement of hydrogen atoms by deuterium in organic molecules has opened many new fields of investigation into the mechanism of organic and biochemical reactions.

12. Tritium.—The mass three isotopes has a half-life of 12.1 years with respect to the β (electron emission) disintegration to form He^3. The β-electron is soft, having an energy of only 0.018 Mev. It may be formed from deuterium by a slow neutron capture,

$$H^2 + n = H^3 + \gamma$$

and by a number of nuclear reactions involving the lighter elements such as,

$$H^2 + H^2 = H^3 + H^1$$
$$N^{14} + n = C^{12} + H^3$$

The latter reaction probably accounts for most of the very small amounts of H^3 and He^3 found in the atmosphere. The neutrons required for the reaction are generated by cosmic radiation. It is estimated that this source produces 0.8 neutrons per second per cm^2 of earth's surface.

Tritium, as well as deuterium, has become most useful in studying the mechanism of reactions involving hydrogen and its compounds. In this case, the radioactivity of the H^3 may be used to follow the course of the reaction. The vapor pressure of liquid tritium at 20.4° K. is estimated to be 45 mm.

Chapter II

INERT GASES: HELIUM, NEON, ARGON, KRYPTON, XENON, RADON

1. As early as 1784, Cavendish showed that air contained a small amount of an unknown gas which was quite nonreactive, but further work on the subject was not published until 1893, when Lord Rayleigh found that the weight of 1 liter of nitrogen prepared from pure nitrogen compounds was 1.2506 g., as compared to 1.2572 g. for atmospheric nitrogen. This discrepancy led to a careful investigation of atmospheric nitrogen by Rayleigh and Ramsey and to the discovery of argon. Ramsey shortly after identified the gas given off by uranium minerals as the unknown element, helium, whose existence Lockyer had postulated in 1868 to account for a prominent yellow line in the solar spectrum. Subsequent investigation by fractional distillation of the crude argon obtained from air led to the discovery of neon, krypton, and xenon, the percentage by volume of the various gases in air being:

He	Ne	A	Kr	Xe
0.00052	0.0018	0.93	0.001	0.00008 per cent

The natural gas fields of Texas and Kansas contain helium in small amounts, a number of these wells, high in nitrogen content, analyzing between 1 and 2 per cent of the gas.

Research on the radioactive elements (Chap. **XXII**) has

shown that the so-called alpha-ray, or particle, is doubly charged helium, and that helium is thus one of the products of the decomposition of these unstable elements. It has been calculated that a gram of radium produces 0.11 cc. of helium per year, and a gram of uranium oxide, U_3O_8, 9.1×10^{-8} cc. The radioactive mineral monazite contains about 1 cc. of helium per gram. The loss of an alpha particle by radium results in the formation of the heaviest member of the inert gas group, radon, also called niton (Chap. **XXII**). Argon, A^{40}, is the product of the β-decay of K^{40} and this accounts for the greater abundance of argon.

2. Physical Properties.—The more important physical properties have been summarized in Table I. The gases are all monatomic, and the low values of the boiling points indicate that their atoms have very little attraction for each other. Indeed, the helium atom is so inert that this element possesses the lowest boiling point of any substance, and by boiling under reduced pressure (below 0.01 mm.), a temperature of 0.7° absolute has been obtained. Considerable pressure (140 atm. at 4.2°) is required to cause liquid helium to solidify and the force of attraction is so small that the heat of solidification at the lowest temperatures is practically zero. Like hydrogen, helium gas heats slightly

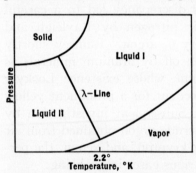

FIG. 1. Diagrammatic representation of the phases in helium at low temperatures.

when expanded at ordinary temperature and the gas must be cooled to the temperature of solid hydrogen (about 11° A.) before it can be cooled by free expansion.

When liquid helium is cooled to 2.2° A. a remarkable transition occurs, for example, the viscosity decreases and the thermal conductivity increases. The substance seems

TABLE I

ATOMIC AND PHYSICAL PROPERTIES

	He	Ne	A	Kr	Xe	Rn
Atomic number	2	10	18	36	54	86
Atomic weight	4.00	20.2	39.91	83.7	131.3	222
Stable isotopes, in order of abundance	4, 3	20, 21, 22	36, 40, 38	84, 86, 82, 83, 80, 78	129, 132, 131, 134, 136, 128, 130, 126, 124	(222) (220)
Electrons in various quantum levels,						
1st	2	2	2	2	2	2
2d		8	8	8	8	8
3d			8	18	18	18
4th				8	18	32
5th					8	18
6th						8
Melting point, °C	−268.9 (140 atm.)	−248.5	−189.3	−156.6	−111.5	−71
°A	4.2	24.6	83.8	116.5	161.6	202
Boiling point °C	−268.9	−245.9	−185.8	−152.9	−108.0	−61.8
°A	4.22	27.2	87.3	120.2	165.1	211.3
Heat of vaporization, cal. per mole, at B.P.	25	405	1,600	2,240	3,100	3,600
Critical temperature, °C	−268	−220	−117	−63	15	
Density of liquid	0.126	1.20	1.40	2.6	3.06	4.4
Potential required to ionize gas atoms, volts,						
1st electron	24.46	21.45	15.68	13.93	12.08	10.70
2d electron	54.14	40.9	27.76	ca 26	ca 21	—

15

to be a solid with properties of a gas. This appears to be a different state of matter and it is referred to as a degenerate gas. The phase relations are indicated in Fig. 1.

The helium isotope of mass three which is present in atmospheric helium to one part in 10^7 (cf. I—12) has a boiling point of 3.2° K. It does not appear to have the degenerate liquid II phase.

The inert gases are somewhat soluble in water and the solubility increases markedly with increasing atomic weight. Helium and neon are not appreciably absorbed by charcoal cooled in liquid air, but the heavier gases are readily absorbed.

The various gases under the influence of a high voltage discharge are luminous, due to the light emitted upon the recombination of the electron with the atom, and the characteristic spectrum of each of the elements, thus produced, serves as a ready means of identification.

3. Electron Structure and Chemical Properties.—The configuration of the electrons in the various atoms of the group is important, not only as explaining their inertness, but also in connection with the interpretation of the formation of the great majority of chemical compounds. Each inert gas marks the completion of an outer shell of eight electrons, except in the case of helium which completes the first quantum group containing but two electrons (Table I). These completed groups are so stable that not only are the ionization potentials of the inert gases very high, but the elements preceding and following each inert gas readily gain or lose sufficient electrons to form ions with the same electronic structure, i.e. the completed octet. This is illustrated by the following ions all with the electron structure of neon:

	O^{--}	F^-	Ne	Na^+	Mg^{++}
Nucleus......................	+8	+9	+10	+11	+12
Electrons in 1st shell...........	2	2	2	2	2
2d shell......................	8	8	8	8	8

Thus the formation of many binary compounds consists in the transfer of electrons from a metallic element to a non-metallic element with the formation of positive and negative ions of the inert gas type, e.g. in the ions shown above: Na + F = $(Na^+)(F^-)$, and crystals of such compounds are lattices built up of these ions (cf. Append. V for many lattice types). However, it is not to be inferred that all positive ions are of the inert gas type, as most of the noble metals form ions of somewhat different structure (cf. **VII—1**).

Although the statement is generally made that the inert gases form no compounds, a few relatively unstable compounds do exist. Thus helium and hydrogen gases subjected to an electrical discharge contain small amounts of the ions, HeH^+ and HeH_2^+, and the large solubility of the heavier members of the group indicates the formation of unstable hydrates. It is claimed that under a pressure of 15 atmospheres at 0°, krypton forms the hydrate, $Kr·5H_2O$. A series of compounds, stable below − 130°, has been reported for argon and boron trifluoride, e.g. $A(BF_3)$, $A(BF_3)_2$, $A(BF_3)_6$.

4. Commercial Preparation and Uses.—The United States government operates a plant in Texas for the extraction of helium from natural gas. During the period 1929 to 1937 approximately eighty million cubic feet of the gas were extracted. The process is one of fractional liquefaction. The gas is used in dirigibles and balloons as it has a lifting power only about 10 per cent less than hydrogen and is, of course, non-combustible.

Helium has assumed considerable importance in deep diving and in deep caisson operations, where men engaged are subject to "caisson disease." This is due to the solution of nitrogen in the blood at high pressure, and its subsequent escape when the pressure is lowered, forming bubbles in the capillaries, or in the brain or spinal cord. It has been shown that the time required in coming out from under high pressure is greatly reduced by the substitution of a mixture of oxygen and helium for compressed air, on account of the small solubility of helium. Mixtures of helium and oxygen are also used in treatment of acute cases of asthma and other diseases where there is constriction of the air passages.

The very low boiling point of helium makes it of special importance in the investigation of the behavior of substances in the neighborhood of absolute zero. Among the more significant changes at these temperatures is the disappearance of the specific heat and coefficient of expansion of solids, and the electrical resistance of many metals. Although, in general, the resistance of metals decreases with decreasing temperature, there is often an abrupt drop a few degrees above absolute zero: thus, at 7° A., the resistance of lead suddenly decreases a million-fold.

The neon tubes used in electric signs contain the gas under low pressure. The commercial source of the element is the fractionation of atmospheric argon.

Argon is now used extensively in filling electric light globes. The presence of the inert gas decreases the rate of evaporation of the filament, retards the blackening of the bulb, and makes possible the operation of the lamp at a higher temperature, thus greatly increasing its efficiency. Argon and also helium are employed to provide an inert atmosphere in welding magnesium and aluminum.

Chapter III

OXYGEN

1. The elements of Group VI,—oxygen, O, sulfur, S, selenium, Se, and tellurium, Te, are characterized by the presence of six outer or valence electrons, and the tendency to complete the octet of the noble gas structure by the addition of two electrons. Consequently these elements readily form compounds in which they have an **oxidation state** of − 2. This tendency is the greatest with the smallest atom; hence oxygen is the strongest oxidizing agent ard tellurium the weakest. On the other hand the six valen :e electrons of the neutral atom may be removed, wholly or in part, giving positive oxidation states up to six. In the case of oxygen this can only be done by high potentials in the gas at low pressure, as no other element is capable of removing electrons from oxygen; hence no ordinary compounds exist in which the oxygen atom must be considered as having a positive charge (with possible exception of F_2O). This separates it considerably in chemical behavior from the other members of the group, and suggests its separate consideration.

2. Occurrence.—Approximately half by weight of the material of the earth's crust is oxygen, and since the atomic weight of oxygen is less than the average atomic weights of the other elements, it follows that more than half of all the atoms of the earth's crust are oxygen. The most abundant of its compounds are those with silicon and aluminum. The element occurs in the free state in the atmosphere, which is one fifth oxygen by volume. Eight ninths by weight of water and between 40 and 50 per cent of all rocks is oxygen. Compounds are known with all the elements except the noble gases.

3. Physical Properties.—In common with the other elements of the family, oxygen exists in several molecular forms. In the gaseous state there are two modifications, ordinary oxygen, O_2, and ozone, O_3. These and probably O_4 also can exist as liquids. Solid oxygen exists in at least three modifications. The more important properties of the oxygen atom and the O_2 molecule are given in Table I.

TABLE I

ATOMIC AND PHYSICAL PROPERTIES OF OXYGEN

Atomic number..........	8	Density g. per cc. 0° C.		
Nucleus { neutrons........	8	and 1 At.,.........		
{ protons (+).....	8	gas................		0.0014290
Atomic weight...........	16.00	liquid − 183°........		1.13
Isotopes................	16	Vaporization at 1 At.		
traces of 17 and 18		Temperature ° A.		90.1
Electrons in various energy		Heat, cals...........		1629
levels, 1st..............	2	Fusion		
2d..............	6	Temperature ° A.		54.4
Ionization potential, volts		Heat, cals...........		105
1st electron.............	13.55	Transition $Solid_1$ = $Solid_2$		
2nd electron............	34.93	Temperature ° A.....		43.7
Electron affinity, volts		Heat, cals...........		177
1st electron.............	2.2	Transition $Solid_2$ = $Solid_3$		
2nd electron............	− 9.5	Temperature ° A.		23.7
Heat of dissociation of O_2		Heat, cals...........		17.5
molecule, kcal..........	117.3	Solubility per 100 g. water		
Dielectric constant of liquid.	1.47	0° C..............		0.007
Magnetic moment of liquid		25° C..............		0.004
O_2 compared to iron as		100° C..............		0.001
unity.................	0.001			
Radius of O^- in crystals,				
cm. $\times 10^8$..............	1.40			

The oxygen molecule O_2 is highly magnetic, and since this property is associated with atoms having an odd number of electrons, it is assumed that the electron formula for the molecule is :Ö:Ö: rather than :Ö::Ö: or :Ö:Ö: .

The variation with concentration of certain of the properties of liquid oxygen dissolved in liquid nitrogen may be explained on the assumption of an equilibrium, $2O_2 = O_4$. The change of this equilibrium with temperature may explain the very large coefficient of expansion of the liquid. In harmony with the assumed structure of O_2 the most likely structure of O_4 would be

$$\overset{..}{:O:}\overset{..}{O:}$$
$$\underset{..}{:O:}\underset{..}{O:}$$

However the small energy of formation of O_4 suggests that the bonds between the two O_2 molecules are not true electron pair bonds.

4. Chemical Properties.—Oxygen combines directly with all other elements except the halogens, the noble gases, and a few of the most noble metals, and in many of these reactions sufficient energy is evolved to heat the products to the point of incandescence, as in the familiar burning of carbon in air. Very often reactions of oxygen which are rapid at high temperatures will not proceed at low temperatures; thus carbon must be heated before it ignites in air, but many oxidations do go slowly in the cold, e.g. the rusting of iron.

A compound of oxygen with another element is called an oxide, and the oxidation state of -2 (except in peroxides, Par. **11**) is assigned to the oxygen indicating that it has gained two electrons, e.g.

$$2Ca : + :\overset{..}{O}: \overset{..}{O}: = 2Ca : \overset{..}{O}:$$

5. The slowness of many oxygen reactions is doubtless connected with the large energy required to dissociate the oxygen molecule into atoms. Indeed the probable mechanism of most reactions of oxygen is first the addition of two electrons to the O_2 to form a peroxide, where the bond between the oxygen atoms remains unbroken, as illustrated by:

$$\text{Ba} : + \begin{matrix} \cdot \ddot{\text{O}} : \\ \cdot \ddot{\text{O}} : \end{matrix} = \text{Ba} \begin{matrix} : \ddot{\text{O}} : \\ : \ddot{\text{O}} : \end{matrix}$$

The process of oxidation may be examined in detail by arbitrarily dividing the formation of an oxide into the following steps. (This does not imply that the process of oxidation ordinarily occurs in this way.) Using copper oxide by way of illustration:

$$\overset{a}{O_2(\text{gas}) \rightarrow} \overset{b}{O(\text{gas}) \rightarrow} O^{-2}(\text{gas})$$

$$\overset{f}{\searrow} \rightarrow \text{CuO(solid)}$$

$$\overset{c}{Cu(\text{solid}) \rightarrow} \overset{d}{Cu(\text{liquid}) \rightarrow} \overset{e}{Cu(\text{gas}) \rightarrow} Cu^{++}(\text{gas})$$

The dissociation of the oxygen molecule, step a, involves the absorption of a large amount of energy, as do also steps c and d, which represents the detachment of copper atoms from the solid mass. The removal of electrons from the metal, step e, requires the absorption of still more energy (i.e. the ionization potential). The addition of two electrons to the oxygen atom, step b, also requires energy; although it is not large, because of the tendency to complete the octet. It is step f which is chiefly responsible for making the net result of the whole process an evolution of energy, and this step must be very large in order to overcome the energy absorption of steps a, b, c, d, and e. Now it is very illuminating to note that step f depends for positive ions of the same charge chiefly upon the size of the ions, being greater the smaller the positive ion. Furthermore, the great stability of oxides, as compared with many other binary compounds, depends upon the fact that the oxygen ion is one of the smallest negative ions. The effect of step f, for example, makes the heat of formation of lithium oxide, 142 kcal., greater than that of sodium oxide,

101 kcal., in spite of the fact that more energy is absorbed in removing the electron from lithium than from sodium.

The above scheme throws light upon differences in the heat of combustion of other substances. Thus a metal of high melting and boiling point, such as platinum, owes its noble character in part to high values for steps c and d, and not entirely to a high value for step e. Again, the high stability of silicon dioxide is related to the large energy evolution of step f, which may be inferred from its high melting point and great hardness.

6. Preparation and Uses.—Commercial oxygen is now prepared on a large scale by the fractional distillation of liquid air. The principle of the method may be understood by considering the liquid vapor diagram, Fig. 1, for solutions of oxygen and nitrogen. Nitrogen boils at $-195°$ C. and oxygen at $-183°$ C. At intermediate temperatures, a solution of the two liquids in equilibrium with the vapors has the composition b and the vapor, the composition a. Since the gas phase is much richer in nitrogen than the liquid, evaporation results

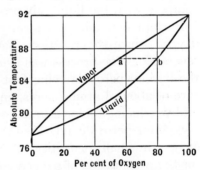

FIG. 1. Temperature-composition diagram for liquid oxygen and nitrogen.

in the liquid becoming richer in oxygen. Simply boiling off the nitrogen from liquid air would not give an efficient separation of the two gases, so the process is carried out in a fractionating column. The cold liquid enters the top of the column; as the liquid evaporates the temperature rises and the liquid increases in oxygen content; the vaporized gas passes up through the colder liquid and loses oxygen, becoming almost pure nitrogen. Oxygen cannot be liquefied above its critical temperature, $-118°$ C., by any pressure, however great; but the fact that compressed air at room temperature cools upon expanding, due to the work done in overcoming the attraction between the molecules (Joule-Thomson effect), makes possible the Linde liquefaction process. Air is compressed to about 3,000 lb. per sq. in. and allowed to expand. The cool expanded air is led back over the incoming highly compressed air and cools it until finally the temperature drops sufficiently below the critical temperature to permit liquefaction. In the Claude process the compressed air is subjected to an additional cooling effect by doing external work. Some commercial oxygen is prepared by the electrolysis of water; however, unless the electrical energy is very cheap and there exists a ready market for the hydrogen produced at the same time, the electrolytic process cannot compete with the liquid air process.

Barium peroxide was formerly an important source of oxygen, since the reaction, $BaO + \frac{1}{2}O_2 = BaO_2$, is easily reversible. The process was usually carried out at 700° C.; the barium peroxide being first formed from air at a pressure of about 3 atmospheres, and the oxygen then pumped off by reducing the pressure.

Sodium peroxide (cf. IV-11) is a convenient source of oxygen in small quantities. A common laboratory method for the preparation of oxygen consists of the decomposition of potassium chlorate using manganese dioxide as a catalyst at about 200° C.: $2KClO_3 = 2KCl + 3O_2$. In the absence of a catalyst, oxygen is evolved but slowly; most of the chlorate being converted into perchlorate, which is much more stable. In the early investigations of oxygen by Scheele, Priestley, and Lavoisier (about 1775) much use was made of the compounds HgO, MnO_2, PbO_2, and KNO_3, all of which give oxygen upon heating.

The present commercial importance of oxygen has resulted from the development of the oxy-acetylene torch in welding and cutting metals. Oxygen for this purpose is sold in heavy cylinders under a pressure of about 2,000 lb.

per sq. inch. The oxy-hydrogen torch, although not producing as high a temperature as the oxy-acetylene flame, is
also of wide industrial use. Pure oxygen is used in the treatment of pneumonia and in cases of asphyxiation; and mixtures of oxygen with nitrous oxide or ether are administered in producing anesthesia. It is also used to maintain
the oxygen content of the air in submarines. The "hardening" of certain oils is accelerated by using pure oxygen.
Charcoal, cotton, or other cellulose soaked in liquid oxygen
form high explosives known as "oxylignite."

7. Oxides, Bases, Acids.—The various types of oxides
with different elements correspond to all the possible oxidation states of the positive elements from $+ 1$, as in Cu_2O,
to $+ 8$, as in OsO_4. In addition, a number of mixed oxides
occur with elements forming oxides of more than one state,
for example Pb_3O_4, which is $(PbO)_2PbO_2$, and Fe_3O_4, which
is $FeO \cdot Fe_2O_3$. In the crystalline state, if the force of attraction between the positive kernel and the oxide ion is not
too great, the oxides crystallize in the completely polar type
of structure: for example, the CaO crystal is a lattice of
Ca^{++} and O^{--} similar to the sodium chloride structure, and
there are no molecules of CaO. On the other hand, large attractive forces allow the molecule to preserve its identity
in the solid as in carbon dioxide.

Oxides of metal ions with small positive charge react
with water to form bases, e.g. $Na_2O + H_2O = 2NaOH$,
$MgO + H_2O = Mg(OH)_2$; while oxides of non-metals, and
even of metals in the higher oxidation states react with
water to form acids: e.g. $Cl_2O + H_2O = 2HOCl$; SO_2
$+ H_2O = H_2SO_3$; $CrO_3 + H_2O = H_2CrO_4$; $As_2O_5 + 3H_2O$
$= 2H_3AsO_4$. In all of these compounds an atom of oxygen
separates a hydrogen atom from the remainder of the molecule; and the basic or acidic character seems to depend
largely upon the relative attractive forces between the oxide
ion and the hydrogen ion, on the one hand, and the remainder of the molecule on the other, modified by the

energy of hydration of the resulting ions. Thus NaOH is a base because the cleavage occurs more easily at a, while HOCl is an acid because it occurs at b.

$$\text{Na} \mid : \overset{\cdot\cdot}{\underset{\cdot\cdot}{\text{O}}} : \mid \text{H} \qquad\qquad : \overset{\cdot\cdot}{\underset{\cdot\cdot}{\text{Cl}}} \mid : \overset{\cdot\cdot}{\underset{\cdot\cdot}{\text{O}}} : \mid \text{H}$$

$$\quad a \quad\quad b \qquad\qquad\qquad a \quad\quad b$$

The bond between the sodium and oxygen is largely that of the coulombic attraction $[E = ee'/(r + r')]$, while the bond between the chlorine and oxygen has considerable covalent (electron pair) character. The greater ability of the chlorine to take electrons away from the oxygen makes the latter more positive in HClO than in NaOH and, in general, the more positive the oxygen the weaker will be its bond with the hydrogen.

The strength of the oxygen acids may be correlated with the formal charge on the central atom which is calculated on the assumption that the electrons in the bond are divided equally between the two atoms. Thus as seen in the formula of HClO, this assumption would give seven electrons

$$: \overset{\cdot\cdot}{\underset{\cdot\cdot}{\text{Cl}}} : \overset{\cdot\cdot}{\underset{\cdot\cdot}{\text{O}}} : \text{H} \qquad : \overset{\cdot\cdot}{\underset{\cdot\cdot}{\text{O}}} : \overset{\cdot\cdot}{\underset{\cdot\cdot}{\text{Cl}}} : \overset{\cdot\cdot}{\underset{\cdot\cdot}{\text{O}}} : \text{H} \qquad : \overset{\cdot\cdot}{\underset{\cdot\cdot}{\text{O}}} : \overset{:\overset{\cdot\cdot}{\text{O}}:}{\underset{\cdot\cdot}{\text{Cl}}} : \overset{\cdot\cdot}{\underset{\cdot\cdot}{\text{O}}} : \text{H}$$

Formal Charge 0   Formal Charge + 1   Formal Charge + 2

on the chlorine and since the neutral atom has seven electrons, the formal charge is zero. Oxygen acids with zero formal charge are very weak and have dissociation constants, K_1, of 10^{-7} or less (cf. Table II).

If the formal charge on the central atom is $+ 1$, as in $HClO_2$ illustrated above, K_1 is approximately 10^{-2}. As a general rule the difference between successive dissociation constants is roughly 10^{-5}, hence K_2 for this class of acids is $\sim 10^{-7}$ and $K_3 \sim 10^{-12}$. Acids with a formal charge of $+ 2$ are strong. K_1 is probably $\sim 10^3$ and $K_2 \sim 10^{-2}$. There are two acids with formal charge of $+ 3$, $HClO_4$ and $HMnO_4$. Both are very strong.

TABLE II

Correlation of Acid Dissociation Constants with Formal Charge

Charge 0		+1		+2	
K_1	K_1	K_2	K_1	K_2
HClO 3×10^{-8}	HClO$_2$ 10^{-2}	—	HClO$_3$ large	—
H$_4$SiO$_4$ 1×10^{-11}	H$_2$SO$_3$ 10^{-2}	10^{-7}	H$_2$SO$_4$ "	1.2×10^{-2}
H$_3$BO$_3$ 6×10^{-10}	H$_3$PO$_4$ 0.7×10^{-2}	6×10^{-8}	H$_2$SiO$_4$ "	1×10^{-2}
H$_3$AsO$_3$ 6×10^{-10}	H$_5$IO$_6$ 2×10^{-2}	$ca\ 10^{-6}$		
HBrO 2×10^{-9}	HNO$_2$ 0.4×10^{-3}	—		

The effect of the formal charge may be interpreted as an increased displacement of the electrons toward the central atom with increasing charge and this in turn weakens the hydrogen-oxygen bond. In some acids there is partial double bond character. This is true in H_2CO_3 and the formal charge is between 0 and $+1$ in this acid.

8. Analytical Properties.—Both oxygen and nitrous oxide will cause a glowing splinter to burst into flame, but oxygen may be distinguished from the latter by the production of dark brown fumes with nitric oxide. The gas is usually determined quantitatively in a mixture of gases by determining the decrease in volume upon contact with various liquids or solids which absorb oxygen, such as, (1) a solution of cuprous chloride in hydrochloric acid, (2) alkaline solution of pyrogallol, (3) phosphorus. A very delicate test for small quantities of oxygen is the deep red color produced by the action of oxygen upon an alkaline solution containing ferrous iron and pyrocatechol.

9. Water.—Water plays such an important role in chemistry that its physical constants are of especial significance. For a substance of low molecular weight, its **melting point,** 0° C., and **boiling point,** 100° C., are extremely high, indicating high attractive forces between the molecules. The high **dielectric** constant, 81 at 18° C., shows that the molecules are highly polar, which would account for the large intermolecular attraction, since two dipoles would attract each other. The unusual solvent action of water for salts is also to be correlated with its high dielectric constant, since the force of attraction between ions varies inversely as the dielectric constant of the medium. Water is unusual in possessing a point, 4° C., of maximum **density** (Append. VIII). This may be connected with the fact that water is one of the few substances whose liquid form ($d = 1.00$ at 4° C.) is denser than the solid ($d = 0.917$). In ice the molecules are combined in a way that involves a looser packing than in the liquid (cf. Fig. 2), and as the tem-

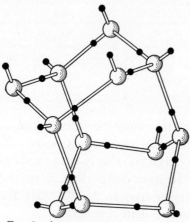

FIG. 2. Arrangement of water molecules in ice.

perature of the liquid approaches 0°, there are doubtless formed an increasing proportion of these same molecules in the liquid. This change counteracts the increase in density uniformly found when only one molecular species is present. Complete **vapor pressure** tables for water and ice are given in Appendix X. The simple phase diagram for "solid, liquid, vapor" is represented in Fig. 3. Since the density of the solid is less than that of the liquid, the melting point is decreased by pres-

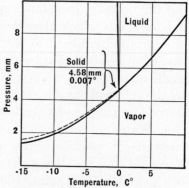

FIG. 3. Temperature-pressure diagram for ice, water, and vapor.

sure. At high pressures ice exists in a number of allotropic modifications, and as several of these are denser than the liquid, they may be obtained under high pressure at temperatures above 0°, as shown in Fig. 4.

The water molecule may be considered as a tetrahedral oxygen with hydrogens attached to two corners. However the angle is only 105° in the gas instead of the tetrahedral angle, 109° 28'. Crystal structure data indicate that in the ordinary form of ice each oxygen atom is surrounded by four other oxygen atoms with a hydrogen atom located on the line joining the oxygens, thus forming a hydrogen bond between the oxygens.

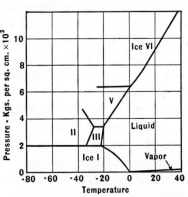

Fig. 4. Modifications of ice at high pressures.

The **heat of fusion** is 80 cal. per gram and the **heat of vaporization,** 540 cal. per gram. The **lowering of the freezing point** and the **elevation of boiling point** per mole of solute in 1,000 g. of water are 1.86° and 0.52° respectively. The lowering of the freezing point of water by common salt is important in refrigeration. The freezing point diagram is given in Fig. 3, Chapter **IV.** One of the lowest eutectics given with water is that of $CaCl_2$·$6H_2O$. A mixture of 7 parts of snow and 10 parts of $CaCl_2$·$6H_2O$ gives a temperature of − 55° C. (cf. Fig. 2, Chap. **V**). The **surface tension** of water at 20° is 72.5 dynes per cm. The **compressibility** at 20° is

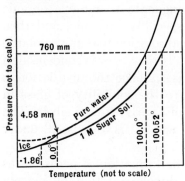

Fig. 5. Diagrammatic representation of the effect of a solute upon the vapor pressure, boiling point, and melting point of water.

43×10^{-6} cc. per megabar. The **specific heat** of 1 g. of water at 15° is taken as unity in the definition of the calorie. The variation of its specific heat with temperature is as follows: 0°, 1.0088; 30°, 0.9988; 50°, 0.9996; 100°, 1.0099. The **heat of formation** per mole of H_2O at 25° is $- 68,270$ cal. The **heat of ionization**, $H_2O = H^+ + OH^-$, 13,200 cal. is of course the negative of the heat of neutralization of dilute solutions of strong acids and bases. The constant for a first **ionization** of water is 1.008×10^{-14} at 25° C. and the constant for the second ionization probably less than 10^{-36}. The **decomposition voltage** of water upon electrolysis is 1.23 volts plus an overvoltage depending upon the nature of the electrodes due to the slowness of the electrode reactions (cf. Append. I). The **specific conductivity** of the purest water at 20° C. is about 1×10^{-7} reciprocal ohms.

10. Water is easily purified from non-volatile substances by distillation; however, to prepare water free from volatile acids, bases, and organic material, elaborate precautions must be taken. This is usually done by first distilling from an alkaline solution of permanganate to remove organic material and volatile acids, especially carbonic, and then redistilling from non-volatile acid solution to remove volatile alkalies, especially ammonium. If the vapor is condensed in air it will contain dissolved gases, hence the distillation is carried out in vacuum. Due to the solubility of glass in water, the condenser is made of quartz, tin, or silver. The so-called "softening of hard water" is discussed under calcium (cf. **V—11**).

11. Hydrogen Peroxide.—The formation of peroxides as intermediate products in the direct oxidation by oxygen has been mentioned (Par. 4). These compounds may be considered as derivatives of hydrogen peroxide, H_2O_2. The oxidation state of the oxygen is $- 1$. In terms of molecular structure peroxides consist of oxygen linked to oxygen to form the group $: \overset{..}{O} : \overset{..}{O} : .$

The oxidation of certain metals by moist oxygen results in the formation of the oxide and hydrogen peroxide: e.g. $Zn + O_2 + H_2O = ZnO + H_2O_2$. The mechanism of this reaction may be the formation of zinc peroxide and its subsequent hydrolysis. Hydrogen peroxide is also formed by the action of ultraviolet light upon water: $2H_2O = H_2O_2 + H_2$. High anodic potentials are capable of oxidizing the oxygen in many of its compounds to the peroxide state: for example, concentrated sulfuric acid is oxidized to per-

$$\begin{matrix} & O & O \\ \text{oxydisulfuric acid } HOSOOSOH. & & \\ & O & O \end{matrix}$$ This acid may then be

hydrolyzed to form hydrogen peroxide and sulfuric acid. Some commercial hydrogen peroxide is prepared in this manner, but the greater portion is prepared by the action of cold sulfuric acid upon hydrated barium peroxide: $BaO_2 + H_2SO_4 = BaSO_4 + H_2O_2$. The peroxide being less volatile than water may be concentrated by evaporation under reduced pressure. Another method of preparation involves the formation of hydrogen peroxide as the product of the oxidation of organic hydrazo-compounds by oxygen. The hydrogen peroxide is removed by distillation and the hydrazo-compound regenerated by reduction with sodium-amalgam.

12. Pure hydrogen peroxide is a faint blue syrupy liquid freezing at $-2°$. It has a vapor pressure of 47 mm. at $80° C$. Violent decomposition occurs if heated much above this temperature. The dielectric constant of the liquid is given as 93, a value even higher than that of water. The water solutions are fairly stable if kept in a cool, dark place. Acetanilid is usually added to the commercial product to act as a preservative. The decomposition into water and oxygen, $H_2O_2 = H_2O + \frac{1}{2}O_2$, is catalyzed by many substances, for example, silver, manganese dioxide, hydrogen bromide, and saliva. The decomposition is more rapid in alkaline solution. The usual 3 per cent commercial preparation is often called a "10 volume solution" since it will evolve about 10 times its volume of oxygen.

Peroxide is a powerful oxidizing agent in both acid and alkaline solutions (Par. **14**), the oxygen being reduced from an oxidation state of -1 to -2. However, it is generally a slow oxidizing agent except with fairly powerful reducing agents. One of the most important reactions of hydrogen peroxide is the quantitative oxidation of iodide: $2I^- + H_2O_2 + 2H^+ = I_2 + 2H_2O$. It also acts as a reducing agent, the oxygen being oxidized from -1 to 0, but a fairly powerful oxidizing agent is required to bring about its oxidation in acid solution. As examples we have the quantitative reduction of permanganate: $5H_2O_2 + 2MnO_4^- + 6H^+ = 2Mn^{++} + 5O_2 + 8H_2O$, and the reduction of silver oxide: $Ag_2O + H_2O_2 = 2Ag + O_2 + H_2O$.

Hydrogen peroxide is used as an antiseptic and as a bleaching agent for hair, silk, feathers, ivory, etc.

Delicate qualitative tests for peroxide are the reactions with chromate or titanic sulfate in acid, forming highly colored peroxy-acids. The peroxychromic acid is a bright blue compound, soluble in ether, and the peroxytitanic acid is yellow.

13. Peroxy-acids.—There are a large number of acids containing peroxy-oxygen. These may be considered as derivatives of oxy-acids formed by the substitution of $-$ OOH in place of OH^-, for example

$$
\begin{array}{ccc}
& OOH & \\
CO & & \\
& OH & \\
\text{monoperoxycarbonic} & & \\
\end{array}
\qquad
\begin{array}{ccc}
& OOH & \\
CO & & \\
& OOH & \\
\text{diperoxycarbonic} & & \\
\end{array}
\qquad
\begin{array}{ccc}
& OOH & \\
CH_3C & & \\
& O & \\
\text{peroxyacetic} & & \\
\end{array}
$$

The elements forming peroxy-acids are B, C, Ti, Ge, Sn, N, P, V, Cb, Ta, S, Cr, Se, Mo, W, and U. Many of these acids are discussed under the respective elements. The most important is probably peroxydisulfuric acid, $H_2S_2O_8$.

14. Ozone.—The density of ozone corresponds to the molecular formula O_3. The reaction, $3O_2 = 2O_3$, absorbs 34.5 kcal. per mole, and the formation of ozone from oxygen is therefore favored by high temperature. The equilibrium mixture of the gas at 3,000° C. probably contains about one per cent of ozone. Sufficient energy to bring about the transformation may be supplied either by ultraviolet radiation or by a silent electrical discharge. The commercial ozonizers usually consist of aluminum plates, separated by insulators, and charged to a potential of about 10,000 volts. When oxygen is passed over the plates, a few per cent of ozone is formed. Ultraviolet radiation of about 2,600 Å. (corresponding to 4.7 volts) is absorbed by oxygen molecules. These highly activated molecules then react to form ozone. The outer portion of the earth's atmosphere must contain large concentrations of ozone formed in this manner by the sun's radiation. The silent electrical discharge is the principal commercial means of forming ozone. This involves the action of electrons shot off from high-potential surfaces upon oxygen molecules. Ozone is also formed under powerful oxidizing conditions, as in the action of fluorine upon water, and by the oxidation of water by a high anodic potential, as, for example, in the electrolysis of aqueous sulfuric acid using a very high current density. The ozone molecule appears to be V-shaped and not a triangular ring as previously postulated.

Reference to the table of oxidation reduction potentials shows that ozone is itself a very powerful oxidizing agent, second only to fluorine. In the reduction in acid solution ordinarily one of the oxygens is reduced to water and the other two liberated as molecular oxygen. The gas is fairly stable toward decomposition into oxygen, and condenses to a blue liquid at − 112.4° C. The melting point is − 249.7°. It has a very pungent, characteristic odor, and unlike oxygen it is not magnetic. Ozone is more soluble in water than is oxygen, and is still more soluble in alkaline solution. The solution contains **perhydroxyl** ion, O_2^-.

$$O_3 + 2OH^- = 2O_2^- + H_2O$$

The latter is unstable in acid solution.

$$2HO_2 = H_2O_2 + O_2$$

The potassium salt KO_2 is formed by the combustion of potassium in air.

Ozone is used in sterilization of water; bleaching of paper pulp, fabrics, and flour; the resinification of oils; and as a deodorant for air in crowded interiors. (Its bactericidal properties in this connection seem not to be very great.) Qualitatively it may be detected by its peculiar odor, by its action upon potassium iodide, and by the blackening of silver.

15. Oxidation-reduction Potentials.—Important oxidation reduction potentials involving oxygen and its oxides have been summarized in Table III. Since the first step in the reduction of oxygen is generally the formation of the peroxide, this potential, equation (2) is an important factor in determining the action of oxygen. However the reverse reaction, that is the oxidation of water, does not involve the formation of peroxide as an intermediate step and depends upon equation (4). A tentative value is also given for the oxidation of water to free hydroxyl which may be formed as an unstable intermediate under some conditions.

TABLE III

OXIDATION-REDUCTION POTENTIALS

		VOLTS$_{25°}$
(1)	$2OH^- = \frac{1}{2}O_2 + H_2O + 2e^-$	$- 0.401$
(2)	$H_2O_2 = O_2 + 2H^+ + 2e^-$	$- 0.68$
(3)	$3OH^- = HO_2^- + H_2O + 2e^-$	$- 0.87$
(4)	$H_2O = \frac{1}{2}O_2 + 2H^+ + 2e^-$	$- 1.229$
(5)	$2H_2O = H_2O_2 + 2H^+ + 2e^-$	$- 1.77$
(6)	$O_2 + H_2O = O_3 + 2H^+ + 2e^-$	$- 2.07$
(7)	$H_2O = OH + H^+ + e^-$	$- 2.82$

The potentials for the reduction of O_2 in steps are given in the following scheme.

Acidic Solution:

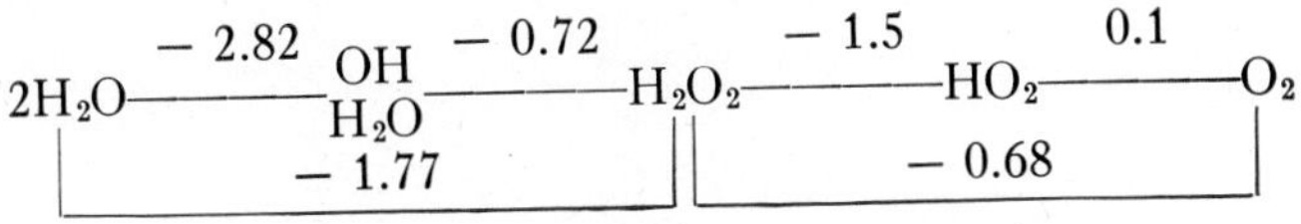

$$2H_2O \xrightarrow{\;-2.82\;} \underset{\substack{H_2O \\ -1.77}}{OH} \xrightarrow{\;-0.72\;} H_2O_2 \xrightarrow[\;-0.68\;]{\;-1.5\;} HO_2 \xrightarrow{\;0.1\;} O_2$$

Basic Solution:

$$2OH^- \xrightarrow{\;-2.0\;} \underset{\substack{OH^- \\ -0.87}}{OH} \xrightarrow{\;0.26\;} HO_2{}^- \xrightarrow[\;0.08\;]{\;-0.4\;} O_2{}^- \xrightarrow{\;0.6\;} O_2$$

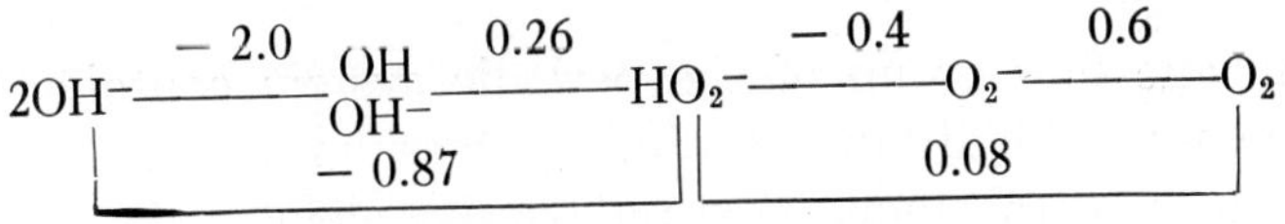

Chapter IV

GROUP I. ALKALI METALS

1. The first group of the periodic system contains the elements stable lithium, sodium, potassium, rubidium, and cesium, and the short-lived radioactive element, francium. They are called the alkali metals because their hydroxides are all soluble bases or alkalies. The most important common characteristics of these elements are the single electron in the outermost energy level of their atoms, and the comparatively low voltage required to detach this electron from the atom, as shown by the ionizing potentials.

Although the outer electron is easily removed, the underlying ones can be removed only by very high potentials; hence ordinary chemical reactions involve the loss or transfer of only a single electron per atom, as illustrated by the equation: $M = M^+ + e^-$. Accordingly these elements display invariably an oxidation state of $+1$ in their compounds.

2. Atomic and Physical Properties.—Many of the physical and chemical properties of these elements may be correlated with the structures of their atoms. (Cf. Table I, also *Prin. of Chem.*, Chap. **XVI.**) Thus in the solid state the electrons are held so loosely that they can readily pass from association with one atom to another under the impulse of an electric potential; hence these elements show in a high degree the conductivity and other properties characteristic of metals. Moreover, since there are not enough outer electrons to serve to bind an atom firmly to all of its neighbors in the solid state, we find these metals to be soft, and easily fusible.

TABLE I
ATOMIC AND PHYSICAL PROPERTIES

ELEMENT	LITHIUM	SODIUM	POTASSIUM	RUBIDIUM	CESIUM
Latin name..........	Lithium	Natrium	Kalium	Rubidium	Cesium
Symbol.............	Li	Na	K	Rb	Cs
Atomic weight.......	6.94	22.997	39.096	85.48	132.91
Atomic number.......	3	11	19	37	55
Melting point. ° C.....	179	97.5	63.5	39.0	28.4
Boiling point ° C......	1367	892	779	679	690
Density 20° C.	0.53	0.97	0.86	1.53	1.90
Stable isotopes.......	6, 7	23	39, (40), 41	85, (87)	133
Nucleus { Neutrons...	3, 4	12	20, 21, 22	48, 50	78
Nucleus { Protons (+)	3, 3	11	19, 19, 19	37, 37	55
Electrons in various quantum levels,					
1st............	2	2	2	2	2
2nd..........	1	8	8	8	8
3rd..........	—	1	8	18	18
4th..........	—	—	1	8	18
5th..........	—	—	—	1	8
6th..........	—	—	—	—	1
Ionizing potentials of gaseous atoms, volts.	5.36	5.12	4.32	4.16	3.87
Potential required to remove electrons from solid metal	2.35	2.12	—	—	—
Potential between metal and normal aqueous soln. of ion; $M = M_{aq}^+ + e^-$....	3.02	2.71	2.92	2.99	3.02
Heat of hydration of gaseous ions, kcal....	123	97	77	70	63
Ionic radius in crystals, cm. $\times 10^8$.........	0.60	0.95	1.33	1.48	1.69

Another phenomenon connected with the easy loss of electrons by these metals is their solubility in liquid ammonia to give highly conducting solutions. The process of solution is accompanied by an ionization of the metal atom whose electron attaches itself to a molecule of ammonia; thus, M (solid) = M^+ (in NH_3) + e^- (ammoniated). The alkali metals all give solutions in ammonia of the same blue color, which is due to the solvated electron, the metal ion being colorless in all cases. The addition of MCl increases the concentration of M^+ and diminishes the blue color in accordance with the mass law. The alkaline earth metals are soluble in liquid ammonia in this way to a smaller extent, and the nobler metals, which hold their electrons more firmly, do not dissolve at all in liquid ammonia.

The metal vapors are somewhat associated into diatomic molecules at the boiling points of the liquids. The heats of dissociation of the Na_2 and K_2 molecules are 18,000 and 12,000 cal. respectively.

The nuclei of potassium, 40, and rubidium, 87, are not altogether stable, as shown by their slight radio-activity (cf. **XIII—4**).

3. Spectra.—Spectra of the alkali metals are easily excited; even the comparatively low temperature of a Bunsen flame suffices to disturb the outer, valence electron; moreover, since the single valence electron alone is disturbed, unless a high voltage spark is used, their spectra are comparatively simple. The wave length (in mm. $\times 10^{-6}$) of the prominent lines in the flame spectra are as follows: lithium, 670 red, 620 orange, fainter; sodium, 590 yellow; potassium, 768 red, 404 violet; rubidium, 780 red, 420 blue, 358 violet; cesium, 457 blue, 388 violet.

4. Chemical Properties.—Since the metals all give up their outer electrons so easily to other substances they are chemically very reactive. Thus, they all decompose water vigorously, the water taking up the electrons and giving hydroxide ion and hydrogen gas: M (solid) $+ H_2O = \frac{1}{2}H_2$ $+ M^+ + OH^-$. With potassium, rubidium, and cesium the amount of heat developed is so great that the metal takes fire almost instantly when thrown upon water.

5. The ease with which an electron is removed from the metal increases regularly in going from lithium to cesium, as shown by the ionizing potentials; hence we would expect that the ease with which the metal forms any one of its compounds would increase from lithium to cesium; and, conversely, the difficulty of reducing the metal from its compounds would be greatest for cesium and least for lithium. This is in general the case, although the simple prediction is somewhat modified by the different sizes and attractions of the resulting ions. The ionizing potentials refer to the reaction: $M(gas) = M^+(gas) + e^-(gas)$, while the reaction between solid metal and water, previously given, involves in addition the hydration of the M^+. This sets free a large amount of energy, and just as the smallest ion, lithium, attracts an electron most strongly, so also it attracts water molecules most strongly, a fact which helps lithium metal to react with water to give it a high electrode potential in water solution, as shown in Table I, instead of the lowest as one would conclude from the ionizing potentials alone.

This point may be clarified by the aid of the following scheme representing the formation of MCl by a series of steps, which give out or absorb energy, as the case may be.

$$
\begin{array}{ccccc}
 & a & & b & \\
M \text{ (solid)} & \to & M \text{ (gas)} & \to & M^+ \text{ (gas)} \\
+ & & + & & + \\
 & c & & d & \\
Cl_2 \text{ (gas)} & \to & Cl \text{ (gas)} & \to & Cl^- \text{ (gas)} \\
+ & & - & &
\end{array}
\quad
\begin{array}{l}
\searrow \ e \\
 \to MCl \text{ (gas)} \xrightarrow{\ f\ } MCl \text{ (solid)} \\
\nearrow \ - \qquad\qquad\qquad\qquad -
\end{array}
$$

We have marked each step + in which the system would absorb heat, and each − in which the system would lose heat. If potassium were substituted for lithium, steps c and d would naturally remain the same; step a would become smaller (Table I) showing that potassium is more easily fused and vaporized; step b would have a smaller positive value (see Ionizing Potentials); but step e would also have a smaller negative value, the last two effects thus tending to offset each other. Although the heats evolved in formation per mole follow for most compounds the order expected from the ionizing potentials, and illustrated by the iodides, bromides, and chlorides in Table II, the fluorides show the reverse order on account of the small size of the lithium and fluoride ions, allowing close approach and a large negative value for step *e*.

TABLE II

HEATS EVOLVED IN FORMATION OF ALKALI HALIDES, KILOGRAM CALORIES PER MOLE

	Li	Na	K	Rb	Cs
Iodides	71	76	85	88	90
Bromides	87	90	97	99	101
Chlorides	97	99	105	105	106
Fluorides	145	137	135	133	132

For the same reason, the compounds with other small atoms usually show the greatest stability with lithium rather than with cesium. Other examples include the hydrides, carbides, nitrides, and oxides.

The smaller size and larger ionizing potential of lithium tends to ally it somewhat with the elements of Group II, particularly magnesium. This is in harmony with the corresponding resemblance between beryllium and aluminum, boron, and silicon. This resemblance is illustrated by the low solubility of its carbonate and phosphate, as well as by the stability of the compounds mentioned in the preceding paragraph.

6. The complete transfer of electrons by the alkali metals in the formation of their compounds is illustrated again by the crystal structure of their halides. All except those of cesium crystallize in a cubic lattice of the sodium chloride type (Append. V; cf. also CsCl type) in which the sodium and chlorine atoms alternate, and each atom of one kind is surrounded by six atoms of the other, *all equidistant from it.* It is not possible to designate any sodium atom as belonging to any particular chlorine atom. There are, therefore, no molecules of NaCl present in the crystal. Now if each sodium atom retained its original electron it would be bound (by an electron pair) to a particular chlorine atom; the absence of such binding shown by the symmetry of the crystal lattice is evidence that the electrons have passed over to the chlorine atoms, giving each an extra electron, making it chloride ion, Cl^-, and leaving the sodium atom as sodium ion, Na^+. Indeed, we have only to melt the crystal, releasing these ions from their fixed positions, and the substance becomes an excellent electric conductor, quite unlike a substance such as sulfur, which is an insulator in the liquid as well as the solid form. The solution of an alkali halide in water merely substitutes the attraction of its ions for water for their attraction for each other. The energy of hydration is very high (Table I) and serves to overcome the large electrostatic force responsible for the cohesion of the crystal.

The fact that lithium has the largest energy of hydration is noteworthy in connection with the high solubility of many of its salts. The salts of low solubility are those where there is an especially high attraction between the lithium ion and the negative ion in the crystal, as in the case of the fluoride.

7. Occurrence.—From the average composition of igneous rocks, the percentage of the alkali metals present is estimated as, sodium 2.85, potassium 2.60, lithium 4×10^{-5}, and rubidium 10^{-6} and cesium 10^{-7}. Spectral lines of lithium and sodium are prominent in the sun. The spectra of the other alkalies are not found in the chromosphere of the sun doubtless because the temperature is sufficient to remove the outer electron completely. Potassium and rubidium can, however, be observed in the cooler portions.

Sea water contains about 2.8 per cent of sodium chloride and 0.08 per cent of potassium chloride, and the evaporation of inland seas has resulted in enormous deposits of these salts. These deposits of chlorides, and also deposits of carbonates, sulfates, and nitrates are discussed under the corresponding salts. Most plants contain from 4 to 6 times as much combined potassium as sodium, a fact responsible for the use of potassium compounds as one of the important fertilizers. The ashes of sea weeds, however, contain more

TABLE III

SUMMARY OF THE MORE IMPORTANT REACTIONS OF THE ALKALI METALS

$4M + O_2 = 2M_2O$	Li, Na at low temperature
$2M + O_2 = M_2O_2$	Li slightly, Rb and Cs spontaneously in dry air
$M + O_2 = MO_2$	K, Rb, Cs, Na at high pressure
$6M + N_2 = 2M_3N$	Li only
$2M + X_2 = 2MX$	With halogens
$2M + S = M_2S$	With Te also
$3M + P = M_3P$	With As, Sb also
$2M + 2H_2O = 2M^+ + 2OH^- + H_2$	
$2M + 2C_2H_5OH = 2C_2H_5OM + H_2$	
$2M + 2NH_3 \text{ (gas)} = 2NH_2M + H_2$	
$3M + AlCl_3 = 3MCl + Al$	At high temperature
$6M + B_2O_3 = 3M_2O + 2B$	At high temperature
$2M + H_2 = 2MH$	
$5M + MNO_3 = 3M_2O + \frac{1}{2}N_2$	

sodium than potassium carbonate, with certain exceptions. The alkalies are found in varying amounts in nearly all silicates. The three commercially important lithium minerals are: amblygonite, $LiAlFPO_4$; spodumene, $LiAl(SiO_3)_2$; and lepidolite, $Li_2[F, OH]_2Al_2(SiO_3)_2$. The principal source of cesium is the mineral pollucite, $H_2Cs_4Al_4(SiO_3)_9$. Potassium feldspar, $KAlSi_3O_8$, is a constituent of granite.

8. Preparation and Uses of the Metals.—Lavoisier, in 1793, predicted that the "alkalies" would prove to be metallic oxides. Sir Humphry Davy isolated sodium and potassium in 1807 by electrolysis of their hydroxides. This method was long employed in the technical preparation of sodium. The metals may also be prepared by the reduction of the hydroxide or carbonate at moderately high temperatures, with iron, calcium, carbon, or other reducing agents. The reduction by less electropositive elements is accomplished through the greater volatility of the alkali metals. The reduction with calcium furnishes probably the simplest laboratory method of preparing rubidium and cesium.

Until recently sodium has been prepared commercially by the electrolysis of the fused hydroxide. Now in America most of the metal is prepared by the Downs process which employs the fused chloride. The normal melting point of the sodium chloride is lowered to about 600° C. by the addition of sodium carbonate. The sodium is liberated at the cathode, rises to the surface of the electrolyte as a liquid and is drawn off. Chlorine is liberated at the anode. Potassium is more difficult to prepare because of its greater solubility in the electrolyte. Some is made by the displacement of potassium from its carbonate by sodium vapor.

About 20,000 tons of sodium produced yearly in America are converted to a lead alloy for use in the synthesis of lead tetraethyl. Other uses are the manufacture of sodium peroxide and cyanide, and in the preparation of organic chemicals where a powerful reducing agent is required. The manufacture of photoelectric cells consumes some cesium but the amount required per cell is small. During the war potassium was burned to form KO_2 for use in oxygen re-breathers or masks, $2KO_2 + CO_2 = K_2CO_3 + \frac{3}{2}O_2$.

9. Alloys.—Sodium amalgamates with mercury with almost explosive violence. The amalgam is often used in place of the solid metal as a reducing agent. An alloy of 24 per cent sodium and 76 per cent potassium is liquid down to $-$ 12.6°. This is sometimes used to remove traces of water from gases. Lithium is more like the elements of the second and third groups (Par. **25**) and therefore alloys with them more readily than do sodium or potassium. Its alloy with aluminum may achieve commercial importance on account of its very low density. A lithium lead alloy is used for cable sheath, and small amounts of lithium are sometimes added to copper alloys as a "deoxidizer."

10. Hydrides.—Compounds of the type MH are formed by the direct action of hydrogen upon the heated metals. These compounds are salt-like in appearance and are of interest because of their analogy to the alkali halides. The electrolysis of the molten hydride results in the liberation of hydrogen at the anode, indicating that the hydrogen possesses a negative charge. Sodium hydride is employed commercially as an agent for descaling iron and other metals: $Fe_3O_4 + 4NaH = 3Fe + 4NaOH$.

11. Oxides.—The direct action of oxygen upon lithium produces the monoxide, Li_2O, and a trace of lithium peroxide, Li_2O_2; with sodium the peroxide, Na_2O_2, is produced; and with potassium, rubidium, and cesium the oxide, MO_2 results. The monoxides cannot be prepared by dehydration of the hydroxides, but may be formed by the action of the metal upon the nitrate, e.g. $5K + KNO_3 = 3K_2O + \frac{1}{2}N_2$. The oxides of the type, M_2O_2, are salts of hydrogen peroxide, while the type MO_2 are derivatives of the unstable compound HO_2 (cf. **III—14**). The only oxide of commercial importance is Na_2O_2 which is used extensively as a source of oxygen and hydrogen peroxide under the name of "oxone." The peroxide hydrolyzes in water with the formation of H_2O_2. When a small amount of water is used upon an excess of sodium peroxide, the liberated hydrogen peroxide decomposes with evolution of oxygen. Sodium peroxide is made commercially by heating sodium in dry air free from carbon dioxide to a temperature somewhat above 300°. The principle of counter currents is employed.

12. Hydroxides.—The older methods of manufacture used the reaction between a dilute solution of the alkali carbonate and milk of lime. $2Na^+ + CO_3^{--} + Ca^{++} + 2OH^- = CaCO_3 + 2Na^+ + 2OH^-$. Half of the hydroxide consumed in this country is produced by this process. The balance is manufactured by the electrolysis of a solution of the alkali chloride, a process which results in the formation of the hydroxide and hydrogen at the cathode and chlorine at the anode. The cell reaction is: $2H_2O + 2Cl^- = 2OH^- + H_2 + Cl_2$. In carrying out this electrolysis the cell must be constructed so as to prevent the interaction of the hydroxide and the chlorine, which would give hypochlorite at low temperatures or chlorate at higher temperatures. This problem is not altogether easy since the hydroxide moves toward the anode under the electric field and the chlorine is somewhat soluble in the brine. The **Nelson** cell used most extensively in the United States, has a carbon anode and perforated steel cathode. The brine percolates through the cell and out of the perforations in the cathode at such a rate that the hydroxide is swept back and prevented from reaching the anode. The liquid coming from the cell contains a mixture of the hydroxide and chloride. Upon evaporation the greater portion of the chloride is precipitated.

The **Castner-Kellner** process takes advantage of the fact that sodium or potassium may be electrolyzed from a concentrated brine solution with a mercury cathode to form a dilute amalgam, and this amalgam will react with water to form a dilute hydroxide solution. The cell employed is in-

TABLE IV

PRODUCTION AND CONSUMPTION OF SODIUM COMPOUNDS
IN UNITED STATES IN 1948

PRODUCTION OF SODIUM COMPOUNDS		CONSUMPTION OF SODIUM CARBONATE	
	Tons		*Tons*
Chloride	15,000,000	Glass	1,360,000
Carbonate	4,900,000	Soap	130,000
Hydroxide	2,300,000	Chemicals	2,100,000
Silicate	500,000	Cleaning compounds	140,000
Sulfate	800,000	Paper	240,000
Bicarbonate	200,000	Water softening	110,000
Borate	400,000	Petroleum	25,000
Phosphate	200,000	Textiles	70,000
Chromate	95,000		
Thiosulfate	50,000	CONSUMPTION OF SODIUM HYDROXIDE	
Sulfide	30,000		
Sulfite	15,000		*Tons*
Hypochlorite	25,000	Soap	110,000
Nitrate	5,000	Chemicals	520,000
Fluosilicate	5,000	Petroleum	170,000
Fluoride	5,000	Rayon	500,000
Metal	25,000	Lye	130,000
Acetate	3,000	Exports	185,000
Benzoate	600	Textiles	100,000
Citrate	1,500	Rubber reclaiming	26,000
		Pulp and paper	140,000
		Miscellaneous	400,000

geniously constructed for the continuous operation of these reactions. The process gives a very pure product.

Commercial sodium and potassium hydroxides may contain, in addition to large amounts of chloride, some carbonate, sulfate, nitrate, phosphate, acetate, and peroxide, as well as small amounts of the other alkalies. The hydroxide, sold as "pure by alcohol," has been dissolved in alcohol which separates out most of the impurities, but leaves a little chloride, carbonate, and acetate. A hydroxide free from the negative impurities may be made by treating a solution of purified alkali carbonate with silver carbonate and boiling the resulting solution with carefully purified lime in a silver dish.

The consumption of sodium hydroxide in the more important industries is given in Table IV. Potassium hydroxide is used less extensively than the sodium compound because of its greater cost. Its principal use is in the manufacturing of soft soap, which owes its properties to the greater solubility of the potassium compound.

13. Sodium Carbonates and Bicarbonates.—Sodium carbonate is found in high concentration in the lakes of many arid regions. Mono Lake and Owen's Lake in California contain millions of tons capable of rather cheap extraction.

The ashes of certain sea plants were formerly the common source of the salt, but it is now manufactured from sodium chloride. The **Le Blanc process** was the earliest (1791) method employed on a large scale for the conversion of chloride to carbonate, but the method is rapidly becoming obsolete. The steps in the process are:

(1) $NaCl + H_2SO_4 = NaHSO_4 + HCl$
(2) $NaHSO_4 + NaCl = Na_2SO_4 + HCl$
(3) $Na_2SO_4 + 2C = Na_2S + 2CO_2$
(4) $Na_2S + CaCO_3 = Na_2CO_3 + CaS$

Reaction (1) occurs readily upon gentle heating, but reaction (2) requires a much higher temperature. The third and fourth steps are carried out in a rotary furnace at a temperature of 700–1,000°, the charge consisting of a mixture of the sodium sulfate with coal dust and limestone. The product, called " black ash," is extracted with water and impure carbonate, $Na_2CO_3 \cdot H_2O$, obtained by crystallization. The sulfide residue is usually oxidized to free sulfur and thus made a profitable by-product.

The **Solvay** or **ammonia** process has now largely superseded the Le Blanc. It is based upon the reactions:

(1) $Na^+ + Cl^- + NH_3 + H_2O + CO_2 = NaHCO_3 + NH_4^+ + Cl^-$
(2) $2NaHCO_3 = Na_2CO_3 + H_2O + CO_2$

Reaction (1) depends upon the slight solubility of sodium bicarbonate in the solution at a temperature of 15° C. or below. The reaction is carried out by first saturating the brine with ammonia, and then with carbon dioxide. Following this the solution is cooled and the bicarbonate removed by filtration. Reaction (2) takes place upon gentle ignition.

The success of the process depends upon the recovery of the ammonia by the reaction: $2NH_4Cl + Ca(OH)_2 = 2NH_3 + CaCl_2 + 2H_2O$. Limestone serves as the source of both the carbon dioxide and the lime: $CaCO_3 = CaO + CO_2$.

The phase relations of the various hydrates are indicated in Fig. 1. The an-

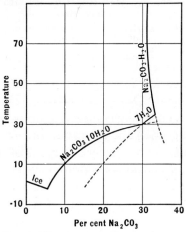

FIG. 1. The system sodium carbonate and water.

hydrous salt is known commercially as **soda-ash** and the decahydrate as **washing soda**. As the salt of a weak acid, sodium carbonate is hydrolyzed in solution, $1N\ Na_2CO_3$

containing about $0.01N$ OH⁻; and many of its uses, such as washing, depend upon this property. As a salt of a weak acid, it is also used to neutralize strong acids and in the preparation of their sodium salts. The consumption of sodium carbonate by various industries is given in Table IV.

Sodium bicarbonate, the common household baking soda, is obtained as a step in the Solvay process. With the excep-

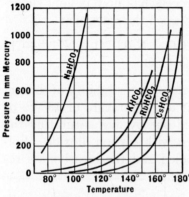

FIG. 2. Decomposition pressures of alkali bicarbonates.

tion of lithium, the alkali bicarbonates are all more insoluble than the carbonates. The conversion of bicarbonate to carbonate by heating becomes more difficult the higher the atomic weight of the alkali, as is indicated in the plot of decomposition pressures (Fig. 2). Advantage may be taken of the reversible reaction, $CO_3^= + CO_2 + H_2O = 2HCO_3^-$, to convert carbonates into bicarbonates. When a bicarbonate solution is evaporated at 100° or above, sodium sesquicarbonate, $Na_3(CO_3)(HCO_3)\cdot 2H_2O$ separates.

The bicarbonate is employed in baking, the use depending upon the liberation of carbon dioxide with acid, as does also its use in certain types of fire extinguishers. The ease of purification of sodium bicarbonate by crystallization renders it a valuable standard in the titration of acids and bases. For this use it is fused to convert to the carbonate and to remove the last traces of water. This operation should be carried out in an atmosphere of CO_2, since the decomposition pressure of Na_2CO_3 is 2.2 mm. at 700° and 6.2 mm. at 1,000°.

14. Potassium Carbonates.—For centuries potassium carbonate was extracted from wood ashes; hence its name, potash. It may be made from the chloride by the Le Blanc process, but not by the Solvay process, since the bicarbonate is not sufficiently insoluble. However the conversion is generally carried out: (1) by the precipitation of $KHCO_3$ ·$MgCO_3$·$4H_2O$ by passing CO_2 under pressure into a suspension of $MgCO_3$ in KCl solution and (2) the recovery of the potassium carbonate from the double salt by decomposition with hot water giving insoluble $MgCO_3$ and a solution of potassium carbonate, $2MgKH(CO_3)_24H_2O$ = $2MgCO_3 + K_2CO_3 + CO_2 + 9H_2O$. Other sources are the mother liquors obtained in the manufacture of beet sugar, wine-lees, and water used in washing crude wool which contains potassium fatty acids. In each case the organic material is ignited to give the carbonate.

Potassium carbonate crystallizes as the dihydrate. It is used in making soap and hard glass, and in the textile industries.

Potassium bicarbonate is similar in chemical properties to the sodium salt but is about three times as soluble.

15. Lithium, Rubidium, and Cesium Carbonates.—Lithium carbonate is the most important commercial compound of that element, is used in medicine, in the preparation of other lithium compounds, in ceramics for producing high glazes, and in the glass industry for making special glasses with high fluidity when molten. Its solubility is sufficiently low so that it may be prepared by precipitation from a solution containing lithium ion by the addition of sodium carbonate. Lithium bicarbonate is soluble.

The rubidium and cesium carbonates and bicarbonates resemble the potassium compounds.

16. Fluorides.—The alkali fluorides do not occur free in nature to any large extent, although sodium aluminum fluoride, Na_3AlF_6, cryolite, occurs in large deposits. The fluorides are usually prepared by the action of hydrofluoric acid upon the carbonate. With excess of the acid they tend to form acid fluorides such as MHF_2 or even MH_3F_4

(cf. **X—10**). These acid compounds are sometimes used as a method of preparing pure hydrogen fluoride, since they readily decompose with the evolution of the gas. Lithium fluoride is but slightly soluble. Sodium fluoride has some use as an insecticide and a wood preservative. It is also used in the preparation of complex fluorides.

17. Chlorides.—Alkali chlorides are found in great deposits resulting from the evaporation of inland lakes or seas.

Sodium chloride. In many places great beds of almost pure sodium chloride have been located and from these salt is taken by ordinary mining operations. In regions removed from naturally occurring salt deposits, sodium chloride is obtained from sea water or salt wells usually by solar evaporation in shallow ponds. Crude salt generally contains traces of calcium and magnesium chlorides which are objectionable because of their deliquescence. Pure sodium chloride may be precipitated from a concentrated brine upon addition of hydrogen chloride gas, due, in part, to the increase in concentration of chloride ion. The reaction qualitatively is that predicted by the Mass Law.

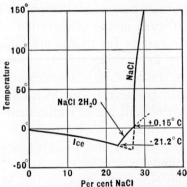

FIG. 3. The system sodium chloride and water.

The solubility of sodium chloride changes but slightly with temperature, being 26.3 per cent at 0° and 28.1 per cent at 100°. Phase relations in the salt-water system are given in Fig. 3. The crystal structure has been discussed in Paragraph **6.**

The production of salt in the United States in 1938 was about nine million tons. Of this three million tons were used in the preparation of the carbonate by the Solvay process. Other important industrial uses include refrigeration; agriculture; household; metallurgy of silver, copper, and lead; tanning; preservative; ceramics; salting out of soap; preparation of hydrochloric acid and sodium sulfate by reaction with sulfuric acid; and the preparation of sodium hydroxide and chlorine by electrolysis.

18. Potassium Chloride.—For many years Germany enjoyed an almost complete monopoly of potassium salts through the possession of the extensive deposits of chloride at Stassfurt in Prussia. Since 1930 there has occurred a rapid development of the potash deposits in the United States. These have been principally the deep lying saline deposits in New Mexico and the natural brines of Searles Lake in California. Over a million tons of potassium salts, chiefly chloride, were produced from these sources in 1948.

The major portion of the potassium chloride of the Stassfurt deposits is in the form of double salts of magnesium and calcium chloride, sulfate, and borate. The most important of these is carnallite, $MgCl_2 \cdot KCl \cdot 6H_2O$, and to a lesser extent kainite, $MgSO_4 \cdot KCl \cdot 3H_2O$. Potassium chloride is extracted by dissolving carnallite in hot magnesium chloride solution; cooling this solution precipitates the greater part of the potassium chloride. The production of potassium chloride at Stassfurt in 1938 was in excess of 1,500,000 tons. The dust from blast furnaces manufacturing pig iron, and the dust from cement kilns, has been shown to contain potassium chloride and also sulfate in recoverable amounts. It is estimated that the United States could produce several hundred thousands of tons yearly from this source. The most important uses of the potassium chloride are as fertilizer (about 90 per cent) and in the production of potassium hydroxide and other potassium compounds. Growing tests indicate that the production of grain in this country could be increased 30 per cent by the average use of 50 lbs of K_2O per acre.

19. Lithium, Rubidium, and Cesium Chlorides.—Lithium chloride is the most soluble of the group. It forms mono-, di-, and tri-hydrates, and in many respects resembles magnesium chloride.

One of the most important sources of rubidium and cesium chlorides is the mother liquor remaining after the extraction of the potassium chloride from carnallite. These elements are usually separated from the liquid by conversion into the relatively insoluble alums through the addition of aluminum sulfate.

20. Bromides and Iodides.—Bromides and iodides occur in sea water and in the various salt deposits. They are not recovered as such, but the halogens are liberated as the free elements, and the salts prepared from the elements by methods discussed under the halogens. Sodium and potassium bromides are used in medicine as sedatives, and in photography for precipitating silver bromide and as retardants in developers. The alkali iodides find limited application in photography, and in medicine to supply iodine to the thyroid gland, and sometimes in tincture of iodine, to increase the amount of iodine that can be dissolved.

21. Cyanides.—Sodium cyanide is made on a large scale from sodium amide (Table III) by reduction with carbon at red heat: $NaNH_2 + C = NaCN + H_2$. A mixture of sodium and potassium cyanides may be prepared by the reduction of potassium ferrocyanide with sodium: $K_4Fe(CN)_6 + 2Na = 4KCN + 2NaCN + Fe$. Potassium cyanide is also manufactured by the action of ammonia upon a mixture of potassium carbonate and carbon at a high temperature: $K_2CO_3 + 2NH_3 + 4C = 2KCN + 3CO + 3H_2$. The alkali cyanides are very soluble in water, and the solution is quite alkaline due to the hydrolysis of the cyanide. The uses of these compounds in gold mining and electroplating depend upon the formation of complex cyanides with gold, silver, and platinum. The sodium salt is now generally used due to the fact that it is cheaper and gives a higher weight of cyanide per pound of salt. Like all substances giving cyanide ion or hydrogen cyanide in solution, these salts are very poisonous.

22. Sulfates.—The alkali sulfates and double sulfates with calcium and magnesium are found in the various salt lakes and salt deposits. Double sulfate of sodium and potassium, as $KNaSO_4$, and various types of sodium and potassium alums are of frequent occurrence in volcanic lava. Sodium sulfate, called salt cake, is a product of the manufacture of hydrochloric acid from sodium chloride. Some potassium sulfate is extracted from the Stassfurt deposits.

Sodium sulfate is used in medicine as a cathartic and in the manufacture of cheap glass to furnish the sodium. Its principal use (over 400,000 tons annually) is in the "sulfate" process for the manufacture of wood pulp. It can be crystallized as $Na_2SO_4 \cdot 10H_2O$, Glauber's salt, below 32.384°, and as the anhydrous sulfate above that temperature. The transition point serves as a convenient "fixed point" in the standardization of thermometers. The solubility of the decahydrate increases rapidly with temperature and the solutions formed at the higher temperatures may be readily cooled in the supersaturated state. If a particle of this solid hydrate is then added, crystallization takes place and the whole solution appears to solidify. An unstable heptahydrate may be crystallized out below 24° C. Potassium sulfate is used in the preparation of potassium alum and also as fertilizer, being preferred to the chloride for this purpose with certain crops, especially tobacco.

23. Nitrates.—Alkali nitrates are formed in nature through the decomposition of organic material. Due to the solubility of these salts, deposits are found only in the rainless regions of the earth. By far the most important occurs in Chile, and is composed chiefly of sodium nitrate. Commercial "Chile saltpetre," consisting of 95 to 98 per cent sodium nitrate, is made by extracting the crude nitre rock with water. Chile saltpetre was formerly almost the only source of the nitric acid and nitrate-fertilizer, but now has been largely replaced by the various processes for the fixation of atmospheric nitrogen (cf. **XII—32**).

The uses of the alkali nitrates which depend upon the oxidizing power of nitrate are discussed under the chemistry of nitrogen. Potassium nitrate absorbs water less readily than sodium nitrate, and for this reason was formerly used more extensively than the sodium salt in gunpowder. Potassium nitrate is prepared from the sodium by double decomposition with potassium chloride, taking advantage of the fact that the solubilities of potassium chloride, potassium nitrate, and sodium nitrate increase rapidly with temperature, while that of sodium chloride is hardly affected. The sodium nitrate is dissolved in hot water and concentrated potassium chloride solution is added, whereupon most of the sodium is precipitated as chloride. The solution is then evaporated, more sodium chloride first separating, followed by potassium nitrate.

The crystal structure of sodium nitrate is similar to the simple cubic arrangement of sodium chloride (Par. **6**), the nitrate group as a whole occupying the positions corresponding to the chloride ion. The alkali nitrates differ from the nitrates of most of the other metals in that upon heating they first decompose into nitrite and oxygen. Upon further heating nitrogen and oxygen are evolved and the oxide and peroxide formed. A mixture of 45 per cent sodium and 55 per cent potassium nitrates melts at 220° and is a convenient high temperature liquid bath.

24. Other Salts of the Alkali Metals.—Compounds of the alkali metals with sulfide, thiosulfate, chlorate, perchlorate, phosphate, borate, and silicate are of importance, but since their properties and uses depend so largely upon the chemistry of negative ions, they are discussed in the chapters dealing with those ions.

25. Chemical and Analytical Properties of Ions.—The outstanding characteristic of the alkali ions is the slight tendency to form insoluble salts or complex ions. As already mentioned, lithium resembles the alkaline earth metals in many respects. Thus lithium fluoride, carbonate, and phosphate are moderately insoluble and the bicarbonate more soluble than the carbonate, like the alkaline earth metals, and unlike the rest of the alkalies. Lithium ion is slightly hydrolyzed. The chloroplatinates, acid tartrates, and alums of lithium and sodium are soluble, while the corresponding salts of potassium, rubidium, and cesium are relatively insoluble. Potassium forms with sodium cobaltinitrite in dilute acid the precipitate, $K_2NaCo(NO_2)_6$. It is the least soluble of the potassium compounds, but this does not serve to distinguish potassium from rubidium, cesium, or ammonium, which form corresponding compounds. Potassium picrate, $C_6H_2(NO_2)_3OK$, potassium perchlorate, $KClO_4$, and sodium and potassium fluosilicates, Na_2SiF_6, K_2SiF_6, are also but slightly soluble. Sodium antimonate, $NaSb(OH)_6$, is the least soluble of the sodium salts. Sodium may be precipitated from solutions containing potassium by use of the uranyl zinc acetate reagent. The formula of the precipitate is $NaZn(UO_2)_3Ac_9 \cdot 6H_2O$. For quantitative determinations the conditions for the precipitation must be carefully controlled.

Potassium ion appears to be more readily adsorbed than sodium ion, and this in part accounts for the much smaller quantity of potassium salts in sea water, although another factor may be its more ready precipitation as an iron silicate, $KFeSi_2O_6$.

In the quantitative analysis of the alkalies, they are usually converted to the chlorides and the mixture weighed. The lithium chloride may be extracted by dissolving in amyl alcohol. Potassium, rubidium, and cesium are converted to the chloroplatinates, and the sodium obtained by difference. Although rubidium and cesium are rarely present in quantity they may be separated from potassium by taking advantage of difference in solubility of the acid tartrates.

In addition to the use of the spectroscope in the identification of the alkalies, advantage is taken of the color imparted to the Bunsen flame by the presence of volatile compounds of these elements. Lithium colors the flame red, sodium yellow, potassium violet, rubidium bluish red, and cesium blue. The sodium flame test is of extraordinary delicacy, being capable of detecting 10^{-10} grams of sodium. Since this quantity of sodium is present in practically every substance, it is necessary in making a flame test for sodium to judge the amount of sodium present largely by the length of time that the intense yellow color persists in comparison to pure sodium chloride as a standard. The potassium flame test is about five thousand times less sensitive than the sodium test. In the presence of any considerable amount of sodium it is necessary to use a thick blue glass to cut out the yellow sodium light in order to detect the potassium.

26. Francium.—The first isotope of element 87 to be discovered was a member of the naturally occurring actinium decay series, (cf. **XXII**). In 1939 M. Perey observed a branching of the decay chain (about 1 per cent) at Ac^{227} which produces Fr^{223} by alpha-emission. The half-life of this isotope is only 21 minutes. Since that date four other radioactive isotopes have been made by nuclear-bombardment reactions. All of these additional isotopes have half-lives shorter than that of Fr^{223}.

Chapter V

GROUP II. ALKALINE EARTH METALS

1. On the basis of their atomic structure the elements with two valence electrons may be divided into a main group consisting of beryllium (formerly often called glucinium from the sweet taste of some of its compounds), magnesium, calcium, strontium, barium, and radium, and a subgroup, zinc, cadmium, and mercury. As a common characteristic the main group elements have kernels with the same number and arrangement of electrons as the preceding noble gas, while the subgroup elements have kernels with eighteen electrons in the outer shell. Beryllium and magnesium are smaller and much less basic than the rest of the main group, and before the fundamental differences in atomic structure were recognized, they were frequently classified with the subgroup elements. The remaining elements of the main group have hydroxides with distinctly alkaline properties and have long been known as the alkaline earth elements, and we shall use the term as applying to all of the main group.

2. Physical Properties of Metals.—The elements in the free state are highly metallic. They have grey white luster when freshly cut, but readily tarnish, especially the heavier members of the group. Although somewhat brittle, they may be hammered and rolled. Beryllium is hard enough to scratch glass, while barium is but slightly harder than lead. The metals are good electrical conductors; the specific conductivity of calcium is about 45 per cent that of silver.

Their melting points (Table I) are much higher than those of the alkali metals.

TABLE I

ATOMIC AND PHYSICAL PROPERTIES OF ALKALINE EARTH ELEMENTS

	Be	Mg	Ca	Sr	Ba	Ra
Atomic number............	4	12	20	38	56	88
Atomic weight............	9.02	24.32	40.8	87.63	137.36	226.05
Isotopes.................	9	24, 25, 26	40, 44, 42, 43, 46, 48	88, 86, 84, 87,	138, 136, 134, 137, 135, 132 130	224, 226
Electrons in various quantum levels, 1st..........	2	2	2	2	2	2
2d..........	2	8	8	8	8	8
3d..........		2	8	18	18	18
4th.........			2	8	18	32
5th.........				2	8	18
6th.........					2	8
7th.........						2
Ionic radius $\times 10^8$ cm.......	0.31	0.65	0.99	1.13	1.35	
Ionization potential of gaseous atom, volts, 1st electron........	'.28	7.61	6.09	5.67	5.19	5
2d electron..........	18.1	14.96	11.82	10.98	9.95	
Potential between metal and molal solution of ion, $M = M^{++} + 2e^-$ in volts .	+ 1.70	+ 2.34	+ 2.87	+ 2.89	+ 2.90	
Heat of hydration of gaseous ions, kcal. approx........		460	395	355	305	
Melting point ° C.........	1284	650	851	771	717	(960)
Boiling point ° C..........	2507	1126	1487	1384	1640	(1140)
Density of metal..........	1.73	1.75	1.55	2.6	3.75	6.0

3. **Chemical Properties.**—In all of their compounds the elements are present in the + 2 oxidation state, i.e. both of the two outer electrons are always lost when the elements enter into chemical reactions. It will be observed (Table I) that the oxidation potential of the heavier members of the group is as great as that of the alkali metals. Thus barium readily reacts with water, losing its electrons to the hydrogen of the water and forming barium ion and molecular hydrogen: $Ba + 2H_2O = Ba^{++} + 2OH^- + H_2$. The mechanism of the reaction involves taking the two electrons away from the barium and this, as given in Table I, requires about five volts for the first electron and ten for the second. These values of the ionization potentials are higher for the alkaline earth metals than for the alkali metals, and the reason that

barium is so readily oxidized to form the ion is to be found in the large heat of hydration of the barium ion. However, the rate of reaction of the second group elements with water is much slower than that of the alkali metals, even in the case of the more electropositive members; and magnesium and beryllium are scarcely attacked by water alone at ordinary temperatures. The metals burn brilliantly when heated in air or oxygen, forming the monoxide, except in the case of barium, which forms the peroxide. A certain amount of the nitride is also formed when burned in air, especially with magnesium, calcium, and radium. Because of their highly electropositive character the metals burn readily when ignited in carbon dioxide, forming the metal oxide and carbon. At low temperatures the metal surfaces are protected from rapid oxidation by oxide films; this is particularly true of beryllium and magnesium. Beryllium does not dissolve with appreciable speed in water even when boiled. Magnesium evolves hydrogen very slowly with cold water, while with calcium a slow stream of bubbles is observed. The metals all dissolve rapidly in acids. Beryllium dissolves in the alkali hydroxides in a manner similar to aluminum: $Be + OH^- + H_2O = HBeO_2^- + H_2$. Due to

TABLE II
REACTIONS OF GROUP II METALS

$2M + O_2 = 2MO$	Ba also forms BaO_2
$M + 2H_2O = M(OH)_2 + H_2$	Very slow with Be and Mg
$M + H_2 = MH_2$	With Ca, Sr, and Ba at high temperature
$M + 2H^+ = M^{++} + H_2$	
$4M + 10H^+ + NO_3^- = 4M^{++} + NH_4^+ + 3H_2O$	With dilute acid: H_2 also evolved
$M + X_2 = MX_2$	$X_2 =$ any halogen
$3M + N_2 = M_3N_2$	High temperature
$3M + 2NH_3 = M_3N_2 + 3H_2$	Heated
$M + S = MS$	Also with Se and Te
$M + 2C = MC_2$	Especially with Ca, Sr. High temperature
$3M + 2P = M_3P_2$	Heated
$2M + CO_2 = 2MO + C$	Burn in CO_2

their action as strong reducing agents the metals are oxidized by many of the negative elements. A summary of the more important types of reactions is given in Table II.

4. Occurrence.—None of the elements of the group exists free in nature. The estimated percentages of the elements in igneous rocks are: calcium, 3.63; magnesium, 2.09; barium, 0.05; strontium, 1.9×10^{-4}; beryllium, 1×10^{-5}; and radium, 10^{-12}. Beryllium compounds do not occur in large deposits but small quantities are found in many minerals and granitic rocks, usually as complex silicates and aluminates. The most important mineral is beryl, $3BeO \cdot Al_2O_3 \cdot 6SiO_2$. Colored dark green with chromium it is known as emerald. A blue-green form is aquamarine. Masses of beryl weighing more than a ton have been found in New Hampshire. The elements are found in combination with practically all of the acid oxides. A few of the more important minerals are: magnesite, $MgCO_3$; talc or soapstone, $H_2Mg_3(SiO_3)_4$; asbestos, $CaMg_3(SiO_3)_4$; dolomite, $MgCO_3 \cdot CaCO_3$; spinel, $Mg(AlO_2)_2$; carnallite, $MgCl_2 \cdot KCl \cdot 6H_2O$; limestone, $CaCO_3$; gypsum, $CaSO_4 \cdot 2H_2O$; fluorspar, CaF_2; apatite, $Ca_5(PO_4)_3X$, (X = Cl or F); strontianite, $SrCO_3$; barites, $BaSO_4$. Magnesium and calcium chlorides and sulfates are present in sea water, the former in somewhat larger concentrations. Both elements are found as integral parts of animal and vegetable matter, although calcium is more prevalent than magnesium.

Radium is widely distributed in almost all rocks but in extremely small quantities. Primary uranium minerals contain about 3.4×10^{-7} grams of radium per gram of uranium (cf. **XXIII**).

5. Metals: Preparation and Uses.—The metals are generally prepared by the electrolysis of their molten chlorides or fluorides to which alkali halides have been added to decrease the melting point. The common commercial electrolyte for magnesium is 70 per cent magnesium chloride and 30 per cent sodium chloride. The recently developed carbothermic and silicothermic processes show considerable promise. In the former a mixture of magnesium oxide and coal is heated to 2300° C. in an electric furnace and magnesium vapor distilled off. In the latter the oxide is reduced by ferro-silicon in the presence of lime. $2MgO + Si(Fe) + 2CaO = 2Mg + Ca_2SiO_4 + (Fe)$. The iron acts as carrier of the silicon and takes no part in the reaction. Calcium is prepared by the electrolysis of a mixture of the chloride and fluoride in a graphite crucible, which acts as the anode. The cathode is an iron rod just dipping into the molten salts. The liberated calcium adheres to the rod which is slowly raised, thus forming a long "stalk" of calcium. Beryllium and magnesium chlorides may be reduced by sodium or potassium at high temperatures and barium oxide is reduced by silicon at 1200° C. As a war emergency, a process was developed for the production of calcium by reduction of calcium oxide by aluminum, the reaction being carried out in vacuum at 1200° C.

Magnesium is used in signal flares and in photographic flash lights, usually in the form of powder; the latter use depends upon the high proportion of ultraviolet light in the flame formed by the combustion of the metal. It is also made into ribbon, the major part of which is now used in the degasification of radio tubes. Its importance in this connection is due to the absorption by the heated metal, not only of oxygen, but also of nitrogen through the formation of the nitride, Mg_3N_2. It is employed as a deoxidizer in casting bronze, nickel-silver, and monel metal. A small per cent of magnesium added to aluminum greatly increases the ease of machining of the latter. The composition of a number of magnesium alloys which are trade-marked, Dowmetal, A. M. Alloys, and Bohnalite X, is given in Table III.

Because of their low density (1.8) and high tensile strength these alloys are now widely used in the construction of airplanes, portable tools, and other machinery where light weight is important. The alloys are frequently treated

TABLE III
Composition of Magnesium Alloys

Use

Mg, 91.8; Al, 2.0; Mn, 0.2; Cd, 2.0; Cu, 4 . . . . Mold
Mg, 89.1; Al, 4.0; Zn, 0.4; Si, 0.5; Sn. 6.0 . . . . Wrought
Mg, 92; Al, 7.0; Zn, 0.75; Mn, 0.2 . . . . Sheet
Mg, 88.2; Zn, 4.5; Mn, 0.8; Si, 0.5; Sn. 6.0 . . . . Press forged
Mg, 9; Al, 91 . . . . Mold

with chromic or selenious acid solutions to give their surfaces a corrosion resistant film.

Calcium metal is used as a deoxidizer in the manufacture of many alloys and special steels. It is volatile at the temperature of molten steel and leaves no metallic residue. Some calcium silicide is used instead of the metal in certain steels. Although pure beryllium is brittle and has no industrial application, its alloys are rapidly becoming useful commodities. A 2.25 per cent beryllium alloy with copper is a remarkable spring material. A beryllium-cobalt-copper alloy combines high electrical conductivity with great hardness. Nickel with 1.8 per cent beryllium can be heat-treated to give values of tensile strengths as high as 260,000 pounds per sq. in. The addition of 0.5 per cent beryllium hardens gold and is said to increase the resistance of silver to tarnish. Because of its nuclear properties, beryllium may become highly important in the construction of nuclear reactors.

Radium amalgam is formed upon the electrolysis of radium chloride solution using a mercury cathode. The mercury may be driven off by heating to leave the radium. The metal is said to blacken quickly due to the formation of the nitride.

COMPOUNDS

6. Oxides.—The monoxides are difficultly fusible (Table IV) and extremely stable, remaining undecomposed at temperatures of 3,000° C. Their heats of hydration increase in order of the atomic weights.

TABLE IV

Oxides of Group II

	BeO	MgO	CaO	SrO	BaO
Common name.............	beryllia	magnesia	lime	strontia	baryta
Melting point ° C..........	2,450	2,642	2,705	2,700	2,000
Heat of formation kcal. per mole...........	135.9	143.9	151.9	141.2	133.4
Heat of hydration $MO + H_2O = M(OH)_2...$		5.4	15.1	17.7	22.3
Solubility moles/liter of $M(OH)_2$ at 20° C.......	5×10^{-9}	3×10^{-4}	0.022	0.065	0.22
Decomposition temp. ° C. $M(OH)_2 = MO + H_2O$ (gas 1 at.)..............			547	778	998

Beryllium oxide is as hard as corundum but the heavier oxides are soft. Beryllium oxide does not react with water. Magnesium oxide, if not ignited too strongly, reacts very slowly, while the rest of the group react rapidly. With lime the hydration reaction is called "slaking." The reaction starts slowly, but the heat evolved soon raises the temperature to a point where the reaction proceeds rapidly. The heat of slaking is sufficient, under some conditions, to cause the ignition of wood or other combustible material; hence the accidental slaking of stored lime often results in destructive fires.

The solid oxides crystallize in the sodium chloride type of ion lattice, with the exception of beryllium oxide, which is similar to zinc oxide (Append. V). The oxides are extremely poor conductors of heat.

The oxides of all except beryllium are generally prepared by the decomposition of the carbonates. The ease of decomposition decreases with increasing atomic weight, that is with increasing basicity of the metal oxide. The manufacture of lime is carried out in tall chimney-like furnaces known as lime kilns. The process is continuous; limestone is fed into the top, is heated and decomposed by a draft of hot gas, and the lime is removed at the bottom of the kiln.

The reaction is carried out at as low a temperature as possible to prevent the fusion of silicates present in the limestone which would render the lime inactive. In order to keep the temperature low the partial pressure of the carbon dioxide must also be kept low. In Fig. 1 are given the pressures of carbon dioxide in equilibrium with the oxide and carbonate at various temperatures. If calcium carbonate is heated in a retort under atmospheric pressure it requires a temperature of 910° C. to bring about decomposition; how-

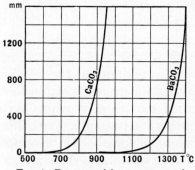

ever, in the operation of the lime kiln the blast of hot gases through the furnace keeps the partial pressure of the carbon dioxide at a low figure and permits the reaction to go to completion at temperatures much below 910°. In the case of barium carbonate, the decomposition temperature is so high that carbon is mixed

FIG. 1. Decomposition pressures of calcium and barium carbonates.

with the charge further to lower the partial pressure of the carbon dioxide: $C + CO_2 = 2CO$. Barium oxide is sometimes prepared from the nitrate, since it decomposes at much lower temperatures.

Magnesia in the form of bricks is used for lining furnaces and other refractory purposes. Mixed with asbestos it is employed as heat insulation for hot water and steam pipes. Other uses include: the manufacture of Sorel cement (Par. 9); absorbent in the manufacture of dynamite; vulcanization of rubber; adulterant of paint. Large quantities of mixed magnesium and calcium oxides are used for some purposes in place of pure magnesia, the mixture being produced by the calcination of dolomite.

The production of lime in the United States in 1948 was 6,000,000 tons. This was consumed chiefly (1) in making the hydroxide (*vide infra*), used in plaster by the building industry, (2) in agriculture for soil treatment, and (3) in the chemical industries. Heated in the oxy-hydrogen flame, lime gives out an intense light, hence its former use in the "lime light." Calcium oxide is often employed as a de-hydrating agent, for example, in the preparation of absolute alcohol and the drying of ammonia gas. A mixture of sodium hydroxide and calcium oxide, "soda-lime," is often em-ployed to remove both water and carbon dioxide from gases. Lime containing more than 5 per cent magnesium oxide does not slake readily and is called "lean."

Barium oxide is the only one of the group which may be converted into the **peroxide**, BaO_2, upon heating in air, although with the exception of beryllium the peroxides may all be prepared by the action of hydrogen peroxide upon the metal ion. Barium peroxide is mentioned in connection with the preparation of oxygen and hydro-gen peroxide. With water it readily forms the hydrate, $BaO_2 \cdot 8H_2O$.

7. Hydroxides.—The formation of the hydroxides from oxides has been discussed above. The alkaline reaction of the hydroxides is limited by their solubilities (Table IV); however, the hydroxides of calcium and the heavier mem-bers of the group may be classed as strong bases. Their salts with strong acids are very slightly hydrolyzed. Barium hydroxide is the only one which is stable enough to be heated to fusion.

Beryllium hydroxide is amphoteric (Hildebrand, *Prin. of Chem.*, p. 214), a fact which is not surprising in view of the very small size of Be^{++} (cf. **III—7**). The freshly precipitated hydroxide is said to have the formula $Be_2O(OH)_2$ and is metastable with respect to the form $Be(OH)_2$. It dissolves in hydrogen ion to form Be^{++} but this ion hydrolizes at low acid to form Be_2O^{++}.

$$2Be^{++} + H_2O = Be_2O^{++} + 2H^+$$

The hydroxide is soluble in hydroxide ion to form BeO_2^{--} or $Be_2O_3^{--}$ (beryllate or deberyllate).

Some **magnesium hydroxide** is prepared by the action of steam upon magnesium chloride: $MgCl_2 + H_2O = MgO + 2HCl$. The hydroxide is precipitated from a solution of magnesium ion upon the addition of a strong base. It belongs to the class of sparingly soluble bases which are soluble in excess of ammonium ion: $Mg(OH)_2 + 2NH_4^+ = Mg^{++} + 2NH_4OH$.

Because of its low cost of production, **calcium hydroxide** is used commercially in many processes requiring hydroxide ion. A suspension of the solid in its saturated solution (milk of lime) is often employed. Among the more important uses are: the preparation of mortar, bleaching powder, ammonia, alkali hydroxide; purification of sugar and illuminating gas; removal of hair from hides; softening of water (Par. **11**). The most extensive use is that in **mortar.** This is made by mixing slaked lime, one volume, with sand, three or four volumes, and water to make a thick paste. The mortar gradually hardens due, first, to the evaporation of water and the cementing action of the deposited hydroxide, and second, to the absorption of carbon dioxide from the air: $Ca(OH)_2 + CO_2 = CaCO_3 + H_2O$. There follows a very slow formation of calcium silicate. The setting is accompanied by a decrease in volume but the presence of the large amount of sand prevents a large total shrinkage and renders the product porous.

Strontium hydroxide is made by heating the carbonate in steam: $SrCO_3 + H_2O = Sr(OH)_2 + CO_2$. This reaction takes place at a lower temperature than the reaction: $SrCO_3 = SrO + CO_2$, due in part to the lowering of the partial pressure of the carbon dioxide by the steam, and in part to the energy of formation of the hydroxide from the oxide. The hydroxide crystallizes as $Sr(OH_2 \cdot 8H_2O$. Strontium hydroxide is employed in the refinement of sugar to recover sugar from dilute solutions. Both calcium and strontium ions form insoluble precipitates (saccharates) with sugar from hydroxide solutions, and these may be decomposed by the action of carbon dioxide. The strontium compound is somewhat the less soluble but the general practice in the sugar industry in the United States is to cool in solution and precipitate the calcium saccharate.

Barium hydroxide crystallizes with eight molecules of water. Its solution is known as "baryta-water," and is often employed as a standard alkali in quantitative analysis. The insolubility of the barium carbonate keeps the solution free from carbonate ion, which is usually present in sodium hydroxide and which is objectionable in titrating acids when certain indicators are used.

8. Carbonates.—Normal beryllium carbonate does not exist, but a basic carbonate is precipitated upon the addition of sodium carbonate to a soluble beryllium salt. The precipitate is soluble in excess of the reagent due to the formation of the beryllate ion, $Be_2O_3^{--}$.

Normal magnesium carbonate, $MgCO_3$, occurs in nature as the mineral, magnesite. A basic carbonate, $Mg_4(OH)_2$-$(CO_3)_3 \cdot 3H_2O$, is precipitated when an alkali carbonate is added to magnesium ion. The precipitate is soluble in excess ammonium ion due to the equilibria: $NH_4^+ + OH^- = NH_4OH$, and $NH_4^+ + CO_3^{--} + H_2O = HCO_3^- + NH_4OH$. The carbonate is also soluble in carbonic acid (see Calcium Carbonate below). The precipitated basic salt is used in medicine under the name "magnesia alba," partly as a mild alkali and partly for the physiological action of magnesium ion. Considerable quantities are consumed in the preparation of tooth powder and of silver polish. The natural carbonate and also the double carbonate with calcium, dolomite, $CaCO_3 \cdot MgCO_3$, are used for the commercial production of carbon dioxide. The compound $MgCO_3(NH_4)_2CO_3 \cdot 4H_2O$ is precipitated upon the addition of ammonium carbonate to magnesium ion in a solution containing 30 per cent alcohol. Advantage is taken of this fact in qualitative analysis.

Calcium carbonate crystallizes in two forms, calcite, rhombohedral, and aragonite, rhombic. The latter is unstable in respect to the former but the rate of transition is slow at ordinary temperatures. The heat of transition is about 300 cal. per mole. The carbonate is the most abundant of the calcium compounds. The most common forms are: Iceland spar, which is almost pure calcite; marble; limestone, which is less crystalline and contains clay and other silicates; chalk, which has been formed from the shells of minute marine organisms; shells and pearls.

The crystal structure of calcite is similar to that of sodium chloride, with the carbonate group replacing the chloride. The three oxygens are symmetrical about the carbon. Because of the size of the carbonate group the unit cube is distorted into a rhombohedron. Calcite is luminescent under the action of cathode rays. The glow persists for some time after the action of the rays has been stopped.

Calcium carbonate is precipitated upon the addition of carbonate ion. If the solution is boiling the precipitate is largely aragonite; in the cold it is finely divided calcite, which becomes coarse grained and distinctly crystalline upon standing. The solubility of calcium carbonate is increased in the presence of hydrogen ion due to the equilibrium, $H^+ + CO_3^{--} = HCO_3^-$ (cf. XIII—10) and hence, $CaCO_3 + H^+ = Ca^{++} + HCO_3^-$. With excess acid, carbon dioxide is, of course, liberated. Due to the fact that the second ionization step of carbonic acid is much less than the first, calcium carbonate dissolves in carbonic acid: $CaCO_3 + H_2CO_3 = Ca^{++} + 2HCO_3^-$. This reaction occurs wherever water comes in contact with rock or soil containing calcium (or magnesium) carbonate, and imparts "hardness" to the water, which is objectionable for certain purposes (Par. 10). The bicarbonate solution upon heating loses carbon dioxide and the carbonate is again precipitated.

Stalactites and stalagmites are formed in caves by the precipitation of calcium carbonate brought about by the loss of carbon dioxide from water, which has been highly charged with the gas and thereby dissolved large quantities of limestone.

In addition to widespread use as building material, limestone is used in the manufacture of cement, lime, and glass. It is used in many metallurgical processes to form a flux with silica through the formation of calcium silicate.

Strontium and barium carbonates occur in nature as strontianite, $SrCO_3$, and witherite, $BaCO_3$, respectively. Next to the sulfates, they are the most important sources of these elements. The stability of the carbonates toward decomposition into the oxides increases, and the solubility in water decreases with increasing atomic weight. The general solubility equilibria of these carbonates with acid is similar to those of calcium, discussed above.

9. Halides.—The halides of beryllium, unlike most metallic halides, are very poor conductors of electricity in the fused state. The beryllium halides are highly hydrolyzed in solution, and the solutions upon evaporation yield basic salts.

The fluorides of the members of the group other than beryllium are insoluble in water, even in the presence of an excess of fluoride ion. The fluorides of calcium, strontium, and barium crystallize in ionic lattices of the so-called "calcium fluoride structure" (Append. V). Calcium fluoride occurs as the mineral fluorite or fluor-spar, and is important as the chief source of fluorine compounds. It is unusually transparent to ultraviolet light, nearly to 0.1 μ.

In the Dow process for extraction of magnesium from sea water, the hydroxide is first precipitated by lime and then converted to chloride by hydrochloric acid. The chloride crystallizes from its water solution at room temperature as $MgCl_2 \cdot 6H_2O$. The anhydrous salt cannot be prepared from the hydrate, as upon heating it loses hydrogen chloride:

$MgCl_2 + H_2O = MgO + 2HCl$. This reaction may be employed for the manufacture of hydrochloric acid. Magnesium chloride combines with the oxide to form a basic chloride, Mg_2OCl_2. The heat of the reaction, 20 kcal., indicates that the compound is very stable. This reaction is the basis for the **Sorel cement** which is now used extensively as a substitute for tile. Magnesium chloride is often present in table salt, and its deliquescent nature frequently causes the salt to "cake" in damp weather. This may be avoided by the addition of enough sodium bicarbonate to form the basic magnesium carbonate.

A number of double compounds of calcium chloride occur as minerals, for example, tachydrite, $CaCl_2MgCl_2 \cdot 12H_2O$, and apatite, $Ca_5(PO_4)_3Cl$ (or $Ca_5(PO_4)_3F$). The chloride may also be recovered from natural brines and salt deposits. Below 30° the salt crystallizes as the hexahydrate. Upon heating it may be dehydrated to form successively tetra-, di-, and monohydrates, and anhydrous salt. The latter contains some oxides formed through the loss of hydro-

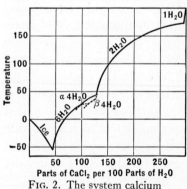

FIG. 2. The system calcium chloride and water.

gen chloride, as in the case of magnesium chloride discussed above. The solubility relations of the various hydrates are given in Fig. 2. The eutectic of the hexahydrate and ice is − 55° C. The anhydrous salt and dihydrate are used extensively as drying agents. The equilibrium pressure of water vapor for the reaction, $CaCl_2 \cdot 2H_2O + 2H_2O = CaCl_2 \cdot 4H_2O$, is 0.92 mm. at 0°, and 3.78 mm. at 20°. Calcium chloride forms compounds with ammonia, $CaCl_2 \cdot 8NH_3$, and with alcohol, $CaCl_2 \cdot 4C_2H_6O$, and hence cannot be used for drying these substances; nor can it be used to dry hydrogen sulfide, which it decomposes somewhat with the evolution of hydrogen chloride.

The deliquescence of calcium chloride and its low cost make it useful in sprinkling roads. Its high solubility and the low freezing point of its solutions render it useful in refrigerating brines. Its principal commercial sources are ammonia recovery plants, $2NH_4Cl + Ca(OH)_2 = 2NH_3 + CaCl_2 + 2H_2O$ (see Ammonia, **XI**—6) and the Solvay soda process (cf. **IV**—13), in both of which it results as a by-product.

Barium chloride is prepared for use as an analytical reagent by heating a mixture of barium sulfate, calcium chloride, and carbon: $BaSO_4 + CaCl_2 + 4C = BaCl_2 + CaS + 4CO$. The chloride is leached out and purified by recrystallization.

Radium is frequently prepared for commercial use in the form of chloride. Both the chloride and bromide are more insoluble than the corresponding barium compounds.

In general the solubilities of the alkaline earth halides increase in order of increasing atomic weight of the halogen, and decrease with increasing atomic weight of the metal.

10. Sulfates.—Beryllium sulfate is very soluble, and forms syrupy liquids from which it is difficult to crystallize a pure compound. The tetra- and hexahydrates have been obtained; the former is apparently unstable in respect to the latter.

Magnesium sulfate is found in many mineral waters and in the bittern of sea water. It occurs as the minerals kieserite, $MgSO_4 \cdot H_2O$, and epsomite (epsom salts), $MgSO_4 \cdot 7H_2O$. Between 1.8° and 48° the rhombic heptahydrate crystallizes from solution; below 1.8° a dodecahydrate separates; and at higher temperatures there are formed a number of lower hydrates. The anhydrous salt cannot be prepared, due to formation of basic sulfates upon heating the hydrates. Magnesium sulfate is used in weighting and sizing cotton, silk, paper, and leather; in fireproofing fabrics;

and in medicine as a purgative, and as a stimulant to increase the secretion of bile.

Calcium sulfate occurs in enormous deposits of **gypsum,** $CaSO_4 \cdot 2H_2O$ (when pure white called alabaster); and less

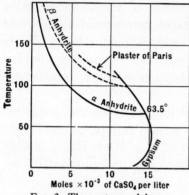

FIG. 3. The system calcium sulfate and water.

extensively as anhydrite, which is the anhydrous salt. The solid phase in equilibrium with the saturated solution is gypsum below 63.5° C., and anhydrite above (Fig. 3). The solubility of the two salts at the transition point is 0.015 mole per liter. The solubility of anhydrite decreases rapidly with rising temperature and is only 0.002 mole per liter at 150° C. This decrease in solubility is partly responsible for the separation of boiler scale from water containing calcium sulfate (Hard Water, Par. **11**). A second unstable and more soluble form of anhydrite also exists.

Upon heating, gypsum loses water to form the hemihydrate: $2(CaSO_4 \cdot 2H_2O) = (CaSO_4)_2 \cdot H_2O + 3H_2O$. The equilibrium pressure of water vapor reaches one atmosphere at 107° C. The hemihydrate is known as plaster of Paris. When it is mixed with water the equilibrium is reversed, and the plaster sets to a mass of gypsum crystals. The setting results in an increase in volume, and the plaster thus fills perfectly any mold into which it may be poured. In making plaster of Paris the gypsum must not be heated too strongly, as the anhydrous salt is then formed which absorbs water very slowly. Such plaster is called "dead burnt." The largest use of sulfate is in the manufacture of plaster for the interiors of buildings. Two varieties of plaster are made: (1) cement plaster, which is plaster of

Paris to which glue, glycerine, and other organic substances have been added as "retarders" to prolong the time of setting; and (2) hard finish plasters, such as Keenes cement, which is made by the calcination of the anhydrous sulfate with alum or borax. This second type of plasters sets very slowly, but gives a hard finish. Large quantities of sulfate are used in the manufacture of stucco and wall board and as a retarder for Portland cement (cf. **XIV—23**). The yearly consumption of gypsum in the United States is about six million tons.

There are two forms of the anhydrous calcium sulfate. One is comparatively unreactive to water but the other, sometimes called soluble anhydrite, absorbs water rapidly. The latter is marketed under the trade name of "Drierite" as a highly efficient desiccant for gases and liquids. Water remaining in air after drying with the reagent at 25° C. is said to be 0.005 mg. per liter.

Strontium sulfate, $SrSO_4$, celestite, and barium sulfate, $BaSO_4$, barite or heavy spar, are the most important minerals of these elements. These sulfates are extremely insoluble in water and dilute acids. They dissolve in concentrated sulfuric acid through the formation of HSO_4^-, and are reprecipitated upon dilution. When the sulfate is treated with sodium carbonate solution, some of the sulfate is converted into carbonate: $BaSO_4 + CO_3^{--} = BaCO_3 + SO_4^{--}$. At equilibrium the ratio of the molal concentration of sulfate to carbonate for the barium salts is about 0.01. If barium sulfate is treated, for example, with 100 cc. of $M\mathrm{Na_2CO_3}$, 0.2 gram of barium carbonate will be formed. By decanting the solution and repeating the treatment, any amount of the sulfate may be converted into carbonate. The sulfate may also be converted into soluble salts by reduction with carbon at about 800° to form the sulfide, which may then be dissolved in acid. Barium sulfate is slowly dissolved by boiling with concentrated HI, because of reduction of the sulfate by iodide.

Barium sulfate is an important pigment. **Lithopone,** a mixture of barium sulfate and zinc sulfide, is prepared by the reaction: $BaS + ZnSO_4 = BaSO_4 + ZnS$. This pigment has excellent covering power and does not darken with hydrogen sulfide. Precipitated barium sulfate is also used as a pigment, especially as an adulterant of white lead, but its covering power is not good. Barium sulfate is further employed as a "filler" in wall paper and in glazed paper. It is taken internally in making X-ray photographs of the intestinal tract, on account of the opaqueness to X-rays of such a heavy atom as barium. The sulfate is the only barium salt which may be used, as it alone is sufficiently insoluble to prevent poisoning by the barium ion.

Radium sulfate is even more insoluble than barium sulfate. In the commercial extraction from uranium ores the sulfate is precipitated along with those of barium and lead, and converted into the chloride by either of the two methods discussed above.

11. Water Softening.—Water containing soluble calcium and magnesium salts is known as **hard water.** It is objectionable in the laundry because soap, which contains sodium or potassium salts of the higher fatty acids, such as stearic or palmitic acid ($C_{17}H_{35}COOH$ and $C_{15}H_{31}COOH$), forms insoluble salts with calcium and magnesium. This results in a waste of soap and the precipitate is a slimy curd which is difficult to remove. Hard water is objectionable in boilers because of the formation of boiler scale. The negative ions present in hard water are principally chloride, sulfate, and bicarbonate. Upon heating to a high temperature much of the dissolved material is precipitated as scale which is composed largely of anhydrite (Par. **10**), calcium carbonate, and magnesium oxy-compounds. Such scale is a very poor conductor of heat, and its formation causes not only a waste of fuel, but also more rapid deterioration of the boiler through overheating at the surfaces where the heat is applied. Water which contains large quantities of bicarbonate may be softened simply by heating: Ca^{++} + $2HCO_3^- = CaCO_3 + CO_2 + H_2O$. Such water is referred to as possessing **temporary hardness.** In many industrial plants water is softened by the addition of lime equivalent to the calcium bicarbonate present, and sodium carbonate equivalent to the additional calcium and magnesium: $2HCO_3^- + 2OH^- + 2Ca^{++} = 2CaCO_3 + 2H_2O$, and $Ca^{++} + CO_3^{--} = CaCO_3$.

In the **zeolite or "permutite" process** water is softened by filtering slowly through artificial or natural zeolite, which is a hydrated sodium aluminum silicate. Although the composition varies somewhat in the different forms, NaH_6AlSiO_7 may be written as an approximate formula. The sodium is replaceable by calcium, magnesium, ferrous, and other + 2 ions. $2NaH_6AlSiO_7 + Ca^{++} = Ca(H_6\text{-}AlSiO_7)_2 + 2Na^+$. The equilibrium is reversible and when the efficiency of the zeolite drops, it may be regenerated by treating for a few hours with a concentrated solution of sodium chloride. The process is inexpensive as only sodium chloride is consumed.

The zeolite minerals are now being replaced by solid synthetic resins of two general types: a) acids for cation exchange, b) bases (such as amine-formaldehyde resin) for anion exchange. Thus sodium chloride may be removed from a water by the following reactions: $RH + Na^+ + Cl^-$ $= RNa + H^+ + Cl^-$ and $RNH_2 + H^+ + Cl^- = RNH_3Cl$. By a combination of the two resin types, it is possible to produce a water of purity comparable with distilled water.

The use of tetrasodium pyrophosphate, $Na_4P_2O_7$, and hexasodium hexaphosphate, $Na_6P_6O_{18}$, is increasing in washing technology. These salts hold the calcium in solution as complex ions, e.g., $Ca_2P_6O_{18}^{--}$, and thus prevent the formation of curds. Since it is the fatty acids, containing the − COOH group which tend to precipitate the calcium in ordinary soap, a number of new detergents have been introduced which do not have this acid radical. The sodium salt of the sulfuric ester of cetyl alcohol, $C_{16}H_{33}$-OSO_3Na and cetyl trimethyl ammonium bromide,$C_{16}H_{33}$-$(CH_3)_3NBr$, are examples.

12. Carbides.—At a very high temperature the metals or their oxides react with carbon forming carbides. The most important is calcium carbide, CaC_2, which is produced on a large scale by heating a mixture of lime and carbon to a temperature of about 3,000° C. in an electric furnace: $CaO + 3C = CaC_2 + CO$. Calcium carbide reacts with water to form acetylene (cf. **XIII—18**): $CaC_2 + 2H_2O = Ca(OH)_2 + C_2H_2$. It may, therefore, be called calcium acetylide. Another important reaction of the carbide is the absorption of nitrogen at about 1,000° C. to form cyanamide: $CaC_2 + N_2 = CaCN_2 + C$. This reaction is the basis for the cyanamide process for the fixation of nitrogen (cf. **XI—8**).

13. Hydrides.—Beryllium and magnesium do not readily form hydrides; but calcium, strontium, and barium react readily with hydrogen at high temperature (about 600°). The large heats of the reactions, e.g., CaH_2, 46 kcal., indicate the stable nature of these hydrides. Like the alkali hydrides, the hydrogen possesses a negative charge and is liberated at the anode upon electrolysis of the molten salts. Calcium hydride, although expensive, is an easily portable source of hydrogen for war balloons. One mole reacts with water to give two moles of hydrogen: $CaH_2 + 2H_2O = Ca(OH)_2 + 2H_2$.

14. Nitrates.—Calcium nitrate is a constituent of fertile soils. The salt is produced for use as fertilizer by the electric arc process for the fixation of nitrogen (cf. **XII—33**). It crystallizes as $Ca(NO_3)_2·4H_2O$ at ordinary temperatures and is very soluble. Strontium nitrate is used in the manufacture of red fire. Barium nitrate is the least soluble of the group, and is precipitated as the anhydrous salt upon the addition of barium ion to solutions containing high concentrations of nitrate. It is sometimes used in making green fire.

15. Sulfides.—The sulfides may be formed by the direct
union of the elements, or by reduction of the sulfates by
carbon. The compounds so prepared dissolve but slowly
in water, but the apparent insolubility is merely a matter
of rate of solution. Solutions of these sulfides, like those
of all soluble sulfides, are highly alkaline due to hydrolysis
of the sulfide ion. Calcium sulfide is used as a depilatory.
The use of barium sulfide has been mentioned in the preparation of lithopone. Both of these sulfides glow in the dark
after exposure to sunlight, and are used in the preparation
of luminous paint. This property is apparently due to the
presence of traces of impurities, especially vanadium and
bismuth. In the regions about the particles of impurities,
the crystal is able to absorb radiant energy through the
displacement of electrons to higher energy levels. The
rate at which the electrons return to the stabler positions is
slow, so that the absorbed energy is re-emitted over a period
of time.

16. Phosphates.—The calcium phosphates are the most
important of the group. They occur as the tri- and di-
calcium orthophosphate, $Ca_3(PO_4)_2$ and $CaHPO_4$; and as
fluor and chlor apatites (Par. **4**). Dried bones consist
largely of calcium phosphate. Millions of tons of the insoluble tricalcium salts are treated yearly with sulfuric acid
to convert into soluble acid phosphate, $Ca(H_2PO_4)_2$, for
use as fertilizer (see Superphosphate, **XI—54**). Ammonium magnesium phosphate, $NH_4MgPO_4 \cdot 6H_2O$, is important
in analytical work (Par. **18**).

17. Other Important Compounds.—A number of compounds containing the alkaline earths are discussed under
other headings: bleaching powder (cf. **X—14**), glass (cf.
XIV—22), cement (cf. **XIV—23**), asbestos (cf. **XIV—19**),
talc (cf. **XIV—19**).

18. Analytical Properties of Alkaline Earth Ions.—The
chemistry of the alkaline earth ions is comparatively
simple, as they form no complexes with other ions (a few

exceptions with beryllium), and few insoluble compounds. The ions are colorless. Beryllium ion has a sweet taste, magnesium ion a bitter taste, and calcium ion is practically tasteless. Be^{++} and Ba^{++} are extremely poisonous. The solubilities of the various hydroxides has been discussed (Par. 7). The solubilities of the chromate and sulfate decrease with increasing atomic weight; and likewise the carbonate, with the exception that strontium carbonate is more insoluble than barium. The group, not including beryllium, is separated from all other positive ions except the alkalies by taking advantage of the fact that they are not precipitated by a solution of ammonium sulfide. Ammonium carbonate precipitates $CaCO_3$, $SrCO_3$, $BaCO_3$; and if about 30 per cent alcohol is present, $MgCO_3 \cdot (NH_4)_2CO_3$. Radium is separated from barium by fractional crystallization of the chlorides, bromides, or chromates, the compounds of the latter being the more soluble. Barium may be separated from the lighter members of the group by the greater insolubility of the chromate. Strontium is separated from calcium in solution by the addition of a dilute solution of sulfate, which precipitates strontium sulfate but not calcium. Magnesium is separated from the heavier elements of the group through the solubility of the carbonate in ammonium salts. The insoluble nature of beryllium hydroxide permits its ready separation from the remainder of the group. It may be distinguished from aluminum by the solubility of the beryllium hydroxide in excess bicarbonate, probably due to the formation of a complex bicarbonate ion.

Calcium may be precipitated quantitatively as calcium oxalate by the addition of ammonium oxalate. The precipitate is composed of larger crystals, and is more easily filtered if precipitated from a slightly acid solution, in which it is somewhat soluble. The final traces of calcium may then be removed by making the solution alkaline with ammonium hydroxide. The oxalate may be dried and weighed as such or ignited to form the carbonate: CaC_2O_4 = $CaCO_3 + CO$.

Barium is usually precipitated and weighed as sulfate (cf. XI—34); while strontium may be determined as sulfate or oxalate. Magnesium ammonium phosphate, NH_4MgPO_4 ·$6H_2O$, is precipitated upon the addition of sodium phosphate and ammonium hydroxide to a solution of a magnesium salt. Upon ignition the pyrophosphate, $Mg_2P_2O_7$, is formed, and may be weighed as such: $2NH_4MgPO_4·6H_2O$ = $Mg_2P_2O_7 + 2NH_3 + 13H_2O$.

The sodium rhodizonate spot test is a convenient method of distinguishing between calcium, barium, and strontium. One drop of an 0.4 per cent solution of the reagent is placed on a filter paper. One drop of test solution is placed on the drop and then one drop of ethyl alcohol. Barium and strontium give red coloration. If the spot is now touched with one drop of $0.3N$ HCl, barium will remain bright red but strontium will dissolve.

Radium sulfate is less soluble than barium sulfate. The separation of the two elements is accomplished by the fractional crystallization of the chlorides or bromides.

19. Spectra.—Beryllium and magnesium compounds do not ionize sufficiently to impart color to the Bunsen flame. Volatile calcium compounds give a brick red, strontium a carmine, barium a yellow green, and radium a crimson flame. The coloration is very intense with the chlorides, but is not satisfactory with the oxides or sulfates due to their low volatility. The electric arc spectra afford a much more delicate means of determining the presence of the alkaline earth elements, 0.002 mg. of calcium being detectable. The material to be analyzed is usually placed upon the positive pole of the arc. The wave lengths in $\mu\mu$ (10^{-6} mm.) of the more prominent lines are: calcium 423, 616; strontium 422, 461; barium 455, 493; magnesium 516.8 to 518.4, a group of three lines.

Chapter VI

GROUP III. BORON, ALUMINUM

1. The third periodic group, like the first and second groups, is divided into a main group with kernels of the noble gas type, and a subgroup with kernels of the eighteen electron type. The elements of the main group are boron, aluminum, scandium, yttrium, lanthanum (and Rare Earths), and actinium; those of the subgroup are gallium, indium, and thallium. Although the Rare Earths may be considered as members of the third main group, they constitute a family which is so unique from the standpoint of atomic structure that it seems advisable to discuss them in a separate chapter (cf. Lanthanide Series **XXI**). Because of the similarity of scandium, yttrium and lanthanum to the Rare Earths, the detailed consideration of these elements will be postponed to that chapter. The elements above atomic number 89 appear to have the same electronic structure as the Rare Earths, and actinium will be discussed with that group (cf. Actinide Series **XXII**).

Boron is a nonmetal, but the remainder of the group are highly metallic. The melting points of the group are fairly high (Table I), and exhibit no regular trend from the light to the heavy elements. An oxidation state of + 3 is shown by these elements in all of their compounds with the exception of a few relatively unstable compounds of boron. The oxides or hydroxides are less basic than those of the alkaline earth elements, as is to be expected from the increased charge on the positive ions. Boron oxide is distinctly acidic and shows only faint basic properties. Aluminum oxide is amphoteric, while scandium, yttrium, and lanthanum show no acid properties and are distinctly, though not strongly, basic. This increase in basic character of the oxides within the group is again to be correlated with the increasing size of the ions of the heavier members (cf. III—7).

The elements are somewhat less electropositive than the alkaline earth metals. The energies required to ionize the electrons from the gaseous atoms are very high, as shown for aluminum in Table I; hence the high values for the electrode potentials of the elements must be due to even greater energies of hydration of the positive ions. In the case of aluminum this is over a thousand kilogram-calories.

TABLE I

ATOMIC AND PHYSICAL PROPERTIES

	B	Al		B	Al
Atomic weight	10.82	26.97	Ionization potentials in		
Atomic number ...	5	13			
Isotopes..........	10, 11	none	volts, 1st.......	8.26	5.96
Electrons in various			2d	25.00	18.74
quantum levels,			3d	37.75	28.31
1st........	2	2	Electrode		
2d	3	8	potential		
3d........		3	$M = M^{+++} +$		
Melting points ° C.	2,040	658	$3e^-$, volts 25°		1.67
Boiling points ° C. .	2,530	2,330	Electral resistivity		
Density..........	2.4	2.70	20° C. ohm-cm.	1.8×10^6	2.62×10^{-6}
			Radius of M^{+++} in crystals,		
			cm. $\times 10^8$	0.20	0.50

BORON

2. Occurrence.—Boron constitutes but a small portion of the earth's crust, estimated as about 0.001 per cent. It occurs as boric acid, H_3BO_3, and as borates. The principal deposits have resulted from the evaporation of inland seas. In the Stassfurt area in Germany the deposits are chiefly magnesium borates; while in the arid regions of western United States they consist largely of colemanite, $Ca_2B_6O_{11}$ $\cdot 5H_2O$, with some borax, $Na_2B_4O_7 \cdot 10H_2O$. Recently large deposits of kernite, $Na_2B_4O_7 \cdot 4H_2O$, have been discovered in Kern County, California. Boron is widely distributed in rocks in complex silicates and aluminates, such as tourmaline, $H_2MgNa_9Al_3(BO)_2Si_4O_{20}$.

3. Preparation and Properties.—No satisfactory electrolytic method has been developed for the production of boron. It is usually prepared by the reduction of the oxide by powdered magnesium: $B_2O_3 + 3Mg = 3MgO + 2B$; but other powerful reducing agents, such as sodium, may be used and the halides may be substituted for the oxide. The product of the reduction is amorphous boron, and, when magnesium is used, it is mixed with magnesium boride, Mg_3B_2, the proportion of which may be minimized by using excess of boric oxide, but in this case some suboxide, possibly B_3O remains. If this product is heated in an electric furnace with an atmosphere of hydrogen a crystalline boron is obtained. When the reduction was first carried out with aluminum the product was thought to be crystalline boron, but further investigation has indicated that it consists of a mixture of aluminum borides, such as AlB_{12}.

Small crystals of boron have been prepared by the reduction of the trichloride with hydrogen when heated by a tungsten filament to a temperature around 1,500° C.

The free element, as usually prepared, is a dark brown powder. The cooled fused material is brittle, almost as hard as diamond, and practically a non-conductor of electricity.

4. Reactions.—Boron oxidizes slowly in air at 100° C., and burns at higher temperatures with a green flame. It ignites in fluorine at room temperature, and in the other halogens at higher temperatures. From the potential + 0.73 volt for the half reaction,

$$3H_2O + B = H_3BO_3 + 3H^+ + 3e^-.$$

the element should dissolve readily in acid. However no reaction occurs, the slowness doubtless being due to the large initial energy required to break the strong bonds in the solid. It does dissolve in fused alkalies due to the stability of the borates. It is readily oxidized by strong oxidizing agents, such as nitric acid, concentrated sulfuric acid, and ferric ion. It does not combine directly with hydrogen. These and other reactions are summarized below.

TABLE II
REACTIONS OF BORON

$4B + 3O_2 = 2B_2O_3$	Burns with green flame
$2B + 3X_2 = 2BX_3$	With halogens
$2B + 3S = B_2S_3$	At about 600°
$2B + N_2 = 2BN$	Above 1,200°
$2B + 2NH_3 = 2BN + 3H_2$	Heated
$2B + 6KOH = 2K_3BO_3 + 3H_2$	Fused with alkali
$B + HNO_3 + H_2O = H_3BO_3 + NO$	
$nB + mM = M_mB_n$	With a large number of metals

5. Oxides.—Boron forms the oxide B_2O_3, and there is evidence of suboxides BO or B_3O. The sesquioxide may be prepared by heating boric acid to red heat. The product is a very hard, brittle glass. The oxide dissolves most metal oxides to form clear glasses. The sesquioxide takes up water rather rapidly to form the acid, and since it is otherwise very non-reactive, it often serves as a convenient dehydrating agent.

6. Boric Acid and Borates.—The addition of strong acids to borates liberates the weak boric acid, and this crystallizes from the water solution as the ortho-acid, H_3BO_3. The solubility increases markedly with temperature; a saturated solution contains 2.6 per cent at 0°, and 28.7 per cent at 100° C. The acid is somewhat volatile from hot solutions, possibly due to the formation of volatile hydrates. Upon heating, the ortho-acid loses water to form first the meta-acid, HBO_2, and then the tetraboric acid, $H_2B_4O_7$. In water solution the ortho-acid acts as a weak monobasic acid i.e., its reactions are those of the meta-acid, HBO_2. The dissociation constant as calculated for the reaction, $H_3BO_3 = H^+ + H_2BO_3^-$, is 5.8×10^{-10}. The equilibrium is complicated, above concentration of $0.5M$ by the formation of $HB_4O_7^-$. The acid is used in medicine, under the name "boracic acid," as a mild antiseptic.

Very few orthoborates are known, and in water solution they hydrolyze:

$$BO_3^{---} + 2H_2O = H_2BO_3^- + 2OH^-$$

Upon the addition of hydroxide to the ortho-acid the equilibrium, $2BO_2^- + 2HBO_2 = H_2O + B_4O_7^{--}$, is established, the equilibrium constant being about 10^3. The constants for the first and second ionization of $H_2B_4O_7$ appear to be about 10^{-4} and 10^{-9}, respectively. Many of the metaborates are but moderately soluble, e.g., $AgBO_2$, $Ba(BO_2)_2$, $Pb(BO_2)_2$. With sodium hydroxide the salt, $Na_2B_4O_7 \cdot 10H_2O$, **borax,** forms, and may be crystallized from the solution below 60° C. Above that temperature a pentahydrate is stable. The naturally occurring kernite, which is the tetrahydrate, is a metastable form and has not been prepared in the laboratory.

Borax is the most important compound of the element. It is but sparingly soluble at 0° C., 1.3 g. per liter, but is very soluble at the temperature of transition to the pentahydrate. The solution is slightly alkaline by hydrolysis, $0.1N$ solution containing about $2 \times 10^{-5}N$ OH^-. Borax is prepared from naturally occurring borates by (1) the extraction of the acid, and (2) the reaction of the acid with sodium carbonate: $4H_3BO_3 + Na_2CO_3 = Na_2B_4O_7 + 6H_2O + CO_2$.

Borax fuses to form a glass which is capable of dissolving metal oxides, since it contains an excess of acid oxide, e.g. $Na_2O \cdot 2B_2O_3 + CuO = Na_2O \cdot B_2O_3 + CuO \cdot B_2O_3$. Upon this property depends its use in soldering and welding to clean the metal surface of coatings of oxides. Many oxides dissolved in fused borax impart characteristic colors, the familiar borax bead tests (Append. VII). The colored glass finds use as artificial gems, and when ground, as pigments. Among other important uses of borax are the manufacture of glass, enamels, and soap, sizing for paper, and as a preservative for wood and meats.

Besides the borates above mentioned there exist a very large number of polyborates, salts of the acids, $(B_2O_3)_n$-$(H_2O)_m$, where n may be as large as six and m is usually one, two, or three.

In boric acid the BO_3 group is planar with the oxygens forming a triangle about the boron. In calcium metaborate the BO_2 groups form chains of triangles linked together by holding oxygen atoms in common, and in potassium metaborate, $K_3B_3O_6$, the structure of the negative ion is,

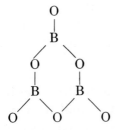

7. Boric acid forms with methyl alcohol the rather volatile methyl borate, $(CH_3)_3BO_3$. This compound burns with a green flame. The corresponding ethyl borate is less volatile. The very slightly basic nature of boric acid is shown by the reaction between boiling boric acid and phosphoric acid to give **boron phosphate,** $H_3BO_3 + H_3PO_4 = BPO_4 + 3H_2O$. Borax fused with ammonium chloride forms boron nitride: $Na_2B_4O_7 + 4NH_4Cl = 4BN + 2NaCl + 7H_2O + 2HCl$. **Boryl sulfate,** $(BO_0)_2SO_4$, is formed by the action of sulfur trioxide upon boron trichloride.

8. Peroxyborates.—Peroxyborates may be prepared by the action of peroxides upon borates or by the electrolytic oxidation of borate solutions. The most important of these compounds is the sodium salt, $NaBO_3 \cdot 4H_2O$. It is used as a bleaching agent, and as an antiseptic constituent of certain tooth powders.

9. Borides.—In addition to the borides of magnesium and aluminum mentioned above, a large number of borides have been prepared, among which the following may be mentioned: AlB_2, CaB_6, BaB_6, CB_4, SiB_6, ThB_4, CrB, WB_2, FeB, Fe_2B, NiB, CoB.

The so-called boron carbide, CB_4, may be made by the reduction of boric acid with carbon in the electric arc furnace. In spite of its great hardness, it may be cast and molded.

10. Halides.—The halides are gases, or easily volatile liquids. The melting and boiling points parallel the corresponding values for the halogens.

	BF_3	BCl_3	BBr_3	BI_3
Boiling point...............	− 101.9	13	90.5	210
Melting point...............	− 128	− 107	− 44	43

They may be prepared by the direct union of the elements, but are usually formed from boric oxide, using hydrogen fluoride in the case of fluorine, $B_2O_3 + 6HF = 2BF_3 + 3H_2O$; and in the case of the other halogens using the halogen and carbon at elevated temperatures: $B_2O_3 + 3C + 3X_2 = 2BX_3 + 3CO$. The fluoride is used commercially as a catalyst, one of the more important reactions being the reaction of an alcohol and carbon dioxide at high temperatures to form an organic acid. The three heavier halides are completely hydrolyzed in water: $BX_3 + 3H_2O = H_3BO_3 + 3H^+ + 3X^-$. The fluoride reacts with water to form boric acid and fluoboric acid: $4BF_3 + 3H_2O = H_3BO_3 + 3HBF_4$. Pure fluoboric acid is unstable, but many of its salts are known. Boron fluoride also forms a complex with ammonia, BNH_3F_3. The probable electronic formulae of the fluoride, the ammonia complex, and fluoboric acid are, respectively:

$$
\begin{array}{ccc}
\ddot{:}\ddot{F}\ddot{:} & H\ddot{:}\ddot{F}\ddot{:} & \ddot{:}\ddot{F}\ddot{:} \\
\ddot{B}:\ddot{F}: & H:\ddot{N}:\ddot{B}:\ddot{F}: & :\ddot{F}:\ddot{B}:\ddot{F}:H \\
:\ddot{F}: & H:\ddot{F}: & :\ddot{F}:
\end{array}
$$

11. Hydrogen Compounds.—The molecule BH_3 does not exist but its dimer B_2H_6 and other compounds of the series having the general formulas B_nH_{n+4} are well known. A few compounds of the series B_nH_{n+6} have also been prepared. The general name, **boranes,** is given to these hydrogen compounds. Some of the physical constants for the more important compounds are given in Table III.

TABLE III

PHYSICAL CONSTANTS OF THE BORANES

NAME	FORMULA	DENSITY	MELTING POINT, ° C.	BOILING POINT, ° C.
Diborane.............	B_2H_6	0.447($-112°$ C.)	-165.5	-92.5
Tetraborane............	B_4H_{10}	0.56($-35°$ C.)	-120	18
Stable pentaborane.......	B_5H_9	0.61(0° C.)	-46.6	48
Unstable pentaborane....	B_5H_{11}	....	-123	63
Hexaborane............	B_6H_{10}	0.69(0° C.)	-65	...
Decoborane............	$B_{10}H_{14}$	0.78(100° C.)	99.7	213

The boranes are of unusual interest in the general theory of valence and chemical bonding since they are all short in the number of electrons required to give an electron pair to each bond. Various theories have been advanced to account for the electronic structures. In diborane two hydrogens appear to be located symmetrically between the two borons, and the assumption has been made that the bond between the boron atoms is a double electron pair with two protons imbedded in the electron cloud. The electron shortage and the suggested solution is illustrated below.

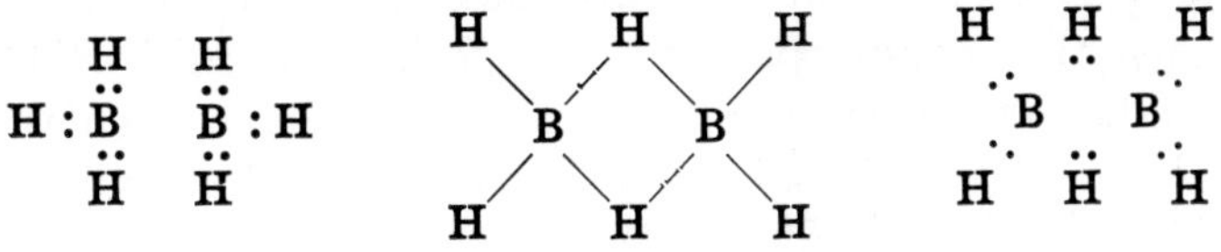

All of the boranes contain at least one of these "protonated double-bonds."

Tetraborane may be prepared by the action of an acid solution upon magnesium boride. $Mg_6B_4 + 12HCl = B_4H_{10} + H_2 + 6MgCl_2$. Diborane is best prepared by passing a mixture of boron tribromide and hydrogen through an electric arc. The reaction is complex and involves bromodiborane, diborane and boron bromide.

Some of the more important reactions of diborane are summarized in Table IV. Many of the products of these

TABLE IV

REACTIONS OF DIBORANE

$5B_2H_6 = 2B_5H_{11} + 4H_2$

$B_2H_6 + 2Na = Na_2B_2H_6$

$B_2H_6 + HI = B_2H_5I + H_2$

$5B_2H_6 + B(CH_3)_3 = 6B_2H_5CH_3$

$B_2H_6 + 2CO = 2BH_3CO$

$B_2H_6 + 2N(CH_3)_3 = 2BH_3N(CH_3)_3$

$3B_2H_6 + 6NH_3 = 2B_3N_3H_6$

$B_2H_6 + 3CH_3OH = 2BH(OCH_3) + 4H_2$

$3B_2H_6 + 2LiC_2H_5 = 2LiBH_4 + 2B_2H_5C_2H_5$

$B_2H_6 + H_2O = 6H_2 + 2B(OH)_3$

reactions are also of considerable interest. Sodium diborane, $Na_2B_2H_6$, may be considered to be a salt of sodium ions with $B_2H_6^{--}$. It is quite stable in dry air and sublimes at 400° C., but since it is a powerful reducing agent, it is highly reactive. Iododiborane B_2H_5I reacts readily with sodium to form tetraborane: $2B_2H_5I + 2Na = B_4H_{10} + 2NaI$. The chloro- and bromo-compounds may also be prepared. Borine carbonyl, H_3BCO, melts at $-137°$ C. and boils at $-64°$ C. It is in some respects similar to the volatile metal carbonyls (cf. **XIX—15**). Lithium borohydride, $LiBH_4$, is a salt-like substance; the BH_4^- radical is the negative counterpart to the positive radical NH_4^+. A number of other metallo borohydrides have been prepared. $Be(BH_4)_2$ is only slightly salt-like and the volatile liquid aluminum compound $Al(BH_4)_3$ is even less so.

TABLE V

COMPARISON OF PHYSICAL PROPERTIES OF BORAZOLE AND BENZENE

PROPERTY	C_6H_6	$B_3N_3H_6$
Molecular Weight	78	80
Boiling point	353° K.	328° K.
Melting point	279° K.	215° K.
Critical temperature	561° K.	525° K.
Density (at boiling point)	0.81 g./cc.	0.81 g./cc.
Heat of Vaporization	7400 cal.	7000 cal.
Molar volume	96 cc.	100 cc.
Carbon-carbon distance	1.42 Å	
Boron-nitrogen distance		1.44 Å

When diborane is heated with ammonia at a temperature of 250–300° C., the product is **borazole**, $B_3N_3H_6$. This compound is remarkably similar to benzene C_6H_6 (cf. **XIII—16**). This is not surprising since they contain not only the same number of atoms but also the same number of valence electrons i.e., boron with three electrons and nitrogen with five electrons are equivalent to two carbon atoms with four electrons each. A comparison of some of the more important physical properties is given in Table V above. Borazole, like benzene, has

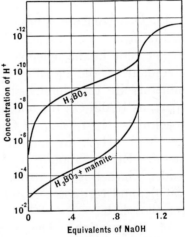

FIG. 1. Titration curves for boric acid.

a ring structure and the vibrational frequencies of the two are also remarkably similar. Like benzene the hydrogens of the ring may be substituted and a number of the methyl derivatives has been prepared.

12. Analytical.—The green flame test of methyl borate is often employed as a qualitative test. The sample is placed in a test tube, and sulfuric acid and methyl alcohol added. The vapors which escape upon gentle warming burn with a green flame when ignited.

Methyl orange does not react acid to boric acid, therefore soluble borates may be titrated with that indicator. Pure boric acid is difficult to titrate with a strong base, as the equivalent point is highly alkaline as indicated in Fig. 1. The addition of glycerol, mannite, or other polyalcohols which form complex ions with BO_2^-, has the effect of increasing the strength of the acid, and bringing the equivalent point into the range of phenolphthalein; hence the acid may be titrated using that indicator.

ALUMINUM

13. Occurrence.—Aluminum ranks third among the elements in order of abundance. The estimated abundance in per cent in the igneous rocks is 8.13. It is the most abundant of the metallic elements. The most common minerals are the aluminosilicates, which include the feldspars, as $KAlSi_3O_8$; the micas, as $H_2KAl_3(SiO_4)_3$; and clays (kaolin), as $H_2Al_2(SiO_4)_2H_2O$. Cryolite, Na_3AlF_6, and bauxite, $Al_2O_3 \cdot nH_2O$, are important in the production of the metal. Ruby, sapphire, and corundum are forms of the oxide. Garnet is, approximately, $[Ca, Mg, Fe]_3[Al, Fe]_2 (SiO_4)_3$; and turquoise, $Al_2(OH)_3PO_4 \cdot H_2O$, colored by copper phosphate.

14. Preparation.—The metal was first prepared commercially about 1850 by the reduction of the chloride by sodium at high temperature. Shortly thereafter methods were developed for the electrolysis of mixtures of molten aluminum, sodium fluorides, and chlorides, but the metal remained rare and expensive until the simultaneous discovery by Hall and by Héroult of the electrolysis of the oxide in molten cryolite in 1886, which laid the foundation of the modern aluminum industry. In the Hall process, the electrolysis is carried out in large iron pots with a thick carbon lining which acts as the cathode. A number of large amorphous carbon rods sticking down into the pot serve as anodes. The carbon rods are first lowered until they touch the cathode and an arc is struck; powdered cryolite is then added and melted by the heat of the arc. When a sufficient liquid bath is obtained, aluminum oxide is added and the anodes drawn farther away from the cathode. The addition of the oxide raises somewhat the resistance of the liquid. The temperature of the bath is kept at about 1,000° C., and since this is above the melting point of the metal, it collects as a liquid in the bottom of the cell and is drawn off at intervals. Oxygen is liberated at the anode and gradually burns away the graphite. The cell reaction is: $2Al_2O_3 = 4Al + 3O_2$. Ordinary commercial aluminum is about 99.0 to 99.5 per cent pure. It is very difficult to refine the impure metal, so the oxide is carefully purified before electrolysis (see Oxide). Recently, however, aluminum of 99.99 per cent purity has been made electrolytically from an alloy of aluminum, copper, and silicon. The cell consists of three liquid layers of decreasing density; the lowest is the alloy, which is made the anode; the middle layer consists of molten salts; and the top layer is pure aluminum, which is made the cathode. Aluminum may be electroplated from a bath containing aluminum chloride and bromide dissolved in ethyl bromide and benzene.

15. Properties.—The metal is extremely light, density 2.7, and possesses relatively high tensile strength. Its electrical conductivity is less than copper, but weight for weight it is twice as good a conductor. It is easily malleable and may be rolled into thin foil. It has a silvery appearance when freshly cut, but the ordinary surface has a dull white luster, since it is covered by a thin, firm coat of oxide which protects the surface from further oxidation.

16. Uses.—In addition to the common use in household utensils, the metal is becoming increasingly important in the construction of airplanes and other machines where light weight is essential. Two important uses are as foil in place of tin foil, and as a "silver" paint. The latter is made by mixing the thin metal flakes with oil. Aluminum wire is used extensively in the United States, chiefly in transmission lines. The metal is used to remove dissolved oxygen in casting iron and steel, and thus to prevent blow holes. It is also used in "thermite" (Par. 17). The metal can be welded, brazed or soldered, but brazing is recommended as the solder lacks resistance to corrosive attack. Alloys with Cu, Si, Mn, Mg, Fe, and Zn are important. The pure metal is difficult to work on the lathe as it sticks to the tools, but many of the alloys may be machined readily. The principal alloy used for construction purposes is Alcoa 24S-T with 4.5 per cent Cu, 0.6 per cent Mn and 0.5 per cent Mg. Its tensile strength of 60,000 lb. per sq. in. is about double that of pure aluminum. "Binary" alloy, 2.5 per cent Mg and 0.25 per cent Cr, is another low magnesium alloy of importance. See also magnesium and copper.

17. Reactions.—Aluminum is a very base metal, but its surface is protected so thoroughly by its oxide coating that it may be melted in air without serious oxidation. However, at high temperatures the metal burns vigorously, and aluminum powder and liquid oxygen unite with a flash if ignited with a match. The metal does not dissolve in water unless the surface is amalgamated. The oxide does not adhere to the amalgamated surface, and the metal is free to show its true electropositive nature by reacting with water or by oxidizing rapidly in air. The metal dissolves readily in hydrochloric acid, and slowly in sulfuric acid, but is rendered passive by nitric acid so that this acid is often shipped in aluminum containers. It dissolves rapidly in nitric acid, however, if a small amount of mercuric salt is present. Nitric oxide is evolved from concentrated acid, and ammonium nitrate formed with dilute. Concentrated alkalies dissolve the metal with the evolution of hydrogen and the formation of the aluminate. The granulated metal reduces many oxides and sulfides upon ignition, the so-called **"Goldschmidt reaction."** A mixture of aluminum and iron oxide, known as **"thermite,"** is used in welding. The heat of the reaction is such that a temperature of about 3,000° is produced, and the iron formed by the reduction can be run as a white hot liquid into the crack to be welded. To start the thermite reaction an ignition powder is required, such as a mixture of barium peroxide and aluminum.

The aluminum electrode is highly irreversible, and extremely difficult to measure directly. The value, 1.67 volts, is calculated from thermal data and indicates that aluminum is almost as electropositive as magnesium.

The irreversibility of the aluminum electrode is made use of in rectifying alternating currents. When acting as anode, the electrode has enormous resistance, but as cathode it has low resistance; hence cells with an aluminum electrode allow one half of an alternating current to pass but not the other. The cell is most effective with a phosphate electrolyte.

TABLE VI

REACTIONS OF ALUMINUM

$4Al + 3O_2 = 2Al_2O_3$

$2Al + 6H^+ = 2Al^{+++} + 3H_2$

$2Al + 2OH^- + 4H_2O = 2H_2AlO_3^- + 3H_2$

$Al(amalgam) + 6H_2O = 2Al(OH)_3 + 3H_2$

$Al(amalgam) + 4H^+ + NO_3^- = Al^{+++} + NO + 2H_2O$ Also forms NH_4^+

$2Al + Fe_2O_3 = Al_2O_3 + 2Fe$ Analogous reaction with many oxides

$2Al + 3X_2 = 2AlX_3$ With halogens

$4Al + 6S = 2Al_2S_3$ At high temperature

$2Al + N_2 = 2AlN$ At high temperature

$6Al + 3CO = Al_4C_3 + Al_2O_3$ At high temperature

$Al = Al^{+++} + 3e^- \quad E° = 1.67$

$Al + 4OH^- = H_2AlO_3^- + H_2O + 3e^- \quad E° = 2.35$

18. Oxide and Hydroxide.—The oxide occurs in nature as corundum. When colored red it is called ruby, and when blue, sapphire. The color in the former is due to a trace of chromium, while that of the latter is attributed to iron and titanium. When it contains magnetite, it is known as emery. Artificial corundum, made by fusing the precipitated hydroxide in an electric furnace, is sold under the name "alundum," and artificial rubies and sapphires are now produced in large quantities. Corundum stands next to diamond and silicon carbide in hardness, and is used as an abrasive, and also in making refractory crucibles. The oxide is formed upon heating the hydroxide. Unless it has been ignited strongly, it will reabsorb water to form the hydroxide, and hence may be employed as a drying agent.

Aluminum hydroxide, $Al(OH)_3$, exists in two forms—gibbsite, stable below 155° C., and bayerite. There are also two forms of the hydroxy-oxide, $AlOOH$—diaspore, stable 280–450° C., and böhmite, stable 155–280° C. Above 450° C. diaspore forms the metastable gamma alumina or the stable corundum. The freshly precipitated gel appears to be hydrous böhmite but gibbsite may be precipitated from aluminate solutions by acidifying with CO_2. The term bauxite is used for the commercial ores which are frequently largely böhmite. The hydroxide is amphoteric and the following are approximate values for the dissociation constants:

$$Al(OH)_3 = Al^{+++} + 3OH^- \qquad K = 1.9 \times 10^{-33}$$
$$Al(OH)_3 = H^+ + H_2AlO_3^- \text{ (or } AlO_2^- + H_2O)$$
$$K = 4 \times 10^{-13}.$$

The hydroxide is dissolved but slightly by ammonium hydroxide, especially in the presence of ammonium salt, to repress the concentration of hydroxide ion. The concentrations of hydroxide and hydrogen ions involved in the precipitation and solution of the hydroxide are indicated in Fig. 2. Soluble carbonates, sulfides, acetates, cyanides, and other salts of weak acids precipitate aluminum hydroxide by complete hydrolysis of both ions.

The pure oxide required for the electrolytic preparation
of the metal is made from bauxite or other hydrated oxides.
The mineral is first dissolved in sodium hydroxide to form
a solution of sodium aluminate; and the hydroxide is then
reprecipitated by passing in carbon dioxide, or by allowing
the solution to stand in contact with crystallized $Al(OH)_3$.
In the latter case, the crys-
tallized and insoluble form
slowly precipitates (see Beryllium Hydroxide). Many
attempts have been made to
prepare the pure oxide from
clay, but no commercial
process has yet been developed.

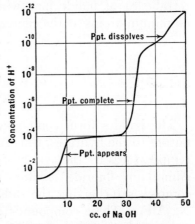

FIG. 2. Precipitation and solution of aluminum hydroxide in alkali.

19. **Aluminates.**—Sodium
and potassium aluminates
are soluble but highly hydrolyzed. Most of the alumi-
nates are, however, insoluble.
The meta aluminates of the
+ 2 ions, $M(AlO_2)_2$, occur as a mineral type known as spinels.
Many complex aluminates exist, but few as simple ortho
salts. The addition of ammonium hydroxide to a solution
of aluminum and zinc salts precipitates aluminum hydroxide
with some zinc aluminate. The formation of blue cobalt
aluminate is mentioned under the analytical properties of
aluminum. Calcium aluminate is an essential constituent
of Portland cement (cf. **XIV**—**23**).

20. **Halides.**—The anhydrous halides may be prepared
by the direct action of the halogen upon the metal, while
solutions of the halides are formed by the action of the
halogen acids upon the metal or hydroxide. Upon evaporation of the solutions, the halides may be obtained as highly
hydrated compounds, e.g., $AlCl_3 \cdot 6H_2O$. When heated, the
hydrates hydrolyze completely to the oxide and the halogen

acid, which is evolved. The anhydrous chloride is employed as a catalytic agent in many organic reactions. It sublimes without melting at ordinary pressures, the sublimation temperature being 183° at 750 mm. The aluminum halide gas molecules have the double formula, Al_2X_6 and their structure may be represented as two tetrahedra of halide ions with an edge in common, and aluminum atoms at the centers of the tetrahedra.

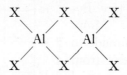

The halides form compounds with ammonia similar in nature to the hydrates, thus $AlCl_3·6NH_3$ forms at ordinary temperatures by the action of ammonia gas upon the salt. Aluminum fluoride exhibits strong tendencies to form complex salts, giving the radical, AlF_6^{---}, as in cryolite, Na_3AlF_6. These compounds are analogous to the aluminate, and owe their stability to the large value of the coulombic attaction of aluminum and fluoride ions. The tendency of the other halides of aluminum to form complexes decreases with increasing weight.

21. Sulfates.—The sulfate, $Al_2(SO_4)_318H_2O$, may be crystallized with difficulty from solutions at ordinary temperatures. It is highly soluble, and gives an acid solution by hydrolysis. A $0.25M$ solution is about 0.5 per cent hydrolyzed, assuming that the hydrolysis reaction is $Al^{+++} + H_2O = Al(OH)^{++} + H^+$. The sulfate is prepared from either bauxite or clay by treating with sulfuric acid. The latter reaction is: $H_2Al_2(SiO_4)_2·H_2O + 3H_2SO_4 = Al_2(SO_4)_3 + 2H_2SiO_4 + H_2O$. The silicic acid is insoluble, and may be filtered off.

, With the alkali sulfates, except lithium, and with ammonium, silver, and thallous sulfates, aluminum sulfate forms isomorphous compounds of the general type, $MAl(SO_4)_2$-

$12H_2O$, known as **alums.** The class is even more general, and the aluminum may be substituted by Fe^{+++}, Cr^{+++}, Mn^{+++}, Ti^{+++}, and other $+3$ ions. The tendency of the alkali elements to form alums increases with increasing atomic weight; cesium forms more alums than the others and these are in general less soluble. The ammonium and potassium alums are the most important commercially. These alums are very soluble in hot water, but much less in cold, so that they may readily be purified by crystallization. Crystal structure data indicate that six of the water molecules form an octohedran about the aluminum ion and the other six water molecules occupy "cavities" in the lattice.

The principal uses of aluminum sulfate and alum depend primarily upon the hydrolysis of the aluminum ion, and may be divided into two classes: (1) those depending upon properties of hydrogen ion, and (2) those depending upon the properties of aluminum hydroxide. In the first class may be mentioned the use in baking powder to furnish acid to cause the liberation of carbon dioxide. The same reaction is employed in certain fire extinguishers, in which solutions of alum are caused to react with solutions of sodium bicarbonate containing organic substances capable of forming very stable foams. To the second class belong the uses as a mordant in dyeing, and as a clarifying agent for water. Aluminum hydroxide, formed by the addition of sodium carbonate or lime to alum or aluminum sulfate, is a very good absorbent for certain dyes, and also attaches itself to the fiber, thus serving to bind the dye to the material. **Mordants** of this nature are frequently necessary in dyeing cotton goods. Certain dyes may also be adsorbed on aluminum hydroxide to form pigments known as **"lakes."** The action of alum in water clarification is again due to the adsorption of suspended material by the gelatinous precipitate. Alum is also used in sizing paper and in fireproofing fabric.

When heated it loses water and some sulfur trioxide; the product, known as "burnt alum," is used in medicine as an "astringent."

22. Ultramarine.—A complex sodium aluminum silicate and sulfide occurs in nature as the mineral lapis lazuli. When ground, it constitutes the blue pigment, ultramarine. The pigment is now manufactured by heating a mixture of clay, sodium sulfate, and carbon, and is much used for laundry blue, as a water color, and in neutralizing yellow tones in linen, starch, paper, and granulated sugar. It is stable toward alkalies, but evolves hydrogen sulfide with acids.

23. Other Compounds of Aluminum.—Aluminum sulfide, Al_2S_3, is formed by the reduction of metallic sulfides by aluminum at high temperatures. It is completely hydrolyzed in water. **Aluminum acetate,** $Al(C_2H_3O_2)_3$, has many uses similar to those of the sulfate. It may be prepared from the sulfate by metathesis with barium acetate. **Kaolin,** the hydrated silicate, is further discussed under silicon.

24. Analytical Properties of Aluminum Ion.—Aluminum ion is colorless, and has a slightly bitter astringent taste. It forms an insoluble amphoteric hydroxide as already discussed. The orthophosphate, $AlPO_4$, is insoluble, and precipitates upon the addition of a soluble phosphate and ammonium hydroxide to aluminum ion. The separation of aluminum from other positive ions, and its identification as the hydroxide, is outlined in the general scheme of analysis (Append. VI). Precipitated aluminum hydroxide is often confirmed by moistening the precipitate with a drop of cobalt nitrate solution and igniting at red heat. A blue residue (cobalt aluminate) indicates the presence of aluminum. The test is capable of detecting 0.2 mg. of aluminum. It is necessary in carrying out the test to have the aluminum oxide in excess, as otherwise the color observed is obscured by the black cobalt oxide. The test is not satisfactory if sodium or potassium salts are occluded in the precipitate in any large amounts.

The formation of a bright red lake (cf. Par. **21**) with the dye aluminon (NH$_4$ salt of aurin tricarboxylic acid) may also be used to detect aluminum. A satisfactory method of carrying out the test is to use an aluminum free filter paper treated with a dilute solution of the dye and ammonium acetate. A drop of test solution is placed on the paper and held for a few seconds in the fumes from an ammonium hydroxide bottle. Red color indicates aluminum.

Complex aluminates may be dissolved by fusion in a platinum dish with potassium acid sulfate or with sodium carbonate, followed by extraction with hydrochloric acid. Silica is removed by evaporating to dryness, boiling again with hydrochloric acid, and filtering.

Aluminum is generally determined in quantitative analysis by precipitating as the hydroxide and weighing as the oxide.

Chapter VII

SUBGROUP I. COPPER, SILVER, AND GOLD

1. The elements of Subgroup I, copper, Cu (cuprum), silver, Ag (argentum), and gold, Au (aurum), differ markedly in properties from the elements of the main group. Unlike the alkalies they are "noble" metals and are not readily oxidized. This property may be correlated (cf. III—5) with the higher boiling points of the metals, indicating greater difficulty in separating their atoms from each other, and with the larger ionization potentials of the gaseous atoms (Table I). Their oxides, of the type M_2O, are much less basic than the alkali oxides, a fact which is related to the smaller size of the ions (cf. Table I, also III—7). These elements also form certain compounds in which they have oxidation states greater than + 1; in fact, the ions of + 2 copper and + 3 gold are in general more stable in respect to reducing agents than the ions of the + 1 state. The outer electron shell of the kernel is not of the noble gas type, but contains 18 electrons, and these higher states exist through the possibility of removing one or two electrons from this shell. This process is impossible in the case of the main group elements, since the energies of their kernel electrons are very much greater.

2. The ions of the subgroup elements possess the property of forming very stable complexes, such as $Cu(NH_3)_4^{++}$, $Ag(CN)_2^-$, $AuCl_4^-$. This property is in general strongly exhibited by all ions with more than eight electrons in the outer shell of the kernel, and may be considered as due to the ability of these positive ions to form definite electron pair bonds. These complexes have been called **coordination compounds,** and the number of groups or ions held by the positive ion is termed its **coordination number.** The electrons of the bond are of course supplied by the coordinating group.

Silver cyanide ion   Chloraurate ion   Cupric ammonia ion

Fluoride ion, which exhibits strong tendencies to form ionic complexes with the smaller ions such as aluminum, does not readily form complexes with the subgroup elements, because its electrons are held so firmly that they are not readily shared in bond formation. The stability of the complexes and also the solubility of the compounds of the ions appear to be related to the electrical distortion or polarization of the negative ions. This relation is illustrated by the following comparison of the solubilities of a number of silver salts with the indices of refraction of the negative ions, which may be taken as a measure of the polarization.

	F^-	O^{--}	Cl^-	Br^-	I^-	S^{--}
Solubility of silver salt moles/liter...	13.5	2×10^{-4}	9×10^{-6}	6×10^{-7}	1×10^{-8}	$< 10^{-8}$
Index of refraction of negative ion per g. atom	2.5	7.0	9.0	12.7	19.2	20.0

Moreover, the interatomic distances correspond in general to those for covalent bonds (cf. Appendix) rather than those for the ionic radii.   Both the $AuCl_4^-$ and $Cu(NH_3)_4^{++}$ given above are square planar structures instead of the customary tetrahedra, which result from a combination of s and p orbitals. The square structures are formed by a combination of one s, two p, and one d orbitals.

3. The basic nature of the oxide (comparing the $+1$ oxides) increases with increasing size of the atom, but the electropositive nature of the metal, i.e. ease of oxidation, decreases; gold being one of the most noble metals. The metals are all excellent electrical conductors.

COPPER

4. Occurrence.—Copper frequently occurs in the free state. As a rule such deposits are small, but in the Lake Superior region masses of native copper have been found weighing many tons. The copper ores may be classified as: (1) sulfide ores, the more important being chalcopyrite, $CuFeS_2$, bornite, approximately Cu_5FeS_4, chalcocite, Cu_2S, and indigo copper, CuS; (2) oxidized ores, consisting of the oxides and their compounds with negative elements, such as cuprite, Cu_2O, melaconite, CuO, malachite, $Cu_2(OH)_2$-CO_3, azurite, $Cu_3(OH)_2(CO_3)_2$, chrysocolla, $CuSiO_3 \cdot 2H_2O$, and atacamite, $CuCl_2 \cdot 3CuO \cdot 3H_2O$. The average percentage of copper in igneous rocks is estimated as 1.0×10^{-4}.

5. Metallurgy.—The methods employed in winning copper from its ores vary greatly with the type of ore. With native copper the rock is crushed, the copper concentrated by mechanical methods, and the metal purified by melting with a flux to remove the remaining gangue. High grade oxidized ores are smelted by heating in a furnace with a mixture of coke and suitable fluxes. Low grade ores may be worked by extraction of the copper with ammonia or other solvents. About 70 per cent of the copper in the United States is produced from sulfide ores. The procedure is somewhat complicated because the sulfide is not

TABLE I
ATOMIC AND PHYSICAL PROPERTIES

ELEMENT	COPPER	SILVER	GOLD
Symbol.................................	Cu	Ag	Au
Atomic number.........................	29	47	79
Atomic weight..........................	63.57	107.880	197.2
Isotopes................................	63, 65	107, 109	197
Number of electrons in various quantum			
levels, 1st............................	2	2	2
2d............................	8	8	8
3d............................	18	18	18
4th............................	1	18	32
5th............................	—	1	18
6th............................	—	—	1
Color of metal.........................	red	silver	yellow
Density................................	8.92	10.5	19.3
Melting point, ° C.....................	1083	960.5	1063
Boiling point, ° C......................	2582	2193	2660
Tensile strength, lb./sq. in..............	60,000	42,000	20,000
Specific resistance at 20°, ohm/cm. $\times 10^6$...	1.72	1.59	2.44
Ionization potential of gaseous atom, volts...	7.68	7.54	9.18
Radius of M^+ in solids, $\times 10^8$ cm.........	0.96	1.26	1.37
Potential of electrode, $M = M^+(aq) + e^-$			
(hydrogen electrode = 0)...............	$- 0.522$	$- 0.799$	$ca - 1.68$

readily reduced, and also because of the difficulty in removing the large amount of iron which is always present. The steps in the process are (1) concentration of the ore (only with low grade ores), (2) roasting, (3) formation of "copper matte," largely Cu_2S and FeS, (4) reduction of the matte to "blister copper," (5) refining of the "blister copper."

The concentration of low grade ores is now usually carried out by the "flotation" methods. The ore is ground with oil and water. The sulfide particles are wet by the oil and the earthy particles by the water. The mass is added to a larger amount of water containing a foaming agent and beaten or blown into a foam. The sulfide particles collect at the surface of the bubbles and are carried off with the foam, while the earthy particles, or "gangue," settle to the bottom. It is claimed that the method will remove as much as 95 per cent of the metal from an ore containing as low as 2 per cent copper.

The roasting step serves to remove volatile oxides of arsenic and antimony, and to oxidize part of the sulfides to the metallic oxides and sulfur dioxide. The next step is the formation of the copper matte by heating the ore with addition of sand or calcium carbonate in the proper proportion to form easily fusible calcium silicate slag. This is carried out either in a reverberatory furnace in which hot flames of burning coal dust are played upon the surface of the charge, or in a blast furnace where a blast of air is blown through the charge. In the latter case coke is added to the mixture, and its combustion supplies the heat. The temperature is kept high enough to melt the charge, and the heavier mixture of the molten sulfides settles beneath the lighter slag. During the process some of the iron is removed as iron silicate, and some of the sulfur is oxidized to sulfur dioxide. The matte consists of cuprous and ferrous sulfides. The next step is now generally carried out in the so-called copper converter, a barrel shaped vessel provided with a number of blast pipes. Air is blown through the charge, to which sand has been added, and the ferrous sulfide is converted to ferrous oxide, which forms ferrous silicate: $2FeS + 3O_2 = 2FeO + 2SO_2$, and $FeO + SiO_2 = FeSiO_3$. When the iron sulfide is all oxidized, the blast is stopped and the slag poured off. The blast is then renewed and metallic copper formed by the oxidation of the sulfur: $Cu_2S + O_2 = 2Cu + SO_2$. The copper is poured into molds, and upon cooling evolves some dissolved sulfur dioxide, which gives the surface a "blistered" appearance.

About 70 per cent of the blister copper in the United States is refined by the electrolytic method, wherein the crude metal is made the anode in a cell containing an acid solution of copper sulfate. A thin plate of pure copper serves as the cathode. By regulating the potential drop across the cell, it is possible to dissolve copper and the baser metals at the anode, leaving behind the more noble metals, such as silver, gold, and platinum as an "anode sludge." The difference in the electro-potential of copper and the base metals, iron, zinc, lead, and nickel, is sufficient so that in the acid solution copper is preferentially deposited at the cathode with a purity of approximately 99.9 per cent.

In the older methods of refining blister copper, the metal is heated in a silica lined vessel, with agitation to bring about oxidation of the base metals by the air. The basic oxides then form a slag with the silica lining. The principal impurity now present is cuprous oxide which is soluble in molten copper; so after skimming off the slag, the metal is stirred with a pole of green wood, and the hot hydrocarbons liberated from the wood reduce the cuprous oxide. The process does not give as pure copper as the electrolytic method, nor does it render possible the recovery of the more noble metals.

6. The Metal.—The more important physical properties are given in Table I. The yearly production of copper is over two million tons, of which the United States produces about 40 per cent. Its principal use, due to its high electrical conductivity and good ductility, is in electrical transmission. For this purpose it must be extremely pure, since the presence of a few tenths of a per cent of certain impurities, especially arsenic, greatly increases the resistance. Because of its high thermal conductivity and comparative inertness, it is used in boilers, water heaters, cooking utensils, steam pipes, etc. It is used in the electrotyping processes now generally employed in reproducing engravings and printing books. A plaster or wax cast is made of each page of type, the cast is coated with graphite to render it conducting, and copper is then deposited upon the cast electrolytically. The deposit of copper is then removed and strengthened by filling the back with lead.

A summary of the composition of the more important

alloys of copper is given in Table II. Bronze is much harder than copper, and also more readily cast into molds. Aluminum bronze resembles gold in color, and is used in gilt paint. Aluminum silicon bronze is quite resistant to corrosion and has a tensile strength about double that of pure copper. Brass foil is often used as a substitute for gold leaf. German silver, as its name indicates, resembles silver in appearance. It is a very poor conductor of heat. Phosphor bronze is employed in bearings. Constantan has a high and very reproducible thermoelectric force against copper, and the copper-constantan thermo-couple is used in the measurement of temperature.

TABLE II
COPPER ALLOYS

Brass...................................	60–90 Cu, 10–40 Zn
Bronze.................................	80 Cu, 15 Sn, 5 Zn
Aluminum bronze........................	90 Cu, 10 Al
Aluminum silicon bronze.................	91 Cu, 7 Al, 2 Si
Phosphor bronze........................	80 Cu, 10 Sn, 9 Sb, 1 P
Manganese bronze.......................	70–95 Cu, 5–30 Mn
Silicon bronze...........................	95 Cu, 5 Si
Gunmetal..............................	90 Cu, 10 Sn
Bell metal..............................	78 Cu, 22 Sn
Constantan.............................	60 Cu, 40 Ni
Manganin..............................	82 Cu, 15 Mn, 3 Ni
German silver..........................	52–60 Cu, 25 Zn, 15–22 Ni
Beryllium alloy.........................	2.5 Be, 97.5 Cu

TABLE III
REACTIONS OF THE METAL

$2Cu + O_2 = 2CuO$	Rapid at about 300°
$4Cu + O_2 = 2Cu_2O$	At about 1,000°
$Cu + F_2 = CuF_2$	Also with Cl_2 and Br_2. I_2 forms CuI.
$2Cu + S = Cu_2S$	Upon heating Also with Se, Te, P
$Cu + 2H^+ + \frac{1}{2}O_2 = Cu^{++} + H_2O$	With any acid not too weak
$Cu + 4NH_3 + \frac{1}{2}O_2 + H_2O = Cu(NH_3)_4(OH)_2$	
$2Cu + O_2 + CO_2 + H_2O = Cu_2CO_3(OH)_2$	Corrosion in air
$Cu + 2H_2SO_4 = CuSO_4 + SO_2 + 2H_2O$	Hot conc. acid
$Cu = Cu^{++} + 2e^-$	In general with oxidizing agents of potential greater than $- 0.34$ volt

7. Oxidation States.—Copper forms compounds in which its oxidation state is $+1$ (cuprous), $+2$ (cupric), and (a few unstable compounds) $+3$. Important potential values dealing with the oxidation and reduction of cuprous and cupric compounds have been summarized in Table IV.

TABLE IV

OXIDATION REDUCTION POTENTIALS OF COPPER

	VOLTS$_{25°}$
$2Cu + S^{--} = Cu_2S + 2e^-$	$+0.95$
$Cu + S^{--} = CuS + 2e^-$	$+0.76$
$2Cu + 2OH^- = Cu_2O + H_2O + 2e^-$	$+0.36$
$CNS^- + Cu = CuCNS + e^-$	$+0.27$
$Cu + 2OH^- = Cu(OH)_2 + 2e^-$	$+0.21$
$Cu + I^- = CuI + e^-$	$+0.19$
$2NH_3 + Cu = Cu(NH_3)_2^+ + 2e^-$	$+0.11$
$Cu_2O + 2OH^- + H_2O = 2Cu(OH)_2 + 2e^-$	$+0.09$
$4NH_3 + Cu = Cu(NH_3)_4^{++} + 2e^-$	$+0.05$
$Cu + Br^- = CuBr + e^-$	-0.03
$Cu + Cl^- = CuCl + e^-$	-0.12
$Cu^+ = Cu^{++} + e^-$	-0.17
$Cu = Cu^{++} + 2e^-$	-0.34
$Cu = Cu^+ + e^-$	-0.52
$CuCl = Cu^{++} + Cl^- + e^-$	-0.57
$CuI = Cu^{++} + I^- + e^-$	-0.88
$Cu^{++} = Cu^{+++} + e^-$	-1.8

In the case of soluble salts giving the ions Cu^+ and Cu^{++}, it is easier to oxidize the metal to the cupric state than to the cuprous, and this also means that the equilibrium, $2Cu^+ = Cu + Cu^{++}$, favors the reactions as written: e.g. cuprous nitrate will decompose into cupric nitrate and copper. Also the reduction of cupric ion in such solutions will yield the metal and not cuprous ion.

However, cuprous ion forms many very slightly soluble salts and very stable complex ions, and with many of these the above equilibria are reversed. The following are a number of important examples:

(a) *Halides.* Cupric chloride and bromide are reduced, e.g. by electrolysis or by the metal, to the cuprous salt. The addition of iodide to cupric ion results in the liberation of iodine: $Cu^{++} + 2I^- = CuI + \frac{1}{2}I_2$.

(b) *Cyanide.* Cupric ion and cyanide give cuprous cyanide ion and cyanogen (or cyanate in ammonia solutions): $2Cu^{++} + 8CN^- = 2Cu(CN)_3^{--} + C_2N_2$. This complex is so stable that the metal will dissolve in hydrogen cyanide, in spite of its weakness, with the evolution of hydrogen: $Cu + 3HCN = H_2Cu(CN)_3 + \frac{1}{2}H_2$.

(c) *Oxide.* The reduction of cupric compounds in alkaline solution gives cuprous oxide, Cu_2O. This is the basis for the common test for sugar (specifically dextrose). An alkaline solution of copper sulfate and Rochelle salts, $NaKC_4H_4O_6 \cdot 4H_2O$, known as **Fehling's solution,** will give a red coloration with extremely small quantities of dextrose, due to the precipitation of Cu_2O.

(d) *Reduction upon Heating.* Cupric compounds are in general unstable in respect to the cuprous upon heating. $2CuO = Cu_2O + \frac{1}{2}O_2$. The partial pressure of oxygen becomes appreciable above 900° C. However, the two oxides appear to form a solid solution in each other so that the partial pressure depends both upon the temperature and the concentration of the two oxides. Cupric sulfide decomposes at red heat: $2CuS = Cu_2S + S$. The cupric halides decompose according to the equation: $2CuX_2 = 2CuX + X_2$. Cupric fluoride decomposes around 500°, and the chloride and bromide at somewhat lower temperatures. The iodide is not stable even at room temperatures.

7. Powerful oxidizing agents, in alkaline solution, oxidize copper to the + 3 state, probably forming CuO_2^-. The calcium salt may be precipitated. This compound is very unstable; it tends to evolve oxygen and it reacts readily with reducing agents.

8. Cuprous Ion and Cuprous Compounds.—Cuprous compounds are prepared from the cupric by methods based upon the reactions discussed in the preceding paragraph. The ion, and in general its complex ions, are colorless. The **oxide** occurs in nature. It has a fine red color, and for that reason is employed in making ruby glass and in coloring porcelain. For the arrangement of the ions in the crystal lattice see Appendix V. It is insoluble in water and alkalies. Alkalies precipitate yellow orange hydrous cuprous oxide from cuprous compounds. Upon heating, it is transformed to the red modification. It reacts with sulfuric, nitric, and hydrofluoric acids to give copper and the cupric salt. It dissolves in ammonia, alkali cyanide, and hydrochloric acid to form the complex ions: $Cu(NH_3)_2{}^+$, $Cu(CN)_3{}^{--}$, and $CuCl_2{}^-$. The cuprous chloride and ammonia solution is oxidized by oxygen to the cupric compound, and advantage is sometimes taken of this in removing oxygen from gas: $2Cu(NH_3)_2{}^+ + 2NH_4OH + \frac{1}{2}O_2 = 2Cu(NH_3)_4{}^{++} + 2OH^- + H_2O$. The **chloride, bromide,** and **iodide** are slightly soluble in water, the solubility decreasing in the order given, as with the corresponding silver halides. They are all soluble in excess of the halide ion: e.g. $CuBr + Br^- = CuBr_2{}^-$. The chloride is hydrolyzed in boiling water: $2CuCl + H_2O = Cu_2O + 2H^+ + 2Cl^-$. A solution of chlorocuprous acid, $HCuCl_2$, is employed in gas analysis to absorb carbon monoxide. The reaction is apparently due to the formation of a rather unstable carbonyl cuprous chloride, $CuCl \cdot CO \cdot 2H_2O$. A solution of cuprous ammonia carbonate is sometimes employed in place of the chloride for the same purpose. The chloride is soluble in cyanide and in ammonia, with the formation of the complex ions. The cyanide ion, $Cu(CN)_3{}^{--}$, gives the smallest concentration of cuprous ion of any of the cuprous compounds. **Cuprous sulfide** is formed by heating together copper and sulfur, by roasting cupric sulfide, by reduction of cupric sulfide by hydrogen, and by precipitation with H_2S from solutions of $CuCl_2{}^-$. Like many sulfides its composition is not constant as the crystal lattice may contain many holes with either of the ions missing. **Cuprous thiocyanate** is also insoluble.

9. **Cupric Ion.**—Cupric ion in dilute aqueous solution probably exists as $Cu(H_2O)_4{}^{++}$, and the characteristic blue color of its solutions is probably due to this complex. Its

most important slightly soluble compounds are the black oxide, CuO; the green hydroxide, $Cu(OH)_2$; the green basic carbonate, $Cu_2CO_3(OH)_2$; the black sulfide, CuS; and red-brown ferrocyanide, $Cu_2Fe(CN)_6$. The most important complex ions are the deep blue cupric ammonia, $Cu(NH_3)_4^{++}$; chlor and brom cuprates, $CuCl_4^{--}$, $CuBr_4^{--}$ (respectively green and brown); and tartrate, $Cu(C_4H_4O_6)_2^{--}$. The soluble cupric salts of strong acids are all slightly acid by hydrolysis.

10. Cupric Oxide and Hydroxide.—The addition of hydroxide ion to a cold solution of cupric ion gives a light bluish green gelatinous precipitate of the hydroxide, but in hot solutions the black oxide is formed. The oxide does not absorb water to form the hydroxide. The hydroxide is a weak base. $Cu(OH)_2 = Cu^{++} + 2OH^-$, $K = 5.6 \times 10^{-20}$. It is not soluble in dilute alkalies, but does dissolve somewhat in $6N$ to $18N$ $NaOH$, forming deep blue solutions of cuprate, $Cu(OH)_2 + 2OH^- = CuO_2^{--} + 2H_2O$, $K = 1.2 \times 10^{-3}$. The sodium cuprate, Na_2CuO_2, may be precipitated from the concentrated alkaline solutions. The hydroxide is soluble in ammonium hydroxide, forming the complex ammonia ion, and in tartrate, forming the complex tartrate (**Fehling's solution**). The oxide is also formed by heating the carbonate or nitrate. At moderately high temperatures, it oxidizes hydrogen, forming water and copper. In quantitative organic analysis, mixtures of the oxide and organic compound are heated to effect the oxidation of the combined carbon and hydrogen to carbon dioxide and water.

11. Cupric Halides.—The fluoride, chloride, and bromide are readily soluble. As mentioned above, the iodide is unstable. The concentrated solution of the chloride is green, and of the bromide, brown. The color appears to be due to existence of part of the copper in the complex ions, $CuCl_4^{--}$ (green), and $CuBr_4^{--}$ (brown). Upon electrolysis, copper moves toward both the cathode and anode. When the concentrated solutions are diluted, the blue of the $Cu(H_2O)_4^{++}$ again predominates. The solid halides absorb ammonia gas to form compounds, such as $CuCl_2 \cdot 6NH_3$. These compounds, of course, give the complex ammonia ion upon solution.

12. Cupric Sulfate.—The sulfate is the most important copper salt. The anhydrous salt is colorless, but it readily absorbs water to form the blue pentahydrate, $CuSO_4$ $\cdot 5H_2O$, known as "blue vitriol." The five molecules of water of hydration may be successively replaced by ammonia. The sulfate is prepared commercially by roasting the sulfide, either to form the sulfate, which may be extracted with water, or to form the oxide, which may be dissolved in sulfuric acid. A $0.2N$ solution is 0.057 per cent hydrolyzed at 25° C. From solutions of copper sulfate and the alkali sulfates, double salts, such as $K_2Cu(SO_4)_2 6H_2O$, may be crystallized. Upon slow addition of alkali to copper sulfate solution, a number of insoluble basic sulfates are formed, for example, $Cu_5(SO_4)_2(OH)_6 2H_2O$. Basic sulfates, made by mixing copper sulfate and slaked lime, are used under the name of **"Bordeaux mixture"** as a fungicide. Copper sulfate is used in calico printing, in electroplating, and electrotyping, and as an electrolyte in the gravity battery. Copper is very poisonous to lower organisms, especially algae, and is used in swimming pools and water works to prevent the growth of such organisms.

13. Cupric Sulfide.—The brownish black sulfide is precipitated from cupric solutions by the action of hydrogen sulfide, even in the presence of high concentrations of acid. When precipitated from neutral solution, it may contain some cuprous sulfide. It is soluble in hot $2N$ HNO_3 because of the oxidation of the sulfur, and in cyanide ion because of the formation of $Cu(CN)_3^{--}$. The sulfide is slightly soluble in ammonium polysulfide, probably through the formation of thiocuprates.

14. Other Cupric Salts.—The **nitrate** crystallizes as blue hexahydrate. Because of the smaller solubility of the hydroxide, the normal carbonate does not exist, but two **basic carbonates,** azurite, $Cu_3(CO_3)_2(OH)_2$, and malachite, $Cu_2CO_3(OH)_2$, occur in nature. The latter is the green coating which forms on copper vessels through the action of oxygen and carbonic acid of the air. A **basic acetate,** verdigris, $Cu_3(C_2H_3O_2)_4(OH)_2$, is used as a green pigment. It is formed by the action of air upon copper in the presence of acetic acid. A mixed acetate and arsenite, $Cu_4(C_2H_3O_2)_2(AsO_3)_2$, **Paris green,** is used as an insecticide. Copper ferrocyanide, $Cu_2Fe(CN)_6$, may be formed as a brown gelatinous precipitate. It has been used in the preparation of semi-permeable membranes for studying osmotic pressure. **Copper phosphate,** $Cu_3(PO_4)_2$, is insoluble and is precipitated, together with basic phosphates, upon the addition of diammonium phosphate to a solution of copper sulfate.

15. Analytical.—Copper is recognized qualitatively by the intense blue color of the ammonia complex, and by the precipitation of the sulfide by hydrogen sulfide in acid solution. Nickel also gives a blue ammonia complex, but its sulfide is not precipitated in acid solution. A strip of iron in a not too acid copper solution will be coated with metallic copper. This is frequently a convenient and delicate test. The detailed methods of separation are indicated in Appendix VI. Copper is often determined quantitatively by the electrolytic precipitation of the metal in acid solution upon an accurately weighed cathode. This method affords a separation from the baser metals as well. A number of reactions are of importance in quantitative determinations. (a) $2Cu^{++} + 5I^- = 2CuI + I_3^-$. The liberated iodine is titrated with standardized thiosulfate. Other oxidizing agents such as ferric ion must be removed. (b) $2Cu(NH_3)_4^{++} + 7CN^- + H_2O = 2Cu(CN)_3^{--} + CNO^- + 2NH_4^+ + 6NH_3$. The ammonia solution is titrated with standardized cyanide to the disappearance of the blue color. This method is not as accurate as the iodide reaction.

(c) $2Cu^{++} + 2CNS^- + SO_2 + 2H_2O = 2CuCNS + 4H^+ + SO_4^{--}$. The precipitate may be ignited and weighed as Cu_2S, or titrated with iodate in the presence of concentrated hydrochloric acid: $4CuCNS + 7IO_3^- + 14H^+ + 14Cl^- = 4Cu^{++} + 4SO_4^= + 7ICl_2^- + 4HCN + 5H_2O$.

SILVER

16. Occurrence.—Native, or free silver is an important source of the element. It is usually alloyed with other of the noble metals. The most important naturally occurring compound is the sulfide, argentite, or silver glance, Ag_2S. It frequently occurs in solid solution with copper and lead sulfide, and as the sulfo-antimonite, Ag_3SbS_3, and arsenite, Ag_3AsS_3. The selenides and tellurides also occur. Silver chloride, AgCl, called horn silver, is an ore of some importance, and often contains the bromide and iodide in small amounts. The sulfate also occurs, being formed through the oxidation of the sulfide. The average percentage of silver in igneous rocks is estimated as 10^{-8}.

17. Metallurgy.—The recovery of silver from copper ores has been mentioned. Much of the lead smelted from lead sulfide contains silver. This is now recovered by Parke's process, which is essentially an extraction of the silver from the molten lead by means of zinc. Solid zinc is but slightly soluble in lead at temperatures just above the melting point of the latter. However, silver at these temperatures is about 3,000 times more soluble in the zinc than in the molten lead. Hence zinc in small amounts, usually 0.8 to 1.5 per cent, is stirred with the molten lead, and the greater portion of the silver is extracted. The zinc is removed from the silver by distillation. The small amount of lead present is removed by oxidation and absorption of the lead oxide on a cupel of bone ash.

The extraction of silver from comparatively pure silver ore is accomplished either by (1) amalgamation, or (2) leaching processes. The first depends upon the conversion of silver sulfide into chloride by copper chloride, $Ag_2S + Cu^{++} + 2Cl^- = 2AgCl + CuS$; and the decomposition of the chloride by mercury, $AgCl + Hg = Ag$ (amalgam) $+ HgCl$. The silver is recovered from the amalgam by distillation of the mercury.

A number of leaching processes have been employed. A sulfide ore may be roasted to convert the sulfide into sulfate, which may then be extracted with water. Or the sulfide may be roasted with salt to convert it into chloride, which is then leached, either with concentrated brine, the solubility being due to the formation of $AgCl_2^-$, or with thiosulfate, forming the complex $Ag(S_2O_3)_2^{---}$. However, solutions of the alkali cyanides are now generally employed, as the metal and all of its compounds are readily dissolved by this reagent in the presence of air: $4Ag + 8CN^- + O_2 + 2H_2O = 4Ag(CN)_2^- + 4OH^-$; $Ag_2S + 4CN^- + \frac{1}{2}O_2 + H_2O = 2Ag(CN)_2^- + S + 2OH^-$; $AgCl + 2CN^- = Ag(CN)_2^- + Cl^-$. The silver is precipitated from the cyanide solution by zinc or aluminum.

18. The Metal.—The more important physical constants have been given in Table I. Silver is the most lustrous of all the metals. In thermal and electrical conductivity it also ranks among the first. It is but little inferior to gold in malleability and ductility. Silver melted in air always has a blistered surface upon cooling, due to the evolution of dissolved oxygen during solidification. The solubility of oxygen under 1 atmosphere pressure at the melting point is 20 volumes per volume of the metal. The cooled solid silver still contains 0.75 volume of oxygen.

The annual production of silver is about 9,000 tons. Silver coins are generally 90 per cent silver with 10 per cent copper to increase the hardness. Jewelry usually contains 20 per cent of copper. The electroplating industry consumes a large proportion of the metal produced. The object to be coated is made the cathode in a cell containing a solution

TABLE V

REACTIONS OF THE METAL

$2Ag + \frac{1}{2}O_2 = Ag_2O$	At 200° with O_2 under pressure
$2Ag + X_2 = 2AgX$	X denotes any halogen
$2Ag + S = Ag_2S$	Also with Se and Te
$2Ag + 2H_2SO_4 = Ag_2SO_4 + SO_2 + 2H_2O$	Hot concentrated acid
$2Ag + 2H^+ + 2Cl^- + \frac{1}{2}O_2 = 2AgCl + H_2O$	
$2Ag + H_2O + 4CN^- + \frac{1}{2}O_2 = 2Ag(CN)_2^- + 2OH^-$	
$Ag = Ag^+ + e^-$	See oxidation reduction table

of sodium silver cyanide, $NaAg(CN)_2$, as electrolyte. The cyanide complex, which gives a very low concentration of silver ion, yields a much firmer deposit than solutions having a higher concentration of the silver ion. Frosted silver ornaments are obtained by roasting the object, made of the ordinary silver-copper alloy, to oxidize the copper on the surface to the oxide; this is dissolved in sulfuric acid, leaving a layer of pure white silver. Silver mirrors are formed by precipitating the metal from a highly alkaline solution containing the silver ammonia complex ion by the aid of some organic reducing agent, such as glucose or formaldehyde. Approximately 150 tons of silver are used yearly in the production of photographic supplies.

19. Stability of Silver Compounds.—Silver ion is colorless. It forms such a very large number of slightly soluble salts and complexes that it is desirable to systematize the chemistry of these substances by arranging the more important in a list in order of decreasing concentration of silver ion in equilibrium with the solid or complex ion, and a $1M$ concentration of the ion or complex forming molecule. For salts of the types Ag_2X or AgY this is not necessarily the order of the solubility in pure water because the square of the Ag^+ concentration enters into the constant for the Ag_2X. The order is Ag_2SO_4, AgAc. $AgNO_2$, Ag_2CO_3, $Ag_2C_2O_4$, Ag_2CrO_4, $Ag(NH_3)_2^+$, Ag_2O, $Ag(SO_3)_2^{---}$, AgCl, AgCNS. AgBr, $Ag(S_2O_3)_2^{---}$, AgCN, AgI, and Ag_2S. Any substance in the list may be formed at the expense of any substance preceding it. Thus silver iodide may be formed from the chloride: $AgCl + I^- = AgI + Cl^-$. Substances which are close together in the list may be present together in equilibrium at appreciable concentrations of both. Thus silver bromide is partially soluble in ammonium hydroxide, and the reaction is easily reversible, depending upon the concentration of ammonia and bromide. The dissociation constant for the ammonia complex ion is, $(Ag^+)(NH_4OH)^2/(Ag(NH_3)_2^+) = 6 \times 10^{-8}$.

The silver halides are soluble in excess of the halide ion to form the complex ions AgX_2^-, and AgX_3^{--} but they have not been included in the list because of the more complicated equilibria.

The potentials of a number of silver complex ions and solids as oxidizing agents are given below. The decrease in oxidizing power is, of course, due to the decrease in concentration of silver ion.

$$Ag = Ag^+ + e^- \dots\dots\dots -0.799$$
$$2Ag + SO_4^{--} = Ag_2SO_4 + 2e^- \dots\dots\dots -0.65$$
$$Ag + C_2H_3O_2^- = AgC_2H_3O_2 + e^- \dots\dots\dots -0.64$$
$$2Ag + C_2O_4^{--} = Ag_2C_2O_4 + 2e^- \dots\dots\dots -0.47$$
$$2Ag + CO_3^- = Ag_2CO_3 + 2e^- \dots\dots\dots -0.46$$
$$Ag + IO_3^- = AgIO_3 + e^- \dots\dots\dots -0.37$$
$$Ag + 2NH_3 = Ag(NH_3)_2^+ + e^- \dots\dots\dots -0.37$$
$$2Ag + 2OH^- = Ag_2O + H_2O + 2e^- \dots\dots\dots -0.344$$
$$Ag + Cl^- = AgCl + e^- \dots\dots\dots -0.222$$
$$Ag + CNS^- = AgCNS + e^- \dots\dots\dots -0.09$$
$$Ag + Br^- = AgBr + e^- \dots\dots\dots -0.07$$
$$Ag + CN^- = AgCN + e^- \dots\dots\dots +0.04$$
$$Ag + I^- = AgI + e^- \dots\dots\dots +0.15$$
$$Ag + 2CN^- = Ag(CN)_2^- + e^- \dots\dots\dots +0.29$$
$$2Ag + S^{--} = Ag_2S + 2e^- \dots\dots\dots +0.71$$

20. Silver Oxide.—The brown oxide, Ag_2O, is precipitated by the addition of soluble alkalies to silver ion. The solid hydroxide is unstable and exists only momentarily. The oxide decomposes at comparatively low temperatures; the partial pressure of oxygen reaches 1 atmosphere at 184° C. However, the rate of decomposition does not be-

come rapid until the oxide is heated much above this temperature. The decomposition is catalyzed by metallic silver.
The oxide is distinctly basic in its reactions. It reacts with
as weak an acid as carbonic to form the normal **carbonate,**
Ag_2CO_3. As indicated above, the oxide is soluble in a large
number of reagents with the formation of complex ions.
The silver ammonia hydroxide, $Ag(NH_3)_2OH$, is a soluble
strong base. Upon standing, the alkaline solution forms a
highly explosive nitride, probably Ag_3N or Ag_2NH.

21. Silver Halides.—Silver fluoride is extremely soluble
and forms a number of hydrates. The solubility of the other
halides is very slight, decreasing with increasing molecular
weight. Their solubility in various reagents has been indicated above. The solubility in excess halide to form the
complexes, such as $AgCl_2^-$, requires a fairly high concentration of the halide. The chloride and bromide are not
oxidized by nitric acid, but the iodide is. The halides form
a number of solid ammoniates, such as $AgCl \cdot 3NH_3$. Silver
chloride, however, is not very soluble in liquid ammonia.
The photochemical properties of the halides are discussed
under the subject of photography. The chloride and bromide have the so-called "sodium chloride" arrangement of
the ions in the crystal, while the iodide has two forms, one
the zinc oxide and the other the zinc sulfide arrangement
(Append. V). The fluoride and chloride are colorless, but
the bromide is light yellow and the iodide a deeper yellow.
Silver chloride may be separated from the bromide by
taking advantage of the difference in solubility in ammonia. A solution containing 32 g. of ammonia and 20 g.
of silver nitrate per liter will dissolve the chloride, but not
appreciable amounts of the bromide.

22. Silver Cyanide.—Silver cyanide is precipitated by
addition of cyanide, and forms the complex ion, $Ag(CN)_2^-$
or $Ag(CN)_3^{--}$, with excess of cyanide. The role of the silver
cyanide complex ion in metallurgy and silver plating has
been discussed. The complex gives the smallest concentra-

tion of silver ion of any of the silver compounds except the sulfide. From the electropotential given above it is evident that, in the presence of cyanide, silver is a powerful reducing agent.

23. Silver Nitrate.—The nitrate is prepared commercially by the action of nitric acid upon silver. The salt is extremely soluble. Its melting point is remarkably low, about 200° C.; cast into sticks it is used in medicine under the name of lunar caustic. At red heat, it is decomposed into metallic silver, oxygen, nitrogen, and nitrogen oxides. Many organic substances reduce it to finely divided metallic silver, as, for example, the black stains produced by the action of the salt upon the skin.

The salt is important in the preparation of other silver compounds. In dilute solutions it is used as an antiseptic, and in more concentrated solutions as a caustic. It is also used in indelible inks, especially in laundry markings.

24. Silver Sulfide.—The sulfide is the least soluble of all the silver salts. It is formed as a black precipitate by hydrogen sulfide, even in highly acid solutions. It is more stable toward decomposition upon heating than the oxide. Strong oxidizing agents dissolve it due to the oxidation of the sulfur. It is also somewhat soluble in concentrated cyanide ion. In the presence of air the reaction proceeds through the removal of the sulfide by oxidation to free sulfur. Metallic silver dissolves slowly in hydrogen sulfide with the evolution of hydrogen, $2Ag + H_2S = Ag_2S + H_2$, in accord with the large positive value for the $Ag - Ag_2S$ couple as given above.

25. Other Silver Salts.—In addition to those given above, the following slightly soluble compounds may be mentioned: the **phosphate,** Ag_3PO_4; **arsenite,** Ag_3AsO_3; **arsenate,** Ag_3AsO_4; **ferricyanide,** $Ag_3Fe(CN)_6$; and **dichromate,** $Ag_2Cr_2O_7$. **Silver nitrite,** $AgNO_2$, is but moderately soluble, and upon standing in contact with the solution decomposes according to the equation: $2AgNO_2 = Ag + Ag^+ + NO_3^-$

+ NO. The reaction is reversible. Silver ion also forms **alums,** such as $AgAl(SO_4)_2 \cdot 12H_2O$.

26. Photography.—The silver halides, as well as the cyanide, show marked changes when exposed to light, especially that of the violet region of the spectrum. There is a change in color; white silver chloride, for example, becomes a deep greyish blue, and is decomposed into silver and the halogen. The primary photochemical process in a crystal lattice, such as silver bromide, composed of silver and bromide ions, appears to be the following:

$$Br^- + h\nu = Br + e^-$$
$$Ag^+ + e^- = Ag$$

The result is a solid solution of silver and atomic halogen in the halide, which, upon further exposure, decomposes with evolution of the halogen. The halide which has been thus "activated" by light is acted upon much more readily by reducing agents than is the unexposed halide.

These photochemical reactions are the basis of the ordinary photographic processes. These may be divided into the following steps: preparation of the plate or film, exposure, development and fixation of the negative, and preparation of the positive, or print.

Dry plates or films are prepared by coating glass or celluloid with a colloidal suspension of silver bromide or chloride in gelatine. The operation must, of course, be carried out in the dark or in faint red light. The size of the particles of the silver halide affects the sensitivity of the plate to light; hence the suspension is warmed and allowed to "ripen" until the desired size of the grains is acquired.

The plate or film is exposed by projecting upon it momentarily an illuminated image. It is then developed by placing in a bath containing a reducing agent (various phenols, such as pyrogallol, metol, and hydroquinone are usually employed). The rapidity of reduction of the silver halide is proportional to the intensity of illumination falling upon it; and as a result the image on the plate is the "negative" of the original in that the bright portions are represented by heavy deposits of silver and the dark portions by faint deposits. The action of the reducing agent is stopped when the proper contrast is obtained, and the plate "fixed" by dissolving out the unreduced silver halide with sodium thiosulfate solution ("hypo").

The process of printing is essentially the same as making the negative, but since the sensitized paper is illuminated through the negative, the image is again reversed, and now appears with the light and dark portions corresponding to the original. On the slower papers silver chloride suspension in albumen is used, while the faster papers employ silver bromide in gelatine. The print may be toned by treating with solutions of sodium chloraurate, $NaAuCl_4$, or potassium chlorplatinite, K_2PtCl_4, which replace the precipitated silver by gold or by platinum. The former gives a red tone, and the latter dark grey. A sepia tone is obtained by treating the print with collodial sulfur which converts the silver to silver sulfur. Blue tones are given by a treatment with ferric chloride and potassium ferricyanide. The silver reduces the ferric to ferrous which then reacts with the ferricyanide to give Prussian blue.

It is possible to reverse a negative to a positive. After developing a film but before fixing, an acid oxidizing agent is used to oxidize and remove the metallic silver. The film is next re-exposed to light to activate the remaining AgBr which was not affected by the initial exposure. The film is then redeveloped and fixed. By this treatment the original dark and light areas of the film are interchanged.

"Orthochromatic" and "panchromatic" plates, more sensitive to the red, yellow, and green light, are prepared by adding to the gelatine various dyes, which absorb these longer wave lengths and thus utilize their energy for the activation of the silver halide.

In **color photography** of the coupler type, the primary process is again the reduction of exposed silver bromide to metallic silver. The emulsion, however, contains a compound, the coupler, which reacts with the oxidation product of the developer to give a dye. Thus if p-aminodiethylaniline is used as the developer it is oxidized by the silver halide and the product of the oxidation reacts with the coupler (for example, acetoacetic ester) to give a green dye. The emulsion is coated with at least three layers, each sensitive to a different region of light frequency. By the use of several couplers with various reducing agents the range of colors is covered. As a final step the metallic silver is removed, and the dyes give the color image.

27. The + 2 and + 3 Oxidation States.—Ozone acts upon solutions of Ag^+ forming AgO^+ and Ag^{++}, probably by the following steps:

$$Ag^+ + O_3 = AgO^+ + O_2$$
$$Ag^+ + AgO^+ + 2H^+ = 2Ag^{++} + H_2O$$

At equilibrium the ratio of Ag^{++}/AgO^+ is quite large. The solutions are highly unstable as the ions oxidize water readily with the evolution of O_2. Powerful oxidizing agents in alkaline solution form AgO and Ag_2O_3. The + 2 oxide is quite stable at ordinary temperatures if kept dry, and is a convenient source of Ag^{++} since it dissolves readily in cold nitric acid. Peroxydisulfate oxidizes Ag^+ in acid solution:

$$S_2O_8^{--} + 2Ag^+ = 2SO_4^{--} + 2Ag^{++}$$

The + 2 ion forms complexes with a coordination number of four. The electrolytic oxidation of a silver nitrate solution in the presence of pyridine forms orange red crystals of the complex salt, $Ag(C_5H_5N)_4(NO_3)_2$. The difluoride AgF_2 may be made by the action of fluorine upon the metal. At its melting point, 690° C., it has about 0.1 atm. pressure of F_2. Approximate values for the standard potentials are:

$$\text{VOLTS}_{25}°$$

$$Ag^+ = Ag^{++} + e^-\ \dots\ -1.98$$
$$Ag^{++} + H_2O = AgO^+ + 2H^+ + e^-\ \dots\ ca\ -2.1$$
$$2OH^- + Ag_2O = 2AgO + H_2O + 2e^-\ \dots\ -0.57$$
$$2OH^- + 2AgO = Ag_2O_3 + H_2O + 2e^-\ \dots\ -0.74$$

28. Analytical.—Silver is detected by the precipitation of the chloride, insoluble in nitric acid, but soluble in ammonium hydroxide. It may be distinguished from the slightly soluble lead and mercurous chlorides by the fact that the former is soluble in hot water, but not in ammonia, while the latter turns black with ammonia. Silver is determined gravimetrically by precipitating and weighing as the chloride, bromide, or as the metal precipitated electrolytically. Silver may be titrated volumetrically with a solution of thiocyanate. Ferric ion is used as an indicator, since the deep red ferric thiocyanate is less stable than the silver salt, and the red color appears only when the silver has been almost completely precipitated. Silver is also titrated in dilute nitric acid with a standardized solution of alkali chloride or bromide, by taking advantage of the coagulation and settling of the precipitate with sufficient rapidity to permit the observation of any precipitate produced by further addition of the halide.

GOLD

29. Occurrence.—Gold is found in nature as the free metal, as the telluride, $AuTe_2$, and also as complex tellurides, e.g. $AuAgTe_4$. The sulfide, selenide, or chloride do not occur. Sea water contains gold to the extent of 0.1 to 0.2 milligram per ton. The name reef gold is given to the deposits of gold occurring in quartz veins. Upon the weathering of the auriferous rocks, the gold has been washed into sand and gravel beds to form alluvial or placer deposits. Native gold nearly always contains silver and the platinum metals.

30. Metallurgy.—The richer deposits of gold have been worked for centuries by methods which recovered only the larger particles of the metal and which could not be applied to low grade ores. The crude methods of placer mining have been the simple agitation or washing of the gravel with water to bring about a separation of the heavy gold particles from the lighter materials. The use of mercury as an aid in the process by the amalgamation of the metal was probably introduced as early as 500 B.C.

The modern metallurgy of gold is quite similar to that of silver. Gold in copper and lead ores is recovered, along with the silver, by methods already discussed. The separation of the gold from the silver is known as "parting," and is usually carried out either by electrolytic methods or by the use of solvents, such as concentrated sulfuric or nitric acids, which dissolve the silver by oxidation, but not the gold. In the former case the impure metal is made the anode, with a solution of chlorauric acid as electrolyte. Pure gold deposits on the cathode. Silver is precipitated as the chloride together with the platinum metals in the anode mud. If excess silver is present, the electrolyte may be silver nitrate solution, in which case gold remains as sludge at the anode and silver deposited on the cathode.

The introduction of the cyanide process by Macarthur and Forest about 1890 has contributed enormously to the world's gold supply through rendering available for commercial treatment low grade ores and also "tailings" from the amalgam process. The potential of the half reaction, $Au + 2CN^- = Au(CN)_2^- + e^-$, is about $+ 0.6$ volt, that is, the gold in the presence of cyanide is a good reducing agent; hence by treating gold ore with a dilute cyanide solution in the presence of air, the metal is easily oxidized by the oxygen: $4Au + 8CN^- + O_2 + 2H_2O = 4Au(CN)_2^- + 4OH^-$. Hydrogen peroxide appears to be formed as an intermediate step (cf. **III—4**). The reaction is not rapid and requires a number of days. The gold is precipitated from the solution by zinc or by electrolysis. High grade ores, after being pulverized in a mill, may first be washed over amalgamated copper plates to remove the larger gold particles which do not dissolve rapidly in the cyanide. The amalgam is scraped off the plates, and the gold recovered by distillation of the mercury.

31. The Metal.—The more important physical properties are given in Table I. Gold is the most malleable and ductile of all metals. It may be rolled into sheets 0.00001 mm. thick and drawn into wire which weighs but 0.0005 g. per meter. The world's yearly production is about 1,000 tons. The gold used in jewelry is alloyed with copper. The copper alloys are redder, harder, and more fusible than pure gold. The temperature-composition curves for the alloy show a minimum melting point at 890° C. with a composition of 82 per cent gold. The purity of the metal is usually expressed in carats, that is, the number of parts of gold in 24 parts of the metal. The best jewelry is 15 to 18 carat gold. American coinage is 21.6 carat (90 per cent). Gold is deposited in electroplating from a solution of aurocyanide, and much cheap jewelry is manufactured by so depositing a very thin coat of gold on copper.

Gold is easily obtained in the **colloidal state,** especially in the presence of other stabilizing colloids. Thus, **purple of Cassius** is finely divided gold adsorbed on a hydrosol of stannic acid. The gold colloids may be formed by reduction of gold solution with chemical agents, or by electrical dispersion, using an arc between gold electrodes under water.

TABLE VI

REACTIONS OF METALLIC GOLD

$2Au + 3Cl_2 = 2AuCl_3$	At about 150°; also with Br_2
$Au + 2Te = AuTe_2$	
$2Au + 6H_2SeO_4 = Au_2(SeO_4)_3 + 3SeO_2 + 6H_2O$	
$Au + 5H^+ + 4Cl^- + NO_3^- = HAuCl_4 + NO + 2H_2O$	Solution in aqua regia
$2Au + 4CN^- + \frac{1}{2}O_2 + H_2O = 2Au(CN)_2^- + 2OH^-$	
$2Au + 2Na_2S_3 = 2NaAuS_2 + Na_2S_2$	
$2Au + I_2 = 2AuI$	

32. Equilibria between Oxidation States.—Aurous ion is unstable in respect to the decomposition: $6Au^+ + 3H_2O = 4Au + Au_2O_3 + 6H^+$ (about 0.3 volt); hence only those aurous compounds and complexes which are relatively less soluble and less ionized than the corresponding auric compound can be prepared in solution. The only aurous compound which appears to be really stable with respect to the auric in solution is the aurocyanide: $Au(CN)_4^- + 2Au + 2CN^- = 3Au(CN)_2^-$.

Oxidation reduction potentials are summarized in Table VII. The value given for the formation of aurocyanide, $+ 0.6$ volt, may be too high, as gold does not appear to dissolve in cyanide solution with the evolution of hydrogen.

TABLE VII

OXIDATION REDUCTION POTENTIALS OF GOLD

$Au = Au^+ + e^-$	ca $- 1.68$
$Au^+ = Au^{+++} + 2e^-$	ca $- 1.29$
$Au + 2CN^- = Au(CN)_2^- + e^-$	$+ 0.6$
$Au + 2Br^- = AuBr_2^- + e^-$	0.96
$2Br^- + AuBr_2^- = AuBr_4^- + 2e^-$	$- 0.82$
$Au + 4Cl^- = AuCl_4^- + 3e^-$	$- 1.0$
$Au + 4OH^- = AuO_2^- + 2H_2O + 3e^-$	ca $- 0.5$

Auric chloride and bromide decompose upon heating to give the aurous halide: $AuCl_3 = AuCl + Cl_2$. Many of the auric compounds, however, decompose, giving the metal. A number of $+ 2$ compounds also exist, but they are all unstable with respect to the reaction, $3Au^{++} = Au + 2Au^{+++}$, with the exception of the sulfide AuS. Like mercuric sulfide this gold sulfide is very slightly soluble and may be precipitated from a solution of auric chloride.

33. Oxides.—The aurous oxide, Au_2O, is said to be formed by the action of dilute potassium hydroxide upon aurous chloride, but it is very unstable and, in excess hydroxide, gives the metal and aurate, AuO_2^-. The addition of hydroxide to auric solutions gives a precipitate of $Au(OH)_3$, or more probably the hydrous sesquioxide, Au_2O_3. This is amphoteric, and is somewhat more acidic than basic. The alkali aurates, such as $KAuO_2$, are soluble; but those of the alkaline earths are not. The oxide forms with ammonia the highly explosive gold **"fulminate,"** probably $AuN \cdot NH_3$. An unstable $+ 2$ oxide, AuO, is also known.

34. Halides.—Fluorine does not attack gold at ordinary temperatures, but at higher temperatures a slight reaction occurs. The fluoride is completely hydrolyzed by water, forming auric hydroxide. Chlorine attacks gold in the neighborhood of 150°, forming $AuCl_3$. At somewhat higher temperatures the aurous chloride, $AuCl$, is formed. This is but slightly soluble in water. Both chlorides are soluble in excess hydrochloric acid, forming, respectively, $HAuCl_4$ and $HAuCl_2$. The latter is unstable, as discussed above. Auric chloride is usually prepared by the action of **aqua regia** upon gold. Sodium chloraurate, $NaAuCl_4 \cdot 2H_2O$, is employed in photography in toning prints. The two bromides, $AuBr$ and $AuBr_3$, are analogous in most respects to the chlorides. Gold is slowly attacked by iodine, forming AuI. However, there appears to be a measurable equilibrium: $2Au + I_2 = 2AuI$. The aurous iodide is also formed by the reaction: $Au_2O_3 + 6HI = 2AuI + 3H_2O + 2I_2$, or by the addition of iodide to the auric chloride. Auric iodide is unstable.

35. Sulfides.—Gold and sulfur do not unite when heated together, but gold is dissolved by molten alkali polysulfides, forming thioaurites and possibly some thioaurates. Hydrogen sulfide in warm acid solution gives with $AuCl_4^-$ a precipitate of gold and sulfur. In cold solution some of the unstable sulfide, AuS, appears to be formed.

36. Other Compounds.—Mention has been made of the occurrence of gold **telluride,** and also of the stability and importance of the **cyanoaurites.** The alkali cyanoaurites, such as $KAu(CN)_2$, are soluble. Auric nitrate and sulfate are so highly hydrolyzed that auric oxide is soluble only in very concentrated solution of these acids.

37. Analytical.—The presence of auric gold may be determined by the rose coloration (colloidal gold) produced upon the addition of a dilute solution of stannous chloride to the auric solution in excess hydrochloric acid. Gold, in the form of auric chloride, is sometimes determined quantitatively by the reaction, $AuCl_4^- + 3I^- = AuI + I_2 + 4Cl^-$, the liberated iodine being titrated with thiosulfate (cf. X—21). Gold ores are usually analyzed by the fire assay. The first step in the assay is the separation of the gangue, and the concentration of gold and silver in a lead "button." This operation may be carried out in a shallow clay dish called a "scorifier," in which the sample of ore is heated with a large amount of lead and a little borax. Much of the lead is oxidized, and the oxide forms an easily fusible flux with the silicates and borates. The rest of the lead serves to collect the gold and silver, and when the molten mass is cooled the lead is found as a small lump or button which may be separated from the slag. This process is sometimes carried out in a crucible with a mixture of ore, fluxing agent, lead oxide, and some reducing agent. The latter reduces some of the lead oxide, and the metal collects the gold and silver as in the scorification process. The second step is the separation of the gold and silver from the lead. The button is heated in a little cup of bone ash called a "cupel." The lead oxidizes, and the liquid oxide is readily absorbed by the bone ash, while the liquid gold and silver remain in a small globule. The third step is the "parting" of the gold and silver. The button is flattened by hammering and treated with nitric acid to dissolve out the silver. Unless there is a considerable excess of silver, more must be added before the separation can be accomplished, as otherwise the silver atoms are removed from the surface of the button but the crystal lattice is not destroyed, and the action soon stops. However, if there is a large excess of silver, the crystal is completely disintegrated, and the finely divided gold remaining may be fused and weighed. Gold is readily separated from the platinum metals by precipitation with hydroquinone in $1.2N$ HCl solutions.

38. Summary of Subgroup I Potentials.—In order to compare the stabilities of the oxidation states of the three elements of Subgroup I, the following summary is given for the potentials in acid solution.

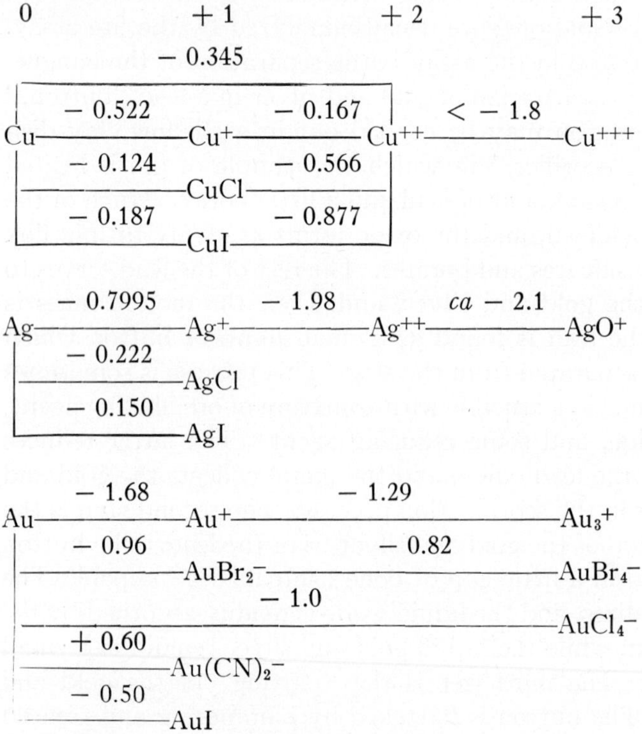

0   + 1   + 2   + 3

                          − 0.345

| − 0.522 | − 0.167 | < − 1.8 |

Cu————————Cu^+————————Cu^{++}————————Cu^{+++}

| − 0.124 | − 0.566 |

————————$CuCl$————————

| − 0.187 | − 0.877 |

————————CuI————————

    − 0.7995   − 1.98 ca − 2.1

Ag————————Ag^+————————Ag^{++}————————AgO^+

    − 0.222

————————————$AgCl$

    − 0.150

————————————AgI

    − 1.68   − 1.29

Au————————Au^+————————————————————Au_3^+

    − 0.96   − 0.82

————————————$AuBr_2^-$————————————————$AuBr_4^-$

                        − 1.0

————————————————————————————————$AuCl_4^-$

    + 0.60

————————————$Au(CN)_2^-$

    − 0.50

————————————AuI

Chapter VIII

SUBGROUP II. ZINC, CADMIUM, AND MERCURY

1. The elements of Subgroup II, zinc, Zn, cadmium, Cd, and mercury, Hg (hydrargyrum), differ from the elements of the main group in much the same way that copper, silver, and gold differ from the alkali metals. Thus the subgroup elements are more noble, their hydroxides are less basic, and their ions have a greater tendency to form complex ions. These properties depend upon the much higher ionization potentials of the atoms and the smaller size of the resultant ions (Table I). The melting points of the elements in Subgroup II are much lower than those of the main group. They all form $+2$ positive ions, but in addition, mercury forms an unusual series of compounds of the ion, Hg_2^{++}, and cadmium appears to form the $+1$ chloride and oxide. These elements are less noble than the corresponding elements of Subgroup I, and their hydroxides are more acidic.

Zinc and cadmium resemble each other much more closely than they do mercury. They are distinctly electropositive, are readily oxidized by hydrogen ion, and their oxides are reduced with difficulty; while mercury is a noble metal, and its oxide is easily decomposed upon simple heating. The solubility of the oxide in water increases with increasing size of the metal ion. Zinc oxide is amphoteric, dissolving readily in both acids and bases. Cadmium and mercuric oxides dissolve in acids, and unstable cadmates and mercurates are also known. Both zinc and cadmium form stable hydroxides, but mercury does not. Mercuric salts are very highly hydrolyzed, notwithstanding the appreciable solubility of mercuric oxide. One of the outstanding characteristics of the subgroup is the slight dissociation of the chlorides, bromides, and iodides. This property is most pronounced with the mercuric ion. In the most stable salts and complexes, the apparent ionic radii are 10 or 15 per cent less than the values given in Table I, as the high attractive force is able to distort the ions from their normal shapes (cf. **VII—2**).

TABLE I

ATOMIC AND PHYSICAL PROPERTIES OF ZINC, CADMIUM, AND MERCURY

	Zn	Cd	Hg
Atomic number	30	48	80
Atomic weight	65.38	112.41	200.61
Isotopes	64, 66, 67, 68, 70	106, 108, 110, 111, 112, 113, 114, 116	196, 197, 198, 199, 200, 201, 202, 204
Electrons in various quantum levels, 1st	2	2	2
2d	8	8	8
3d	18	18	18
4th	2	18	32
5th		2	18
6th			2
Radius of M^{++} in crystals $\times 10^8$ cm	0.74	0.97	1.10
Ionization potential of gaseous atoms in volts, 1st electron	9.36	8.96	10.38
2d electron	17.89	16.84	18.65
Melting point ° C	419.4	320.9	− 38.87
Boiling point ° C	907	767	356.9
Density of solids	7.14	8.6	14.19 at − 40°
Electrical resistance ohm-cm. $\times 10^6$	6	7.5 at 20°	21.3 at − 50°
Potential of electrode: $M = M^{++} + 2e^-$ in volts	+ 0.762	+ 0.402	− 0.854
Solubility of $Zn(OH)_2$, $Cd(OH)_2$, and HgO, g. per liter	2.6×10^{-6}	2.6×10^{-4}	5×10^{-2}

ZINC AND CADMIUM

2. Occurrence.—The principal zinc ores are the sulfide, ZnS, called sphalerite or zinc blende; and the carbonate, $ZnCO_3$, smithsonite. Other ores are: willemite, Zn_2SiO_4; calamine, $Zn_2(OH)_2SiO_3$; zincite, ZnO; and franklinite, [Fe, Zn, Mn]$(FeO_2)_2$. The average percentage of zinc present in igneous rocks is estimated as 4×10^{-5}.

Most zinc ores contain some cadmium. The average ratio of zinc to cadmium is about 200 to 1. The yellow cadmium sulfide sometimes occurs fairly pure and is known as greenockite.

3. Metallurgy.—The major portion of the zinc ore is smelted by reduction with carbon, although more than a hundred thousand tons of pure zinc are now produced yearly by a process which combines the extraction of the ore by leaching, and the electrolytic reduction of the metal from the solution. In the former process the ore is first crushed and concentrated by washing out the lighter rocks, or, in the case of the sulfide, by "flotation" methods (see Metallurgy of Lead). Sulfide and carbonate ores are roasted to convert them into the oxide: $2ZnS + 3O_2 = 2ZnO + 2SO_2$. Much of the sulfur dioxide liberated is recovered and made into sulfuric acid. The oxide is mixed with coal, and the mixture heated in small clay retorts (4 to 5 feet long). A temperature of 1,200 to 1,300° C. is required for reduction, and as the boiling point of the metal is only 907°, the metal is vaporized as soon as it is liberated: $ZnO + C = Zn + CO$. A sufficient excess of coal is employed to prevent the formation of carbon dioxide, since zinc is oxidized by the dioxide. A small condenser is placed over the mouth of the retort, and its temperature is controlled so as to condense the metal to the liquid state. If the temperature of the condenser is below the melting point of the zinc, the metal collects in the form of a fine powder called zinc dust, which also contains a small per cent of zinc oxide. Even under the best conditions, some zinc dust is formed, and 10 per cent or even more of the zinc escapes from the condenser along with the carbon monoxide. The liquid is drawn off and cast into molds, forming what is known as "spelter." It usually contains, as the principal impurities, a per cent or so of lead and smaller amounts of iron and cadmium. The metal may be purified by distillation in vacuum or in hydrogen, but it is difficult to effect a complete separation from the lead.

In the electrolytic process sulfide ore is first carefully roasted at a low temperature, and under these conditions forms largely sulfate. The ore is then leached with dilute sulfuric acid, and the acid sulfate solution treated with a small quantity of zinc dust to precipitate the nobler metals, as these would deposit along with the zinc upon electrolysis of the solution. Although the potential required to precipitate zinc is 0.762 volt greater than the reversible reduction potential for hydrogen ion, the overvoltage of hydrogen on pure zinc is sufficiently great (1.23 volts in $1N$ H^+) to permit the deposition of zinc in acid solution if a high cathodic current density is used. Electrolytic zinc is very pure, and commands a higher price for that reason. The annual production of zinc is over a million tons.

Cadmium is both more easily reduced and more volatile than zinc; consequently, it is concentrated in the first portions of the distillate in zinc smelting, and may be recovered from the zinc by fractional distillation. However, most of the commercial product now comes from the electrolytic zinc process, the cadmium being precipitated along with the more noble metals in the purification of the electrolyte.

4. The Metals.—The more important physical properties have been summarized in Table I. Zinc takes a good white metallic luster upon polishing, but the surface quickly tarnishes to the familiar blue-grey tinge. Zinc is hard and brittle at ordinary temperatures, but between 100° and 150° it becomes malleable enough to permit rolling and drawing. At somewhat higher temperatures, it becomes so brittle that it may be pulverized in a mortar. These changes appear to be due to allotropic forms, but the transitions from one form to another have not been definitely determined.

Zinc is used in making brass (see Copper) and many other alloys. It is used in dry cells (see Manganese) and the preparation of zinc pigments (see Oxide, Sulfate, and Sulfide). The largest use of the metal, however, is in galvanizing iron. The process is carried out in three different ways: (1) dipping the iron into molten zinc, (2) depositing the zinc upon the iron by electrolytic reduction, (3) exposing the iron to the action of zinc vapor, called "sherardizing." Galvanized iron resists the action of weather better than pure iron, largely due to the impervious coating of basic zinc carbonate on the surface, but in part to the fact that the electropositive character of the zinc tends to prevent a hole wearing through the iron by furnishing electrons in place of the iron. Zinc dust is employed as a reducing agent in the manufacture of dyes.

Cadmium has a silver white color with a slight bluish tinge. It is not as hard as zinc, and at ordinary temperatures is much more ductile and malleable. Like zinc, however, it becomes very brittle at higher temperatures, the change likewise appearing to be due to a crystalline transition. The electrical conductivity of cadmium is somewhat less than that of zinc.

Cadmium is used as a substitute for tin in antifriction metals and solders, its principal use being in bearing metals for automobiles. Its presence in small amounts in copper wire adds strength with but small reduction in the conductivity. Cadmium plating is now used to rust-proof wires, tools, and other iron and steel articles. After plating, the articles are heat-treated, thus alloying the cadmium and iron. Corrosion tests indicate that cadmium plate and zinc plate have about the same resistance.

5. Reactions of the Metals.—Zinc dust is subject to spontaneous combustion in moist air, but in more compact forms does not burn readily until heated above 500° C. Pure zinc is almost insoluble in dilute hydrogen ion, due to the very large overvoltage of the hydrogen. If, however, the metal be touched with some metal with a low overvoltage for hydrogen, such as nickel or platinum, the evolution of hydrogen takes place rapidly on the surface of the other metal, and the zinc dissolves. The high positive value of the oxidation-reduction potential (Table I) renders it possible to dissolve zinc by a number of oxidizing agents. The metal is soluble in rather concentrated alkali with the evolution of hydrogen and formation of zincate. These and other reactions are summarized in Table II.

TABLE II
REACTIONS OF ZINC METAL

$2Zn + O_2 = 2ZnO$	Upon heating
$Zn + 2H^+ = Zn^{++} + H_2$	Slow with pure zinc
$Zn + 2H_2O = Zn(OH)_2 + H_2$	With steam at high temperature
$Zn + OH^- + H_2O = HZnO_2^- + H_2$	With concentrated alkali
$Zn + S = ZnS$	Also with Se, Te, P, As, etc.
$Zn + X_2 = ZnX_2$	X is any halogen
$Zn = Zn^{++} + 2e^-$	0.762 volt
$Zn + CO_2 = ZnO + CO$	At red heat
$4Zn + 2O_2 + 3H_2O + CO_2 = Zn_4CO_3(OH)_6$	The protective coating on zinc surfaces

The reactions of cadmium are, in general, similar to those of zinc, but the lower positive value of the oxidation reduction couple, 0.402 volt, renders it considerably less reactive with oxidizing agents. Unlike zinc, it does not dissolve in alkali.

6. Zinc and Cadmium Ions.—The ions Zn^{++} and Cd^{++} are colorless and poisonous to most organisms, cadmium more so than zinc. Zinc ion is rather highly hydrolyzed, while cadmium ion is only slightly so. Zinc ion forms as its more important slightly soluble compounds: $Zn(OH)_2$, $ZnCO_3 \cdot nZn(OH)_2$, $ZnNH_4PO_4$, $Zn_3(PO_4)_2$, ZnP_2O_7, ZnC_2O_4,

$Zn(CN)_2$, $Zn(IO_4)_2$, $Zn_2Fe(CN)_6$, and ZnS. Its most stable complex ions are $Zn(NH_3)_4^{++}$, $Zn(CN)_4^{--}$, and $HZnO_2^-$. Cadmium ion forms the precipitates: $Cd(OH)_2$, $CdCO_3$ $\cdot nCd(OH)_2$, $Cd(CN)_2$, $Cd_2Fe(CN)_6$, and CdS; and the complex ions, $Cd(NH_3)_4^{++}$, $Cd(CN)_4^{--}$, and CdI_4^{--}.

7. Oxides and Hydroxides.—Zinc oxide, ZnO, occurs as the mineral zincite. It is an important commercial commodity, and is prepared by the oxidation of the metal or directly from the oxidized ores by heating a mixture of carbon and ore in an air blast. The carbon reduces the oxide, but the zinc vapor is immediately reoxidized, and the oxide carried along as a fine dust in the flue gas, from which it is finally recovered by the use of filter bags. This oxide is used extensively as a white pigment, generally mixed with white lead. It is employed in the manufacture of automobile tires, and in medicine as a base for various ointments. It may be formed by gently heating the hydroxide, but it will not combine with water to form the hydroxide. It is yellow when hot, and white when cold. The arrangement of the zinc and oxide ions in the crystal lattice is given in Appendix V.

The hydroxide is precipitated upon the addition of hydroxide ion to a solution of zinc ion. It is amphoteric, and readily soluble in excess hydroxide and in acids:

$$Zn(OH)_2 = Zn^{++} + 2OH^- \qquad K = 4.5 \times 10^{-17};$$
$$Zn(OH)_2 = ZnO_2^{--} + 2H^+ \qquad K = 1 \times 10^{-29}.$$

The solid zincates, such as K_2ZnO_2, are prepared by fusion of the two oxides, but are highly hydrolyzed in solution. Zinc hydroxide is soluble in ammonium hydroxide, due to the stability of the complex, $Zn(NH_3)_4^{++}$. The value for the dissociation constant of the complex is $K = 9.8 \times 10^{-10}$. Peroxides in alkaline solution form with zinc salts the hydrated zinc peroxide, $ZnO_2 \cdot 2H_2O$.

The brown cadmium oxide, CdO, is formed by methods similar to those discussed for zinc oxide. Cadmium hydroxide, (solubility product, 1.2×10^{-14}), is more soluble and more basic than zinc hydroxide. It does not dissolve in excess hydroxide ion, but cadmates are said to be formed by fusing cadmium oxide in potassium hydroxide. Cadmium hydroxide is soluble in ammonium hydroxide, and cyanides with the formation of the complex ions: $Cd(NH_3)_4^{++}$ ($K = 2.5 \times 10^{-7}$), and $Cd(CN)_4^{--}$ ($K = 1 \times 10^{-17}$). A hydrated cadmium peroxide similar to the zinc peroxide exists, and **cadmous hydroxide,** $Cd_2(OH)_2$, appears to form when a base is added to the unstable cadmous chloride. The hydroxide is a powerful reducing agent.

8. Halides.—Although zinc and cadmium fluorides are but moderately soluble, the other halides are readily soluble. They crystallize from their solutions as hydrated salts, usually with 4 moles of water at low temperatures, and one mole at higher temperatures. Solutions of the zinc salts are distinctly acid by hydrolysis, and readily precipitate basic halides upon the addition of dilute alkali. Concentrated solutions of zinc chloride dissolve zinc oxide and set to form a cement, ZnOHCl, similar to the magnesia cement. The chloride in the fused state also dissolves metal oxides, and is much used as a flux in soft soldering.

In their concentrated solutions, the halides appear to be slightly ionized, due to the formation of complex ions. This property is exhibited somewhat by the zinc salts and markedly by the cadmium. The latter forms, for example, $CdCdCl_4$ and $CdCdF_4$. The complex ion, CdI_4^{--}, is fairly stable, the value for the dissociation constant being about 5×10^{-7}.

Cadmous chloride, Cd_2Cl_2, appears to be formed by heating the dichloride and metal together at about 800°. It is hydrolyzed by water to $Cd_2(OH)_2$.

9. Sulfates.—The crystallization of an aqueous solution of zinc sulfate at ordinary temperature forms the heptahydrate, $ZnSO_4 \cdot 7H_2O$; and solutions of cadmium sulfate form the hydrate, $3CdSO_4 \cdot 8H_2O$. A number of other hydrates also occur at higher and lower temperatures. These hydrates are very soluble in water. Large quantities of zinc sulfate are used in the preparation of the white pigment, **lithopone,** the reaction being: $ZnSO_4 + BaS = BaSO_4 + ZnS$. This pigment does not blacken with hydrogen sulfide, as does white lead, and possesses fair covering power. Cadmium sulfate is employed in the manufacture of "standard cells" for electrical measurements. These cells have an anode of cadmium amalgam, a cathode of mercurous sulfate in contact with mercury, and an electrolyte of cadmium sulfate solution.

10. Sulfides.—Zinc sulfide is the only common white metallic sulfide. Cadmium sulfide is yellow. Zinc sulfide is precipitated by the addition of alkali or ammonium sulfides to solutions of zinc salts. Its solubility is increased by hydrogen ion: $ZnS + H^+ = Zn^{++} + HS^-$; but it may be fairly completely precipitated in a solution of acetic acid with sodium acetate added to reduce the hydrogen ion concentration. The value for the solubility product is 4.5 $\times 10^{-24}$. Cadmium sulfide is much less soluble ($K = 1.4 \times 10^{-28}$), and may be precipitated from highly acid solutions. Neither sulfide is soluble in excess of sulfide ion, but both are slightly soluble in high concentrations of ammonium hydroxide, due to the formation of the complex ammonia ions. Cadmium sulfide is also soluble in iodide, as mentioned under the halides, but it is not soluble in cyanide. Cadmium sulfide is an excellent yellow pigment, but is too expensive for extensive application.

11. Other Salts.—The **nitrates** are readily prepared by dissolving the metals or oxides in nitric acid. Normal **zinc carbonate** exists in nature, and may be precipitated from zinc solution with sodium bicarbonate, but basic carbonates are precipitated from solution by the alkali carbonates. Cadmium shows less tendency to form basic carbonates than does zinc. Basic zinc phosphate, made from the oxide and phosphoric acid, is important as a cement in dentistry. See also Appendix XIX.

12. Analytical.—The separation of zinc and cadmium from other metallic elements is indicated in the standard scheme of analysis (Append. VI). The separation of aluminum from zinc, by the precipitation of aluminum hydroxide with excess ammonium hydroxide, carries down considerable zinc as zinc aluminate, and, for this reason, in detecting small amounts of zinc, it is preferable to precipitate the aluminum as $AlCl_3 \cdot 6H_2O$, by adding ether and hydrogen chloride gas. The insolubility of cadmium sulfide in excess sulfide ion distinguishes it from arsenic, antimony, and tin; and its solubility in hot nitric acid gives a separation from mercuric sulfide. The precipitation of cadmium sulfide in the presence of cyanide ions serves to distinguish cadmium from copper.

Zinc may be determined quantitatively by precipitating as the sulfide, igniting, and weighing as the oxide; by precipitation as $ZnNH_4PO_4$, and weighing as $Zn_2P_2O_7$; or by precipitation by cathodic reduction from an acetic acid-acetate buffer solution. In the electrolytic determination, it is difficult to obtain a complete precipitation of the metal. The most satisfactory volumetric method is the titration of zinc with ferrocyanide. The formation of a brown color with an uranyl solution as an outside indicator is used to determine the end-point, or a few drops of ferrous ion may be added to the zinc solution, in which case the color changes from light blue to pea-green at the end-point. This latter color change appears to be due to the presence of a trace of ferricyanide, which gives a blue color until an excess of ferrocyanide is obtained.

Cadmium may be determined gravimetrically by precipitating as carbonate and weighing as oxide; or, similarly to zinc, precipitating as phosphate and weighing as $Cd_2P_2O_7$. It is impossible to precipitate the sulfide pure enough to weigh as such, as it forms complexes, e.g., Cd_2Cl_2S. Cadmium may also be determined electrolytically by reduction from a solution of the cyanide complex.

MERCURY

13. Occurrence.—Mercury occurs native and in amalgams of gold and silver, but the principal ore is cinnabar, HgS. Complex selenides, tellurides, and chlorides also occur, but they are of slight economic importance. The average percentage of mercury in the igneous rocks is estimated as 10^{-7}.

14. Metallurgy.—The extraction of mercury from the sulfide ore is comparatively simple, since the sulfide may readily be converted into the volatile metal, either by roasting in air: $HgS + O_2 = Hg + SO_2$; or by roasting with lime: $4HgS + 4CaO = 3CaS + CaSO_4 + 4Hg$. The mercury vapor is more easily condensed from the furnace gases than is zinc, because of the greater weight of the molecules of vapor, and also because the vapor is not readily reoxidized by air. The metal is filtered through chamois skin and purified by washing with nitric acid, or mercurous nitrate solution; or by distillation in the presence of oxygen, or other oxidizing agents, which will remove the base metals, especially zinc and cadmium.

15. The Metal.—The more important physical properties have been given in Table I. The metal is a silvery-white liquid with a vapor pressure of 0.001 mm. at 20° and 0.28 mm. at 100°. Its boiling point is 356.90°. A table of densities of the liquid is given in Appendix IX. The vapor is monatomic, and does not conduct electricity in the cold, but if an arc is once struck it conducts readily with the emission of the characteristic mercury spectrum which is very rich in green and ultra-violet light. This mercury vapor arc is much used as a current rectifier, and as a source of ultra-violet light for the treatment of certain diseases. The cubical coefficient of expansion of mercury between 0°

and 300° is represented by the expression: $\alpha = 1.8006 \times 10^{-4} + 2 \times 10^{-8}t$. Due to this rather uniform expansion and to the fact that the pure liquid does not "wet" glass, mercury is extensively used in thermometers. Its low vapor pressure and high density makes it useful in barometers. With the exception of iron and platinum, metals readily dissolve in, or are wet by mercury to form amalgams; many of these have been mentioned in connection with other metals, e.g. sodium, aluminum, gold, and silver. An amalgam of thallium (8.5 per cent Tl) has a very low melting point and may be used in thermometers down to $- 60°$ C. Amalgams of tin, silver, gold, and other metals are employed in dentistry. Many attempts have been made to use mercury in heat engines, as the higher boiling point offers a very substantial increase in the theoretical efficiency over the steam engine, and two plants are now in operation in the United States. These installations employ 300,000 pounds of mercury.

TABLE III
REACTIONS OF THE METAL

$2Hg + O_2 = 2HgO$	Slowly around 350°
$Hg + X_2 = HgX_2$	X is any halogen
$Hg + S = HgS$	Upon subliming together
$3Hg + 2NO_3^- + 8H^+ = 3Hg^{++} + 2NO + 4H_2O$	Excess acid
$6Hg + 2NO_3^- + 8H^+ = 3Hg_2^{++} + 2NO + 4H_2O$	Excess mercury
$Hg + SO_4^{--} + 4H^+ = Hg^{++} + SO_2 + 2H_2O$	Hot concentrated acid

16. Equilibria between Oxidation States.—The mercurous ion is stable in respect to the decomposition into mercuric ion and mercury: i.e., mercuric ion is reduced by mercury: $Hg^{++} + Hg = Hg_2^{++}$. However, the value for the potential of the reaction corresponds to an equilibrium concentration of Hg_2^{++} at 25° C., only 166 times that of Hg^{++}; hence the equilibrium is easily reversed in case the mercuric compound is much less soluble than the mercurous: e.g., $Hg_2S = HgS + Hg$ and $Hg_2O = HgO + Hg$. Due to the insolubility of the basic ammonia mercuric salts (Par. **25**), all mercurous compounds are decomposed by a.mmonia. The equilibrium lies in the direction of the mercuric form at higher temperatures. In this respect the higher oxidation state is different from copper, since cupric oxide upon heating gives cuprous oxide and oxygen, while mercuric oxide gives mercury and oxygen. Mercuric sulfate, however, decomposes at high temperatures according to the equation: $2HgSO_4 = Hg_2SO_4 + SO_2 + O_2$.

The couple Hg^{++}-Hg^+ is a stronger oxidizing couple than Hg^{++}-Hg (Table IV); hence reducing agents first reduce mercuric ion to mercurous. Since the potential of the couple Hg^+-Hg is almost as large, most reducing agents capable of reducing mercuric ion will, in excess, reduce the mercurous ion to mercury as a second step: e.g., $2Hg^{++} + Sn^{++} = 2Hg^+ + Sn^{++++}$, and $2Hg^+ + Sn^{++} = 2Hg + Sn^{++++}$. It also follows from the potential values that fairly powerful oxidizing agents, e.g., bromine water and hot nitric acid, are required to oxidize mercurous compounds to mercuric, unless, of course, the mercuric compound is much less soluble or less ionized.

TABLE IV

OXIDATION-REDUCTION POTENTIALS OF MERCURY

	VOLTS$_{25°}$
$Hg + S^{--} = HgS + 2e^-$	+ 0.70
$Hg + 4CN^- = Hg(CN)_4^{--} + 2e^-$	+ 0.37
$Hg + 4I^- = HgI_4^{--} + 2e^-$	+ 0.04
$2Hg + 2I^- = Hg_2I_2 + 2e^-$	+ 0.04
$Hg + 2OH^- = HgO + H_2O + 2e^-$	− 0.098
$2Hg + 2Br^- = Hg_2Br_2 + 2e^-$	− 0.14
$2Hg + 2SCN^- = Hg_2(SCN)_2 + 2e^-$	− 0.22
$2Hg + 2Cl^- = Hg_2Cl_2 + 2e^-$	− 0.2675
$2Hg + CO_3^{--} = Hg_2CO_3 + 2e^-$	− 0.32
$2Hg + C_2O_4^{--} = Hg_2C_2O_4 + 2e^-$	− 0.41
$2Hg + SO_4^{--} = Hg_2SO_4 + 2e^-$	− 0.615
$2Hg = Hg_2^{++} + 2e^-$	− 0.789
$Hg = Hg^{++} + 2e^-$	− 0.854
$Hg_2^{++} = 2Hg^{++} + 2e^-$	− 0.920
$HgS = S + Hg^{++} + 2e^-$	− 1.05

MERCUROUS COMPOUNDS

17. Mercurous ion is strikingly similar to silver ion in the solubility of its salts, and in the potential of reduction to the

metal. However, the mercurous ion is peculiar in that it is associated into the double ion, Hg_2^{++}, not only in solution, but in its compounds in the solid and gaseous state. Indeed it is somewhat doubtful if the undissociated ion Hg^+ exists. From the standpoint of atomic structure, the mercurous ion is quite unusual. The variations in the oxidation states of the Subgroup I elements arises through the possibility of removing electrons from the kernel, but the mercurous ion consists of the kernel plus one valence electron. Many examples may be given of the association of molecules containing an odd number of electrons; and the formation of $(\mathbf{Hg:Hg})^{++}$ may be correlated with this general behavior of "odd" molecules. The mercurous ion does not form complex ions with the ammonia, cyanide, iodide, or thiosulfate, as does silver ion.

18. Mercurous oxide, Hg_2O, is formed by the action of alkalies upon soluble mercurous salts. It is not soluble in excess hydroxide ion. The oxide decomposes rapidly into mercury and mercuric oxide. X-ray patterns of a fresh precipitate show only HgO and Hg.

19. Mercurous chloride, Hg_2Cl_2, or calomel, is the most important mercurous salt. It is usually prepared by subliming a mixture of mercuric chloride and mercury: $HgCl_2 + Hg = Hg_2Cl_2$. It is formed as a white precipitate by the addition of chloride to a solution of mercurous nitrate. Mercurous chloride sublimes without melting, and if dry, the vapor consists of Hg_2Cl_2 molecules, but moisture catalyzes its decomposition into mercury and mercuric chloride. Light causes a partial decomposition of the salt at room temperature. Mercurous chloride turns dark when treated with ammonia, due to the formation of finely divided mercury and the ammono-basic mercuric chloride (Par. **25**). The use of calomel in medicine depends upon its stimulating action upon the liver and other secretive organs. The potential of the reaction: $2Hg + 2Cl^- = Hg_2Cl_2 + 2e^-$ is -0.2675 volt (i.e., molal chloride ion activity and referred

to the potential of hydrogen arbitrarily chosen as zero);
and the electrode: mercury—solid mercurous chloride—
chloride ion, is often employed as a reference electrode in
potential measurements. The potential of the electrode
changes slightly in air. Thus with $1M$ KCl the values are
$- 0.2825$ in air and $- 0.2812$ in absence of air. Much work
has been done on the absolute value of this electrode potential, and the value 0.56 volt is usually accepted; the
mercury is positive with respect to the solution.

20. Mercurous fluoride, bromide, and iodide resemble
the corresponding silver salts in respect to solubility in
water. The iodide is unstable, especially with excess iodide,
and decomposes into mercury and mercuric iodide.

21. Mercurous sulfide may be formed momentarily by
the action of hydrogen sulfide upon mercurous salts, but it
immediately decomposes into mercury and mercuric sulfide.
Mercurous nitrate and **sulfate** may be prepared by the
action of nitric acid and of hot concentrated sulfuric acid,
respectively, upon excess mercury. The nitrate is readily
soluble, but the sulfate only sparingly so. Both are hydrolyzed, and unless excess acid is present, form slightly
soluble basic salts, such as $Hg_2(OH)NO_3$ and $Hg_2OHg_2SO_4$
$\cdot H_2O$.

Mercurous phosphate, nitrite, chromate, bromate, and
iodate, are but slightly soluble. Alkali carbonates precipitate **mercurous carbonate** from soluble mercurous salts.
The carbonate is unstable if warmed slightly: Hg_2CO_3
$= Hg + HgO + CO_2$. **Mercurous cyanide** is not stable.

MERCURIC COMPOUNDS

22. Mercuric oxide, HgO, is slowly formed as a red
powder when mercury is heated in air just below its boiling
point. It is usually prepared by heating the nitrate or a
mixture of the nitrate and mercury: $Hg(NO_3)_2 + Hg$
$= 2HgO + 2NO_2$. The partial pressure of oxygen over
mercuric oxide is 985 mm. at 500° C. The oxide precipitates

upon the addition of a strong base to a solution of a mercuric salt. Precipitated in the cold, the color is yellow, but from hot solutions, the color is red. The difference in color seems to be merely a question of the state of subdivision of the solid, as the two forms appear to have the same crystal structure and very nearly the same energy content. The yellow is the more reactive and also the more finely divided. The hydroxide is unstable, but a hydrate, $HgO \cdot 3H_2O$, exists. The oxide is soluble in excess iodide due to the formation of the complex iodide: $HgO + 4I^- + H_2O = HgI_4^{--} + 2OH^-$. Its solubility increases slightly in alkali, due to weak acidic properties and the formation of $HHgO_2^-$.

$$HgO + OH^- = HHgO_2^- \qquad K = 3 \times 10^{-5}$$

Mercuric ion in solution is more highly hydrolyzed than is to be expected from the value for the solubility of the oxide, Table I. However, the value for the oxide electrode: $Hg + 2OH^- = HgO + H_2O + 2e^-$, -0.098 volt, indicates that the concentration of Hg^{++} in the solution is very small.

23. Mercuric chloride, $HgCl_2$, "bichloride of mercury" or "corrosive sublimate," may be made by heating mercury in an atmosphere of chlorine. The reaction is accompanied by green radiation. It is usually prepared, however, by subliming a mixture of mercuric sulfate and common salt. The chloride is moderately soluble in water, and the solubility is increased by excess chloride ion due to the formation of complex ions, probably $HgCl_4^{--}$. The salt in solution is but slightly ionized, even less than cadmium chloride, as is indicated by its low electrical conductivity, and by the value of the chloride as an oxidizing agent: $Hg_2Cl_2 + 2Cl^- = 2HgCl_2 + 2e^-$, -0.53 volt. This value is 0.3 volt lower than the Hg_2^{++}-Hg^{++} couple in spite of the small solubility of the mercurous chloride. The solution is only slightly hydrolyzed, but the addition of dilute alkali results in the formation of various basic chlorides, such as $HgCl_2 \cdot HgO$. The chloride is much used as an antiseptic and is highly poisonous. It forms a slightly soluble compound with albumen, and advantage is taken of this fact in administering egg white as an antidote. As a poison it acts partly through the destruction of kidney cells to such an extent that death results in about two weeks from the inability of the body to eliminate its waste products. The commercial preparation is usually mixed with sodium chloride to increase the rate of solution.

24. **Mercuric fluoride** is more soluble and much more hydrolyzed than the chloride. The **bromide** is sparingly soluble, and the **iodide** still less soluble. The iodide exists in two modifications, a scarlet form stable below 128°, and a yellow form stable above that temperature. The yellow iodide may be super-cooled below the transition temperature, but readily changes to the scarlet when touched. Mercuric iodide dissolves in excess iodide forming the very stable complex iodide, HgI_4^{--}. A solution of the potassium complex iodide is known as **Nessler's reagent,** and is used in detecting small amounts of ammonia (see below).

25. **Mercuric ammonia compounds** exist in interesting variety, divisible into four types: (1) Soluble complexes giving the ion $Hg(NH_3)_4^{++}$. This ion is stable only at very high $(12N)$ concentrations of NH_4OH; (2) with ammonia of crystallization, such as $HgCl_2 \cdot 2NH_3$; (3) basic salts of the ammonia system, that is, they are formed from the negative ions of ammonia, NH_2^-, NH^{--}, and N^{---}, similar to negative ions of water OH^- and O^{--}, the simplest being of the type $HgNH_2Cl$; (4) salts which are both ammonolyzed and hydrolyzed. Many complex salts of this latter type exist. The most important are derivatives of Millon's base, $OHHgNHHgOH$, or $Hg_2NOH \cdot H_2O$. The addition of ammonium hydroxide to mercuric chloride solution precipitates the ammonobasic chloride, $HgNH_2Cl$. With mercurous chloride, the same compound mixed with mercury is formed. The ammonobasic chloride is soluble in hydrochlo-

ric acid and dissolves more readily if some ammonium ion is present. Ammonia and mercuric nitrate solution form $Hg_2N\cdot NO_3$ and a number of other complex salts. Nessler's reagent (Par. **24**) gives, with ammonia, a yellow precipitate, the iodide of Millon's base, $Hg_2NI\cdot H_2O$.

26. Mercuric Sulfide.—Crystalline mercuric sulfide is red, both as found in nature, cinnabar, and as prepared by subliming together mercury and sulfur; but the sulfide precipitated from solution by hydrogen sulfide is black and amorphous. The black form is transformed slowly into the red by digestion with sodium sulfide. Mercuric sulfide is the least soluble ($K = 3 \times 10^{-53}$) of all the metal sulfides, and does not dissolve in hydrochloric or nitric acids. It is, however, soluble in aqua regia and in bromine water, due to the stability of the complex halides. Hot concentrated nitric acid converts it into the difficultly soluble white complex, $Hg(NO_3)_2\cdot 2HgS$. The sulfide has weak acidic properties, and is somewhat soluble in a solution of an alkali sulfide but not in ammonium sulfide. The red sulfide is used as a pigment under the name of vermilion.

27. Mercuric nitrate and **sulfate** are formed by the action of excess nitric and hot concentrated sulfuric acids upon the metal. Both are soluble, but are rather highly hydrolyzed, and precipitate as basic salts, such as $Hg(NO_3)_2\cdot HgO$ and $HgSO_4\cdot 2HgO$, unless excess acid is present. Normal mercuric carbonate does not exist, but **basic carbonates,** such as $HgCO_3\cdot 2HgO$, may be precipitated. **Mercuric cyanide,** $Hg(CN)_2$, is soluble, but is even less ionized than the halides, and like them forms a complex ion, $Hg(CN)_4^{--}$. When heated, it decomposes into mercury and cyanogen: $Hg(CN)_2 = Hg + C_2N_2$. This complex gives the smallest concentration of mercuric ion of any of the mercuric compounds except the sulfides.

Mercuric fulminate, $Hg(CNO)_2$, is formed by the addition of alcohol to a hot solution of mercury in nitric acid. The dry precipitate explodes upon being struck, and is used extensively in percussion caps. **Mercuric thiocyanate,** $Hg(CNS)_2$, is slightly soluble. "Pharaoh's serpents" are prepared from this salt by making it into a paste with gum-water. When dried and ignited it burns and forms a voluminous ash which assumes serpentine forms.

28. Analytical.—Mercurous ion, like silver, gives a curdy, white precipitate with chloride but, unlike silver chloride, the precipitate blackens with ammonia (Par. **25**). The insolubility of mercuric sulfide in nitric acid and in ammonium polysulfide serves to identify mercuric ion. The addition of stannous chloride to mercuric ion in small amounts gives a white precipitate of mercurous chloride, and in excess, a grey precipitate of mercury. With mercurous ion, stannous chloride in small amounts gives an immediate precipitate of mercury. A copper wire in either mercurous or mercuric solutions becomes coated with a grey or silvery deposit of mercury.

Mercury may be precipitated and weighed quantitatively as the sulfide, or electrolytically as the metal on a platinum cathode. It is sometimes determined by heating the sample in a combustion tube and passing the vapors through a weighing tube containing gold leaf to absorb the mercury. Mercurous salts may be precipitated and weighed as the chloride. Mercuric salts are sometimes analyzed volumetrically by titration with iodide.

Chapter IX

SUBGROUP III. GALLIUM, INDIUM, AND THALLIUM

1. The elements of Subgroup III are extremely rare and of slight industrial importance. They form compounds in which they have an oxidation state of + 3, and, in the case of thallium, compounds also of the + 1 state. In spite of the higher positive charge on their ions, they do not show as great tendencies to form "coordination compounds" or complexes as do the elements of Subgroup II. The first electron is rather easily removed, and as a consequence, compounds of the elements give characteristic colors in hot Bunsen flames; in fact, all of the elements of this group were discovered (between 1860–1875) through spectroscopic means. The name thallium (from Latin thallus, a budding twig) refers to its green spectrum; and the name indium, to its indigo-blue spectral lines. Gallium was named in honor of France (Latin, Gallia).

The + 3 compounds are similar to those of aluminum; with the exception that the acid character of the hydroxides decreases with increasing size of the atoms, and the potential of the ions as oxidizing agents increases.

2. Occurrence.—The elements occur widely distributed, but only in minute quantities. The average percentages of the elements present in igneous rocks are given as: gallium, 10^{-11}; indium, 10^{-11}; and thallium, 10^{-10}. Gallium is a common constituent of zinc, iron, aluminum, and chromium ores, but is seldom present in quantities as high as 0.01 per cent. In small amounts, it is a very common impurity in pig iron and in commercial aluminum. Indium is usually associated with zinc blende, and often with ores of lead and tin. Its principal source is zinc ores, in which it sometimes occurs to the extent of 0.1 per cent. It is estimated that several thousand tons of gallium and indium could be recovered yearly as by-products of the zinc and coal industries. Thallium is associated with the alkalies, and also with iron, zinc, lead, tellurium, and other elements. It is most commonly obtained from the flue dust of sulfuric acid works in which thalliferous pyrites are burned.

3. Preparation of Metals.—The extraction of the metals is largely a problem of separating the small quantities of their compounds from other metallic constituents, and is, therefore, best considered after a discussion of the properties of the various ions. The metals are easily obtained by reduction with zinc, or by electrolysis.

TABLE I

ATOMIC AND PHYSICAL PROPERTIES

ELEMENT	GALLIUM	INDIUM	THALLIUM
Symbol.........................	Ga	In	Tl
Atomic weight...................	69.72	114.76	204.39
Atomic number..................	31	49	81
Isotopes........................	69, 71	113, 115	203, 205
Ionization potential of gaseous atoms in volts, 1st electron.............	5.97	5.76	6.07
2d electron..............	20.43	18.79	20.32
3d electron..............	30.6	27.9	29.7
Radius of ion in crystals, cm. $\times 10^8$...	0.62	0.81	0.95 (ic) 1.15 (ous)
Melting point ° C.................	29.78	156.4	303.5
Boiling point ° C.................	2,071	1,450	1,457
Density.	5.91	7.3	11.85
Electrical resistivity, ohm/cm. $\times 10^6$.	53 at 0°	9 at 20°	18.1 at 20°
Electrode potential, $M = M_{(aq.)}^{+++} + 3e^-$ volts.......	+ 0.52	+ 0.34	− 0.72
Principal spectral lines, wave lengths, cm. $\times 10^8$....................	4,172.2 4,033.2	4,511.55 4,101.95 3,256.22 3,039.46	3,519.37 3,775.89 5,350.70

4. The Metals.—Many of the properties of the metals have been summarized in Table I. **Gallium** is a hard, brittle, grey metal. It melts just above room temperature, and remains a silver white liquid of low vapor pressure through a temperature range of about 1,500 degrees. The metal expands upon changing from liquid to solid. The liquid supercools readily and may be kept in the liquid state even at 0° C. A possible application is in the construction of high temperature thermometers using quartz tubes. **Indium** is a lustrous silver metal almost as soft as lead, and is both ductile and malleable. It is now available in commercial quantities. As a coating for bearings it improves corrosion resistance and permits the surface to retain a more complete oil film. **Thallium** is bluish-white in color, easily cut with a knife, malleable, but of low tensile strength. The metal exists in two crystalline modifications with a transition at 226° C. Like the other two metals, the liquid is stable over a very long range of temperature.

5. Reactions of the Metals.—Gallium is only superficially oxidized in air at red heat; indium is not appreciably oxidized in air at 25°, but burns with a blue flame when heated, forming In_2O_3; thallium oxidizes slowly at 25°, and rapidly at higher temperatures, forming both Tl_2O and Tl_2O_3. Gallium and indium dissolve fairly readily in hydrogen ion with the evolution of hydrogen gas and the formation of the ions; thallium dissolves forming thallous ion or thallous salts. They unite directly with the more electronegative elements, and are, of course, oxidized by even moderately strong oxidizing agents, as indicated by their oxidation-reduction potentials (Table I).

6. Gallic Ion and Its Compounds.—Gallic ion is colorless and its salts with colorless negative ions are white. **Gallic oxide,** Ga_2O_3, resembles aluminum oxide. Gallous oxide, Ga_2O, is known but it is unstable with respect to its decomposition into the + 3 oxide and the metal. The **hydroxide,** $Ga(OH)_3$, is precipitated by alkali and ammonium

TABLE II

REACTIONS OF THE METALS

$4M + 3O_2 = 2M_2O_3$	Ga slowly. Tl also forms Tl_2O
$2M + 6H^+ = 2M^{+++} + 3H_2$	With Ga and In. Tl forms Tl^+
$2M + 2OH^- + 2H_2O = 2MO_2^- + 3H_2$	With Ga
$2M + 3X_2 = 2MX_3$	X denotes halogens. Tl also forms TlX
$2M + 3S = M_2S_3$	Analogous reactions with Se, Te, P, As.

hydroxides, and the precipitate is soluble in excess of the reagent, forming **gallates**. Approximate values for the basic and acidic dissociation constants are:

$$Ga(OH)_3 = Ga^{+++} + 3OH^- \qquad K = 5 \times 10^{-37}$$
$$H_3GaO_3 = H_2GaO_3^- + H^+ \qquad K = 1 \times 10^{-15}$$

Gallic ion, like aluminum, in the presence of carbonate ion, is completely hydrolyzed, leading to the precipitation of the hydroxide. The **sulfates, nitrates,** and **halides** are soluble, but the solutions are highly hydrolyzed and precipitate basic salts upon boiling. A **dichloride,** $GaCl_2$, appears to be formed by heating the trichloride with excess of the metal. The salt evolves hydrogen in water and forms basic gallic chloride. Gallic ion readily forms **alums.** The **ferrocyanide** is insoluble, even in solutions strongly acid with hydrochloric acid. The white **sulfide,** Ga_2S_3, is not precipitated except in the presence of other sulfides, such as zinc, copper, or arsenic, and then only when the solution is alkaline or but slightly acid.

7. Analytical.—Gallium is precipitated with the iron aluminum zinc group in qualitative analysis. It may be separated from the other elements of the group, except ferric iron, by converting to the chloride and extracting with an ether-hydrogen chloride solution. The iron may be removed by reduction to ferrous and repeating the ether separation. The commercial separation from the zinc, with which it is usually associated, may be effected by converting into the chlorides, and fractional precipitation by sodium carbonate. The gallium concentrates in the first precipitate. It is separated from indium by taking advantage of the greater solubility of gallium hydroxide in excess alkali. The separation from zinc and indium may also be accomplished by fractional electrolytic precipitation. Quantitatively gallium is precipitated with aqua ammonia, removing the excess ammonia by boiling, and is weighed as the sesquioxide.

8. Indic Ion and Compounds.—The ion, In^{+++}, is colorless; ammonia or alkali hydroxides precipitate it as the **hydroxide,** $In(OH)_3$. The hydroxide forms the **sesquioxide,** In_2O_3, upon heating, and upon strong ignition the oxide, In_3O_4. Heated to 300° in hydrogen, the oxide, In_2O_2, appears to be formed. The hydroxide is soluble to a very small extent in strong alkali hydroxide (but not in dilute ammonium hydroxide), probably forming **indate** ion, InO_2^-. The carbonate is but slightly soluble, and, unlike gallium, is but slightly hydrolyzed. It is soluble in excess ammonium carbonate, but not in excess sodium carbonate. The **nitrate, sulfate, alums,** and **halides** are soluble. The halides resemble the cadmium compounds in that they are weak salts. **Mono-** and **dihalides** are formed by heating the trichlorides with excess metal, but these lower halides are unstable in water solutions: $3In^+ = In^{+++} + 2In$, and $3In^{++} = 2In^{+++} + In$. From analogy to mercurous ion the $+ 2$ ion should have the formula In_2^{+4}. Yellow indium **sulfide,** In_2S_3, is precipitated by hydrogen sulfide in the presence of very dilute acid. It is somewhat soluble in a very high concentration of sulfide ion. The **cyanide** is but slightly soluble in water, but dissolves in excess cyanide. The **ferrocyanide** and **chromate** are also but slightly soluble.

9. Analytical.—The separation of indium from indiferous zinc, the principal source of the element, is usually accomplished by dissolving the metal in acid, and precipitating indium and iron by the addition of ammonium hydroxide.

The indium is separated from the iron present by dissolving the hydroxides and precipitating indium sulfide in acetic acid solution by hydrogen sulfide.

In the systematic qualitative separation, indium, like gallium, is precipitated with the iron-aluminum-zinc group. It is similar to zirconium and titanium in that the hydroxide is not dissolved when boiled with NaOH and Na_2O_2, but differs in the precipitation of the sulfide from a fluoride solution by NH_4OH and $(NH_4)_2S$.

10. Equilibria between Thallous and Thallic Ions.— Thallic ion, Tl^{+++}, is a strong oxidizing agent (Table III), being reduced to thallous ion, Tl^+. Further reduction requires a fairly powerful reducing agent. The reaction, $Tl^{+++} + 2Tl = 3Tl^+$, takes place practically to completion. Hot water is decomposed by thallic ion: $Tl^{+++} + H_2O = Tl^+ + 2H^+ + \frac{1}{2}O_2$. Thallic compounds decompose in general, upon heating, with the formation of the thallous compound: e.g. $TlCl_3 = TlCl + Cl_2$, and $Tl_2S_3 = Tl_2S + 2S$.

TABLE III

OXIDATION-REDUCTION POTENTIALS OF THALLIUM

	VOLTS
$Tl + I^- = TlI + e^-$	0.77
$Tl + Br^- = TlBr + e^-$	0.66
$Tl + Cl^- = TlCl + e^-$	0.56
$Tl = Tl^+ + e^-$	0.336
$Tl^+ = Tl^{+++} + 2e^-$	− 1.2

11. Thallous Ion and Compounds.—In the solubilities of most of its salts, thallous ion resembles plumbous ion; while in size and other physical properties, basic nature of the hydroxide, and lack of tendency to form complex ions, it resembles potassium. Thallous ion is like stannous and plumbous ions in having a pair of valence electrons left in the valence energy level. **Thallous oxide,** Tl_2O, readily absorbs water to form **thallous hydroxide,** TlOH. The latter is fairly soluble and is a strong base. The decomposition pressure of steam over the hydroxide, $2TlOH = Tl_2O$

+ H_2O, reaches one atmosphere at 139° C. The **chloride, bromide,** and **iodide** are but sparingly soluble, and the solubility is decreased by the presence of excess halide ion. However, the **cyanide** appears to be soluble in excess cyanide ion. **Thallous sulfide,** Tl_2S, is precipitated in neutral or alkaline solution. The solubility product of the sulfide is given as 1.2×10^{-24}. **Thallous carbonate** is fairly soluble. The **chromate,** normal **phosphate, chloroplatinate,** and **cobaltinitrite** are sparingly soluble. Thallous sulfate is sometimes used in the preparation of poison grain to kill rodents.

12. Thallic Ion and Its Compounds.—Thallic ion resembles aluminum ion except that it is larger, and its **hydroxide** does not possess acid properties. The hydroxide is extremely insoluble and the soluble thallic compounds such as **sulfate** and **nitrate** are highly hydrolyzed. Oxygen reacts with thallium just below red heat to form thallic oxide, Tl_2O_3; at higher temperatures mixed thallic and thallous oxides are formed. Chlorine, passed into a suspension of thallous chloride, produces **thallic chloride.** Upon evaporation, the hydrate, $TlCl_3 \cdot 3H_2O$, may be obtained, and in the presence of ammonia the ammoniate, $TlCl_3 \cdot 3NH_3$, separates. The trichloride forms complex ions with excess chloride, and a complex **thallous chlorthallate** exists, $TlTlCl_4$. The **bromide** is quite similar to the chloride, but the **iodide,** TlI_3, is probably thallous triiodide. The **sulfide,** Tl_2S_3, is very unstable, and forms thallous sulfide and sulfur.

13. Analytical.—Thallous chloride is soluble in hot water and its solubility is not increased in ammonia. It thus resembles lead chloride. The iodide is much less soluble than the chloride and is considered the most satisfactory test for thallous ion. It is but slightly soluble in thiosulfate. The extraction of thallium from the flue dust of sulfuric acid plants is based upon the slight solubility of the chloride, the non-precipitation of thallous carbonate by alkali carbonates, the precipitation of thallous sulfide by ammonium sulfide, and the reduction of the compounds to the metal by zinc. Quantitatively, thallium is usually precipitated and weighed as the thallous iodide. It may also be determined by titrating with standard permanganate, which in acid solution oxidizes thallous salts to thallic.

14. Potential Diagram Summary.—

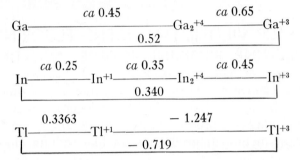

Chapter X

GROUP VII. THE HALOGENS: FLUORINE, CHLORINE, BROMINE, IODINE, ASTATINE

1. The elements of Group VII, fluorine, F, chlorine, Cl, bromine, Br, iodine, I, are called the halogens from a Greek word meaning salt-producing, since they all combine with the alkali metals to produce salts like sodium chloride. Element number 85, the heaviest member of the group, is known only in minute amounts as highly radioactive isotopes produced by nuclear reactions. It has been named astatine, symbol At, from a Greek word meaning "unstable." Very little is known of its physical and chemical properties. Since it is still impossible to discuss the chemistry of astatine in relation to the other elements of the group in any detail, it will be treated separately at the end of this chapter.

Fluorine and chlorine are gases; bromine is a volatile liquid; and iodine is a solid, easily melted and vaporized. The chemical behavior of these elements is related to the fact that each has 7 valence electrons (Table I). The removal of one of the 7 valence electrons requires a rather high potential, as shown by the value of the ionization potential of the gaseous atoms. This group tends to add an extra electron so as to produce the octet of the noble gas element of next higher atomic number (Chap. **II**). With increasing size of the atoms, i.e., going down the periodic group, the attraction for the electrons decreases, as is shown by the decreasing ionization potential and electron affinity.

because of their high electron affinity the halogens are powerful oxidizing agents, $X_2 + 2e^- = 2X^-$, although much of the energy of the reaction in water arises from the energy of hydration of the negative ion. Fluorine not only has the largest electron affinity, but, due likewise to its small size, the ion has the highest energy of hydration; consequently fluorine is the most powerful oxidizing agent the chemist can prepare.

These elements, with the exception of fluorine, also give compounds in which their oxidation state is positive, as illustrated by the following:

	HClO	HClO$_2$	HClO$_3$	HClO$_4$
Oxidation state	+ 1	+ 3	+ 5	+ 7

It is arbitrary to assume that the halogen has lost electrons to the oxygen in such compounds, for the electrons are probably in reality shared by both, as indicated by the electron formulas, such as

$$H : \overset{..}{\underset{..}{O}} : \overset{\overset{\displaystyle :\overset{..}{O}:}{}}{\underset{\underset{\displaystyle :\overset{..}{O}:}{}}{\overset{..}{\underset{..}{Cl}}}} : \overset{..}{\underset{..}{O}} :$$

From this picture, it is obviously untrue that the actual charge upon the chlorine atom is + 7. The concept of the oxidation state of + 7 is most useful in correlating oxidation and reduction reactions. The *half reaction* which relates chlorine and perchlorate in aqueous acid solutions is,

$$\tfrac{1}{2}Cl_2 + 4H_2O = ClO_4^- + 8H^+ + 7e^-$$

Thus the oxidation of the element to perchlorate involves the loss of seven electrons. Actually this loss is shared between the chlorine and the oxygen but for simplicity we ascribe all of it to the chlorine and say the oxidation state is + 7. The concept of the formal charge (cf. **III—7**) which assumes that the electrons of the bond are equally shared by the two atoms, gives an approximate value for the actual charge upon each atom. While the formal charge is useful in correlating many properties such as acid strengths, its use in determining the electrons gained or lost in oxidation-reduction reactions is considerably more complicated than use of the oxidation state concept since it would require a summation of the change in charge of all of the atoms in the reacting and product molecules. In addition to the terms oxidation state and formal charge, it is frequently convenient to employ a term which describes the number of electron pair bonds on the central atom. The term coordination number is frequently employed in this sense but in organic chemistry the term valence is used to express the number of bonds. For the example of chlorine in $HClO_4$, the oxidation state is $+ 7$, the formal charge is $+ 3$ and the valence or coordination number is 4.

The tendency to form an octet with the valence electrons is made evident in the free element by the formation of the diatomic molecules in which the 2 atoms share their 7th electrons, so that each is in at least partial possession of an octet.

$$: \overset{..}{\underset{..}{X}} : \overset{..}{\underset{..}{X}} :$$

As might be expected, the bond grows weaker with increasing atomic radius, as shown by the increasing ease of dissociation, and also by the decreased constraint under which the shared electrons are held, which is evident from the increasing dielectric constant.

2. Occurence.—The estimated per cent of the halogens in the earth's crust is: F, 0.1; Cl, 0.2; Br, 0.001; I, 0.001. Sea water contains about 2 per cent of chloride ion, and 0.006 per cent of bromide ion. The greater portion of the fluorine is in the form of fluorspar, CaF_2, and cryolite, Na_3AlF_6. The occurrence of great deposits of the alkali halides is discussed under the alkali elements. In addition to the alkali halides, there are found in nature chlorides, bromides, and iodides of the alkaline earths, silver, lead, copper, mercury, and bismuth. The major portion of the bromine of commerce formerly came from the bromo-

TABLE I

PROPERTIES OF THE HALOGENS

NAME	FLUORINE	CHLORINE	BROMINE	IODINE
Symbol............................	F	Cl	Br	I
Melting point ° C................	− 223	− 102.1	− 7.3	113
Boiling point ° C.................	− 188.3	− 34.7	58.0	183
Color of gas.....................	Light yellow	Greenish yellow	Reddish brown	Violet
Atomic volume of solid, cc........	17.15	23.52	27.13	34.23
Atomic weight..................	19.0	35.46	79.92	126.92
Isotopes.......................	19	35, 37	79, 81	127
Atomic number.................	9	17	35	53
Electrons in various quantum levels, 1st...................	2	2	2	2
2d....................	7	8	8	8
3d....................	—	7	18	18
4th....................	—	—	7	18
5th....................	—	—	—	7
Ionizing potential of gaseous atoms, volts......................	17.34	12.95	11.80	10.6
Electron affinity of gaseous atoms, volts......................	4.13	3.75	3.53	3.22
Radius of X⁻ in crystals, cm. × 10⁸	1.36	1.81	1.95	2.16
Heat of vaporization, cals. per mole	1,640	4,420	7,418	10,388
Heat of fusion, cals. per mole......	—	1,615	2,580	3,650
Reaction } { Heat, cals. per mole.	62,600	56,900	45,200	35, 000
X₂ = 2X } { Dissoc. constant at 1000°...........	—	10⁻⁸	0.008	0.1
Dielectric constant of solid........	—	2.0	3.2	4.0
Solubility in water, moles of X₂ per liter, 20°.....................	Decomposes	0.090 (1 atm.)	Liq. 0.210	Sol. 0.00133
Distribution ratio, solubility CCl₄/H₂O, 0°................	—	20.0	27.0	85.5

carnallite, $MgBr_2 \cdot KBr6H_2O$, of the Stassfurt (Germany) deposits, and from various American salt brines, especially those of the Saginaw Valley, Michigan. With the introduction of the modern method for the extraction of bromine from sea water, this source now supplies most of the American market. The principal source of iodine is the Chile deposits, where it occurs largely in the form of iodate, $NaIO_3$, and periodate, $NaIO_4$. The largest source in the United States is from the oil well brines in California. Blood contains approximately 0.25 per cent chlorine as chloride

ion, and the gastric juices 0.2 to 0.4 per cent free hydrochloric acid. Iodine is found in the various human tissues,
the thyroid gland containing the highest per cent. Many
marine plants exercise a selective absorption of iodide, even
in the presence of far greater concentrations of chloride and
bromide; hence dried seaweed is another important source
of iodine.

3. Preparation and Uses of Free Elements.—Fluorine
was first prepared by Moissan (1886) by the electrolysis of
potassium fluoride in liquid hydrogen fluoride in a platinum
vessel. Cells with this type of electrolyte are still used but
for large scale production a fused KHF_2 electrolyte is
generally employed, using a copper vessel and a graphite
anode. Copper is attached by fluorine but the surface
layer of copper fluoride protects the metal from rapid
corrosion. The electrolyte melts around 250° C. and the
cell is generally operated slightly above 275° C. At this
temperature there is considerable pressure of HF above the
electrolyte: $KHF_2 = KF + HF$. As the cell operates, hydrogen fluoride is decomposed and it is necessary to re-
generate the electrolyte by the addition of more gaseous
hydrogen fluoride. There is also an increasing use of cells
with $KF \cdot 2HF$ as an electrolyte at a temperature of 80° to
120° C. The development of the fluorocarbons has greatly
increased the commercial production of fluorine.

Chlorine. Although the greenish yellow fumes formed by
the oxidation of chlorides by various oxidizing agents had
long been observed, it remained for Scheele (1774) to clean
up their meaning. He prepared chlorine by heating a mixture of manganese dioxide and hydrochloric acid. He considered the gas to be "dephlogisticated muriatic acid,"
meaning muriatic acid (hydrochloric) freed from phlogiston
(the element of combustion).

Davy (1810) established its identity as an element.
Scheele's method is still the one usually used for its laboratory preparation. It is also prepared by dropping dilute

hydrochloric acid upon potassium permanganate: $2KMnO_4 + 16HCl = 8H_2O + 2KCl + 2MnCl_2 + 5Cl_2$, and by the action of dilute sulfuric acid upon bleaching powder: $CaCl(ClO) + H_2SO_4 = CaSO_4 + H_2O + Cl_2$.

Most of the chlorine of commerce is prepared by the electrolysis of brine as described under the preparation of sodium hydroxide. The annual production in the United States is over 400,000 tons. From the equilibrium electrode potentials (Append. II), one would expect oxygen to be liberated upon electrolysis of a brine solution; and this is the case in low concentration of salt: $0.2N$ NaCl yields about 20 per cent oxygen and 80 per cent chlorine at the anode. However, the oxygen evolution requires a high overvoltage (Append. I), and in more concentrated solutions only 1 or 2 per cent of oxygen is liberated.

The Deacon process, employing the oxidation of hydrogen chloride by oxygen (Par. **5**), has been of some importance in the past. Attempts have also been made to operate the reaction, $MgCl_2 + \frac{1}{2}O_2 = MgO + Cl_2$, commercially at a high temperature. The magnesium oxide is reconverted to the chloride by hydrochloric acid.

Approximately two thirds of the chlorine manufactured is used in bleaching, chiefly of pulp and paper. Large quantities are also used in water purification as a germicide, and in the manufacture of organic dyes, explosives, and chemicals. It is usually liquefied and sold in cylinders, or converted into bleaching powder, $CaCl(ClO)$, by action upon lime (Par. **5**). The chlorine is again liberated from the bleaching powder upon the addition of acid. It was used extensively in the World War, at first directly as a poison gas, and later in the preparation of most of the other war gases, such as phosgene, $COCl_2$, and "mustard gas," $(C_2H_4Cl)_2S$.

Bromine may be prepared from the bromides by any of the methods used for chlorine. It is recovered commercially in Germany from the waste liquors of the potash industry, and in America from various salt brines. The method depends upon the oxidation of bromide by chlorine. A commercial process has been developed for the recovery of bromine from sea water. Free bromine is liberated by chlorine, and precipitated as tribromoaniline upon the addition of aniline. The process is capable of extracting a pound of bromine from 1,800 gallons of sea water.

Liquid bromine is used in the preparation of most of the bromides and other compounds of the element. Like chlorine, it is used in the preparation of intermediate products in the synthesis of organic compounds, an example being the lead-tetraethyl now added in small amounts to gasoline to prevent "knocking." The major portion of the American production of bromine is consumed in this process; ethylene dibromide is the intermediate compound which is first formed.

Iodine is extracted from kelp by oxidation of the iodides with chlorine, or manganese dioxide in acid, or even by sulfuric acid. The principal source is, however, the Chile deposits containing sodium iodate and periodate. Iodine is liberated by reduction with sodium bisulfite: $2IO_3^- + 5HSO_3^- = I_2 + 5SO_4^{--} + H_2O + 3H^+$: it is then removed and purified by sublimation.

Iodine is used in synthesis of aniline dyes, and iodides are employed somewhat in photography. It is also used in medicine as an antiseptic; in alcohol solution, known as tincture of iodine; in iodoform, CHI_3; and as metallic iodides, in the prevention and cure of goiter, and other disorders of the thyroid gland.

4. Physical Properties.—Table I gives the colors of the elements in the gaseous state. In the liquid state, the colors are, of course, deeper. Liquid bromine and iodine are opaque except in very thin layers. Solid iodine is dark grey with a slight luster.

Solutions of chlorine and bromine in water show colors closely resembling those of the gases. Iodine dissolves in many solvents, such as carbon tetrachloride, chloroform, and hexane, with a violet color resembling that of the vapor; but in solvents of high dielectric constant such as water and alcohol, its solution is brown. The progression in color in the gaseous halogens with increasing atomic weights is due to an absorption band, which in fluorine is nearly all in the ultraviolet, removing only a little of the visible light at the violet end of the spectrum, thus causing the transmitted light to have an excess of the complementary color, yellow. With chlorine this band has moved down into the blue, and so on, until with iodine the band removes the middle portions of the visible spectrum allowing only red and violet light to be transmitted.

The density in the gaseous state corresponds to molecules of 2 atoms each, which is confirmed by the figures for the same elements in solution. Heated to sufficiently high temperatures, the diatomic molecules gradually break down into single atoms. The dissociation of iodine in this way becomes noticeable below 700°. Progressively higher temperatures would be necessary for the corresponding dissociation as we go from iodine to the lighter halogens, as indicated by the dissociation constants and heats of dissociation given in Table I.

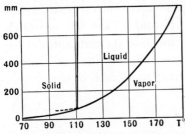

FIG. 1.   Temperature-pressure diagram of iodine

Although solid iodine may be melted at 1 atmosphere pressure, it sublimes without melting below a pressure of 100 mm. as is indicated in the phase diagram, Fig. 1.

The halogens, with the exception of fluorine, are soluble in water (Table I). Chlorine and bromine form the hydrates, $Cl_2 \cdot 8H_2O$ and $Br_2 \cdot 10H_2O$. The former is stable up to 28.7° under a pressure of 6 atm. of chlorine, and the latter to 6.2° under a pressure of 93 mm. of bromine vapor.

Above 28.7°, chlorine under pressure forms with water two liquid layers. Bromine likewise forms two liquid layers, but the lower layer contains only a very small amount of water, 0.04 per cent at 10°.

5. Reactions of the Halogens.—The chemical behavior as related to atomic structure, has been discussed in Paragraph **1.** Fluorine and chlorine are capable of oxidizing all metals, while bromine and iodine can oxidize all but the noblest. The products of these reactions are halides. The halogens do not react directly with oxygen or nitrogen. Fluorine reacts directly with all other elements except nitrogen, oxygen, chlorine, and the noble gases; and chlorine with all but these and carbon. Bromine and iodine are less reactive.

The reactions of the halogens with hydrogen are discussed in detail under the hydrogen halides. The halogens act upon many hydrocarbons, displacing hydrogen and forming the halogen acid: e.g. $CH_4 + Cl_2 = CH_3Cl + HCl$. They also unite directly with many unsaturated compounds: $C_2H_4 + Cl_2 = C_2H_4Cl_2$ and $CO + Cl_2 = COCl_2$. They readily oxidize sulfur in most of its compounds: e.g. $CS_2 + 2Cl_2 = CCl_4 + 2S$. Excess of chlorine (or bromine but not iodine) will oxidize sulfur to sulfate in water solution.

TABLE II

OXIDATION-REDUCTION POTENTIALS OF HALOGEN-HALIDE COUPLES

	VOLTS$_{25}$°
$I^- = \frac{1}{2}I_2 + e^-$	− 0.535
$Br^- = \frac{1}{2}Br_2 + e^-$	− 1.07
$Cl^- = \frac{1}{2}Cl_2 + e^-$	− 1.359
$F^- = \frac{1}{2}F_2 + e^-$	− 2.87

The oxidation-reduction potentials (Table II) of the free elements to the halide ions are extremely important, especially in connection with the general table (Append. II) in predicting many reactions. Thus, bromine will oxidize iodide, $I^- + \frac{1}{2}Br_2 = \frac{1}{2}I_2 + Br^-$, but will not oxidize chloride or fluoride; and all of the halogens except iodine will oxidize ferrous ion to ferric: $Fe^{++} = Fe^{+++} + e^-$, $- 0.77$ volt.

The halogens undergo two important **reactions with water:**

$$(1) \quad X_2 + H_2O = 2H^+ + 2X^- + \tfrac{1}{2}O_2$$
$$(2) \quad X_2 + H_2O = H^+ + X^- + HXO$$

The potential values at 25° for reaction (1) in volts are: F_2, 2.0; Cl_2, 0.6; Br_2, 0.3, and I_2, $- 0.3$ (i.e., in the reverse direction). Thus fluorine reacts vigorously with liquid water, liberating not only oxygen but ozone; chlorine reacts slowly in sunlight, liberating oxygen. On the other hand, moist hydrogen chloride gas reacts with oxygen with the aid of a catalyst to give a detectable amount of chlorine. Bromine liberates oxygen only very slowly from water, and the reaction is reversed if the hydrobromic acid has a high concentration. Iodine, on the other hand, is liberated from a solution of hydrogen iodide by oxygen, the speed of the reaction increasing rapidly with an increase in hydrogen ion concentration.

At a temperature of 450°, an equilibrium is reached between chlorine, steam, hydrogen chloride, and oxygen by means of which it is possible to convert two thirds of the hydrogen chloride into chlorine. This is the basis for the **Deacon process** once used for the manufacture of chlorine. Hydrogen bromide is completely oxidized to bromine at this temperature.

Reaction (2), the hydrolysis of the halogen, likewise takes place less completely, the higher the atomic weight of the halogen. In the case of fluorine the reaction cannot be observed because of the rapidity of reaction (1). With the other halogens a reversible equilibrium is established. At 25°, the equilibrium constants are: for Cl_2, 4.8×10^{-4}; for Br_2, 5×10^{-9}; for I_2, 3×10^{-13}. The hydrolysis may in every case be largely repressed by the presence of acid, and increased by the addition of alkali. Thus, hydrogen chloride added to hypochlorite liberates chlorine; and chlorine in sodium hydroxide solution is converted completely into chloride and hypochlorite. For a $0.01M$ Cl_2 solution, the above equilibrium constant corresponds to about 85 per cent hydrolysis. The electronic picture of the hydrolysis consists of a splitting of the halogen molecule and a union of the positive halogen atom with water.

Electron formulas

$$: \ddot{\ddot{X}} : \ddot{\ddot{X}} : + H : \ddot{O} : H = : \ddot{\ddot{X}} : + H + : \ddot{\ddot{X}} : \ddot{O} : H$$

Ordinary formulas

$$X_2 + H_2O = X^- + H^+ + XOH$$

TABLE III

SUMMARY OF IMPORTANT REACTIONS OF HALOGENS

X = halogen

$X_2 + H_2 = 2HX$	cf. Par. 7
$X_2 + H_2O = 2HX + \frac{1}{2}O_2$	cf. Par. 5
$X_2 + H_2O = H^+ + X^- + HXO$	cf. Par. 5
$nX_2 + 2M = 2MX_n$	With most metals
$3X_2 + 2P = 2PX_3$	Also with As, Sb, Bi
$5X_2 + 2P = 2PX_5$	Not with I_2. Also As, Sb with F_2 and Cl_2
$X_2 + RH = RX + HX$	RH many organic hydrocarbons
$mX_2 + 2C_nH_m = XmHX + 2nC$	At high temperature. Less readily with Br_2 and I_2
$X_2 + CO = COX_2$	With Cl_2 and Br_2
$X_2 + SO_2 = SO_2X_2$	With F_2 and Cl_2
$X_2 + H_2S = 2HX + S$	Excess H_2S
$X_2 + 2S = S_2X_2$	With Cl_2 and Br_2. F_2 forms SF_6, Cl_2 also forms SCl_4
$4X_2 + S_2O_3^{--} + 10OH^- = 2SO_4^{--} + 8X^- + 5H_2O$	
$I_2 + 2S_2O_3^{--} = S_4O_6^{--} + 2I^-$	Neutral or slightly acid solution
$3X_2 + 8NH_3 = 6NH_4X + N_2$	With F_2, Cl_2, Br_2
$3Cl_2 + NH_4^+ = NCl_3 + 4H^+ + 3Cl^-$	I_2 forms $NI_3 \cdot NH_3$ with NH_3
$2X_2 + TiO_2 + 2C = TiX_4 + 2CO$	With Cl_2 and Br_2. Also SiO_2, Cr_2O_3, etc.

COMPOUNDS OF THE HALOGENS

6. Halogen Halides.—In view of the great difference in the electronegative character of the halogens, it is not surprising that the more positive form compounds with the more negative. Thus, iodine forms IF_7 (m.p. 5°), IF_5 (m.p. −9.6°), ICl (2 forms m.p. α 27.2°, β 13.9°), ICl_3 (m.p. 33°), and IBr (m.p. 36°); and bromine forms BrF_5 (m.p. −61.3°), BrF_3 (m.p. 9°), BrF (m.p. −33°) and BrCl (m.p. −66°) and chlorine forms ClF_3 (m.p. −83°) and ClF (m.p. −154°). The positive character of the larger halogen in these compounds is indicated, for example, by electrolysis of liquid iodine chloride, ICl, and also by its solution in sulfur dioxide, whereby iodine is liberated at the cathode, and chlorine at the anode. Hydrolysis gives the corresponding oxy-acid of the positive halogen, and the halide ion of the other. $IF_5 + 3H_2O = IO_3^- + 5F^- + 6H^+$. Because of the instability of the lower oxy-acids, the first step is not always realized: thus, $5ICl + 3H_2O = 2I_2 + 5Cl^- + IO_3^- + 6H^+$.

Iodine monochloride is formed by the direct action of chlorine upon iodine, and by the reaction, $HIO + HCl = ICl + H_2O$. By the latter reaction, iodine monochloride is often formed through the reduction of iodates, or the oxidation of iodides in moderately concentrated hydrochloric acid. It hydrolyzes in dilute acid.

The chloride reacts with excess chloride ion to form the complex ion

$$ICl_2^- = ICl(aq.) + Cl^- \qquad K = 6 \times 10^{-3}$$

and the potential of the oxidation of iodine to the complex ion,

$$2Cl^- + \tfrac{1}{2}I_2 = ICl_2^- + e^-$$

is given as − 1.06 volts. (Cf. Par. **18.**) If the formation of iodine monochloride in concentrated hydrochloric acid is accompanied by the liberation of chlorine, iodine trichloride, ICl_3, results. Salts, such as $KICl_4$, are known.

7. Hydrogen Halides. Preparation.—The hydrogen halides may be formed by direct union of the elements. As shown in Table IV, the reaction: $X_2 + H_2 = 2HX$, decreases in energy with increasing atomic weight of the halogen. Fluorine and hydrogen combine instantly, even at a temperature of $-253°$ C., where fluorine is solid and hydrogen liquid. The rate of combination of hydrogen and chlorine is slow in the dark, but takes place with explosive violence in the sunlight, or at 250° C. The increased speed under these conditions is doubtless due to the absorption of radiant energy by the chlorine molecule, and the more rapid reaction of this activated molecule. Of course, as soon as a few molecules react, enough energy is liberated to activate many molecules. Some idea of the force holding the HCl molecules together is given by the consideration that the formation from hydrogen and chlorine involves the dissociation of Cl_2, 56,900 cal., and H_2, 103,730. The reactions of hydrogen with bromine and iodine are very slow at room temperature, and are catalyzed by light and by platinum at higher temperature.

TABLE IV

PROPERTY OF HYDROGEN HALIDES

		HF	HCl	HBr	HI
Boiling point		20	$- 85$	$- 67$	$- 36$
Melting point		$- 83$	$- 114$	$- 87$	$- 51$
$\frac{1}{2}H_2 + \frac{1}{2}X_2 = HX$	Heat kcal...	64.0	22.0	13.5	$- 0.8$
	Per cent dissociation at 1000°..		1.34×10^{-13}	0.144	29.0
Solubility in water 1 at. and 20° C. g. per 100 g. of solution		35.3	42	49	57
Heat of solution at infinite dilution, kcal		11.6	17.3	19.9	19.2
Constant boiling mixture, 1 at.	Temp	120	110	126	127
	Density	1.14	1.10	1.49	1.70
	Wt. per cent of acid	35.37	20.24	47	57.0
Dielectric constant of liquid		66	9	6	3
Heat of neutralization of dilute acid in kcal		16.2	13.4	13.4	13.4

Hydrogen fluoride and chloride are usually prepared by the action of the less volatile sulfuric acid upon a halide salt, such as CaF_2 and $NaCl$. In the case of hydrogen chloride, the reaction is the first step in the LeBlanc carbonate process (cf. **IV—13**). The acid sulfate is first formed: $NaCl + H_2SO_4 = HCl + NaHSO_4$, and the mixture is heated to a temperature of about 500°, in order to complete the second step: $NaCl + NaHSO_4 = HCl + Na_2SO_4$. Because of the oxidation of bromide and iodide by hot concentrated sulfuric acid, $H_2SO_4 + 2HI = I_2 + SO_2 + 2H_2O$, this acid is replaced usually by phosphoric acid in the preparation of hydrogen bromide and iodide. The acids may be prepared by the hydrolysis of the halides of the more negative elements, such as phosphorus, sulfur, or arsenic: $PBr_3 + 3H_2O = H_3PO_3 + 3HBr$. The halides of the noble metals may be reduced with hydrogen at a high temperature to form the hydrogen halide: $2AgCl + H_2 = 2Ag + 2HCl$. These acids are also formed by the action of the halogens upon many organic hydrocarbons: $C_6H_6 + Br_2 = C_6H_5Br + HBr$. A solution of hydrogen iodide is conveniently prepared by the action of hydrogen sulfide upon a suspension of iodine in water: $H_2S + I_2 = S + 2HI(aq.)$. With gaseous HI this reaction is reversible.

8. Properties.—The hydrogen halides are all colorless gases; they possess a disagreeable pungent odor, fume strongly in moist air, are extremely soluble in water; their water solutions, with the exception of hydrogen fluoride, are strongly acidic. The water solutions are called hydrofluoric acid, hydrochloric acid, etc. In the pure liquid state, they have a low electrical conductivity, of about the same magnitude as that of pure water. The approximate values for the dielectric constants of the liquids indicate that the electrical polarization decreases with increasing molecular weight. Hydrogen fluoride gas polymerizes, forming $(HF)_6$. At 20° C. and 745 mm., 80 per cent of the HF is so polymerized. This property is not shown by the other gases.

The water solutions exhibit the phenomena of **boiling point maxima.** The temperature composition diagram for hydrochloric acid is given in Fig. 2. The curve represents the temperature at which a given composition of the acid will boil, i.e. the temperature at which the sum of the pressures of hydrogen chloride and water equals atmospheric pressure. As a given solution boils, its composition changes toward that of the maximum boiling mixture. When this composition is reached, the solution boils without further change in composition. The composition of the maximum boiling mixture depends upon the

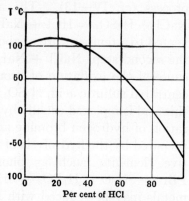

FIG. 2. Boiling point-composition curve for HCl.

total pressure. For hydrogen chloride, 1 atmosphere, the value is 20.24 per cent HCl and the temperature 110°; for 2,500 mm., the composition is 18 per cent; and for 50 mm. it is 23.2 per cent. Advantage is often taken of these fixed concentrations to prepare acids of known concentrations for quantitative analysis.

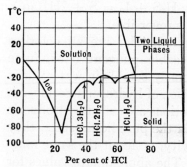

FIG. 3. The system water-hydrogen chloride.

Hydrogen chloride forms three definite hydrates, as indicated in Fig. 3. The eutectic, $- 86°$, is remarkably low. Hydrogen bromide forms a di-, tri-, and tetrahydrate; and hydrogen iodide, tri-, and tetrahydrates.

The **ionization** of these acids in dilute solution is 100 per cent, as judged by the lowering of vapor pressure and freezing points, and by electrical conductivity. The apparent ionization at higher concentrations is discussed in Appendix IV. Hydrofluoric acid is much weaker than the other acids ($HF_{aq} = H^+ + F^-$, $K = 7.2 \times 10^{-4}$). In fairly concentrated solutions, it forms the ion HF_2^- ($F^- + HF = HF_2^-$, $K = 5.5$). In dilute solutions, its heat of neutralization is about 3 kcal. more than that of typically strong acids, which is unusual, as the heat of neutralization of

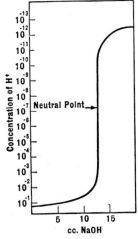

other weak acids is less than that of strong acids. The change of concentration of hydrogen ion in hydrochloric acid, upon titration with hydroxide, is given in Fig. 4.

9. Uses.—Hydrogen fluoride is used in etching glass. This remarkable property results from the action of hydrogen fluoride upon silicon dioxide: $SiO_2 + 4HF = SiF_4 + 2H_2O$. The silicon fluoride escapes as a gas. Etched designs, such as buret graduations, are made by covering the glass with paraffin, which is scraped away where etching is desired, and then treating with a solution of the

Fig. 4. Titration of HCl with NaOH.

acid. A mixture of ammonium fluoride and hydrogen fluoride is used in frosting glass. The acid is also used in quantitative analysis, in dissolving complex silicates, since most silicates are decomposed through the removal of the silica. It has certain application in the curing of crude rubber, in cleaning the exterior of stone buildings, and in cleaning castings.

Hydrochloric acid is used in the preparation of metal chlorides, especially those of zinc and tin; in cleaning metal surfaces, particularly iron before galvanizing; and in the manufacture of glue, soap, glucose, dyes, and many other materials.

10. Halides and Halide Ions.—**Fluoride.** The fluorides of lithium, the alkaline earth, and the rare earth metals are sparingly soluble. Fluoride forms more stable complexes than do the other halides with small positive ions, for example, BF_4^-, SiF_6^{--}, AlF_6^{---}. These complexes are analogous to the corresponding oxygen acids, and their stability is doubtless due to high electrostatic attraction for the small fluoride ions. On the other hand, the fluoride ion is not as polarizable as the larger halides (cf. **VII—2**), and does not readily form coordination complexes with the ions of the noble metals.

The metal fluorides form acid salts of the type KHF_2, and even KH_3F_4, and the crystal structure of these compounds indicates that the hydrogen ion serves to bind two fluoride ions together:

$$: \ddot{F} : H : \ddot{F} :$$

11. Chloride. Among the most important sparingly soluble chlorides are those of Ag^+, Hg_2^{++}, Tl^+, Cu^+, Pb^{++}, Au^+, Pt^{++}, Pt^{++++}, SbO^+, and BiO^+.

The solubility of all metallic chlorides is decreased by a small excess of chloride ion, but a larger concentration often leads to an increase in solubility through the formation of complex ions. The alkali and alkaline earth elements do not form complex chlorides, but practically all of the subgroup and transition elements do. Thus ions of the type $[XCl_6]^{-6+n}$ are formed by the $+3$ ions of the following elements: Al, In, Ir, Mo, As, Rh, Sc, Tl, and V; the $+4$ ions of: Ge, Hf, Ir, Os, Pd, Pt, Pb, Re, Sb, Si, Sn, Ti, Tl, and Zr; and the $+5$ ions of Cb, Sb, and Ta. Ions of the type $[XCl_4]^{-4+n}$ are formed by the $+2$ ions of Be, Co, Cu, Cd, Hg, Pd, Pt, and Zn, and by the $+3$ ions of Au, B, Bi, In, Re, Tl, V, and Y. With Ag^+ and Cu^+ the complex chlorides are XCl_2^-, XCl_3^{--} and possibly XCl_4^{---}. The ions $[XCl_4]^{-6+n}$ are octahedral but the $[XCl_4]^{-4+n}$ are of the two types, tetrahedral and square planar.

There is some evidence for the formation of trichloride

Cl_3^- when chlorine is passed into concentrated hydrogen chloride (see Triiodide below).

Certain of the chlorides, especially the volatile chlorides of metals of higher valence, may be prepared by the action of chlorine upon a heated mixture of the oxide and carbon: e.g. $TiO_2 + 2Cl_2 + 2C = TiCl_4 + 2CO$.

Chlorides of the non-metals, e.g. CCl_4, PCl_5, SCl_4, are discussed under these elements.

Bromide. Bromide ion is very similar to chloride ion in the character of its slightly soluble compounds and complex ions, though in general the sparingly soluble bromides are somewhat less soluble than the corresponding chlorides.

Alkali bromides are usually prepared from bromine, by first forming ferrous bromide by action of bromine upon iron, and then carrying out the double decomposition with the alkali carbonate: e.g. $FeBr_2 + K_2CO_3 = FeCO_3 + 2KBr$.

Iodide. The iodide ion, being the largest and most easily polarized (cf. **VII—2**) of the halides, forms very insoluble salts, and very stable coordination complex ions with the subgroup metals. The stability of many of these compounds is limited, however, by the ease of oxidation of iodide to the free element. The method of formation of the alkali iodides is similar to that of the bromides, *vide supra.*

Iodide ion readily dissolves iodine with the formation of **triiodide:** $I^- + I_2$ (aq.) $= I_3^-$, the constant $(I^-)(I_2)/(I_3^-)$ $= 1.4 \times 10^{-3}$ at 25°. This reaction is important as a means of bringing iodine into aqueous solution. Higher polyiodides are formed in very concentrated solutions.

In neutral solution, iodide is not readily oxidized by oxygen in the air; but in acid solution, the reaction becomes rapid: $6I^- + O_2 + 4H^+ = 2I_3^- + 2H_2O$. The quantitative oxidation of iodide by powerful oxidizing agents, e.g. H_2O_2 or $KMnO_4$, is extremely important in quantitative analysis (Par. **21**).

12. Oxygen Compounds of the Halogens.—Fluorine forms the fairly stable oxide, F_2O, and at low temperatures the oxides F_2O_2 and F_2O_3. Bromine forms no stable oxides, though the unstable oxides Br_2O and BrO_2 have recently been prepared. Chlorine forms the oxides Cl_2O, ClO_2, and Cl_2O_7; and iodine, the oxides I_2O_4 and I_2O_5. A number of additional oxides as ClO_3, ClO_4, and I_2O_3 have been described, but they are extremely unstable. None of these oxides are formed by direct union of the elements. The oxides with an odd oxidation state of the halogen are anhydrides of the corresponding acids. The oxygen acids of the halogens are given in the following summary. The halous acids and their salts are of the least importance. Indeed the existence of $HBrO_2$ and HIO_2 is but momentary, usually as an intermediate reaction step.

TABLE V

OXYGEN ACIDS OF THE HALOGENS

OXIDATION STATE	NAME	CHLORINE	BROMINE	IODINE	NAME OF ION
+ 1	hypo-ous	HClO	HBrO	HIO	hypo-ite
+ 3	-ous	$HClO_2$	$(HBrO_2)$	(HIO_2)	-ite
+ 5	-ic	$HClO_3$	$HBrO_3$	HIO_3	-ate
+ 7	per-ic	$HClO_4$	—	HIO_4 and H_5IO_6	per-ate

TABLE VI

OXIDATION-REDUCTION POTENTIALS OF HALOGEN ACIDS AND IONS

Volts$_{25°}$

COUPLE	Cl	Br	I
Acidic solution			
$\frac{1}{2}X_2 + 4H_2O = 8H^+ + XO_4^- + 7e^-$	− 1.34	—	(− 1.38)
$\frac{1}{2}X_2 + 3H_2O = 6H^+ + XO_3^- + 5e^-$	− 1.47	− 1.52	− 1.195
$\frac{1}{2}X_2 + 2H_2O = 3H^+ + HXO_2 + 3e^-$	− 1.63	—	—
$\frac{1}{2}X_2 + H_2O = H^+ + HXO + e^-$	− 1.63	− 1.59	− 1.45
Basic solution			
$X^- + 8OH^- = XO_4^- + 4H_2O + 8e^-$	− 0.42	− 0.71	(− 0.32)
$X^- + 6OH^- = XO_3^- + 3H_2O + 6e^-$	− 0.59	—	− 0.26
$X^- + 4OH^- = XO_2^- + 2H_2O + 4e^-$	− 0.76	—	—
$X^- + 2OH^- = XO^- + H_2O + 2e^-$	− 0.88	− 0.76	− 0.49

The halogen oxyacids are powerful oxidizing agents, as is indicated in the table on page 174, which gives the potential in volts for their reductions to the elements in acid and to the halides in alkaline solutions. These values may be used to calculate the potentials of the reduction in steps. The potential diagrams for all of the halogens are summarized in Par. **23**. Periodic acid is the most powerful oxidizing agent of all the oxyacids.

Since the oxyacids of chlorine and bromine are sufficiently powerful oxidizing agents to liberate oxygen from water ($2H_2O = O_2 + 4H^+ + 4e^-$, $- 1.23$ volts), it follows that water solutions of these acids are unstable. These decompositions are slow, but are catalyzed by certain substances.

It may also be observed from the table that the oxidizing potentials of the halates decrease with increasing atomic weight, so that iodine will replace bromine in bromate, and bromine will replace chlorine in chlorate: e.g. $2BrO_3^- + I_2 = 2IO_3^- + Br_2$. The reactions take place in highly acid solution, and while they are often called replacement reactions, they are in reality complicated oxidation-reduction reactions.

With the exception of perchloric acid, the potentials of the oxygen acids are greater than those of the halogens to halide (cf. Table II); hence, these acids are reduced by the halide ion. $HClO + H^+ + Cl^- = Cl_2 + H_2O$; $IO_3^- + 6H^+ + 5I^- = 3I_2 + 3H_2O$.

The $+ 1$ state is unstable in regard to its own oxidation and reduction into halate and halide; thus $3XO^- = XO_3^- + 2X^-$. Because of the reduction of the oxygen acids by the halide as mentioned above, this reaction in acid approaches the stoichiometric equation: $5HXO = XO_3^- + H^+ + 2X_2 + 2H_2O$. The speed of decomposition increases rapidly in order from hypochlorous to hypoiodous. In the case of chlorate ion, we encounter instability with respect to perchlorate and chloride ions, according to the equation:

$4ClO_3^- = 3ClO_4^- + Cl^-$. This occurs readily in the fused state.

13. Oxides of Fluorine.—The oxide (probably better called the fluoride), F_2O, is formed by passing fluorine into a dilute solution of sodium hydroxide.

$$2F_2 + 2OH^- = F_2O + 2F^- + H_2O$$

The oxide boils at $-146.5°$ and in the absence of reducing agents is a stable gas at room temperature. It does not react with water but is a very powerful oxidizing agent.

$$H_2O + 2F^- = F_2O + 2H^+ + 4e^-\ E° = -2.1$$

and an even higher potential may be given for the reaction

$$2F^- + \tfrac{1}{2}O_2 = F_2O + 2e^-\ E° = -3.1$$

but it appears unlikely that the second reaction can be realized experimentally. The dioxide, F_2O_2, may be prepared at low temperatures by the direct combustion of oxygen and fluorine under the activation of an electrical discharge, $O_2 + F_2 = F_2O_2$. It melts at $-163.5°$ C. and boils at $-57°$ C. but is highly explosive above $-100°$ C.

14. Chlorine Monoxide and Hypochlorite.—Chlorine monoxide, Cl_2O, is the anhydride of hypochlorous acid, $HClO$. Its reaction with water, $Cl_2O + H_2O = 2HClO$, is reversible. The gas, at 1 atmosphere and $0°$, is in equilibrium with a solution containing about 200 volumes of the gas per volume of solution. It is most conveniently prepared by the action of chlorine upon finely divided mercuric oxide: $2HgO + 2Cl_2 = Cl_2O + Hg_2OCl_2$. The reaction is carried out at about $0°$, at which temperature the gas condenses to a liquid. The gas and liquid have a deep yellowish red color, and are highly explosive.

The hydrolysis of chlorine (Par. **5**) yields hydrochloric acid and hypochlorous acid. The equilibrium is displaced by hydroxide through the neutralization of these acids:

$Cl_2 + 2OH^- = H_2O + Cl^- + ClO^-$. A solution containing chloride and hypochlorite is easily prepared by the electrolysis of a solution of NaCl in a cell permitting the chlorine produced at the anode to react with the OH^- produced at the cathode. This solution is a cheap, efficient, and widely used disinfectant and bleaching agent. For household use, it can be purchased under the name of "chlorox."

When chlorine is passed over slaked lime, a reaction occurs which is closely related to the one given above: $Cl_2 + Ca(OH)_2 = H_2O + CaCl(ClO)$. The resulting product, represented by CaCl(ClO), is known as **"bleaching powder,"** or **"chloride of lime"** and is a complex mixture of $CaCl_2$, $Ca(ClO)_2$ and $Cu_3(OH)_4(ClO)_2$. Upon solution in water it gives the corresponding ions; hence, when an excess of acid is added, chlorine is liberated, corresponding to the shift of the hydrolysis equilibrium of chlorine. Bleaching powder is extensively used for bleaching and disinfecting. Any solution containing both Cl^- and ClO^- can be made to yield chlorine in almost any desired concentration by suitably fixing the hydrogen ion concentration. However small the equilibrium concentration of chlorine, it will nevertheless be approximately maintained as the chlorine is used up. Such a solution is much used in surgery under the name "Dakin's solution."

One equivalent of acid, acting upon bleaching powder, liberates the weak hypochlorous acid, HClO, which may be distilled from the solution and thus separated from chloride ion. The dissociation constant of the acid is 5.6×10^{-8}.

The familiar odor of bleaching powder is due to hypochlorous acid liberated by the carbonic acid of the air.

Hypochlorite solutions readily give off oxygen (Par. **5**) in the presence of a catalyst, e.g. cobalt hydroxide. Heated in the absence of a catalyst, the following reaction occurs: $3ClO^- = ClO_3^- + 2Cl^-$. The rate is increased if the solution is slightly acid.

15. Chlorites and Chlorine Dioxide.—Although chlorine dioxide and the chlorites are of different oxidation states, they are discussed together because of the formation of chlorite by the reaction of the oxide in alkaline solution: $2OH^- + 2ClO_2 = ClO_2^- + ClO_3^- + H_2O$. Chlorine dioxide is one of the few "odd molecules" $:\overset{..}{O}:\overset{..}{\underset{.}{Cl}}:\overset{..}{O}:$, i.e. possessing an odd number of electrons; and the mechanism of the above reaction may be considered to be the transfer of the odd electron from one molecule of the oxide to another, forming ClO_2^- and ClO_2^+. The latter adds a molecule of hydroxide to form $HClO_3$. Chlorous acid is unstable except in very dilute solutions. The sodium salt $NaClO_2$ may be obtained commercially.

The formation of chlorine dioxide from chloric acid is mentioned below (Par. **16**). It may also be prepared by the action of chloric acid upon oxalic acid: $2HClO_3 + H_2C_2O_4 = 2ClO_2 + 2CO_2 + 2H_2O$. A new commercial process prepares chlorine dioxide by the action of chlorine upon dry sodium chlorite: $NaClO_2 + \frac{1}{2}Cl_2 = NaCl + ClO_2$. The dioxide is used for bleaching flour, paper and textiles and in controlling blue mold.

Approximate values for the potentials of the dioxide are:

VOLTS $_{25°}$

$2H_2O + Cl^- = ClO_2 + 4H^+ + 5e^-$.............................. -1.50
$4OH^- + Cl^- = ClO_2 + 2H_2O + 5e^-$.......................... -0.8

16. Chloric Acid and Chlorates.—Chlorates are easily prepared by decomposition of the hypochlorite (Par. **12**). The process may be carried out, either by passing chlorine into hot alkaline solution, or by the electrolysis of a hot chloride solution with agitation so as to bring the chlorine from the anode into contact with the hydroxide of the cathode. Chloric acid decomposes upon distillation, and cannot be prepared in the pure state. A solution may be obtained by treating a solution of barium chlorate with dilute sulfuric acid: $Ba^{++} + 2ClO_3^- + 2H^+ + SO_4^{--} = BaSO_4 + 2H^+$

+ $2ClO_3^-$. It is a strong acid and is much less stable than its salts. In addition to the decomposition into perchlorate and chloride and into oxygen and chloride, it may decompose according to the equation: $4HClO_3 = 4ClO_2 + O_2 + 2H_2O$. If concentrated sulfuric acid is added to solid chlorate, the above reaction takes place, and usually the ClO_2 formed explodes with great violence.

Potassium chlorate is the most important salt of chloric acid. While readily soluble in hot water, its solubility is but 3.1 g. per 100 grams of water at 0°. Advantage is taken of this behavior in preparing potassium chlorate by adding potassium chloride to a hot solution containing chlorate ion made from calcium hydroxide and chlorine, and then cooling.

Potassium chlorate decomposes at moderate temperatures as follows: $2KClO_3 = 2KCl + 3O_2$. This reaction is catalyzed by manganese dioxide, and furnishes a convenient laboratory method for the preparation of oxygen. If carefully heated to avoid the evolution of oxygen, potassium chlorate may be converted into the perchlorate: $4KClO_3 = 3KClO_4 + KCl$.

The oxidizing power of potassium chlorate renders it useful in making matches and pyrotechnics. Explosive mixtures may be made, using potassium chlorate with combustible substances such as charcoal, sugar, or sulfur; they are too treacherous to be of practical value. A solution of potassium chlorate is sometimes used as a gargle in throat infections.

All of the chlorates are at least moderately soluble. **Lithium chlorate** is one of the most soluble of all salts, 100 g. of water dissolves 315 g. of the salt at 18°.

17. Perchloric Acid and Perchlorates.—As mentioned in the previous section, perchlorates may be prepared by carefully heating chlorates. They may also be prepared by anodic oxidation in the electrolysis of concentrated chlorate solutions: $ClO_3^- + H_2O = ClO_4^- + 2H^+ + 2e^-$. Although this half reaction only requires a calculated potential of about one volt, it is difficult to find an oxidizing agent capable of bringing it about, since the oxidizing agent must at the same time be more powerful than chlorate; peroxysulfuric acid or sodium bismuthate may, however, be used for this purpose. Perchloric acid may be distilled from a solution formed by the addition of sulfuric acid to a perchlorate. This reaction is subject to violent explosions. The anhydrous acid is best prepared by the action of nitric and hydrochloric acids upon a solution of ammonium perchlorate. The pure acid is a volatile liquid at ordinary temperatures, and decomposes at 92° under atmospheric pressure. The acid reacts explosively with strong reducing agents. It combines with water to form the solid hydrate, $HClO_4 \cdot H_2O$, with the evolution of much heat. It is interesting to note that this hydrate, OH_3ClO_4, has the same crystal structure as NH_4ClO_4. The addition of phosphorus pentoxide to perchloric acid, cooled below 0°, results in formation of **perchloric anhydride:** $6HClO_4 + P_2O_5 = 2H_3PO_4 + 3Cl_2O_7$. This oxide is a colorless liquid which may be heated to its boiling point, 82°, without decomposition. It is easily detonated, however, by a sudden shock.

The perchlorates are safer to handle than the chlorates. They are used in matches, fireworks, and explosives. They are as a rule readily soluble, potassium, rubidium, and cesium perchlorates being the least soluble. Due to its slight solubility, potassium perchlorate is easily prepared and purified. It is probably the most important of the salts.

If silver perchlorate is treated with bromine, silver bromide and **free perchlorate radical,** ClO_4, result: $2AgClO_4 + Br_2 = 2AgBr + 2ClO_4$. This substance also has an odd number of valence electrons, and is extremely reactive and unstable.

18. Hypobromite and Hypoiodite.—The hydrolysis of the halogens decreases markedly with increasing atomic weight (Par. **5**); however, in strongly alkaline solution both bromine and iodine are almost completely converted into the halide and hypohalite. Hypobromous acid, and more especially hypoiodous acid are very unstable, decomposing within a few minutes into the halide and halate. They are also extremely weak acids. In fact, the reaction, $IOH + HCl = ICl + H_2O$, indicates certain basic tendencies in the latter. Hypobromites and hypoiodites decompose much more readily than hypochlorites to give halate and halide. The unstable **monoxide,** Br_2O, has been prepared by the action of bromine upon mercuric oxide at 50°: $2HgO + 2Br_2 = Br_2O + Hg_2OBr_2$.

19. Bromate and Iodate.—In addition to the methods of preparation analogous to the chlorine compounds, bromic and iodic acids may be prepared from the elements by the action of powerful oxidizing agents such as hypochlorous, chloric, and nitric acids, and hydrogen peroxide. Bromic acid cannot be prepared in the pure state, as the concentrated solutions decompose, forming oxygen and bromine. The bromates are in general less soluble than the chlorates, and may be distinguished from the latter by the insolubility of silver bromate. They have some industrial applications as oxidizing agents.

Iodic acid is a white solid and is very soluble in water. It is most conveniently prepared in a pure state by the action of a slight excess of chloric acid upon iodine, or by the action of hydrogen peroxide in acid solution upon iodine. It may be dehydrated by careful heating to form the **pentoxide,** I_2O_5. This is a white solid which may be heated to about 300° before decomposition becomes rapid. Sodium iodate, occurring in the Chile nitre beds, has been mentioned as the most important source of the element. The iodates are much less soluble and much more stable than the other halates, and are easily distinguished from them by the insolubility of their barium and lead salts. Iodates in highly acid solution oxidize chloride. Neither the acid nor the salts show any tendency to decompose to form the periodates. Potassium iodate and bi-iodate, $KH(IO_3)_2$, are of considerable importance in analytical chemistry (Par. **21**), because of the quantitative reduction to iodine in dilute acid and to iodine chloride in moderately concentrated hydrochloric acid by many reducing agents. The potential for the latter reduction is $-$ 1.23 volts corresponding to the half reaction:

$$3H_2O + ICl_2^- = IO_3^- + 6H^+ + 2Cl^- + 4e^-$$

19. Iodine Tetroxide.—The oxide, I_2O_4, may be prepared by the action of concentrated sulfuric acid upon iodic acid, similar to the preparation of chlorine dioxide. It reacts with water according to the equation: $5I_2O_4 + 4H_2O = 8HIO_3 + I_2$. With sulfuric acid, it forms a complex compound, $(I_2O_4)H_2SO_4$.

20. Periodic Acid and Periodates.—Strong oxidizing agents convert the iodates into periodates. There is a long series of polybasic periodic acids which may be considered as derived from the anhydride, I_2O_7, by the addition of n molecules of water, $I_2O_7 \cdot nH_2O$, where n has the values 1 to 7: e.g. $I_2O_7 + H_2O = 2HIO_4$; $I_2O_7 + 2H_2O = H_4I_2O_9$; $I_2O_7 + 7H_2O = 2H_7IO_7$. The existence of H_7IO_7, or its salts, is somewhat doubtful, but the acid, H_5IO_6, is probably the principal constituent of the water solution. The constant for the first ionization is 5×10^{-4} and for the second about 10^{-7}. The second step of the neutralization appears also to involve the equilibrium, $H_4IO_6^- = IO_4^- + 2H_2O$. The higher polybasic acids may be dehydrated to form the meta acid, HIO_4; but the anhydride, I_2O_7, cannot be prepared, as further heating causes decomposition into oxygen and the pentoxide. The fact that the iodine atom in periodic acid is surrounded by as many as six oxygen atoms, while the chlorine atom in perchloric acid is limited to four may be correlated with the larger size of the iodine atom.

The preparation of periodates is usually accomplished by heating iodate with chlorine in alkaline solution: $2Na^+$

$+ IO_3^- + 3OH^- + Cl_2 = Na_2H_3IO_6 + 2Cl^-$. The product, disodium paraperiodate, is but moderately soluble. In highly acid solution the periodates are extremely powerful oxidizing agents, being capable of oxidizing manganous ion to permanganate, which requires a potential of -1.5 volts. Excess periodate, in even low acid concentration, is reduced to iodate by iodide: $2H^+ + IO_4^- + 2I^- = IO_3^- + I_2 + H_2O$. With excess iodide, the product is triiodide.

21. Analytical Properties.—Advantage is taken of the insolubility of silver chloride, bromide, and iodide in both the qualitative and quantitative determination of these halides (cf. **VII—28**). Iodides and bromides are readily distinguished from chlorides by the liberation of bromine or iodine by chlorine water, and the production of the characteristic colors upon extraction of the free halogen with carbon disulfide.

The oxygen compounds of the halogens may be determined qualitatively by the reduction to the free element or halide, and identified as such. Quantitatively they may be reduced by excess reducing agent, such as stannous chloride, or titanous chloride, and the excess reducing agent titrated with permanganate; or they may be reduced with excess iodide and the iodine formed titrated (at low H^+) with thiosulfate: $I_3^- + 2S_2O_3^{--} = 3I^- + S_4O_6^{--}$.

The reaction just given for the oxidation of thiosulfate by iodine or triiodide is one of the most important in chemical analysis. It provides a general method for the determination of oxidizing agents, as indicated above, by the addition of excess iodide and the titration of the iodine by thiosulfate, As an end point indicator in this titration, soluble starch is added to the solution, giving a deep blue color as long as an appreciable concentration of iodine is present. Strong reducing agents may be titrated by direct oxidation with triiodide.

22. Astatine.—The most stable isotopes of element 85 have the mass numbers 210 and 211 (cf. all **XXII**—), their half-lives being 8.3 hours and 7.5 hours respectively. Astatine 211 is readily prepared by bombarding bismuth with alpha-particles in the energy range of 21–29 Mev. Because of the very short half-life, all experiments on the chemistry of astatine have been carried out on minute quantities of the element. In general the concentrations in solution have been less than $10^{-10} M$. At^{211} is an α-emitter and it is possible to follow the course of the element in a chemical reaction by means of its radioactivity. However, the behavior of an element in tracer amounts is often erratic, and the observations so far made are open to reinterpretation.

The element in the zero oxidation state is fairly volatile and may be separated from bismuth by distillation at 270° C. It is reduced by zinc or sulfur dioxide in acid solution to the −1 state and is oxidized by ferric ion, bromine and nitric acid to a positive state, probably HAtO. Like iodine the element is readily soluble in carbon tetrachloride or benzene. In alkaline solution the element is unstable with respect to its disproportionation, probably into At^- and AtO^-.

The −1 state is completely precipitated with Ag^+ using AgI as a carrier. There are two positive oxidation states, probably the +1 and +5. Powerful oxidizing agents in acid solution such as hypochlorous acid and peroxysulfate are required to oxidize the element to the higher state. An interpretation of the chemistry gives the following tentative values for the oxidation reduction couples in acid solution:

$$At^- = \tfrac{1}{2}At_2 + e^- \quad E° = ca - 0.3$$
$$H_2O + \tfrac{1}{2}At_2 = HAtO + H^+ + e^- \quad E° = ca - 0.7$$
$$2H_2O + HAtO = HAtO_3 + 4H^+ + 4e^- \quad E° = ca - 1.3$$

The +1 (?) state does not precipitate completely with silver iodate as a carrier but the higher oxidation state carries completely with this precipitate.

23. Potential Diagrams.—For a comparison of the oxidation-reduction properties of the members of the halogen family, the following summary is given:

Acidic Solutions:

$$F^-\overset{-\,2.87}{\rule{3cm}{0.4pt}}F_2$$

$$Cl^-\overset{-\,1.36}{\rule{1.5cm}{0.4pt}}Cl_2\overset{-\,1.62}{\rule{1.5cm}{0.4pt}}HClO\overset{-\,1.63}{\rule{1.5cm}{0.4pt}}HClO_2\overset{-\,1.21}{\rule{1.5cm}{0.4pt}}ClO_3^-\overset{-\,1.19}{\rule{1.5cm}{0.4pt}}ClO_4^-$$
$$\underset{-\,1.47}{\rule{6cm}{0.4pt}}$$

$$Br^-\overset{-\,1.07}{\rule{1.5cm}{0.4pt}}Br_2\overset{-\,1.59}{\rule{1.5cm}{0.4pt}}HBrO\overset{-\,1.49}{\rule{1.5cm}{0.4pt}}BrO_3^-$$
$$\underset{-\,1.52}{\rule{5cm}{0.4pt}}$$

$$I^-\overset{-\,0.53}{\rule{1.5cm}{0.4pt}}I_2\overset{-\,1.45}{\rule{1.5cm}{0.4pt}}HIO\overset{-\,1.14}{\rule{1.5cm}{0.4pt}}IO_3^-\overset{ca\,1.70}{\rule{1.5cm}{0.4pt}}H_5IO_6$$
$$\underset{-\,1.06}{\rule{3cm}{0.4pt}}ICl_2^-\underset{-\,1.23}{\rule{3cm}{0.4pt}}$$
$$\underset{-\,1.20}{\rule{5cm}{0.4pt}}$$

$$At^-\overset{(-\,0.3)}{\rule{1.5cm}{0.4pt}}At_2\overset{(-\,0.7)}{\rule{1.5cm}{0.4pt}}HAtO\,(?)\overset{(-\,1.3)}{\rule{1.5cm}{0.4pt}}AtO_3^-\,(?)$$

Basic Solutions:

$$F^-\overset{-\,2.85}{\rule{1.5cm}{0.4pt}}F_2$$

$$Cl^-\overset{-\,1.36}{\rule{1.5cm}{0.4pt}}Cl_2\overset{-\,0.40}{\rule{1.5cm}{0.4pt}}ClO^-\overset{-\,0.65}{\rule{1.5cm}{0.4pt}}ClO_2^-\overset{-\,0.35}{\rule{1.5cm}{0.4pt}}ClO_3^-\overset{-\,0.36}{\rule{1.5cm}{0.4pt}}ClO_4^-$$
$$\underset{-\,0.88}{\rule{3cm}{0.4pt}}$$

$$Br^-\overset{-\,1.07}{\rule{1.5cm}{0.4pt}}Br_2\overset{-\,0.45}{\rule{1.5cm}{0.4pt}}BrO^-\overset{-\,0.54}{\rule{1.5cm}{0.4pt}}BrO_3^-$$
$$\underset{-\,0.71}{\rule{4cm}{0.4pt}}$$

$$I^-\overset{-\,0.53}{\rule{1.5cm}{0.4pt}}I_2\overset{-\,0.45}{\rule{1.5cm}{0.4pt}}IO^-\overset{-\,0.14}{\rule{1.5cm}{0.4pt}}IO_3^-\overset{ca\,-\,0.7}{\rule{1.5cm}{0.4pt}}H_3IO_6^{--}$$
$$\underset{-\,0.49}{\rule{3cm}{0.4pt}}$$

$$At^-\overset{(-\,0.3)}{\rule{1.5cm}{0.4pt}}At_2\overset{(0.2)}{\rule{1.5cm}{0.4pt}}AtO^-\overset{(-\,0.3)}{\rule{1.5cm}{0.4pt}}AtO_3^-$$
$$\underset{(-\,0.05)}{\rule{3cm}{0.4pt}}$$

Chapter XI

GROUP V. NITROGEN, PHOSPHOROUS, ARSENIC, ANTIMONY AND BISMUTH

1. The elements of Group V, nitrogen, phosphorus, arsenic, antimony, and bismuth, have a maximum positive oxidation state of five in agreement with the presence of five valence electrons. The nitrogen atom, the smallest of the group, shows strong tendencies to add three additional electrons and thus complete the octet; but this property decreases with increasing size so that bismuth forms no stable compounds in which it has a negative oxidation state. Nitrogen and phosphorus are non-metallic in their properties, but the heavier elements of the group are increasingly metallic. Each of the elements forms an acid pentoxide, though the acidic nature of the oxide decreases markedly with increasing size of the positive ions. The elements also form sesquioxides which are acidic with the lighter members, but become basic with the heavier. The elements of the group thus show a complete transition from non-metallic to metallic character.

Nitrogen, like the first member of other groups, differs in many respects from the other elements. For this reason, and also because its importance warrants a more detailed treatment, it will be considered separately. A further discussion of the group properties is given in Paragraph **40**.

NITROGEN

2. Occurrence.—Four fifths by volume of the atmosphere is free nitrogen, N_2. All fertile soils contain the element in the form of ammonium salts, nitrates, or nitrites; and nitrogen is a constituent of all proteins. The occurrence of deposits of alkali nitrates has been mentioned (cf. **IV—23**). The amount of nitrogen in the primary rocks is so small that nitrogen ranks among the less abundant elements, constituting but 0.03 per cent of the earth's crust and atmosphere.

3. Preparation.—Atmospheric nitrogen is the cheapest source of the element, and large quantities are prepared commercially from the air by fractional liquefaction (cf. **III—6**). This process concentrates the argon somewhat (to about 3 per cent), but the gas is sufficiently pure for most commercial purposes. Nitrogen may, of course, be prepared from the air by the absorption of oxygen by chemical agents, such as heated copper. Pure nitrogen is usually prepared, either by passing ammonia over copper oxide: $2NH_3 + 3CuO = N_2 + 3H_2O + 3Cu$, or by heating a solution containing ammonium and nitrite ions: $NH_4^+ + NO_2^- = N_2 + 2H_2O$. Once the latter reaction is started, it proceeds rapidly or even explosively unless cooled. Other reactions producing nitrogen under appropriate experimental conditions are: $MnO_2 + 4NH_4NO_3 = Mn(NO_3)_2 + 8H_2O + 3N_2$; $(NH_4)_2Cr_2O_7 = Cr_2O_3 + 4H_2O + N_2$; $2P + 5NH_4NO_3 = 2H_3PO_4 + 7H_2O + 5N_2$; $CO(NH_2)_2 + 2HNO_2 = CO_2 + 2N_2 + 3H_2O$.

4. Properties of Molecular Nitrogen.—The more important physical properties of atomic and molecular nitrogen are summarized in Table I. The gas is colorless and tasteless. The low boiling point is indicative of the stability of the molecule. Although the arrangement of the 10 valence electrons in the molecule is not known, the formulae

$$: N :: N : \quad \text{and} \quad : N :: \ddot{N} :$$

probably represent the two most important resonating states of the molecule. The molecule is diamagnetic. The

TABLE I
PHYSICAL AND ATOMIC PROPERTIES OF NITROGEN

Atomic weight	14.008	Radius of M^{-3} ion, cm.	
Atomic number	7	$\times 10^8$	1.71
Isotopes	14, 15	Melting point, ° C	− 210.0
Electrons in various quantum		Boiling point, ° C	− 195.8
levels, 1st	2	Density of liquid, g./cc.	0.808
2d	5	Heat of vaporization cal. per	
Ionization potentials of gaseous		mole	1,350
atoms, volts		Solubility of N_2 at 1 atm. in	
1st electron	14.48	g. per 100 g. water, 20° C.	0.00189
2d electron	29.47	100° C.	0.00069
3d electron	47.40	Density of gas at 0° C. and 1	
4th electron	77	atm., g./liter	1.2506
5th electron	97	Heat of dissociation of N_2 in	
		kcal. per mole	226

heat of dissociation is probably greater than that of any other diatomic molecule, and is doubtless the chief factor in its very slight reactivity. It may be calculated from thermal data, that at 8,000° C., the gas is only about 40 per cent dissociated into atomic nitrogen. Under the influence of a high voltage discharge, i.e. high velocity electrons, the nitrogen molecule is "activated." Active nitrogen appears to be atomic nitrogen, in which one or more electrons are raised to higher energy levels. Active nitrogen continues to glow for some time after the discharge has been stopped. It combines readily with many elements, phosphorus, sulfur, sodium, etc., with which ordinary nitrogen does not react.

The more important reactions of the element are given in Table II and will be discussed further in connection with the various compounds.

TABLE II
REACTIONS OF NITROGEN

$N_2 + 3H_2 = 2NH_3$	See ammonia
$N_2 + O_2 = 2NO$	See nitric acid
$N_2 + CaC_2 = CaCN_2 + C$	See cyanamide process
$N_2 + 3Mg = Mg_3N_2$	Also Li_3N, Ca_3N_2, BN, AlN, TiN, etc.
$N_2 + Al_2O_3 + 3C = 2AlN + 3CO$	
$N_2 + 4C + Na_2CO_3 = 2NaCN + 3CO$	See also **XIII—24**

Compounds of Nitrogen and Hydrogen

6. Nitrogen forms with hydrogen compounds in which its oxidation state is -3, -2, and -1, and a trinitride with an average polar number of $-1/3$. The most important of these are the -3 compounds, ammonia and its derivatives. The compound, NH_2, exists only in the double molecule, N_2H_4, hydrazine, and the compound NH is known only as the hydrate, NH_2OH, hydroxylamine, and its derivatives. The probable electronic structures of these compounds are given below:

$$H : \ddot{N}: + H_2O \rightarrow H : \ddot{N} : H : \ddot{O} : H$$

Ammonia   Ammonium hydroxide

$$2H : \ddot{N}\cdot \rightarrow H : \ddot{N} : \ddot{N} : H$$

Hydrazine

$$H : \ddot{N} + H_2O = H : \ddot{N} : \ddot{O} : H$$

Hydroxylamine

$$: \ddot{N} :: N :: \ddot{N} : H$$

Hydrazoic acid

The three nitrogen atoms in hydrazoic acid are linear, which corresponds to double bonds between the tetrahedral atoms, but there is probably resonance with other electronic structures.

6. Manufacture of Ammonia.—Ammonia was formerly made by the destructive distillation, in the absence of air, of hoofs, horns, and other nitrogenous organic substances; and the solution of the gas was called "spirits of hartshorn." Coal, due to its vegetable origin, contains nitrogenous matter, and one of the chief sources of ammonia has been the **"by-product ammonia,"** from coke ovens and coal gas works, in which ammonia produced by the distillation of the coal is separated from the other coal-tar products. The gas is usually washed with water to separate it from the tar, then with sulfuric acid which removes the ammonia as ammonium sulfate. Pure ammonia may be prepared from this by evaporation and treatment with calcium hydroxide.

7. One of the most important industrial developments of recent years has been the **production of synthetic ammonia** through the direct reaction of hydrogen and nitrogen: $3H_2 + N_2 = 2NH_3$. The reaction evolves 24,000 cal.; hence, the formation of ammonia is favored by low temperatures, and because of the volume change, by high pressure (cf. Principle of Chatelier, Hildebrand, *Prin. of Chem.*, p. 244), as is indicated in the following table.

TABLE III

VOLUME PER CENT AMMONIA IN EQUILIBRIUM WITH A 1 TO 3 MOLAL MIXTURE OF N_2 AND H_2

t ° C.	ATMOSPHERES				
	30	100	300	600	7000
200.......	67.6	81.5	90.0	95.4	98.3
300.......	30.3	52.0	71.0	84.2	92.5
400.......	10.2	25.1	47.0	65.2	79.9
500.......	3.5	10.6	26.4	42.1	57.5
600.......	1.4	4.2	13.8	23.1	31.4
700.......	0.7	2.2	7.3	12.6	12.9

The rate of reaction is slow at the lower temperatures, and the commercial process has been dependent upon the development of efficient catalysts. The Haber process, developed in Germany, employed according to the original patents, iron oxide containing other metals, such as molybdenum, uranium, or cobalt. Recently developed plants employ, as a catalyst, iron made by the reduction of fused iron oxide (magnetite) containing small amounts of both basic and acidic oxides, such as 0.5 per cent Al_2O_3 and 0.5 per cent K_2O; and operate at pressures of 100–200 atmospheres and temperatures of 550–600° C. The French Claude process attempts to utilize the greater yields at higher pressures by working at 600–1,000 atmospheres. Under these conditions, ordinary sheet iron is very permeable to hydrogen, and the containers must be constructed of special chrome-steel alloys. The American production of synthetic ammonia, in 1946 was about 725,000 tons of contained nitrogen as compared to 220,000 tons of by-product ammonia.

8. Another source of ammonia is **calcium cyanamide,** $CaCN_2$, which is formed by the action of nitrogen upon calcium carbide (Table II) at about 1,200°. When treated with steam, cyanamide is hydrolyzed: $CaCN_2 + 3H_2O = CaCO_3 + 2NH_3$. Much of the cyanamide is used directly as fertilizer. The world production of cyanamide in 1938 was 300,000 tons of contained nitrogen.

9. Attempts have been made to manufacture ammonia commercially by the hydrolysis of aluminum nitride in hot sodium hydroxide solution: $AlN + 3H_2O = Al(OH)_3 + NH_3$. The nitride is made by heating aluminum oxide and carbon in an atmosphere of nitrogen to about 1,700°. The reaction is slow, and the process is unable to compete with the direct synthesis from the elements. Ammonia may also be prepared by the hydrolysis of sodium cyanide: $NaCN + 2H_2O = HCOONa + NH_3$.

The historical laboratory method for the preparation of ammonia has been the reaction between an ammonium salt and a strong base (usually calcium hydroxide): $NH_4^+ + OH^- = NH_3 + H_2O$.

10. Physical Properties and Uses of Ammonia.—Ammonia boils at − 33.4°, melts at − 78°, has a critical temperature of about 133°, and a critical pressure of 112 atm. The vapor pressure of the liquid at 25° is 9.90 atm., hence it is easily liquefied by pressure at that temperature. If the pressure upon the liquid is decreased to one atmosphere, the temperature of the liquid, of course, falls to − 33.4°, and the liquid evaporates with the absorption of 330 cal. per g. of ammonia vaporized. This cycle of compression and evaporation is utilized in refrigeration.

The liquid has a density of 0.677 at − 34°, and a dielectric constant of 18.9 at 5° C. The specific conductivity at − 33° is about 10^{-8} reciprocal ohms. As a solvent for polar salts, it resembles water more closely than any other substance, although, due to the lower dielectric constant, salt solutions have a much lower activity (Append. IV).

The remarkable ability of liquid ammonia to ionize the alkali metals to give a solution containing the "free" electron has been mentioned (cf. **IV—2**). The potential of $e_{NH_3}{}^- = e_{metal}{}^-$ couple at $-33°$ against a hydrogen electrode is given as about 1.90 volts. The solubilities of the ammonium salts in liquid ammonia are remarkably large. For example, the values in grams per 100 grams of NH_3 are for NH_4NO_3, 390, and NH_4I, 369 at 25°.

The structure of the ammonia molecule is a pyramid with the nitrogen at the apex. The N-H distances are 1.016 Å and the height of the pyramid 0.360 Å. The dipole moment of the gas is 1.46×10^{-18} e.s.u. The nitrogen atom has two equally stable positions, one above the plane of the hydrogen atoms and the other below the plane and vibrates back and forth between these positions. The frequency of this cycle is 2.387013×10^{10} per second and is the basic time unit in the ammonia "atomic" clock.

Liquid ammonia is sold under pressure in iron cylinders, and is the most convenient source of the gas. The greater part of the ammonia produced is absorbed in sulfuric acid and sold as fertilizer. Household ammonia, or aqua ammonia, is used in washing and cleaning. Large quantities of ammonia are now oxidized to nitric acid (Par. **32**). The most important fields of consumption are given in Table IV.

TABLE IV

AMMONIA IN U. S. 1948

Production	TONS OF N_2
Coke ovens	232,000
Synthetic	1,090,000
Consumption	
Fertilizer	860,000
Manufacture of HNO_3	270,000
Aqua ammonia	50,000
Liquid, largely for refrigeration	30,000
Salts	30,000

11. Reactions of Ammonia.—Ammonia does not react readily with air, but in pure oxygen it burns to water and nitrogen: $4NH_3 + 3O_2 = 2N_2 + 6H_2O$; 301 kcal. In the presence of platinum as a catalyst, the reaction goes to nitric oxide: $4NH_3 + 5O_2 = 4NO + 6H_2O$, 215 kcal. This selective oxidation is the basis for the commercial preparation of nitric acid from ammonia (Par. **32**). The gas is also oxidized to nitrogen by passing over many heated oxides, e.g. CuO, and by chlorine and bromine (Par. **22**). The oxidation of ammonia and ammonium ion in water solutions is discussed in subsequent paragraphs.

Ammonia reacts with water to form ammonium hydroxide (Par. **13**). It is absorbed by many salts with the formation of ammoniated compounds similar to solid hydrates, e.g., $CaCl_2 \cdot 2NH_3$, $CaCl_2 \cdot 4NH_3$. Ammonia forms complex ions with solutions of many metal ions which possess pronounced "coordination" tendencies (cf. **VII—2**), e.g., $Ag(NH_3)_2^+$, $Cu(NH_3)_4^{++}$.

TABLE V

ANALOGY OF WATER AND AMMONIA SYSTEMS

	WATER SYSTEM	AMMONIA SYSTEM
First ionization step..........	H^+ and OH^- or OH_3^+ and OH^-	H^+ and NH_2^- or NH_4^+ and NH_2^-
Ionization constant..........	10^{-14} at 25°	ca 10^{-33} at − 33°
Base....................	KOH	KNH_2
Acid....................	HCl (OH_3Cl)	NH_4Cl
Neutralization reaction.......	$KOH + (H_3O)Cl = KCl + 2H_2O$	$KNH_2 + NH_4Cl = KCl + 2NH_3$
Dehydration or deammoniation products of base..........	K_2O	K_2HN and K_3N
Basic salts..................	$Mg(OH)Cl$	$Hg(NH_2)Cl$
Solvates....................	$CaCl_2 \cdot 2H_2O$	$CaCl_2 \cdot 2NH_3$

Ammonia shows acid properties, in that the three hydrogens are replaceable by metals as illustrated by the following: $NaNH_2$, sodium amide; Ag_2NH, silver imide; Li_3N, lithium nitride. These compounds are formed by heating the metals in ammonia gas: $2Na + 2NH_3 = 2NaNH_2 + H_2$.

The acid ionization of ammonia, however, is extremely small, and even sodium amide is completely hydrolyzed in water: $NaNH_2 + 2H_2O = Na^+ + OH^- + NH_4OH$. The amides may be considered as the analogues of the hydroxides of water systems (Table V).

12. Many acids exist, both inorganic and organic, which may be thought of as formed by the replacement of the OH^- by NH_2^-, e.g.,

$$O_2S\big\langle{}^{OH}_{OH} \qquad O_2S\big\langle{}^{NH_2}_{NH_2} \qquad CH_3{-}C\big\langle{}^{O}_{OH} \qquad CH_3{-}C\big\langle{}^{O}_{NH_2}$$

| Sulfuric acid | Sulfuryl amide | Acetic acid | Acetamide |

On the other hand, such acids may be considered as compounds in which one or more of the hydrogen atoms of ammonia is replaced by an acid radical, e.g.,

$$N\big\langle{}^{H}_{H}{-}H \qquad N\big\langle{}^{HSO_3}_{H}{-}H \qquad N\big\langle{}^{HSO_3}_{H}{-}HSO_3 \qquad N\big\langle{}^{HSO_3}_{HSO_3}{-}HSO_3$$

| Ammonia | Amidosulfonic acid | Imidosulfonic acid | Nitrilosulfonic acid |

The compound NH_2NO_2, **nitramide,** results from the substitution of the nitro-group for one of the hydrogens of ammonia. It is a solid which melts at $72°$ with decomposition. The constant for its dissociation in aqueous solution into H^+ and $NHNO_2^-$ is 2.55×10^{-7}. The acid solution slowly decomposes, $NH_2NO_2 = N_2O + H_2O$. The decomposition is rapid in alkaline solution. The compound is an isomer of hyponitrous acid.

13. Ammonium Hydroxide.—Ammonia is extremely soluble in water (1,300 vol. per vol. of H_2O at $0°$ and 700 vol. at $20°$), forming solutions of ammonium hydroxide, NH_4OH. The hydroxide is a weak base: $NH_4OH = NH_4^+ + OH^-$, $K_{25°} = 1.81 \times 10^{-5}$. A $1N$ solution thus contains $0.0042N$

OH^-. To account for the weakness of ammonium hydroxide, it is generally assumed that a hydrogen atom acts as a bond as indicated by the formula:

$$\overset{\displaystyle H}{\underset{\displaystyle \ddot{H}}{H : \ddot{N} : H : \ddot{O} : H}}$$

Values for the specific gravity of aqueous solutions of ammonia are given in Table VI.

TABLE VI

SPECIFIC GRAVITY OF AQUEOUS AMMONIA AT 15° C.

SPECIFIC GRAVITY	PER CENT AMMONIA	SPECIFIC GRAVITY	PER CENT AMMONIA
0.998	0.45	0.940	15.63
0.994	1.37	0.930	18.64
0.990	2.31	0.920	21.75
0.980	4.80	0.910	24.99
0.970	7.31	0.900	28.33
0.960	9.91	0.890	31.75
0.950	12.72	0.882	34.95

Water and ammonia react to form solid ammonium hydroxide and the **oxide**, $(NH_4)_2O$, at $- 79°$. These pure compounds decompose upon heating, so only the water solutions of ammonium hydroxide are known at room temperature.

14. Ammonium Amalgam.—The free ammonium radical, NH_4, may be prepared as an amalgam by the reduction of ammonium ion in the presence of mercury: $NH_4^+ + e^-$ $= NH_4$. The reduction may be accomplished electrolytically, using a solution of ammonium sulfate and a mercury cathode, or by the action of sodium amalgam upon an ammonium solution. At ordinary temperature, the radical is unstable, decomposing into ammonia and hydrogen, and the amalgam is a spongy mass, due to the bubbles of gas, but at low temperatures the amalgam is a hard, stable substance. In forming an amalgam, the ammonium radical thus appears to possess distinctly metallic properties.

15. Ammonium Salts.—Ammonium ion resembles thallous and potassium ions in the solubility and crystalline form of its salts. The four hydrogen atoms are arranged in tetrahedral form about the nitrogen, and the approximate diameter of the ion in crystals is 1.50×10^{-8} cm. Two points of dissimilarity from thallous and potassium ions are the weakness of ammonium hydroxide, and the volatility of ammonium salts. All ammonium salts volatilize at temperatures around 300°, except compounds, such as the nitrate and dichromate, which decompose with the oxidation of the ammonia. The vapor of the sublimed salt is largely dissociated into ammonia and the acid, e.g. NH_4Cl (s) = NH_3 (gas) + HCl (gas). In fact, it is this dissociation taking place on the crystal surface which is probably responsible for the ready volatility of the salt. Ammonium salts are highly ionized, and slightly acid by hydrolysis. The constant for the hydrolysis, $K = (NH_4OH)(H^+)/(NH_4^+)$, is 5.5×10^{-10} at 25° C. A $1N$ NH_4^+ solution thus contains $2.3 \times 10^{-5}N$ H^+.

16. Ammonium chloride is made by absorbing ammonia in hydrochloric acid. It crystallizes from solution in feathery crystals of the regular system, having the same type of crystal lattice as cesium chloride, but changing at higher temperatures into the sodium chloride lattice. The vapor pressure of the solid reaches one atmosphere at 338° C. The salt is used in "galvanizing" iron, and in soldering, to clean metal surfaces of oxides, the action being due to the presence of free hydrochloric acid in the vapor. It is also used in "dry" batteries (cf. **XVIII—9**), and in textile dyeing. Its common name is sal ammoniac.

Ammonium bromide and **iodide** are similar to the chloride.

The **nitrate** exists in five crystalline modifications between the temperatures of − 20° and 125°. When heated gently, it decomposes into nitrous oxide and water. The compound is really a high explosive, but is extremely diffi-

cult to detonate. However, disastrous explosions have occurred. It is employed extensively as an explosive mixed
with trinitrotoluene under the name of amatol.

17. Ammonium carbonate solutions are highly hydrolyzed, and lose ammonia to form the bicarbonate: $2NH_4^+$
$+ CO_3^{--} = NH_4^+ + HCO_3^- + NH_3$. The so-called solid
ammonium carbonate is a mixture of the bicarbonate and
ammonium carbamate, and is made by heating a mixture
of the ammonium sulfate and calcium carbonate in iron
retorts. It may also be formed by the reaction of ammonia and carbon dioxide.

$$2NH_3 + CO_2 \text{ equals } H_2N-\overset{\overset{\text{O}}{\|}}{C}-O-NH_4 \text{ or } \left[H : \overset{..}{\underset{..}{N}} : \overset{..}{\underset{..}{C}} : \overset{..}{\underset{..}{O}} : \right] NH_4$$

Upon heating, ammonium carbamate loses water to form
urea: $NH_4CO_2NH_2 = CO(NH_2)_2 + H_2O$.

Ammonium sulfate, prepared by passing "by-product"
ammonia into sulfuric acid, has been the principal source
of ammonium compounds. Synthetic ammonia has, however, now become the greatest potential source of ammonium compounds. The sulfate is employed extensively
as a fertilizer, but if a cheaper method of preparing phosphoric acid from phosphate rock can be developed, the sulfate will doubtless be replaced by the **phosphate,** as the
absorption of ammonia in this acid will serve to eliminate
the cost of the sulfuric acid and at the same time give a
compound, both constituents of which are valuable fertilizers.

Ammonium sulfide, $(NH_4)_2S$, solutions, made by passing
hydrogen sulfide into ammonium hydroxide, are largely
hydrolyzed to the bisulfide, NH_4HS. The use of these
solutions is frequently referred to in connection with the
precipitation of metal sulfides in qualitative analyses. The
sulfide readily absorbs sulfur forming polysulfides (cf.

XI—26). The polysulfide also forms through the action of the oxygen of the air upon solutions of the sulfide.

Ammonium thiocyanate, NH_4SCN, is used in dyeing to prevent injurious action of iron salts upon the color (see $Fe(SCN)_3$). It is sometimes prepared by the reaction of ammonia and carbon disulfide: $CS_2 + 2NH_3 = NH_4SCN + H_2S$. Ammonium **dithiocarbamate,** $NH_4S_2CNH_2$, forms as an intermediate compound.

Ammonium peroxysulfate, $(NH_4)_2S_2O_8$, formed by the electrolysis of a concentrated solution of the acid sulfate, is an important oxidizing agent.

18. Analytical.—The perchlorate, cobaltinitrite, chloroplatinate, and acid tartrate, may be precipitated similarly to the potassium salts; but a more delicate test for ammonium compounds is the formation of ammonium hydroxide upon the addition of a strong base and the subsequent volatilization of ammonia gas: $NH_4^+ + OH^- = NH_4OH$ and $NH_4OH = NH_3 + H_2O$. The ammonia is detected by its odor, or by its action upon moistened red litmus paper placed over the solution. Quantitatively, ammonium salts are determined by treating the sample with excess sodium hydroxide, and distilling the ammonia into a known volume of standard acid. The excess acid is then titrated with standard base, using methyl orange as an indicator. Small amounts of ammonia are determined by means of Nessler's reagent (cf. **VIII—25**).

19. Hydrazine.—Ammonium salts may be oxidized electrolytically to hydrazine, if certain viscous substances, such as glue or starch are added to the electrolyte. Hydrazine is usually prepared by treating dilute ammonia (in the presence of glue, etc.) with chlorine to form the monochloramine, NH_2Cl; and then adding an excess of ammonia: $2NH_3 + Cl_2 = NH_2Cl + NH_4Cl$, and $2NH_3 + NH_2Cl = N_2H_4 + NH_4Cl$. The sulfate, $N_2H_4 \cdot H_2SO_4$, or $(N_2H_5)_2SO_4$, is not very soluble, and hydrazine is readily purified by crystallization as such. It may also be prepared by the reduction of the potassium sulfite-nitric oxide complex, $K_2SO_3 \cdot 2NO$, with sodium amalgam, and by the reduction of a number of organic nitrogen compounds. With water hydrazine forms the weak base, N_2H_5OH, which gives in acid solution the ion, $N_2H_5^+$. For the dissociation, $N_2H_4 + H_2O = N_2H_5^+ + OH^-$, the value for K is 8.5 $\times$ 10^{-7}. The constant for $N_2H_6^{++}$ is 8.9 $\times$ 10^{-16}. The pure substance may be prepared as a fuming liquid by distilling hydrazine hydrate with barium oxide: $N_2H_4H_2O + BaO = N_2H_4 + Ba(OH)_2$. The liquid boils at 113.5° without decomposition. Hydrazine is a good reducing agent even in acid solution. It is oxidized quantitatively to nitrogen by iodate, chlorine, bromine, and iodine. It is also oxidized by chloric acid with osmium salts as a catalyst. The alkaline solution is readily oxidized by oxygen. Many oxidizing agents which gain one electron per molecule react with hydrazine to form both nitrogen and ammonia: $N_2H_5^+ + Fe^{+++} = Fe^{++} + \frac{1}{2}N_2 + NH_4^+ + H^+$. Hydrazine reacts with nitrous acid to form hydrazoic acid (Par. 21). Hydrazine is not easily reduced to ammonia. It reacts readily with metallic sodium to form NaN_2H_3. The relation of hydrazine to ammonia is analogous to that of hydrogen peroxide to water.

20. Hydroxylamine.—Hydroxylamine, NH_2OH, prepared by the reduction of 1 mole of nitrous acid with 2 moles of sulfurous acid (Par. 30). The reduction is carried out at 0° in neutral solution ($NaHSO_3$) and forms first the ion of hydroxylaminedisulfonic acid: $NO_2^- + SO_2 + HSO_3^- = NOH(SO_3)_2^{--}$. This is then hydrolyzed by heating in acid solution: $NOH(SO_3)_2^{--} + 2H_2O = H_3NOH^+ + H^+ + 2SO_4^{--}$. Hydroxylamine is also obtained by the reduction of nitric and nitrous acid in dilute solution, by strong reducing agents such as tin, and zinc. The electrolytic reduction of nitric acid with most metal electrodes yields ammonia, but with a mercury cathode, hydroxylamine is formed. Hydroxylamine in solutions of acids forms the ion,

NH_3OH^+, and upon evaporation of the solution, salts such as $NH_3OH \cdot Cl$, are obtained. $NH_2OH + H_2O = NH_3OH^+ + OH^-$, $K = 6.6 \times 10^{-9}$. The anhydrous compound may be prepared by distilling, under reduced pressure, an alcoholic solution of the hydrochloride with sodium methylate: $NH_3OH \cdot Cl + CH_3ONa = NH_2OH + CH_3OH + NaCl$. The melting point is 33°, and at 57°, the vapor pressure is 22 mm. At higher temperatures the liquid is very explosive. Ferric ion (in excess) in acid solution oxidizes hydroxylamine quantitatively to nitrous oxide, and more powerful oxidizing agents give nitrate. If the H^+ is low and NH_2OH is in excess, nitrogen is largely formed. Hydroxylamine is reduced by moderately powerful reducing agents.

As indicated above, the hydrogen atom of hydroxylamine may be substituted by sulfonate groups. Although the resulting acids are unstable many of their salts are well-known, e.g., $K[HONHSO_3]$, potassium hydroxylamine monosulfonate, and $K_3[SO_3ON(SO_3)_2]$, potassium hydroxylamine trisulfonate. Both a di- and an isodisulfonate are known.

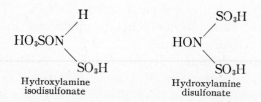

Hydroxylamine
isodisulfonate

Hydroxylamine
disulfonate

21. Hydrazoic Acid.—Nitrous oxide reacts with sodamide at 200° to form sodium azide: $N_2O + H_2NNa = NaN_3 + H_2O$. Hydrazine and its derivatives react in the cold with nitrous acid or trichlornitride to form hydrazoic acid: $N_2H_4 + O_2NH = HN_3 + 2H_2O$. The dissociation of hydrazoic acid is about like acetic acid $K = 1.8 \times 10^{-5}$, and the ion, N_3^-, resembles chloride ion in the solubility of its salts and in its reversible reaction with hypochlorous acid: $HClO + HN_3 \rightleftharpoons ClN_3 + H_2O$.

The product, chlorazide, like chlorine, is a gas, but is highly explosive. The iodo-azide also exists. Sodium azide tastes like sodium chloride, and is highly poisonous. The free acid boils at 37°, but the warm liquid is violently explosive, as the compound is highly endothermic (62 kcal.). The acid is both a powerful oxidizing agent and a powerful reducing agent. $NH_4^+ + N_2 = HN_3 + 3H^+ + 2e^-$, -1.82 volts and $HN_3 = \frac{3}{2}N_2 + H^+ + e^-$, 2.8 volts. The acid reacts quantitatively with ceric ion: $2Ce^{++++} + 2HN_3 = 3N_2 + 2Ce^{+++} + 2H^+$. The crystal structure of the azides from X-ray data show that the three nitrogen atoms are in line, with a distance between the atomic centers of 1.16×10^{-8} cm. Lead azide is now used extensively in the manufacture of percussion caps.

22. Halogen Nitrides.—Trichlornitride, also called nitrogen trichloride, Cl_3N, is formed almost quantitatively by the action of excess chlorine or hypochlorous acid with ammonium ion in excess of strong acid: $NH_4^+ + 3Cl_2 = Cl_3N + 4H^+ + 3Cl^-$, and $NH_4^+ + 3HClO = Cl_3N + H^+ + 3H_2O$. With low concentration of hydrogen ion, nitrogen is evolved, probably through the reaction: $NCl_3 + NH_4^+ = N_2 + 4H^+ + 3Cl^-$. With dilute equimolal solutions of ammonia and hypochlorite, **chloramine** is formed: $NH_3 + ClO^- = NH_2Cl + OH^-$. Both substances are highly explosive, oily liquids, and are partially hydrolyzed by water to ammonia and hypochlorous acid. Because of this type of hydrolysis and the method of preparation, the nitrogen is often considered as being in the -3 oxidation state but the classification is not very significant in view of the non-polar character of the bonds between the nitrogen and chlorine.

$$: \overset{..}{\underset{..}{Cl}} : \overset{..}{N} : \overset{..}{\underset{..}{Cl}} : \qquad \qquad H : \overset{..}{N} : \overset{..}{\underset{..}{Cl}} :$$
$$\quad\; : \overset{..}{\underset{..}{Cl}} : \qquad\qquad\qquad\qquad H$$

Trichlornitride   Chloramine

Iodine reacts with ammonia, forming a dark brown solid.

the so-called **nitrogen triiodide,** $I_3N \cdot NH_3$. When dry, it explodes with the slightest touch. It may also be prepared by the addition of iodine chloride in concentrated hydrochloric acid to an excess of concentrated ammonia. The formation of ammonium hypoiodite, NH_4IO, appears to be an intermediate step. Bromine reacts with ammonia to liberate nitrogen, and the reaction is frequently employed to remove bromine from a solution. **Nitrogen trifluoride** has been prepared by the electrolysis of anhydrous ammonium fluoride, NH_4HF_2. It is fairly stable.

23. Nitrogen and Sulfur.—Sulfur nitride, S_4N_4, may be prepared by the action of liquid ammonia upon sulfur, or by the action of ammonia on sulfur chloride in benzene. The compound is orange-red and may be sublimed under reduced pressure at 100°, but explodes at higher temperatures. It hydrolyzes in water to form ammonia, sulfurous, and thiosulfuric acids. When N_4S_4 is heated with CS_2 a deep red oil, said to be N_2S_5 is formed. The highly explosive compounds $(Se_4N_4)_x$ and Te_3N_4 have been prepared.

OXIDES AND ACIDS OF NITROGEN

24. Nitrogen forms oxides, in which it possesses the oxidation states $+1$ to $+5$, inclusive, and acids corresponding to the $+1$, $+3$, and $+5$ states. In addition, there is a nitrogen peroxide, and a peroxyacid, and the sodium salts of **hydronitrous acid** H_2NO_2 and of **nitrohydroxylamic acid,** H_2ONNO_2, have been prepared but these are relatively unimportant. Electronic formulae are given below. These must not be interpreted as representing the actual position of the electrons, but simply as a representation of the total number of electrons and a distribution which appears to be in harmony with known facts relating to the various compounds. In molecules which do not have completed octets of electrons, there doubtless is resonance of electrons between atoms with completed octets and those with incomplete octets. The relative positions of the atoms in the molecule are known, in a majority of cases, from X-ray data on the solid crystals.

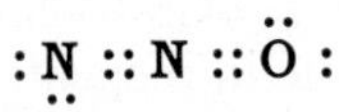

:N :: N :: Ö :
Nitrous oxide (+ 1)

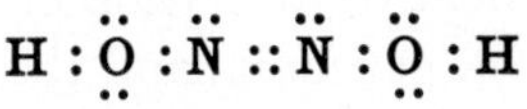

H : Ö : N̈ :: N̈ : Ö : H
Hyponitrous acid (+ 1)

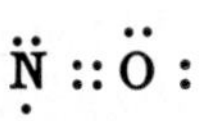

N̈ :: Ö :
Nitric oxide (+ 2)

:Ö :
  N : Ö : N̈ :
:Ö :
Nitrous anhydride (+ 3)

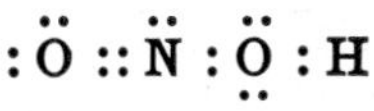

:Ö :: N̈ : Ö : H
Nitrous acid (+ 3)

:Ö :
N ·
:Ö :
Nitrogen dioxide (+ 4)

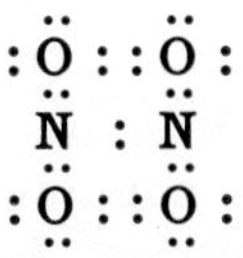

:Ö :: Ö :
N : N
:Ö :: Ö :
Nitrogen tetroxide (+ 4)

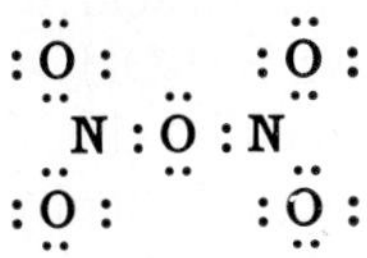

:Ö :   :Ö :
  N : Ö : N
:Ö :   :Ö :
Nitric anhydride (+ 5)

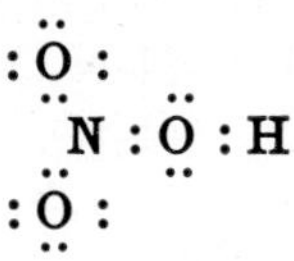

:Ö :
  N : Ö : H
:Ö :
Nitric acid (+ 5)

25. Nitrous Oxide.

Nitrous oxide is prepared commercially by the decomposition of ammonium nitrate through gentle heating: $NH_4NO_3 = N_2O + 2H_2O$. The reaction must be carefully controlled, as overheating may result in the explosive decomposition into nitrogen, oxygen, and water. The oxide is also a product of various other reactions, including: $NH_3OH \cdot NO_2 = N_2O + 2H_2O$; $HN_3 + HNO_2 = N_2 + N_2O + H_2O$; $N_2H_4 \cdot HNO_2 = N_2O + NH_3 + H_2O$. The oxide is a colorless gas which may be liquefied by a pressure of 50 atmospheres at 20°. The critical temperature is 35°. It is soluble to the extent of 1.3 per vol. of water at 20°, and at low temperatures forms a hydrate, $N_2O \cdot 6H_2O$. Band spectra data on the gas show all three atoms of the molecule to be in a line, with the oxygen on one end.

The heat of formation of nitrous oxide is negative, about 19.7 kcal. per mole; and the gas is unstable in respect to the decomposition into its elements. However, the rate of decomposition is not appreciable at ordinary temperatures. A glowing splinter bursts into flame in nitrous oxide, and phosphorus and sulfur burn readily, nitrogen being liberated in the reaction. Strong oxidizing agents, such as permanganate, oxidize nitrous oxide to nitric oxide. Metals do not tarnish readily in nitrous oxide, and it does not combine with nitric oxide as does oxygen. The gas is employed extensively as an anaesthetic. Inhaled in small amounts, it often produces a type of hysteria, hence its common name "laughing gas." The pure liquid oxide is put on the market in heavy steel containers.

26. Hyponitrous Acid.—Hydroxylamine is oxidized by mercuric oxide or nitrous acid to hyponitrous acid: $2NH_2OH + 2HgO = H_2N_2O_2 + 2Hg + 2H_2O$; $NH_2OH + HNO_2 = H_2N_2O_2 + H_2O$. The ion is also formed by the reduction of nitrite with sodium amalgam or electrolytically with a mercury cathode. The silver salt, $Ag_2N_2O_2$, is slightly soluble, and the free acid may be formed by treating the silver salt with an ether solution of hydrogen chloride. Upon evaporation of the ether, the acid is obtained as a highly explosive solid. In water solution the acid slowly decomposes into nitrous oxide and water: $H_2N_2O_2 = H_2O + N_2O$. The reaction is not reversible. The double formula is assigned from measurements of the molecular weight in various solvents. The following potentials relate hyponitrous acid to nitrous acid and hydroxylamine, $2H_2O + H_2N_2O_2 = 2HNO_2 + 4H^+ + 4e^-$, -0.80 volt, and $2NH_3OH^+ = H_2N_2O_2 + 6H^+ + 4e^-$, -0.44 volt. The ionization constants of $H_2N_2O_2$ are $K_1 = 9 \times 10^{-8}$ and $K_2 = 1 \times 10^{-11}$.

The compound, **nitroxyl**, NOH, appears to be formed as

an intermediate step in the oxidation of hydroxylamine or the reduction of nitrous acid. Under various conditions it may react to give N_2O or $H_2N_2O_2$ or it may react with excess hydroxylamine to give nitrogen, $NH_2OH + NOH = N_2 + H_2O$. By its reaction with excess of nitrous acid nitric oxide may be formed. Sodium reacts with nitric oxide at low temperatures to form NaNO, which may be considered to be a salt of NOH. The sodium compound liberates N_2O with water.

27. Nitric Oxide.—Pure nitric oxide is formed by the addition of dilute nitric acid (sp. gr. 1.2) to a boiling solution of ferrous sulfate and dilute sulfuric acid: $3Fe^{++} + 4H^+ + NO_3^- = 3Fe^{+++} + NO + 2H_2O$. It may also be formed by the reduction of dilute nitric acid by various metals, such as copper or silver, although usually contaminated by some nitrogen, nitrous oxide, or nitrogen dioxide.

Nitric oxide is highly endothermic, but is the most stable of the nitrogen oxides at high temperatures. It is formed to a small per cent in a mixture of nitrogen and oxygen in an electric arc, the reaction being the basis for the various arc processes for the fixation of nitrogen (see Nitric Acid). The oxide is also an intermediate step in another important process for the manufacture of nitric acid, namely, the oxidation of ammonia (Par. **32**).

Nitric oxide resembles nitrogen and oxygen in physical properties. The critical temperature is $- 93°$, and the boiling point $- 150.2°$. The heat of dissociation into N_2 and O_2 is $- 21$ kcal., and into atomic nitrogen and oxygen about $- 150$ kcal. It is doubtless this latter large heat that renders the rate of decomposition so slow at low temperatures. The molecule contains an odd number of valence electrons, but possesses only slightly the general tendency of such compounds to form double molecules, nor is it colored. In the liquid state, however, it appears to be about 90 per cent associated into $(NO)_2$. The oxide is magnetic, its magnetic susceptibility being approximately half that of oxygen, which contains two unpaired electrons (cf. III—3).

At ordinary temperatures, nitric oxide reacts with oxygen or air to form brown nitrogen dioxide; but the equilibrium is reversed at higher temperatures (Table VII): $2NO + O_2 \leftrightarrows 2NO_2$. Vigorously burning wood or phosphorus continues to burn in nitric oxide, but it does not support the combustion of more feebly burning substances, such as sulfur or a tallow candle. The oxide is somewhat soluble in water, 4.7 vol. per 100 vol. of water at 20° and 1 atm. It is, however, very soluble in solutions of ferrous salts due to the formation of the dark brown colored complex ion, $FeNO^{++}$ (cf. Par. 39). Complex ions with cupric, cobaltous, and platinous also exist, as well as the complex sulfite, $K_2SO_3 \cdot 2NO$.

28. Nitrogen Sesquioxide, and Di- or Tetra-oxide.—The sesquioxide, N_2O_3, is the anhydride of nitrous acid: $N_2O_3 + H_2O = 2HNO_2$. The acid is very unstable and readily evolves the oxide, or, more correctly, a mixture of nitric oxide and nitrogen dioxide, since the sesquioxide is itself unstable at ordinary temperatures: $N_2O_3 = NO + NO_2$. The equimolal mixture of oxides may be condensed to a dark blue liquid boiling at 3.5°. If the liquid is completely dried, it may be vaporized without dissociation.

The dioxide, NO_2 (also incorrectly called peroxide), is largely polymerized in the liquid to tetroxide, N_2O_4. At the boiling point, 21.3°, the gaseous tetroxide is only about 20 per cent dissociated into the dioxide, but at 135° the dissociation is 99 per cent. Above 150°, the dioxide begins to dissociate into nitric oxide and oxygen.

TABLE VII

DISSOCIATION OF NITROGEN DIOXIDE

$t°$ C.	130	185	350	500	620
Per cent dissociated	0	5	20	57	100

The dioxide is an "odd molecule," and like the majority of such molecules, in addition to its tendency to polymerize, it is colored, the color in this case being a deep red-brown. The pure tetroxide, however, is colorless, and upon heating, therefore, undergoes a striking color change.

$$N_2O_4 \overset{0° \rightleftharpoons 140°}{\underset{}{=\!=\!=\!=}} 2NO_2 \overset{150° \rightleftharpoons 620°}{\underset{}{=\!=\!=\!=}} 2NO + O_2$$

Color- less	Deep brown	Color- less

29. These oxides are involved in three important equilibria with water, nitric, and nitrous acids: (1) In small concentrations, nitrogen dioxide reacts with water in the cold to give a blue solution of nitric and nitrous acids: $2NO_2 + H_2O = HNO_2 + H^+ + NO_3^-$, $K = 10^5$. It follows from the equilibrium constant that in a dilute solution of the two acids the concentration of nitrogen dioxide is very small. (2) Nitrous acid is unstable in respect to the decomposition: $3HNO_2 = H^+ + NO_3^- + 2NO + H_2O$, $K = 30$. This equilibrium is comparatively slow in cold dilute solutions, and, from the value of the constant, is rather easily reversed. (3) In warm concentrated solutions of nitric acid, the quantity of nitrous acid, which may be present, is very small, and the principal equilibrium is the following: $3NO_2 + H_2O = 2NO_3^- + 2H^+ + NO$, $K = 2 \times 10^3$. Although the equilibrium constant favors largely the formation of nitric acid from the dioxide, concentrated nitric acid may, however, be reduced by nitric oxide. The third reaction is extremely important in connection with synthetic nitric acid processes (Par. **32**). With alkaline solutions only reaction (1) occurs, i.e. nitrate and nitrite are formed and the equimolal mixture of NO and NO_2 gives almost pure nitrite.

It follows from these equilibria that the concentration of nitric acid affects greatly the reduction products of the acid. This concentration effect is illustrated by the following summary of the products formed by the action of nitric acid upon arsenous oxide:

DENSITY OF HNO_3	1.20	1.25	1.35	1.45
Product..........	Almost pure NO	Mostly NO, a little NO_2	Equimolal mixture, NO, NO_2	1 part NO, 10 parts NO_2

30. Nitrous Acid and Nitrites.—The formation of nitrous acid, HNO_2, from the dioxide or sesquioxide has been discussed above. A solution containing nitrous acid may also be formed by the hydrolysis in dilute acid of nitrosylsulfuric acid: $NO_2HSO_3 + H_2O = 2H^+ + SO_4^{--} + HNO_2$. A solution of nitrous acid is conveniently formed by the addition of sulfuric acid to a nitrite in the cold. Nitrous acid is weak, the dissociation constant being 4.5×10^{-4}. The solution has a slight bluish color. The decomposition of the water solution has been discussed (Par. **29**). Nitrous acid is a rapid and fairly strong oxidizing agent:

$$NO + H_2O = H^+ + HNO_2 + e^-, -0.99 \text{ volt}$$

It thus oxidizes iodide quantitatively to iodine. Certain strong reducing agents, e.g., stannous ion, are able to reduce nitrous acid to the negative oxidation states, but with many equally strong reducing agents, e.g., titanous ion, the reduction stops at NO. In general, such reductions involve a number of steps, but only in the case of sulfurous acid has the mechanism been worked out.

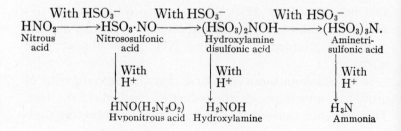

The reactions indicated on the horizontal are reversed in strong alkali. The reduction products may be hydrolyzed in acid solution to form the compounds indicated by the vertical arrows. The reduction potential of nitrous acid to ammonium ion is:

$$2H_2O + NH_4^+ = HNO_2 + 7\bar{H}^+ + 6e^-, - 0.86 \text{ volt}$$

and in alkaline solution:

$$7OH^- + NH_3 = NO_2^- + 5H_2O + 6e^-, + 0.15 \text{ volt}.$$

Nitrous acid may also act as a reducing agent:

$$HNO_2 + H_2O = 3H^+ + NO_3^- + 2e^-, - 0.94 \text{ volt}.$$

A strong oxidizing agent is thus required, but the reaction is quantitative with permanganate.

Nitrites are usually prepared by heating the alkali nitrates either alone, $2KNO_3 = 2KNO_2 + O_2$, or with carbon or lead, to decrease the temperature of conversion: $2KNO_3 + C = 2KNO_2 + CO_2$.

Nitrite forms complex ions with many positive ions, including cobaltic, ferrous, chromic, cupric, platinous; the most important being that with cobaltic ion, $Co(NO_2)_6^{---}$. The alkali nitrites are extremely soluble, but the silver nitrite is but slightly soluble. The silver salt in contact with solution decomposes upon heating, according to the equation: $2AgNO_2 = Ag + NO + Ag^+ + NO_3^-$.

Nitrous acid reacts with ammonia and with organic primary amines to form nitrogen: $NH_3 + HNO_2(NH_4^+ + NO_2^-) = N_2 + 2H_2O$; $RNH_2 + HNO_2 = N_2 + ROH + H_2O$; $CO(NH_2)_2 + 2HNO_2 = 2N_2 + CO_2 + 3H_2O$. The reaction with urea, $CO(NH_2)_2$, is often employed to remove nitrites from solution. Nitrous acid forms nitrosoamines with secondary amines: $R_2NH + HNO_2 = R_2N \cdot NO + H_2O$. With aniline hydrochloride in the cold, nitrous acid forms diazonium chloride: $C_6H_5NH_2 \cdot HCl + HNO_2 = C_6H_5N_2Cl + 2H_2O$. This reaction is important in the synthesis of many organic compounds. Due to the weakness of nitrous acid, soluble nitrites are slightly hydrolyzed. Nitrites are readily distinguished from nitrates by the fact that ferrous ion is oxidized in dilute acid (acetic) by nitrite, but not by nitrate, to give (with excess of the ferrous ion) the characteristic brown color of the $Fe(NO)^{++}$ ion. Nitrites are quite poisonous.

31. Nitric Acid.—Pure nitric acid is a colorless liquid, density 1.54, freezing point $-41.6°$, boiling point $86°$ under atmospheric pressure, and $35°$ under pressure of 20 mm. The concentrated acid is usually colored yellow, due to the presence of a percentage of the dioxide formed by the slow decomposition: $4HNO_3 = 4NO_2 + 2H_2O + O_2$. The speed of the decomposition is increased by higher temperature and by light. The acid fumes strongly in moist air; the water solution has a constant boiling mixture of 68 per cent acid, density 1.41, and boiling point of $120.5°$. Upon repeated distillation of the pure acid, the constant boiling mixture is obtained through the formation of water by the decomposition reaction.

The **anhydride or pentoxide** may be formed by the action of phosphorus pentoxide upon concentrated nitric acid: $2HNO_3 + P_2O_5 = N_2O_5 + 2HPO_3$. It is a white solid which readily sublimes, and is easily decomposed into the dioxide and oxygen. The freezing point composition curves for the acid and water show the existence of mono-, di-, and tri-hydrates at low temperatures. Water solutions of nitric acid are highly ionized (Append. IV).

32. Three processes for the **manufacture of nitric acid** are now in use: (1) the older process of preparation from Chile saltpeter and sulfuric acid, (2) from nitric oxide formed by the oxidation of ammonia, (3) from nitric oxide formed by the direct union of the elements.

For many years, Chile saltpeter (cf. **IV**—**23**) was practically the only source of nitric acid. The acid is produced from the salt by heating with concentrated sulfuric acid:

$NaNO_3 + H_2SO_4 = HNO_3 + NaHSO_4$. The reaction proceeds because of the greater volatility of nitric acid, and is carried out under reduced pressure in order to operate at the lowest possible temperature, and thus keep down the decomposition of the acid. The reaction mixture is heated in iron retorts, and nitric acid condensed and collected in glass tubes and vessels. The sodium acid sulfate is valuable because of its acid properties, and is used in various industries.

Since it is now possible to make ammonia synthetically at as low a cost per pound of nitrogen as Chile nitrate can be mined and extracted, ammonia has become the principal commercial source of the acid. In 1938 the production of nitric acid in the United States was approximately 160,000 tons from ammonia and only 20,000 tons from nitre. The oxidation is carried out by passing a mixture of ammonia (about 10 per cent) and air over a heated platinum gauze: $4NH_3 + 5O_2 = 4NO + 6H_2O$. The platinum gauze is maintained at a temperature of 900–1000° C. The gaseous mixture is heated to about 300° before entering the catalyst, and the heat of oxidation is sufficient to maintain the catalyst at the high temperature once the reaction is started. The efficiency of oxidation is about 96 per cent of the ammonia. The gas from the catalyst passes into absorption towers: $2NO + O_2 = 2NO_2$ and $3NO_2 + H_2O = 2HNO_3 + NO$. The first of these reactions is rather slow, but is catalyzed by most surfaces. The second reaction has been discussed at length under the oxide. The final two or three per cent of the oxide is absorbed in sodium carbonate solution to give a mixture of nitrate and nitrite. An important factor in the successful development of the process has been the use of chrome-steel alloys in the absorption towers, as this metal is practically unattacked by nitric acid.

33. Synthesis of nitric acid from its elements can only be carried out at extremely high temperatures as indicated in Table VIII.

TABLE VIII

EQUILIBRIUM IN THE REACTION $N_2 + O_2 = 2NO$

$t°$ C....	1227	1727	2227	2627	2927	3927
Per cent of $N_2 + O_2$ combined..	0.1	0.6	1.8	3.2	4.2	10.0

The existence of nitric oxide at ordinary temperatures is obviously due to a very slow rate of decomposition, and this rate becomes rapid only at high temperatures.

TABLE IX

ESTIMATED TIME REQUIRED FOR HALF DECOMPOSITION OF NO

$t°$ C............	721	1227	1627	1827	2627
Time..........	81.6 years	1.3 days	2.1 min.	5.1 sec.	3×10^{-5} sec.

A process for the direct synthesis of nitric oxide must, then, involve the heating of a mixture of oxygen and nitrogen to about 2000° C., followed by the rapid cooling of the equilibrium mixture. This is carried out commercially (chiefly in Norway) by blowing the gases through an electric arc. The gases pass through the arc and are cooled rapidly by coming in contact with the walls of the tube. Under the best working conditions, the yield of nitric oxide is only about 2.5 per cent: it is difficult for the process to compete with nitric acid from ammonia. Recently a somewhat simpler process has been developed in which a temperature of 2100° is reached in a MgO pebble bed by burning a mixture of gas and air. The hot gases are quickly cooled by mixing with more gas and passing through a second pebble bed. The air flow is then reversed and the cycle repeated. NO concentrations of about one per cent are obtained. In nature fixation of nitrogen during thunder storms is doubtless very large.

34. Nitric Acid as an Oxidizing Agent.—The conditions for the reduction of nitric acid to NO, NO_2^-, or NO_2 have been discussed (Par. **29**). The further reduction to NH_3 with SO_2 has also been treated (Par. **30**) and this step may be carried out with Zn and other powerful reducing agents. The values for a number of the oxidation-reduction potentials at molal concentration are given below, but it must be pointed out that in the majority of the reactions the rates are slow, and that the speed becomes a factor of equal importance with the energy in determining what reactions will occur.

TABLE X
OXIDATION-REDUCTION POTENTIALS OF HNO_3 AND NO_3^-

Acidic solution   VOLTS$_{25^\circ}$

$H_2O + NO_2 = NO_3^- + 2H^+ + e^-$	$- 0.81$
$H_2O + HNO_2 = NO_3^- + 3H^+ + 2e^-$	$- 0.94$
$2H_2O + NO = NO_3^- + 4H^+ + 3e^-$	$- 0.96$
$5H_2O + N_2O = 2NO_3^- + 10H^+ + 8e^-$	$- 1.11$
$3H_2O + \frac{1}{2}N_2 = NO_3^- + 6H^+ + 5e^-$	$- 1.24$
$2H_2O + NH_3OH^+ = NO_3^- + 8H^+ + 6e^-$	$- 0.73$
$6H_2O + N_2H_5^+ = 2NO_3^- + 17H^+ + 14e^-$	$- 0.84$
$3H_2O + NH_4^+ = NO_3^- + 10H^+ + 8e^-$	$- 0.87$

The potentials for the oxidation of ammonia by steps in both acidic and basic solutions are shown in the following scheme:

Acidic solution:

$$\begin{array}{ccccccc} & -1.24 & & -1.46 & & 1.87 & & -1.77 \\ NH_4^+ & \!\!\!\!—\!\!\!\! & N_2H_5^+ & \!\!\!\!—\!\!\!\! & NH_3OH^+ & \!\!\!\!—\!\!\!\! & N_2 & \!\!\!\!— \end{array}$$

$$\begin{array}{ccccccc} -1.59 & & -0.99 & & -1.07 & & -0.81 & \\ N_2O & \!\!\!\!—\!\!\!\! & NO & \!\!\!\!—\!\!\!\! & HNO_2 & \!\!\!\!—\!\!\!\! & N_2O_4 & \!\!\!\!—\!\!\!\! & NO_3^- \end{array}$$

Basic solution:

$$\begin{array}{ccccccc} & -0.10 & & -0.74 & & 3.04 & & -0.94 \\ NH_4OH & \!\!\!\!—\!\!\!\! & N_2H_4 & \!\!\!\!—\!\!\!\! & NH_2OH & \!\!\!\!—\!\!\!\! & N_2 & \!\!\!\!— \end{array}$$

$$\begin{array}{ccccccc} -0.76 & & 0.46 & & -0.88 & & 0.85 & \\ N_2O & \!\!\!\!—\!\!\!\! & NO & \!\!\!\!—\!\!\!\! & NO_2^- & \!\!\!\!—\!\!\!\! & N_2O_4 & \!\!\!\!—\!\!\!\! & NO_3^- \end{array}$$

Although the reduction to free nitrogen appears to give the greatest potential, this reaction is seldom realized, and then usually through the formation, first, of a compound of nitrogen of negative oxidation number which reacts with nitrogen compounds of the same positive oxidation number, e.g. $NH_4^+ + NO_2^- = N_2 + H_2O$ and $NH_2OH + NOH = N_2 + 2H_2O$ (Par. **26**). The values in the table show that nitrate in alkaline solution is not a powerful oxidizing agent. The values in the table apply to molal concentrations and cannot be used to predict the action of concentrated nitric acid, which is a far more powerful oxidizing agent, especially when heated. Nitric acid is reduced by sulfurous acid or acid sulfites through the formation of nitrosylsulfuric acid, $HONO_2 + H_2SO_3 = NO \cdot HSO_4 + H_2O$, and its subsequent hydrolysis in dilute acid.

35. Nitric acid reacts with chloride ion according to the equation: $4H^+ + NO_3^- + 3Cl^- = NOCl + Cl_2 + 2H_2O$. The compound, $NOCl$, is **nitrosyl chloride,** a liquid boiling at $-5.6°$, and upon heating, it very readily decomposes into nitric oxide and chlorine. The mixture of nitric and hydrochloric acids, known as **aqua regia,** is capable of dissolving gold and platinum, which will not dissolve in nitric acid alone. This, however, is not due to an increase in the oxidizing potential of the nitric acid in the presence of the chloride, but rather to an increase in the reduction potential of these metals in the presence of the chloride (cf. **VII—31**). Fluorine reacts with nitric acid to form gaseous **fluorine nitrate,** NO_3F. The fluorine is bonded to an oxygen.

36. Nitric acid reacts with organic hydroxides to form nitrates, for example with glycerine to form "nitroglycerine," $C_3H_5(OH)_3 + 3HNO_3 = C_3H_5(NO_3)_3 + 3H_2O$, and with hydrocarbons, such as benzene, to form nitro compounds such as nitrobenzene: $C_6H_6 + HNO_3 = C_6H_5NO_2 + H_2O$. In both of these reactions, water is produced, so that the reaction is favored by the presence of concentrated sulfuric acid to lower the activity of this product. Large quantities of the mixed concentrated acids are manufactured for this purpose. At present, the major portion of the nitric acid manufactured is consumed in some form of organic nitrate or nitro-compound, the more important being the explosives, plastics, varnishes, and dyes (cf. **XIII—29**).

37. Nitrates.—The nitrates of the metals are, in general, readily soluble in water. The nitrate group shows but slight tendencies to form coordination compounds. The alkali nitrates decompose upon heating to form nitrites: $2NaNO_3 = 2NaNO_2 + O_2$. The nitrates of the more noble metals form the dioxide, e.g. $2Cu(NO_3)_2 = 2CuO + 4NO_2 + O_2$. Ammonium nitrate decomposes into nitrous oxide and water: $NH_4NO_3 = N_2O + 2H_2O$.

X-ray data on the crystalline nitrates show that the three oxygen atoms are arranged symmetrically about the nitrogen atom in the same plane.

The properties of many nitrates have been discussed under the various positive constituents, the more important being the salts of sodium, potassium, ammonia, and calcium. Formerly the largest use of a nitrate was in the manufacture of **gunpowder,** consisting of potassium nitrate, 75 per cent; charcoal, 15 per cent; and sulfur 10 per cent. This mixture is moistened, ground, and the dried product granulated. When ignited, the powder burns and liberates a large volume of gases consisting mainly of nitrogen, carbon dioxide, carbon monoxide, and some sulfur dioxide. This type of powder is not smokeless, since solid particles of potassium sulfide and oxide are dispersed in the gas phase.

38. Peroxynitrogen Compounds.—Nitric oxide appears to unite with oxygen at low temperature ($- 180°$) to form the peroxide, NO_3, which decomposes upon heating. The silver salt of the peroxynitric acid, HNO_5, is said to be formed by the electrolysis of a concentrated solution of silver nitrate, but neither the free acid nor other salts have been prepared. The highly unstable acid, HNO_4, is formed by the action of hydrogen peroxide upon nitrogen pentoxide: $H_2O_2 + N_2O_5 = HNO_4 + HNO_3$.

39. Analytical.—The ferrous sulfate test for nitrates depends upon the reduction of nitrates by ferrous ion in concentrated hydrogen ion solution and the formation of the brown complex ion, $Fe(NO)^{++}$. The test may be carried out by the addition of about 5 cc. of ferrous sulfate solution to a few cc. of unknown solution. Holding the tube in an inclined position, $36N$ H_2SO_4 is carefully poured down the side of the tube so that the two liquids do not mix. A brown ring at the junction of the two liquids indicates nitrate. The test is not satisfactory in the presence of chlorate, iodine, bromine, nitrite, ferrocyanide, or ferricyanide. The diphenylamine test for nitrates consists of the addition of a solution of $(C_6H_5)_2NH$ in sulfuric acid to 2 or 3 cc. of unknown solution on a watch glass. Upon gentle heating, a blue color is produced if a nitrate is present.

The quantitative determination of nitrate is usually carried out either by reduction to ammonia and the determination as such, or the reduction to nitric oxide, and its estimation as a gas (nitrometer method). In the former process, aluminum or Devarda's alloy (Al 45, Cu 50, Zn 5) in alkaline solution is used as the reducing agent. The ammonia is distilled into excess standardized sulfuric acid, and the excess of acid titrated with sodium hydroxide. The nitrometer process depends upon the reaction: $2NO_3^-$ $+ 8H^+ + 3SO_4^{--} + 6Hg = 3Hg_2SO_4 + 4H_2O + 2NO$. The nitric oxide is collected in a gas burette or nitrometer and the quantity of nitrate calculated from the volume of gas. The base diphenylendoanilohydrotriazole, $C_{20}H_{16}N_4$, called **nitron,** forms a slightly soluble nitrate, $C_{20}H_{16}N_4$ $\cdot HNO_3$, and this reagent can be used for the quantitative separation and estimation of nitric acid.

PHOSPHORUS, ARSENIC, ANTIMONY, AND BISMUTH

40. The elements of this group form an especially interesting series in that they involve a complete transition from non-metallic to metallic character in both physical and chemical properties. It is, however, noteworthy that this transition is by no means uniform, but that there is rather an alternation in properties. Thus, nitrogen, arsenic, and bismuth form no pentachlorides, while phosphorus and antimony do. Figure 1 illustrates this alternation for the heats of formation of the trioxides and trichlorides when plotted against atomic numbers. This alternation extends to neighboring groups, as illustrated first by figures for the heats of formation of the dioxides of Group VI and second, in Group VII, by the stability of oxides of chlorine and iodine, but not of fluorine or bromine. Various other evidences of

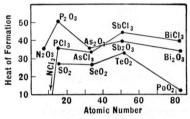

Fig. 1. Heats of formation in kcal. per equivalent against atomic numbers.

alternation may be discovered, such as the enhanced tendency towards hydration of the oxides of phosphorus and antimony as compared with those of their immediate neighbors.

41. Occurrence.—Phosphorus is the only member of the group which is never found free in nature. It occurs principally as calcium phosphate, $Ca_3(PO_4)_2$, and as apatite, $Ca_5F(PO_4)_3$ and $Ca_5Cl(PO_4)_3$. The first of these is found in large deposits of phosphate rock in Florida, Tennessee, Montana, and neighboring states, and in northern Africa. It is the principal mineral constituent of bones and teeth, and bone ash is largely calcium phosphate. Apatite occurs in many rocks, and important deposits are located in Canada. Many plant and animal tissues contain phosphoproteins, complex compounds of protein with phosphoric acid derivatives, such as casein in milk, and vitellin in eggs. The average human body daily excretes phosphorus compounds containing about 2 g. of the element.

Arsenic and antimony are occasionally found free, and

bismuth is generally so found. Their most important minerals are the sulfides: arsenical pyrite, FeAsS; orpiment, As_2S_3; realgar, As_2S_2; stibnite, Sb_2S_3; bismuthinite, Bi_2S_3. Oxides also occur such as claudetite, As_2O_3; senarmontite, Sb_2O_3; and bismite, $Bi_2O_3 \cdot H_2O$, and less frequently selenides and tellurides. Arsenides, such as $FeAs_2$, $CoAs_2$, and NiAs are not infrequent, and arsenic is a common impurity in sulfuric acid made from pyrites, in pig iron, and in commercial zinc. The most extensive deposits of antimony are located in China. The average percentage of the metals in the igneous rocks is given as: arsenic, 10^{-6}, antimony 10^{-7}, and bismuth 10^{-8}.

42. Properties of the Elements.—The more important physical constants are summarized in Table XI. Like the corresponding elements of Group VI, phosphorus, arsenic, and antimony exist in a number of crystalline modifications. **Phosphorus** has the two familiar forms known as "white" and "red." The white modification is formed by rapidly cooling phosphorus vapor. It is a wax-like substance, of low melting point, very low heat of fusion (157 cal. per g. atom), high volatility even at room temperature (Fig. 2) and is readily soluble in carbon disulfide (90 g. per 100 g. sol. at 10°). It ignites spontaneously in air and is, therefore, usually kept and worked under water in which it is only very slightly soluble (1 in 300,-000). It is extremely poisonous, about 0.1 g. being a fatal dose, and the continued consumption of small amounts leads to chronic poisoning, one of the symptoms of which is necrosis of the jaw. The white is a metastable form and upon heating or exposure to sunlight turns yellow and then red. The transition is catalyzed by iodine: a trace of the latter causes a

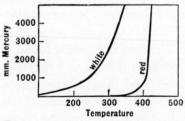

FIG. 2. Vapor pressure of phosphorus.

very rapid reaction at 200°. The heat of the transition is 3,700 cal.

The red modification does not have definite density or melting point and appears to be a transition form or mixture of the white and the real stable modification, **violet phosphorus.** The latter is difficult to prepare pure, but may be obtained by crystallization from a solution in molten lead. The properties of red phosphorus are essentially those of the violet. It is much less volatile than the white and is not appreciably soluble in carbon disulfide or other solvents. Red phosphorus sublimes without melting, unless heated under pressure, and from the shape of the vapor pressure curves there does not appear to be a transition point between the two modifications. Red phosphorus is not especially reactive, only slightly poisonous, and does not ignite below 240°. White phosphorus has a molecular weight corresponding to P_4 in its solutions and in the vapor state, but the red or violet is not sufficiently soluble to enable its molecular weight to be determined. Above 1,500°, the vapor is somewhat dissociated into P_2. A third solid modification, **black phosphorus,** is formed when a pressure of 4,000 atmospheres is applied to the element at 200°.

Arsenic exists in a reactive metastable crystalline modification, the so-called "yellow" arsenic, and a grey semi-metallic form. **Yellow arsenic** is formed by passing the vapor into cold carbon disulfide. The rate of transition into the grey form is rapid even at low temperature and instantaneous at room temperature in the sunlight. Yellow arsenic volatilizes readily, is extremely poisonous and phosphoresces in air at room temperature. Its molecular weight in solution corresponds to As_4. The **metallic form** is steel grey in color with a bright luster, very brittle, and is a good conductor of heat but a rather poor electrical conductor. It sublimes without melting unless heated under pressure.

Antimony occurs in modifications similar to those of

arsenic. **Yellow antimony** is transformed so rapidly into the stable form that it can be kept only at low temperature. Antimony also forms a metastable metallic modification known as **explosive antimony** from the character of its transition into the stable form when struck or scratched. The reaction evolves 20 cal. of heat per gram. Yellow antimony is formed by the action of oxygen upon liquid stibine, SbH_3, at $-90°$, and the explosive form by the electrolysis of a concentrated solution of antimony trichloride. The explosive form always contains some trichloride, and is probably a solid solution of the chloride in yellow antimony. The stable modification is a silvery white, metallic appearing substance. It is extremely brittle and much less volatile than arsenic.

Bismuth is known only in the one crystalline metallic form. It is grey white with a slight red tinge, hard and brittle, a very poor conductor of heat, and, although its melting point is low, the boiling point is high.

43. Preparation of the Elements.—Phosphorus is generally prepared from calcium phosphate through the reaction, $Ca_3(PO_4)_2 + 2SiO_2 + 5C = Ca_3Si_2O_7 + 5CO + P_2$, which is carried out at high temperatures, usually in an electric arc furnace. Phosphorus vapor leaves the furnace along with the carbon monoxide and is condensed under water, while the calcium silicate is drawn off as liquid slag. The element was first prepared by Brandt in 1669, by the destructive distillation of the solid residue from the evaporation of urine.

Arsenic, antimony, and bismuth may be obtained by the reduction of the oxides with carbon, e.g., $As_2O_3 + 3C = 2As + 3CO$. In case the ore is a sulfide, it may first be roasted to the oxide: $2As_2S_3 + 9O_2 = 2As_2O_3 + 6SO_2$; or iron may be used as the reducing agent: $Sb_2S_3 + 3Fe = 2Sb + 3FeS$. Native bismuth is easily extracted by taking advantage of its low melting point, and simply heating the ore and running off the metal. Most of the bismuth is obtained as a by-product of copper, lead, gold, and silver ores, generally from the flue dust of the smelters.

TABLE XI

ATOM AND PHYSICAL PROPERTIES OF PHOSPHORUS, ARSENIC, ANTIMONY, AND BISMUTH

	P	As	Sb	Bi
Atomic weight	31.02	74.91	121.76	209.00
Atomic number	15	33	51	83
Stable Isotopes	31	75	121, 123	209 (210) (214)
Electrons in various quantum states,				
1st	2	2	2	2
2d	8	8	8	8
3d	5	18	18	18
4th		5	18	32
5th			5	18
6th				5
Ionization of gaseous atom, volts	10.75	10.5	8.5	7.3
Size of M^{+5} ion, cm. $\times 10^8$	0.34	0.47	0.62	0.74
Molecular formula of gas at boiling point	P_4	$As_4 - As_2$	$Sb_2 - Sb$	$Bi_2 - Bi$
Melting point	W 44.1° V 590 (43 atm.)	814° (36 atm.)	630.5°	271°
Boiling point	280°	610° (sub.)	1440°	1420°
Density	W 1.82 V 2.34	M 5.7 Y 3.9	M 6.58 Y 5.3	9.8
Electrical resistivity, ohm-cm.	$W10^{11}, 10°$	$35 \times 10^{-6}, 0°$	$39 \times 10^{-6}, 20°$	$115 \times 10^{-6}, 20°$
$G + 3H_2O = H_3GO_3 + 3H^+ + 3e^-$ volts	0.49	$- 0.25$	$Sb = SbO^+ - 0.21$	$Bi = BiO^+ - 0.32$

44. Commercial Applications of the Elements.—The electric furnace production of phosphorus has increased rapidly since 1937. The element is shipped in tank cars and most of it is later burned to P_4O_{10} and made into various phosphates. A large amount of the phosphorus is consumed in the preparation of the sulfide, P_4S_3 (Par. **62**), for use in **matches.** Formerly matches were made by dipping wood splints into a paste containing white phosphorus, lead dioxide, powdered glass, and glue. Due to its poisonous nature, the use of white phosphorus is now prohibited in most countries and in its place the trisulfide is substituted. When struck, the friction raises the temperature to the point where the phosphorus sulfide is rapidly oxidized by the lead dioxide and the match bursts into flame. In the so-called "bird's eye" match, the phosphorus sulfide is present only in the small tip. The safety matches now used so extensively contain no phosphorus in the match head, but the box is coated with a mixture of red phosphorus, glue, and abrasive. The match contains a mixture of good oxidizing agents, such as potassium chlorate or chromate or lead dioxide, and reducing agents, as antimony sulfide. It may be ignited by striking on some surface of low heat conductivity, such as glass, and more readily on the surface of the box, since a trace of the red phosphorus is ignited by the friction and the heat kindles the match head.

Phosphorus is used in tracer bullets, and burning phosphorus is employed for the preparation of smoke screens. Ground with flour and grease, white phosphorus is used as a poison for rodents.

Very little free arsenic is consumed. The annual consumption in the United States is around 100 tons. A small amount of element (0.5 per cent) is usually added to lead in making shot to harden it and also to increase the surface tension. The latter aids in obtaining perfect spheres when the shot is made by allowing molten drops to fall from a height. The use of arsenic as a metal-tempering material is increasing. Arsenical copper alloys are now employed in products which require soldering, as their annealing temperature is high and the substance does not suffer loss of strength during heating. The trioxide is an important commercial compound.

Antimony is a cheap metal which can be used in certain instances as a substitute for more expensive metals. Most of the world's supply comes from China. The annual consumption in the United States is about 20,000 tons. Its principal use is in the manufacture of alloys, especially those of lead and tin, the most important being type metal, white metal, hard metal, britannia, babbitt, and antifriction metal (see Alloys of Lead and Tin). The presence of antimony adds to the hardness of the metal and also contributes the property of expanding upon solidification, which makes these alloys very useful in the preparation of sharp castings. About half of the American consumption goes into a lead alloy for battery plates.

Bismuth alloys also expand upon cooling and make good castings. A number of bismuth alloys can be prepared which melt below the boiling point of water, e.g.

	M.P.	Bi	Pb	Sn	Cd
Lipowitz metal	60°	50	27	13	10
Woods metal	71°	50	25	12.5	12.5
Rose metal	94°	50	27.1	22.9	—

Alloys of this type are used in automatic fire extinguishers which depend upon plugs of the alloy melting and releasing water sprinklers, closing fire-doors, etc. Such alloys are also employed in safety plugs in steam boilers to guard against over-heating. An alloy of 55.5 per cent Bi and 44.5 per cent Pb is utilized as a master pattern metal in the foundry industry. An aluminum alloy (Al, 93.5; Cu, 5.5; Pb, 0.5; Bi, 0.5) is free cutting and is used as the material for aluminum screws.

45. Reactions of the Elements.—The reactions of phosphorus are markedly different for the two modifications. Yellow phosphorus in moist air at ordinary temperature emits a pale greenish light and gives off white fumes of the sesquioxide, and the reaction is accompanied by the formation of ozone. The light is not true temperature radiation but results from the conversion of some of the reaction energy directly into light (**chemiluminescence**). The glow appears to be connected with the formation of trioxide and does not occur if the partial pressure of the oxygen is considerably increased, although oxidation to the pentoxide then takes place. Yellow phosphorus ignites at about 45°, the red at about 260°. The yellow modification likewise ignites spontaneously in chlorine, but the red must be heated to start the reaction. Yellow phosphorus is also soluble in hot alkalies liberating phosphine while the red is not although the energy of the reaction is favorable. Phosphorus reacts with sulfur forming sulfides and with the halogens (Par. **61**). Moderately strong oxidizing agents oxidize phosphorus to phosphoric acid; $P + 4H_2O = H_3PO_4 + 5H^+ + 5e^-$; $+ 0.3$ volt. The potential value indicates that even hydrogen ion should be capable of oxidizing the element but the oxidation appears to be slow with all weak oxidizing agents.

Arsenic, antimony, and bismuth form surface films of oxide in moist air, and burn to the trioxide when heated (Sb also forms some Sb_2O_4). Like phosphorus, they unite directly when heated with sulfur (Par. **62**), the halogens (Par. **61**), and various metals (Par. **63**). The oxidation of the elements to the $+ 5$ state becomes increasingly difficult with increasing atomic weight. Concentrated nitric acid, acting upon the elements, forms H_3AsO_4, Sb_2O_5, and $Bi(NO_3)_3$. The reactions are summarized in Table XII.

TABLE XII
Reactions of Phosphorus, Arsenic, Antimony, and Bismuth
(G = any element of the group)

$4G + 3O_2 = 2G_2O_3$	See also P_2O_5 and Sb_2O_4
$2G + 3X_2 = 2GX_3$	X = halide. See also Par. **61** for GX_5, etc.
$2G + 3S = G_2S_3$	See Par. **62** for other sulfides
$nM + mG = M_nG_m$	Formation of metal phosphides, arsenides, antimonides, and bismuthides

46. Hydrogen Compounds.—Gaseous hydrogen compounds the analogues of ammonia, are formed by all members of the group: **phosphine**, PH_3; **arsine**, AsH_3; **stibine**, SbH_3; **bismuthine**, BiH_3. They are frequently referred to as hydrides, but since the hydrogen is undoubtedly more positive, the name does not appear to be appropriate.

TABLE XIII

PHYSICAL PROPERTIES OF HYDROGEN COMPOUNDS

	NH_3	PH_3	AsH_3	SbH_3	BiH_3
Melting point, °C.........	− 75	− 132.5	− 119	− 88	?
Boiling point, °C..........	− 33.5	− 86.2	− 55	− 18	?
Heat of formation, kcal.....	10.2	1.9	− 36.7	− 34?	?
$XH_3 = X(\frac{1}{2}N_2) + 3H^+ + 3e^-$ volts..................	− 0.27	0.03	0.54	0.51?	(0.8)

47. Unlike ammonia, the other members of the group cannot be prepared by the direct union of the element and hydrogen. Phosphine decomposes readily upon heating; stibine decomposes explosively, and the bismuth compound is so unstable that a quantity of the gas is 80 per cent decomposed in 50 minutes at room temperature. The decomposition of arsine and stibine is further considered under the Marsh test (Par. **64**).

A general method of preparation is the hydrolysis of a binary metal compound similar to the hydrolysis of magnesium nitride to form ammonia: $Ca_3P_2 + 6H_2O = 3Ca(OH)_2 + 2PH_3$; $Na_3As + 3H_2O = 3NaOH + AsH_3$; $Zn_3Sb_2 + 6H_2O = 3Zn(OH)_2 + 2SbH_3$; $Mg_3Bi_2 + 6H_2O = 3Mg(OH)_2 + 2BiH_3$.

Phosphine may also be prepared by boiling white phosphorus with a solution of an alkali: $4P + 3OH^- + 3H_2O = 3H_2PO_2^- + PH_3$. There are usually present in the gas traces of the compounds P_2H_4 and P_4H_2.

Arsine may be formed by cathodic reduction, or by the reduction of arsenic compounds in acid solution by zinc or magnesium: $H_3AsO_3 + 3Zn + 6H^+ = AsH_3 + 3Zn^{++} + 3H_2O$. This reduction gives, of course, a mixture of the gas and hydrogen. The same method is also applicable to the preparation of stibine, but the more powerful reducing agent, magnesium, must be used for bismuthine.

These compounds are all extremely poisonous and it is dangerous to inhale even small amounts. Because of the presence of arsenic in many acids and metals, arsine is a common impurity in hydrogen prepared through their interaction, and such hydrogen should, therefore, not be inhaled unless it has been passed through permanganate solution.

Phosphine ignites spontaneously in air. The gas burns to phosphoric acid: $PH_3 + 2O_2 = H_3PO_4$. If bubbled through water into air, the bubbles ignite at the surface and form beautiful smoke rings. Arsine and stibine readily burn in air, forming the trioxides. If, however, a piece of cold porcelain is placed in the flame, it is coated with the free element. The liquid compound, P_2H_4, decomposes in the light into phosphine and a hydrogen phosphide, P_4H_2, or possibly $P_{12}H_6$, which is a solid: $5P_2H_4 = 6PH_3 + P_4H_2$.

48. Unlike ammonia, these compounds are only slightly soluble in water (PH_3, 11 vol. in 100 vol. water at 15°), and the solutions are not alkaline. The basic nature of the compounds decreases with the increasing size of the elements. Indeed, phosphine is the only one which resembles ammonia in the formation of salts, the **phosphonium compounds,** and these are far less stable than the ammonium compounds.

Phosphonium iodide, PH_4I, is formed by the reaction: $PH_3 + HI = PH_4I$. It crystallizes in beautiful, large, highly refracting, square, prisms which sublime at 62°. It is a powerful reducing agent, and is decomposed by water with the liberation of phosphine. Phosphonium bromide resembles the iodide, but the chloride can only be formed at room temperature under pressure (at 14° the dissociation pressure, $PH_4Cl = PH_3 + HCl$, is about 20 atmospheres). Phosphine reacts with solutions of certain metallic ions, e.g. Cu^{++}, with the formation of slightly soluble metal phosphides, which usually are of uncertain composition. Arsine passed into a solution of silver nitrate gives metallic silver and arsenious acid: $AsH_3 + 6Ag^+ + 3H_2O = 6Ag + H_3AsO_3 + 6H^+$. Under the same conditions, stibine gives silver antimonide: $SbH_3 + 3Ag^+ = 3H^+ + Ag_3Sb$. Arsenic forms no compounds analogous to hydrazine but organic derivatives are known, such as $As_2(CH_3)_4$, **cacodyl.**

OXIDES AND ACIDS

49. The oxides and acids are summarized in Table XIV.

TABLE XIV

ACIDS AND OXIDES OF PHOSPHORUS, ARSENIC, ANTIMONY, AND BISMUTH

OXIDATION STATE		P	As	Sb	Bi
	Oxides				
2	Monoxide	....	....	....	BiO
3	"Trioxide" (or X_4O_6)	P_2O_3	As_2O_3	Sb_2O_3	Bi_2O_3
4	Tetroxide	P_2O_4	$As_2O_4(?)$	Sb_2O_4	Bi_2O_4
5	"Pentoxide" (or X_4O_{10})	P_2O_5	As_2O_5	Sb_2O_5	Bi_2O_5
	Acids				
1	Hypo-us	H_3PO_2			
3	-ous { meta	HPO_2	$HAsO_2$	$HSbO_2$	....
	{ ortho	H_3PO_3	H_3AsO_3	H_3SbO_3	$Bi(OH)_3$
4	Hypo-ic	$H_4P_2O_6$	....	....	....
	{ meta	HPO_3	$HAsO_3$	$(HSbO_3)$	$HBiO_3$
5	-ic { ortho	H_3PO_4	H_3AsO_4	$HSb(OH)_6$	....
	{ pyro	$H_4P_2O_7$	$H_4As_2O_7$	....	....
	{ tri	$H_5P_3O_{10}$	....	....	....

Peroxyacids of phosphorus, $H_4P_2O_8$ and H_3PO_5, also exist. The pentoxides, with the exception of that of phosphorus, readily evolve oxygen upon heating, forming the sesquioxides. These oxides are formed also upon burning the elements in air. Measurements of gas density show that the sesquioxides, generally called the trioxides, are associated into double molecules, X_4O_6. Phosphorus pentoxide has an enormous affinity for water, even removing it from concentrated sulfuric acid. The oxides of arsenic react slowly with water, while the oxides of antimony and bismuth show almost no such reaction. With increasing size of the atoms, the oxides become less acidic.

50. Oxides and Acids of Phosphorus.—The sesquioxide, $P_2O_3(P_4O_6)$, is produced by the combustion of phosphorus in a limited supply of air. It dissolves slowly in cold water, to form phosphorous acid, and violently in hot water, to form phosphoric acid and phosphine: $2P_2O_3 + 6H_2O = PH_3 + 3H_3PO_4$. When heated in a sealed tube, it decomposes into the tetraoxide and phosphorus: $4P_2O_3$

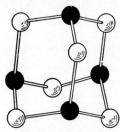

= $3P_2O_4 + 2P$. The trioxide is readily separated from the pentoxide by the greater volatility of the former. The heat of formation of P_2O_5 from its elements is about 370 kcal., and the heat of solution in water to form orthophosphoric acid, H_3PO_4, is about 35 kcal. The pentoxide appears to exist in a number of forms, one of which sublimes at about 350°. The

Fig. 3. Structure of P_4O_6 and As_4O_6.

vapor density of the higher oxide corresponds to the formula P_4O_{10} even at 1500°. Frequent mention has been made of the oxide as an extremely efficient drying agent.

Electronic formulas for the more important phosphorus acids are given below:

$$
\begin{array}{cc}
& \text{H} \\
:\!\overset{..}{\text{O}}\!: & :\!\overset{..}{\text{O}}\!: \\
\text{H}:\!\overset{..}{\text{P}}\!:\!\overset{..}{\text{O}}\!:\text{H} & \text{H}:\!\overset{..}{\text{P}}\!:\!\overset{..}{\text{O}}\!:\text{H} \\
\text{H} & :\!\overset{..}{\text{O}}\!:
\end{array}
$$

Hypophosphorous acid   Phosphorous acid   Hypophosphoric acid

$$
\begin{array}{ccc}
\text{H} & & \text{H} \\
:\!\overset{..}{\text{O}}\!: & :\!\overset{..}{\text{O}}\!: \quad :\!\overset{..}{\text{O}}\!: & :\!\overset{..}{\text{O}}\!: \\
\text{H}:\!\overset{..}{\text{O}}\!:\!\overset{..}{\text{P}}\!:\!\overset{..}{\text{O}}\!:\text{H} & \text{P} & \text{H}:\!\overset{..}{\text{O}}\!:\!\overset{..}{\text{P}}\!:\!\overset{..}{\text{O}}\!:\!\overset{..}{\text{P}}\!:\!\overset{..}{\text{O}}\!:\text{H} \\
:\!\overset{..}{\text{O}}\!: & :\!\overset{..}{\text{O}}\!: & :\!\overset{..}{\text{O}}\!: \quad :\!\overset{..}{\text{O}}\!:
\end{array}
$$

Orthophosphoric acid   Metaphosphoric acid   Pyrophosphoric acid

The formulas for hypophosphorous acid and phosphorous acid have been written with two and one hydrogen atoms, respectively, attached to the phosphorus.   This is in agreement with the fact that the former acts only as a monobasic acid and the latter generally as a dibasic acid, and also that these acids all have about the same strength as phosphoric acid—see Table XV), whereas the general rule that the higher the positive oxidation state, the stronger the acid, would predict that they would be very weak acids, since phosphoric acid is, itself, only moderately strong. In other words, it seems probable that the hydrogen attached to phosphorus serves to attract electrons, and thus increase the formal charge on the central atom.

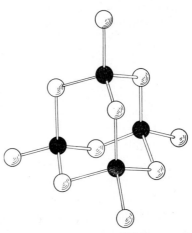

Fig. 4. Structure of P_4O_{10}.

TABLE XV

DISSOCIATION CONSTANTS OF PHOSPHORUS ACIDS

	H_3PO_2	H_3PO_3	H_3PO_4
K_1.............................	1×10^{-2}	1.6×10^{-2}	0.8×10^{-2}

51. Salts of **hypophosphorous acid,** $H(H_2PO_2)$, are obtained by the action of phosphorus on an alkaline solution (Par. **47**). The free acid may be prepared by treating the barium salt with sulfuric acid. The acid is a strong reducing agent and a poor oxidizing agent:

$$H_2O + H_3PO_2 = H_3PO_3 + 2H^+ + 2e^-, 0.50 \text{ volt}$$
$$2H_2O + P = H_3PO_2 + H^+ + e^-, \qquad 0.51 \text{ volt}$$

When heated, it decomposes into phosphine and phosphoric acids. The sodium salt, NaH_2PO_2, is used in medicine under the belief that phosphorus can thus be supplied to the body tissues. As mentioned above, the acid is monobasic and only partially ionized in solution.

52. Phosphorous acid, $H_2(HPO_3)$, is formed by the action of the trioxide upon cold water, or by the hydrolysis of the trichloride: $PCl_3 + 3H_2O = H_3PO_3 + 3HCl$. The further addition of the chloride gives the pyro-acid, $H_4P_2O_5$. The acid decomposes upon heating to give pure phosphine and phosphoric acid. The acid is oxidized to phosphoric acid: $H_3PO_3 + H_2O = H_3PO_4 + 2H^+ + 2e^-$, $+ 0.3$ volt but a moderately strong oxidizing agent is required as the first step is probably $2H_3PO_3 = H_4P_2O_6 + 2H^+ + 2e^-$, $(- 0.4)$ volt. The meta-acid, HPO_2, forms when phosphorus burns in air but it reacts with water to give the ortho-form.

53. Hypophosphoric acid, $H_4P_2O_6$, may be formed, mixed with phosphorous acid, by the slow oxidation of phosphorus in a limited supply of moist air. It is tetrabasic, and its salts are relatively unimportant. P_2O_4 does not give $H_4P_2O_4$ with water: $P_2O_4 + H_2O = H_3PO_3 + H_3PO_4$.

54. The Phosphoric Acids and Phosphates.—The product of the addition of phosphorus pentoxide to an excess of water is a solution of the orthophosphoric acid, H_3PO_4. This acid, or its hydrate, $2H_3PO_4 \cdot H_2O$, may be crystallized from the solution by evaporating under reduced pressure. The pure acid melts at $42.3°$ and the hydrate at $29.4°$. The acid is tribasic, and thus forms three series of salts. The ionization constants for the acid are, respectively, $K_1 = 7.5 \times 10^{-3}$, $K_2 = 6.2 \times 10^{-8}$, $K_3 = 10^{-12}$. The values for the molal concentration of H^+ in molal solutions of the following are: H_3PO_4, 0.1; NaH_2PO_4, 2×10^{-4}; Na_2HPO_4, 10^{-8}; Na_3PO_4, 10^{-13}.

Phosphoric acid is but a very weak oxidizing agent (Par. **52**). In this respect, it differs greatly from the other $+ 5$ acids of the group.

Impure commercial acid is made by heating pulverized phosphate rock with sulfuric acid: $Ca_3(PO_4)_2 + 3H_2SO_4$

$= 2H_3PO_4 + 3CaSO_4$. The greater portion of the calcium sulfate formed in the reaction is precipitated and separated by filtration. The acid is also manufactured by a method similar to the preparation of the free element by heating phosphate rock with carbon and sand, but differing in that air is introduced to oxidize the phosphorus vapor to the pentoxide, which is absorbed in water.

The most important salts of orthophosphoric acid are the calcium compounds. The occurrence of enormous deposits of the slightly soluble **tricalcium phosphate** has been mentioned. Soluble phosphate constitutes an important constituent of fertile soils and large quantities of phosphate rock (U. S. production about 7,000,000 tons yearly) are mined and con-

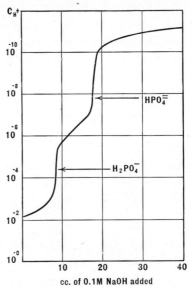

FIG 5. Titration curves for phosphoric acid.

verted into the soluble salt, $Ca(H_2PO_4)_2$, for use as fertilizer: $Ca_3(PO_4)_2 + 2H_2SO_4 + 4H_2O = Ca(H_2PO_4)_2 + 2CaSO_4 \cdot 2H_2O$. The mixture of acid phosphate and gypsum is sold under the name of **"superphosphate of lime."** **Triple superphosphate** is made by the action of phosphoric acid on phosphate rock, $Ca_3(PO_4)_2 + 4H_3PO_4 = 3Ca(H_2PO_4)_2$. It seems likely that **ammonium phosphate** will to a certain extent replace the superphosphate as a fertilizer (Par. **17**).

Most of the normal orthophosphates are but slightly soluble. The compounds, **ammonium magnesium phosphate,** $MgNH_4PO_4 \cdot 6H_2O$, and **ammonium phosphomolybdate,** $(NH_4)_3PO_4 \cdot 12MoO_3$, are mentioned under analytical properties. **Microcosmic salt,** $Na(NH_4)HPO_4$, is used in bead tests similar to the borax bead. The **disodium phosphate**, $Na_2HPO_4 \cdot 12H_2O$, is employed as a laboratory reagent. This compound loses water upon heating, forming, at about 95°, the anhydrous salt. Sodium and calcium diacid phosphates are used in one type of baking powder.

If the ortho-acid is heated to 215°, water is lost and **pyrophosphoric acid** is formed: $2H_3PO_4 = H_4P_2O_7 + H_2O$. When this acid is dissolved in cold water, the rate of transformation back into the ortho-acid is slow, but the transformation is rapid in hot water. Hydrolysis does not occur in neutral or alkaline solutions. All four hydrogen ions are replaceable by metals, and the four ionization constants are: $K_1 = 1.4 \times 10^{-1}$, $K_2 = 1.1 \times 10^{-2}$, $K_3 = 2.9 \times 10^{-7}$, $K_4 = 3.6 \times 10^{-9}$. The silver salt, $Ag_4P_2O_7$, is but slightly soluble, and the magnesium salt, $Mg_2P_2O_7$, is of analytical importance. Sodium pyrophosphate is readily formed upon heating disodium hydrogen phosphate, Na_2HPO_4. The pyro-acid may be distinguished from the other phosphoric acids through the formation of a precipitate with zinc acetate.

Metaphosphoric acids, $(HPO_3)n$ are formed by strongly heating the ortho- and pyro-acid, and sodium salts may be prepared by heating NaH_2PO_4, $Na_2H_2P_2O_7$ or $NaHNH_4PO_4$. There is no good evidence for the existence of the monomer, HPO_3, but the di, tri, tetra, and hexapolymers of the acid or their salts have been prepared. **Dimetaphosphoric acid** may be prepared by heating H_3PO_4 a short time at 300°. It is soluble in water but hydrolyzes rapidly to the pyrophosphate. The lead salt is slightly soluble. When NaH_2PO_4 is heated for several hours at 500°, sodium **trimetaphosphate,** $Na_3P_3O_9$, is formed. It is readily soluble in water and gives no precipitate with Ag^+, Pb^{++} or Ca^{++}. Copper **tetrametaphosphate** is prepared by heating CuO and H_3PO_4 up to 400°. The free acid may be obtained from the copper salt by treatment with H_2S. It is readily soluble and gives precipitation with Pb^{++} and Ca^{++} but not with Ag^+. Sodium **hexametaphosphate** $Na_6P_6O_{18}$, is prepared by fusing a sodium metaphosphate at 650° and then quenching. The salt is readily soluble in water (973 g./liter H_2O at 20°). The lead salt is slightly soluble. The sodium salt has commercial importance in water

TABLE XVI

REACTIONS OF PHOSPHORIC ACIDS

REAGENT	H_3PO_4	$H_4P_2O_7$	$H_6P_6O_{18}$
Ag^+	Yellow Ag_3PO_4	White $Ag_4P_2O_7$	White ppt.
Ca^{++}	$Ca_3(PO_4)_2$ in alkali	$Ca_2P_2O_7$ in alkali	Complex unless Ca^{++} in excess
$Zn (Ac)_2$	No ppt.	White $Zn_2P_2O_7$	No ppt.
Al^{+++}	Ppt. sol. in HAc	Ppt. insol. in HAc	Ppt. insol. in HAc
Albumin	No ppt.	No ppt.	White ppt.

softening and scale removal because it forms a complex with calcium ion, $Na_2Ca_2P_6O_{18}$. This complex is so stable that solutions of the hexametaphosphate will decompose Portland cement by the removal of the calcium. Insoluble high polymers (molecular weight around 100,000), known as **Kurrols salt,** are formed by heating NaH_2PO_4 below fusion for long periods.

The sodium salt of triphosphoric acid $Na_5P_3O_{10}$ is formed by heating mixtures of NaH_2PO_4 and Na_2HPO_4. Like the hexametaphosphate it forms complex ions with calcium.

A series of **fluophosphoric** acids may be prepared by the substitution of oxide by fluoride, e.g., monofluophosphoric acid, H_2PO_3F; difluophosphoric acid, HPO_2F_2; hydrofluophosphoric acid, HPF_6.

55. The Peroxyphosphoric Acids.—H_3PO_5 and $H_4P_2O_8$ (compare Peroxysulfuric Acid), are formed by the electrolysis of solutions of the salt, K_2HPO_4, containing a little potassium fluoride and dichromate. The former is the principal product at high current density and the latter at lower current densities. The former may also be prepared by treating the pentoxide with cold 30 per cent hydrogen peroxide.

56. Oxides and Acids of Arsenic.—The **trioxide,** As_2O_3, (As_4O_6), generally known as **white arsenic,** is commercially the most important compound of the element (cf. Fig. 3). Its most important source is the flue dust of smelters roasting arsenic-containing ores, and it is recovered from the dust by resubliming. The vapor condenses to a vitreous form which slowly changes to an octahedral crystalline modification. A monoclinic form may be prepared by heating for some time at 200°. The oxide is slightly soluble in cold water and more soluble in hot water. The rate of solution in both cases is very slow. The solution contains **arsenious acid,** H_3AsO_3. The acid is but slightly ionized, $K_1 = 6 \times 10^{-10}$. About 60 per cent of the white arsenic consumed in the United States (40,000 tons per annum) is used in the manufacture of insecticides, 25 per cent in the manufacture of weed killers, and about 5 per cent in the manufacture of glass. Smaller quantities are used in the preparation of ant paste and rodent poison, as a mordant in dyeing, and as a wood preservative. The fatal dose of the oxide is 0.06–0.2 g., but a toleration may be developed that will permit the consumption of several times this amount without harmful effects. A number of organic arsenic compounds are used in medicine, which are highly toxic to lower organisms, but which can be tolerated in fairly large quantities by the human body.

Although the trioxide is somewhat amphoteric, it is more acidic than basic and dissolves readily in alkalies forming **arsenites.** Salts of the types Na_3AsO_3, $NaAsO_2$, and $Na_2As_4O_7$ may be obtained, but the free poly-acids are not stable and decompose to give the oxide. The soluble salts are highly hydrolyzed, due to the weakness of the acid. Ferric and magnesium arsenites are very slightly soluble, and suspensions of the hydroxides of these ions are administered in cases of arsenic poisoning. Sodium arsenite is used

extensively in the preparation of poison bait for grass-
hoppers, crickets, beetles and as a weed killer. A number of
copper arsenites are important insecticides and pigments,
such as **Paris green,** $Cu_4(C_2H_3O_2)_2(AsO_3)_2$, and **Scheele's
green,** $CuHAsO_3$.

The trioxide dissolves in concentrated hydrochloric acid
to form a **trichloride,** but this compound is completely hydrolyzed in dilute acid solution.

Arsenious acid may be oxidized to arsenic acid:

$$H_3AsO_3 + 2H_2O = H_3AsO_4 + 2H^+ + 2e^-, \quad -0.559 \text{ volt}$$

As is evident from the potential value, a fairly strong oxidizing agent is required. In neutral solution the reaction with
iodine is quantitative, but in acid solution, the reaction is
reversed and arsenic acid oxidizes iodide quantitatively. A
value of -0.234 volt is given in Table XI for the metal-
arsenite couple.

57. Orthoarsenic acid is obtained upon evaporating a
solution made by dissolving the trioxide in nitric acid. It
crystallizes as $2H_3AsO_4 \cdot H_2O$. When heated, water is lost
to form the pentoxide, As_2O_5, which readily dissolves again
in water to form the acid.

Arsenates resemble the phosphates in solubility and
crystalline form. The sodium salts, Na_2HAsO_4 and Na_4-
As_2O_7, are used in the preparation of the **lead arsenates,**
$Pb_3(AsO_4)_2$ and $PbHAsO_4$, and the corresponding **calcium
arsenates.** The former are employed extensively to provide
protection against fruit insects, and the latter for controlling
the cotton boll weevil. The value of arsenic as an oxidizing
agent has been discussed above.

58. Oxides and Acids of Antimony.—The so-called **trioxide,** Sb_2O_3 (or Sb_4O_6), together with some tetroxide, is
formed when antimony burns in air. The tetroxide may be
prepared from the trioxide by heating in air to moderate
temperature (300–400°), but at higher temperatures (about
900°) it decomposes again to the trioxide. The trioxide is

amphoteric. It dissolves in concentrated acids, but only basic salts can ordinarily be crystallized from the solutions, e.g. $(SbO)_2SO_4$, $(SbO)NO_3$, and $K(SbO)C_4H_4O_6$. In hot water, these salts are completely hydrolyzed. The basic radical, SbO, is known as **antimonyl,** and the potassium antimonyl tartrate has long been used in medicine under the name of **tartar emetic.** The antimonyl ion gives only a very small concentration of Sb^{+++}.

The trioxide dissolves in alkalies, forming salts of **antimonous acid.** The sodium metaantimonite, $NaSbO_2 \cdot 3H_2O$, may be crystallized from the solution in sodium hydroxide. Salts of the ortho- and pyro-acids are also known.

The **tetroxide** is acidic in properties, dissolving in alkalies, but not acids. Two **hypoantimonates** occur as minerals, $CaSb_2O_5$ and $CuSb_2O_5$.

Antimony pentoxide, like the corresponding oxide of arsenic, may be prepared by the action of nitric acid upon the trioxide. Antimonic acid appears to have the formula $HSb(OH)_6$. The oxide and acid are only slightly soluble in water, but they dissolve easily in alkali. The so-called potassium acid pyroantimonate, probably $KSb(OH)_6$, is very soluble in water, but the corresponding sodium compound is the least soluble of all sodium salts, and is sometimes employed as a test for sodium. As the solubility is about 0.03 g. per liter, the test is not delicate. The acid is a good oxidizing agent:

$$SbO^+ + 5H_2O = HSb(OH)_6 + 3H^+ + 2e^-; ca - 0.7 \text{ volt}$$

59. Bismuth Oxides, Hydroxides, and Acids.—Bismuth monoxide is prepared by heating basic bismuth oxalate: $(BiO)_2C_2O_4 = 2BiO + 2CO_2$. It is readily oxidized to the **sesquioxide.** The latter oxide occurs in nature, and may be formed upon heating the metal in air. It has a yellow color, a comparatively high melting point, and exists in several crystalline modifications. This oxide is not soluble in bases but dissolves in acids, and normal salts may be obtained by evaporating the acid solutions. When treated with water in the absence of acid, these salts are hydrolyzed to basic compounds, e.g., **basic nitrate** (also called subnitrate), $Bi(OH)_2NO_3$, **basic sulfate**, $(BiO)_2SO_4$, and **oxychloride**, $BiOCl$. A **basic carbonate** is known, and this and also the basic nitrate, are employed in medicine in the treatment of infections of the alimentary canal. The **hydroxide**, $BiOOH$, is precipitated from the salt solutions by alkalies. It is not soluble in excess of the reagent.

The hydrolysis of Bi^{+++} gives some bismuthylion, BiO^+, but complex ions such as Bi_2O^{+4} and $Bi_3O_2^{+5}$ may also be present. Bismuthyl ion is readily reduced to the metal (cf. Par. **65**).

60. Bismuth pentoxide, Bi_2O_5, is formed by the action of very strong oxidizing agents upon the trioxide, e.g. $NaClO$ in weakly alkaline solution. It is comparatively non-reactive. In concentrated sodium hydroxide it forms **sodium bismuthate**, $NaBiO_3$. In water or acid, this compound hydrolyzes to the acid, which is a very powerful oxidizing agent:

$$BiO^+ + 2H_2O = HBiO_3 + 3H^+ + 2e^-; ca - 1.6 \text{ volts}$$

The acid will even oxidize manganous ion to permanganate in acid solution. Orthobismuthates are not known, although a tetroxide, Bi_2O_4, which is formed along with the pentoxide by the action of chlorine in alkaline solution upon the trioxide, is considered to be bismuth orthobismuthate, $Bi(BiO_4)$.

61. Halogen Compounds.—The various halogen compounds are summarized on page 238.

The halides may, in general, be prepared by the direct action of the elements. The compounds, AsX_3, SbX_3, and BiX_3, may also be prepared by treating the corresponding oxide with the concentrated halogen acid. The relatively unstable PCl_2 is formed by passing an electric spark through mixtures of PCl_3 vapor and hydrogen.

TABLE XVII

HALIDES OF PHOSPHORUS, ARSENIC, ANTIMONY, AND BISMUTH

X = any halogen

P	As	Sb	Bi
P_2Cl_4, P_2I_4	AsI_2		BiCl
PX_3	AsX_3	SbX_3	$BiCl_2$, $BiBr_2$
		$SbCl_4$ in Rb_2SbCl_6	BiX_3
PX_5 (except I)	AsF_5	SbX_5 (except I)	$BiCl_4$
			BiF_5

The salt-like nature of the compounds increases with the increasing size of the elements of the group; thus phosphorus trichloride is a non-conductor of electricity, while molten bismuth trichloride conducts readily. The halides are hydrolyzed by water, e.g., $PCl_5 + 4H_2O = H_3PO_4 + 5HCl$. Often an oxyhalide forms as the first step, e.g., $POCl_3$, SbOCl, and BiOCl. The more basic the oxide, the less is the tendency of the halide toward hydrolysis: thus the hydrolysis of antimony and bismuth trichloride at ordinary temperatures stops at the oxychloride, and the reaction is readily reversed by acid. On account of its ready hydrolysis, phosphorus trichloride is used extensively in organic chemistry to replace hydroxide by chloride, e.g. $3CH_3CO \cdot OH + PCl_3 = 3CH_3COCl + H_3PO_3$. Antimony trichloride early received the name of **butter of antimony** and was employed for medicinal purposes. It was prepared by the reaction: $Sb_2S_3 + 3HgCl_2 = 3HgS + 2SbCl_3$. Bismuth triiodide is soluble in excess iodide, forming salts of the complex iodide BiI_4^-. The antimony tetrachloride is known only in complex salts.

62. Sulfides.—The following sulfides are known:

P	As	Sb	Bi
P_4S_3	AsS		BiS
	As_2S_3	Sb_2S_3	Bi_2S_3
		Sb_2S_4	
P_4S_{10}	As_2S_5	Sb_2S_5	
P_4S_5, P_4S_7			

The **sulfides** of **phosphorus** may be prepared by heating together the elements in equivalent amounts. Only two of the compounds, P_4S_{10} and P_4S_3, are important. The pentasulfide is used as a reagent in organic chemistry. The trisulfide, P_4S_3, has been mentioned in connection with the manufacture of matches. P_4S_{10} reacts with BiF_3 to form the sulfofluoride PSF_3.

Arsenic monosulfide, AsS, occurs as the mineral **realgar.** It may be formed by heating together the elements, or by the reaction: $FeS_2 + FeSAs = 2FeS + AsS$. The yellow trisulfide, As_2S_3, also occurs as a mineral, **orpiment.** It is precipitated from solutions of arsenites by hydrogen sulfide. With pure arsenious acid, the precipitate is colloidal, but is coagulated by hydrogen ion or other positive ions. The sulfide is not soluble in concentrated hydrochloric acid. The sulfide is acidic in nature and dissolves in excess sulfide ion, forming **thioarsenite:** $As_2S_3 + 3S^{--} = 2AsS_3^{---}$. In polysulfide, it is oxidized to **thioarsenate:** $As_2S_3 + 2S_2^{--} + S^{--} = 2AsS_4^{---}$. The yellow trisulfide changes to a red form at 170°. The pentasulfide, As_2S_5, is formed by passing hydrogen sulfide into an acid solution of an arsenate. It is soluble in sulfide ion, forming the thioarsenate: $As_2S_5 + 3S^{--} = 2AsS_4^{---}$, and is reprecipitated from this compound by acid. The sulfide is not very stable and decomposes rather easily into the trisulfide and sulfur.

The mineral **stibnite,** Sb_2S_3, is black, but the antimony trisulfide, precipitated from solutions of the trichloride or antimonites, is orange red. It is soluble in concentrated hydrochloric acid, but not in dilute. It dissolves in sulfide and polysulfide, forming **thioantimonites** and **thioantimonates,** similar to arsenic trisulfide. When the thioantimonates are acidified, the **tetrasulfide** and sulfur are precipitated: $2SbS_4^{---} + 6H^+ = Sb_2S_4 + S + 3H_2S$. The tetrasulfide forms a mixture of thioantimonite and thioantimonate with excess sulfide ion, and is soluble in concentrated acid.

Black **bismuth sesquisulfide** is formed by heating together the element or by the action of hydrogen sulfide upon bismuth salts. It is not soluble in dilute hydrogen ion, but is dissolved by hot dilute nitric acid with the oxidation of the sulfur. It is not soluble in sulfide or polysulfide.

63. Metal Compounds.—Phosphides may be prepared (1) by heating together phosphorus and the finely divided metal or, (2) metal oxide; or by the action of (3) phosphorus, or (4) phosphine upon solutions of metal salts. Examples of (1) are Hg_3P_4, MnP_2, Sn_3P (used in phosphor bronze), K_2P_5, PbP_5; (2) Ca_3P_2; (3) Ag_3P, Cu_3P_2 and (4) Hg_3P_4, Cu_2P.

Arsenic unites with almost all metals at red heat, e.g., $CoAs_2$, $FeAs_2$, Fe_4As_3, $NiAs$, $MnAs$. Antimony forms a series of compounds with an apparent oxidation state -2, e.g., $CuSb$, $NiSb$, $ZnSb$, $PtSb_2$; and also compounds of the -3 state, e.g., Ag_3Sb, Mg_3Sb_2, Cd_3Sb_2, Fe_3Sb_2. Bismuth also forms a number of metal compounds, e.g., Mg_3Bi, although not so many as antimony.

ANALYTICAL

64. Phosphorus compounds are usually detected and determined as phosphate, since nitric acid readily oxidizes all of the lower states to this ion. In the absence of heavy metals whose phosphates are insoluble in ammonia, the phosphates may be precipitated as magnesium ammonium phosphate, $MgNH_4PO_4$, by a solution of magnesium chloride, ammonium hydroxide, and ammonium chloride. In quantitative determinations, this is ignited and weighed as $Mg_2P_2O_7$. Ordinarily the phosphate is precipitated in dilute nitric acid as the ammonium phosphomolybdate: $H_3PO_4 + 12(NH_4)_2MoO_4 + 21HNO_3 = (NH_3)_2PO_4 \cdot 12MoO_3 + 21NH_4NO_3 + 12H_2O$. This precipitate is usually not weighed as such but is (1) dissolved in ammonium hydroxide and the phosphate reprecipitated as $MgNH_4PO_4$ or (2) titrated with standard hydroxide: $(NH_4)_3PO_4 \cdot 12MoO_3$

$\llcorner 23OH^- = HPO_4^{--} + 3NH_4^+ + 12MoO_4^{--} + 11H_2O$.
A colorimetric determination of phosphate is based upon
the fact that the MoO_3 in the phosphomolybdate is reduced
to molybdenum blue much more readily than is a solution
of molybdic acid. The reducing agent employed is benzi-
dine or stannous chloride. Advantage may be taken of the
slight solubility of bismuth phosphate, $BiPO_4$, to remove
phosphate from acid solution. This is desirable in qualitative analysis since the presence of phosphate results in the
precipitation of many slightly soluble compounds, e.g.,
$CaHPO_4$, when NH_4OH is added.

Arsenic, antimony, and bismuth are usually detected by
precipitation as sulfides in dilute acid solution. The properties of these compounds have been discussed, and the systematic scheme of separation (Append. VI) should also be
consulted for the outline of the analysis. Arsenic is sometimes determined quantitatively as the ammonium ar-
senomolybdate similar to phosphate given above. It is more
often determined by the oxidation of arsenite to arsenate in
the presence of bicarbonate by iodine. Antimony may
likewise be determined by the oxidation of antimonite to antimonate by iodine in alkaline solution, or better by the
reduction of antimonic acid by iodide in acid solution. Bismuth may be precipitated and weighed as the oxychloride,
BiOCl, or precipitated as the hydroxide and weighed as the
trioxide.

Small quantities of arsenic and antimony are determined
by the **Marsh test,** in which arsine and stibine are formed
by reduction with zinc in hydrochloric acid, and the mixture
of the gases with hydrogen passed into silver nitrate solution. Any antimony present is precipitated as silver antimonide, while the arsine is oxidized to arsenious acid. Upon
filtering, the arsenic is confirmed in the filtrate by repre-
cipitation as sulfide, while the antimony in the precipitate
is dissolved in hot concentrated tartaric acid and then reprecipitated as the sulfide. The test for arsenic may be modi-

fied by first separating the arsenic from the antimony by volatilizing the former as $AsCl_3$ from a hydrochloric acid solution, and then, after reduction with zinc, detecting the arsine by placing a strip of paper wet with copper sulfate solution in the stream of gas. From the depth of color of the copper arsenide formed on the paper, the quantity of arsenic may be estimated. The method is capable of detecting 0.001 milligram of arsenic.

65. Potential diagrams.—For comparison of the group properties the following potential diagrams are given for acid solution:

-3	0	$+3$	$+4$	$+5$

$$\overset{-0.27}{NH_4^+ \underline{\qquad}} \overset{-1.44}{N_2 \underline{\qquad}} \overset{-1.07}{HNO_2 \underline{\qquad}} \overset{-0.81}{N_2O_4 \underline{\qquad}} NO_3^-$$
$$|\underline{\qquad -0.94 \qquad}|$$

$$\overset{0.06}{PH_3 \underline{\qquad}} \overset{0.49}{P \underline{\qquad}} \overset{(-0.40)}{H_3PO_3 \underline{\qquad}} \overset{(0.9)}{H_2PO_3 \underline{\qquad}} H_3PO_4$$
$$|\underline{\qquad 0.30 \qquad}|$$

$$\overset{0.54}{AsH_3 \underline{\qquad}} \overset{-0.247}{As \underline{\qquad}} \overset{-0.56}{H_3AsO_3 \underline{\qquad}} H_3AsO_4$$

$$\overset{0.51}{SbH_3 \underline{\qquad}} \overset{-0.212}{Sb \underline{\qquad}} \overset{-0.68}{SbO^+ \underline{\qquad}} \overset{-0.5}{Sb_2O_4 \underline{\qquad}} Sb_2O_5$$
$$|\underline{\qquad -0.58 \qquad}|$$

$$\overset{(0.8)}{BiH_3 \underline{\qquad}} \overset{-0.32}{Bi \underline{\qquad}} \overset{(-1.6)}{BiO^+ \underline{\qquad}} \overset{(-1.6)}{Bi_2O_4 \underline{\qquad}} HBiO_3$$
$$|\underline{\qquad (-1.6) \qquad}|$$

Chapter XII

GROUP VI. SULFUR, SELENIUM, TELLURIUM AND POLONIUM

1. The relation of the three elements, sulfur, selenium, and tellurium to oxygen has been discussed in Chapter **II.** The outstanding characteristics of these elements is the six valence electrons and the tendency to add two more electrons to complete the octet. Thus the members of the group all form compounds with the electropositive elements, in which they exhibit an oxidation state of minus two, and with the more electronegative elements compounds in which the oxidation state varies from one to six, the most important of these being the $+ 4$ and the $+ 6$ states. The elements are all solids with relatively low melting points. Sulfur is distinctly a non-metal, but selenium and tellurium, especially the latter, show certain metallic properties. A marked characteristic of the group is the existence of a number of allotropic modifications. In addition to these three elements, the extremely rare, unstable, and highly radioactive element, polonium, belongs to this group. The few known facts relating to its chemical behavior are given in Par. **35.**

2. Occurrence.—The amount of sulfur in the earth's crust is estimated at 0.1 per cent. Most of this occurs primarily as iron sulfide, but oxidation has given rise to large deposits of sulfate, chiefly of calcium and magnesium. The sulfides of all the heavy metals, except gold and platinum, occur as minerals, the most extensive deposits being those of iron pyrites, FeS_2. Free sulfur occurs in numerous

TABLE I

ATOMIC AND PHYSICAL PROPERTIES

	S	Se	Te
Atomic number............	16	34	52
Atomic weight............	32.06	78.96	127.61
Isotopes.................	32, 33, 34, 36	74, 76, 77, 78, 80, 82	120, 122, 123, 124, 125, 126, 128, 130
Density..................	R 2.07	G 4.80	6.24
	M 1.96	R 4.50	
Melting point, ° C.........	114.5	217.4	456
Boiling point, ° C.........	444.6	684.8	1,087
Size of X^{--} in crystals, cm. $\times 10^8$..................	1.84	1.98	2.21
Heat of fusion cal.........	350	1,660	4,200
Heat of vaporization X_{liquid} $= X_2$ cal...............	29,100	29,500	24,000
X_2 (gas) $= X$ (gas) cal......	83,000	62,300	53,100
Entropy X_2 gas 298.1° K....	54.42	60.3	64.1
Ionization potential, volts ..	10.36	9.75	9.01

deposits, of special importance being those in Louisiana and Texas, and in Sicily.

Selenium and tellurium are much less abundant than sulfur, the estimated percentage in the igneous rocks being 10^{-8} and 10^{-9} respectively. The former occurs in the free state in most of the sulfur deposits, as selenides of many of the heavy metals, especially copper, silver, and lead; and less frequently selenites of copper, lead, cobalt, and other metals. Tellurium occurs chiefly as tellurides of copper, lead, silver, gold, iron, or bismuth. Tellurites and free tellurium are of rare occurrence.

THE FREE ELEMENTS

3. Sulfur.—Sulfur vapor at the boiling point has a molecular weight of 230 and is mostly S_8, with some S_6 and S_2. At 1000° it is largely S_2 and at 2000° is about half dissociated into atomic sulfur. This tendency of sulfur to form complexes is a common characteristic of the group and may be attributed to the readiness with which a sulfur atom, $\overset{\cdot\cdot}{\underset{\circ\bullet}{S}}:,$

will share its electrons with other sulfur atoms in an effort
to complete the octet. Liquid sulfur contains two molec-
ular species called S_λ and S_μ (probably S_8 and S_6), and
possibly one or two others. The
structure of S_8 is an eight membered
ring with the $S-S-S$ angle of $105°$.
The S_6 is probably irregular chains.
At $120°$ the equilibrium liquid contains 3.6 per cent S_μ and at the boiling point 35 per cent. The heat of
the transition is 416 calories. Such an
equilibrium is probably not infrequent in liquids but the unusual fea-

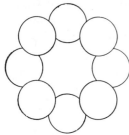

FIG. 1. Molecule of
rhombic sulfur, S_8.

ture with sulfur is the slowness with which the equilibrium
state is reached. The time required is still further increased
by the presence of traces of iodine or sulfuric acid, but is
decreased by ammonia. Near the melting point sulfur
is a light yellow mobile liquid; as the temperature is increased it becomes darker and more viscous with increasing
content of S_μ. The viscosity reaches a maximum around
200°, and falls off rapidly
as the boiling point is ap-
proached.

Solid sulfur exists in two
crystalline forms, rhombic
and monoclinic, Fig. 2.
There have been prepared,
also, two other monoclinic,
one triclinic and one rhombohedral form, but they are
unstable with respect to the

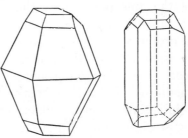

FIG. 2. Crystal forms of sulfur; sulfur rhombic (left) and sulfur monoclinic
(right).

common forms. There are also a number of amorphous and
colloidal forms whose characteristics doubtless depend
chiefly upon the degree of dispersion. Rhombic sulfur is in
equilibrium with monoclinic at 96° C. The reaction is rather
slow, however, and by rapidly cooling sulfur, held for some

time just above its melting point, the long needle-shaped monoclinic crystals may be obtained. At room temperature they are transformed into rhombic in about a day. The heat of the transition is 70 cal. Rhombic sulfur melts at 112.8°, in equilibrium with S_λ, and at 110.4° to form the equilibrium mixture $S_{\lambda\mu}$. Monoclinic sulfur melts at 119.2° to form S_λ and 114.5 to form $S_{\lambda\mu}$. Both forms are soluble in CS_2. At 25° the solubility of the monoclinic is 1.28 times that of the rhombic. The molecular form of the solute in both cases is S_8. By heating sulfur near its boiling point, and suddenly cooling, a very plastic substance is obtained which consists of a mixture of rhombic crystals and an amorphous form not soluble in carbon disulfide. The latter form is essentially the super-cooled liquid. After some time it becomes very hard. The rate of change of the amorphous into the rhombic form requires years at ordinary temperature, but is rapid at 90°. There is at least one other amorphous modification, this form being

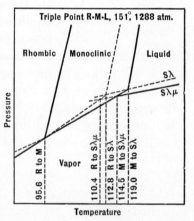

FIG. 3. Pressure-temperature diagram for sulfur; diagrammatic as actual vapor pressures are not known.

soluble in carbon bisulfide. Finely divided sulfur prepared by precipitating sulfur from calcium polysulfide by the addition of acid is known as **milk of sulfur,** and finely divided sulfur formed by sublimation is known as **flowers of sulfur.**

The various forms of sulfur are all non-conductors of electricity and are insoluble in water.

4. The salt domes of Louisiana and Texas have now supplanted the mines of Sicily as the world's most important source of sulfur. These enormous domes consist of a salt core covered with a cap of gypsum, dolomite, and limestone

in which the sulfur occurs. It is extracted by the ingenious
Frasch Process. Water heated to about 180° under pressure
is pumped down bore holes and forced into the deposits;
the sulfur is liquefied, and when a quantity of it collects at
the bottom of the cavity it is forced to the surface by an
air lift and discharged into bins. A small amount of sulfur
is obtained from the purification of illuminating gas (Par.
8). The production of sulfur in the United States in 1948
was 4,000,000 tons. The major portion of this is made into
sulfuric acid. Smaller amounts are consumed in the vulcanization of rubber, in the manufacture of sulfites and
thiosulfates, in bleaching dried fruit, and for dusting and
spraying plants.

Sulfur is both a fairly good reducing agent and oxidizing
agent. It combines directly with all of the elements except
gold, platinum, and the inert gases.

5. Selenium.—Selenium vapor at the boiling point consists of mixtures of $Se_8 - Se_2$. The liquid also doubtless
contains a number of molecular complexes but the problem
has not been carefully investigated. The solid exists in
three crystalline modifications, two of them rather similar
monoclinic forms, red in color, soluble in carbon disulfide,
and unstable with respect to the third form, a hexagonal
rhombohedral structure known as metallic or grey selenium.
The monoclinic forms are relatively stable below 100° and
melt somewhat below 200°, the exact temperature being in
doubt due to their rapid transformation, upon heating, into
the grey form. The latter form melts at 220° and is insoluble
in carbon bisulfide. Like sulfur, there is an amorphous
modification, vitreous and black in color, which may be
prepared by quickly cooling the liquid. Reduction of selenates results in the formation of two red modifications, one
crystalline and the other amorphous. A number of colloidal
forms of selenium have been prepared.

The electrical conductivity of the grey form is poor, but
is greatly increased by light. This property makes selenium

useful in the construction of apparatus for the measurement of light intensity, as in photometers for measuring the intensity of radiation coming from the stars, and for the automatic turning of lights on and off at night and morning, respectively.

Large quantities of selenium could be recovered from the flues of the sulfur burners in sulfuric acid plants, and from the anode mud of electrolytic copper refineries. The free element has no extensive commercial applications. The largest consumption is in the glass works for making ruby red glass, and to neutralize the green color of glass, due to the presence of ferrous silicate. Some selenium is used in place of sulfur in the vulcanizing of certain types of rubber goods, and a small amount of selenium is added to copper alloys and stainless steel to make them more machinable.

The reactions of selenium are similar to those of sulfur, but the element is both a poorer reducing agent and a poorer oxidizing agent than sulfur, cf. Table II and Par. **13.**

6. Tellurium.—The vapor of tellurium at the boiling point contains a much smaller per cent of the higher molecular complexes than in the case of sulfur and selenium, being mostly Te_2. The solid crystallizes in a silver white, semi-metallic, rhombohedral form, isomorphic with grey selenium, and in a second modification as yet little known. It may be precipitated in an amorphous modification by reduction and like the other members of the group readily forms various colloidal solutions. The amorphous form changes to the crystalline extremely slowly at ordinary temperatures, but rapidly just below the melting point. The metallic modification is insoluble in carbon bisulfide. Its density is 6.24. It is the poorest electrical conductor of any of the metals, specific resistivity being 2×10^{-1} ohm-cm. Tellurium with an atomic number of 52 has a higher atomic weight than iodine, atomic number 53. This situation arises through a preponderance of the heavier isotopes of tellurium. Fairly large quantities of tellurium could be recovered from a number of metallurgical processes, especially the electrolytic copper refineries. Like selenium it imparts free-cutting properties to steel. A 0.05 per cent alloy with lead increases the corrosion resistance of that metal.

7. Hydrogen Compounds.—The compounds, H_2S, H_2Se, H_2Te, are much less polar liquids than water, as is indicated by their lower melting and boiling points. Their stability decreases and their power as reducing agents (Table II) increases with increasing atomic weight; that is, with increasing size of the atom, it becomes easier to pull off the two extra electrons. Hydrogen selenide and hydrogen telluride are endothermic. These compounds all possess very disagreeable odors and are extremely toxic.

TABLE II

HYDROGEN COMPOUNDS OF SULFUR GROUP

	H_2S	H_2Se	H_2Te
Melting point, ° C.	− 85.4	− 64	− 48
Boiling point, ° C.	− 60.3	− 41.3	− 2.2
$H_2 + X = H_2S$ (gas); kcal	+ 5.3	− 18.5	− 34
H_2X (gas) $= X + 2H^+ + 2e^-$, in volts	− 0.14	+ 0.35	+ 0 69
$H_2X = H^+ + HX^- K_1$	1.15×10^{-7}	1.9×10^{-4}	2.3×10^{-3}
$HX^- = H^+ + X^{--} K_2$	1×10^{-15}	ca 10^{-10}	ca 10^{-5}
Solubility moles/liter (P = 760 mm)	0.102	0.034	< 0.08

8. Hydrogen Sulfide.—Hydrogen sulfide may be formed by passing hydrogen into boiling sulfur, but is usually prepared by the action of acid upon a sulfide, particularly ferrous sulfide: $FeS + 2H^+ = Fe^{++} + H_2S$. The gas is soluble in water at 20° and 1 atm. to the extent of 290 volumes per 100 volumes of water. The resulting concentration is about $0.1M$. In solution, it behaves as an extremely weak dibasic acid; the first ionization constant, $H_2S = H^+ = HS^-$, is 1.15×10^{-7}, and the second ionization constant, $HS^- = H^+ + S^{--}$, 1.0×10^{-15}. The soluble sulfides are, accordingly, highly hydrolyzed, $0.1N$ Na_2S containing about $0.085N$ OH^-. The acid sulfides or hydrosulfides, such as NaSH, are much less alkaline; $0.1N$ NaSH contains $0.001N$ OH^-. A saturated solution of H_2S in the presence of $10^{-4}M$ H^+ has a sulfide ion concentration of $10^{-15}M$, and at $0.3M$ H^+ the sulfide concentration is $10^{-22}M$. The concentration of sulfide in $1M$ $(NH_4)_2S$ is $10^{-6}M$.

The sulfides of nearly all the metals except those of the main groups I, II, and III are insoluble in water. Extensive use is made in qualitative analysis of the varying degrees of solubility of the sulfides. Due to the weakness of hydrogen sulfide, the solubility of all sulfides is increased in acid. However, certain of the sulfides are so extremely insoluble that even large concentrations of hydrogen ion do not increase the solubility sufficiently to dissolve them in appreciable amounts. In general practice the metal sulfides are divided into two groups: (1) those precipitated in $0.3N$ H^+ by H_2S, and (2) those not precipitated under these conditions. For details of the classification and separation, reference may be made to the general scheme of analysis, Appendix VI.

Hydrogen sulfide burns in excess of air to form sulfur dioxide and water. In a limited amount of air, the free element is formed, as the dioxide and hydrogen sulfide react according to the equation: $2H_2S + SO_2 = 3S + 2H_2O$. Advantage is taken of the oxidation in a limited quantity of air to remove hydrogen sulfide from illuminating gas, where it is objectionable because of its odor and the corrosive nature of its combustion products, the process being carried out by admitting a small amount of oxygen and heating the mixture. The sulfur precipitated by the reaction is sold as a by-product.

Hydrogen sulfide tarnishes the surface of even such a noble metal as silver: $2Ag + H_2S = Ag_2S + H_2$. The action of hydrogen sulfide here as an oxidizing agent with the liberation of hydrogen is, of course, due to the great stability of silver sulfide. The absorption of sulfur by the alkaline sulfides is discussed later under the polysulfides (par. 26).

9. Hydrogen Selenide and Telluride.—The direct combination of hydrogen with selenium and tellurium shows less tendency to take place than with sulfur: however, the reactions do proceed to some extent at high temperatures. The compounds can be prepared, respectively, by the action of acid upon iron selenide or upon magnesium or aluminum telluride. They are gases with very disagreeable odors, and dissolve in water to form dibasic acids, probably slightly stronger than hydrogen sulfide. The selenides and tellurides of the heavy non-alkali metals are insoluble in water. Hydrogen telluride decomposes above $0°$.

10. Oxides.—Sulfur forms the oxides SO, S_2O_3, SO_2, SO_3, and SO_4; selenium SeO_2 and SeO_3 (unstable); and tellurium TeO, TeO_2, and TeO_3. The slight tendency of selenium to form oxides is interesting in connection with the same characteristic of bromine, which occupies a position but one atomic number higher than selenium (cf. **X—12**). The heat of formation of selenium $_{\bullet}$dioxide is also less than either of the others, the values in kcals. being: SO_2(gas) 71, SeO_2(solid) 56, and TeO_2(solid) 77.6.

11. SO and S_2O_3.—Sulfur reacts with concentrated sulfuric acid or with the trioxide to form the unstable solid sesquioxide, S_2O_3. It is not an acid anhydride, although its oxidation state corresponds to the hyposulfurous acid, $H_2S_2O_4$. When a mixture of SO_2 and sulfur vapor is subjected to an electrical discharge SO gas is formed. It is highly unstable. It reacts with water. $3SO + H_2O = H_2S_2O_4 + S$.

12. Sulfur Dioxide and Sulfurous Acid.—Sulfur dioxide is a gas condensing to a liquid at $-10°$. It is formed by the oxidation of sulfur or sulfides, and by the reduction of sulfuric acid: $S + O_2 = SO_2$; $4FeS_2 + 11O_2 = 2Fe_2O_3 + 8SO_2$; $2H_2SO_4 + Cu = CuSO_4 + SO_2 + 2H_2O$. Due to the instability of sulfurous acid, the gas is liberated by the action of strong acids upon sulfites: $Na_2SO_3 + H_2SO_4 = Na_2SO_4 + SO_2 + H_2O$. The gas is, however, moderately soluble in water, 50 volumes per unit volume of water at 20° and 1 atmosphere, forming sulfurous acid in solution. In terms of the electron structures, this reaction is:

$$: \overset{\cdot\cdot}{\underset{\cdot\cdot}{O}} : \overset{\cdot\cdot}{\underset{\cdot\cdot}{S}} : \overset{\cdot\cdot}{\underset{\cdot\cdot}{O}} : + H : \overset{\cdot\cdot}{\underset{\cdot\cdot}{O}} : H = H : \overset{\cdot\cdot}{\underset{\cdot\cdot}{O}} : \overset{\cdot\cdot}{\underset{: \overset{\cdot\cdot}{\underset{\cdot\cdot}{O}} :}{S}} : \overset{\cdot\cdot}{\underset{\cdot\cdot}{O}} : H$$

Sulfurous acid is a rather weak dibasic acid, somewhat resembling carbonic acid. Its first ionization constant is 0.012 and the second 6.2×10^{-8}. Sulfurous acid is a fair oxidizing agent (Table III). It is unstable with respect to the decomposition: $3H_2SO_3 = 2SO_4^{--} + 4H^+ + S + H_2O$; 0.33 volt. This reaction is slow but takes place under the influence of violet light and upon heating. Its most important reaction, however, is its oxidation to sulfuric acid (Table III). Many of its industrial uses depend upon this action as a reducing agent.

TABLE III

OXIDATION-REDUCTION POTENTIALS OF SULFUROUS
AND SULFURIC ACIDS

	VOLTS $_{25}°$
$S + 3H_2O = H_2SO_3 + 4H^+ + 4e^-$	-0.45
$H_2SO_3 + H_2O = SO_4^{--} + 4H^+ + 2e^-$	-0.20

The alkali sulfites are but slightly hydrolyzed. The sulfites of many of the heavy metals are insoluble. The acid sulfites occur in two types, such as $NaHSO_3$ and $Na_2S_2O_5$, the latter being the anhydride of the former: $2HSO_3^- = S_2O_5^{--} + H_2O$.

At 20°, sulfur dioxide may be liquefied by a pressure of about 3 atmospheres. Because of its ease of liquefaction it is employed in refrigeration processes. The commercial product is usually sold as the liquid, in metal cylinders. Sulfurous acid has a powerful toxic action upon vegetable organisms, and thus finds many applications as a fungicide and as a preservative in the preparation of beverages and foods. Sulfurous acid and sulfites are used extensively as bleaching agents for silk and woolen textiles, straw hats, feathers, and dried fruits. Sulfites have a digesting action upon wood, tending to separate the fibers as well as bleaching them, and their largest use is probably in the pulp and paper industry.

13. Selenium Dioxide and Selenites.—The same general methods of preparing sulfur dioxide are applicable to selenium dioxide. This dioxide is a solid which sublimes without melting. It has a characteristic odor which is described as that of "rotten horse-radish." It dissolves in water to form weak selenious acid, H_2SeO_3. Upon evaporating the solution, the free acid separates, and upon further heating, decomposes to the oxide. The acid is a much more powerful oxidizing agent than sulfurous acid:

$$3H_2O + Se = H_2SeO_3 + 4H^+ + 4e^-, \ -0.74 \text{ volt}$$

It thus oxidizes sulfurous acid to sulfuric: $2H_2SO_3 + H_2SeO_3$ $= 4H^+ + 2SO_4^{--} + Se + H_2O$. The selenium first separates as a red transparent colloid. When a solution of selenious acid is boiled with hydrogen bromide, the volatile tetrabromide escapes. Some attempts have been made to use the selenites as insecticides in fruit orchards, but they are so extremely toxic that they damage the growing plants. The acid constants are: K_1, 2.4×10^{-3} and K_2, 5×10^{-9}.

14. Tellurium Dioxide and Tellurites.—Tellurium burns more readily than does selenium to form the dioxide. The dioxide is also formed by the action of other strong oxidizing agents upon the metal, and by reduction of tellurates. It does not unite readily with water but may be dissolved in alkali to form tellurites from which the slightly soluble acid may be obtained, upon acidifying, as a white solid. The oxide is somewhat soluble in acid, $TeO_2 + H^+ = TeO_2H^+$, $K = 8.9 \times 10^{-3}$. The acid may also be obtained by the oxidation of tellurium by nitric acid. Salts of the **"telluryl"**

radical, TeO^{++}, or even $Te_4O_7^{++}$ are known. With hydrogen iodide the acid forms the slightly soluble iodide, TeI_4. The acid forms a number of acid complexes of the general formula, $H_2TeO_3 \cdot nTeO_2$. The oxide (or acid) is a fair oxidizing agent but not so strong as selenous acid. $2H_2O + Te = TeO_2 + 4H^+ + 4e^-$, -0.53 volt. It is not easily oxidized to telluric acid. The dioxide forms, upon heating with tellurium, the **monoxide**, TeO. This oxide may also be formed by the hydrolysis of the chloride, $TeCl_2$.

15. Sulfur Trioxide and Sulfuric Acid.—Sulfur trioxide, SO_3, is a colorless liquid, freezing at $15°$ and boiling at $46°$. The solid soon changes from a transparent glassy form to the polymer, S_2O_6, an opaque mass of needle shaped crystals which can be sublimed without melting. The trioxide possesses a remarkable affinity for water, forming sulfuric acid:

$$:\!\ddot{O}\!: \quad H \qquad\qquad :\!\ddot{O}\!:$$
$$:\!\ddot{O}\!:\!\ddot{S} + :\!\ddot{O}\!:\!H = H:\!\ddot{O}\!:\!\ddot{S}:\!\ddot{O}\!:\!H$$
$$:\!\ddot{O}\!: \qquad\qquad :\!\ddot{O}\!:$$

This reaction takes place with a hissing sound resulting from the large quantity of heat evolved, 38 kcal. The trioxide dissolves in concentrated sulfuric acid, forming the bi- or pyrosulfuric acid, $H_2S_2O_7$, called "fuming sulfuric acid" or "oleum."

16. Contact Process.—Sulfur trioxide is formed by the action of oxygen (air) or other powerful oxidizing agents upon sulfur dioxide. The reaction, $SO_2 + \frac{1}{2}O_2 = SO_3$, has, at $25°$ and partial pressures of 1 atm., a potential of 0.35 volt. Like many direct oxidations by O_2, this reaction is extremely slow. However, the rate can be increased by certain surface catalysts, including ferric oxide, vanadium pentoxide, and metallic platinum, the latter two being very effective. This catalysis is the basis for the "contact process" for the manufacture of sulfuric acid. The efficiency of platinum as a catalyst increases with temperature, reaching a maximum about 500°, but the per cent of trioxide formed at equilibrium decreases at high temperature (Table IV).

TABLE IV

EQUILIBRIUM CONSTANTS FOR THE REACTION, $SO_2 + \frac{1}{2}O_2 = SO_3$

$t°C$.............	300	527	680	790	900
K.............	8×10^3	28	3.6	1	0.38

The reaction is generally carried out between 380 and 450° with excess air, under which conditions 97 to 99 per cent of the dioxide is converted into trioxide. The efficiency of the catalyst depends upon the extent of active surface. The platinum is obtained in a finely divided state by heating chlorplatinic acid, H_2PtCl_6, and is dispersed upon a base of asbestos fibers, magnesium sulfate, or silica gel. In recent years the cheaper vanadium pentoxide has replaced much of the platinum.

One of the factors in the successful operation of the process is the removal from the sulfur dioxide of all impurities which may "poison" the catalyst and render it inactive. It is particularly important to remove traces of solid sulfur, selenium dioxide, mercury, and compounds of phosphorus and arsenic. The sulfur trioxide formed by the reaction is more readily absorbed from the excess of oxygen by concentrated sulfuric acid than by water. The discovery of this curious fact aided materially in the development of the process. The explanation appears to be in the formation of a fog through the absorption of water vapor by the sulfur trioxide when water is used as the absorbing medium. The fog particles are small drops of sulfuric acid, and their thermal motion, compared with gas molecules, is very slow. With concentrated sulfuric acid, no fog is formed, and the rapidly moving sulfur trioxide molecules are more readily absorbed when the gas is bubbled through the acid. As the trioxide dissolves, water is added to keep the acid at any desired concentration, usually at about 98 per cent acid. One of the mechanical problems is the temperature control. Since the reaction liberates heat, the temperature is kept from becoming too high by means of heat interchange between the incoming and outgoing gases. The reaction is carried out in cast iron containers, iron being insoluble (passive) in concentrated sulfuric acid.

17. Lead Chamber Process.—Many industries employ dilute sulfuric acid of no high degree of purity. It is cheaper to make this type of acid by the action of oxygen and steam upon sulfur dioxide, using nitric oxide as a catalyst. This process is known as the lead chamber process, from the large lead-lined reaction chambers employed. The presence of steam increases the ease of oxidation of sulfur dioxide, $SO_2 + O_2 + H_2O = H_2SO_4$, 1.1 volts at 25° C., as compared to 0.35 volt for the oxides. Although the various steps involved in the action of the gases with the catalyst are apparently quite complicated, the net result is that the nitric oxide acts as an oxygen carrier:

$$NO + \tfrac{1}{2}O_2 = NO_2$$
$$NO_2 + SO_2 + H_2O = NO + H_2SO_4$$

The reaction is carried out in immense lead chambers of approximately 200,000 cu. ft. capacity. The sulfuric acid condenses and is drained off at the bottom of the chamber. The nitrogen oxides are recovered by passing the gas coming from the lead chamber through concentrated sulfuric acid. The probable reaction is: $N_2O_3 + 2H_2SO_4 = ONHSO_4 + H_2O$. This reaction is reversed upon dilution; the water and nitrosyl sulfonic acid, $ONHSO_4$, again forming sulfuric acid and nitrogen oxides. Advantage is taken of this reversal to restore the oxides of nitrogen to the system by diluting the nitrogen containing acid, and by passing the sulfur dioxide, which also aids in the reversal by removing NO_2, through the solution before entering the lead chambers. This is carried out in a large tower employing the counter current principle. Thus the nitrogen oxides are again restored to the chambers and at the same time the chamber acid is concentrated. The ordinary chamber acid is about 60 to 70 per cent sulfuric acid and large quantities are sold at these concentrations. Further concentration may be carried out by evaporating in lead pans until a concentration of 77 per cent is reached. Below this concentration the lead is not rapidly oxidized because of a protective layer of sulfate. Above this concentration, however, the sulfate is soluble, and the concentration process is usually continued in iron vessels. The use of silica and silicon iron containers for the further concentration is becoming more general.

Formerly a large fraction of the sulfur dioxide consumed in the manufacture of sulfuric acid in this country was made by roasting iron pyrites, FeS_2, but at present the major portion is made by burning sulfur. However, two thirds of the world's production of sulfuric acid is still made from pyrites. Some sulfur dioxide is utilized from the stacks of the copper, zinc, and lead smelters.

18. Properties of Sulfuric Acid.—The specific gravity of sulfuric acid solutions increases rapidly with concentration, becoming 1.85 for 100 per cent acid. The pure acid melts at 10.5°, but the melting point is greatly lowered by the presence of either water or sulfur trioxide. The boiling point is 270° at 755 mm., but is without special significance since the solution loses sulfur trioxide and changes in composition until the constant boiling mixture of 98.3 per cent sulfuric acid is reached at 338°. In addition to the compounds, $SO_3 \cdot H_2O$, (H_2SO_4) and $2SO_3 \cdot H_2O$, $(H_2S_2O_7)$, the freezing point curves, Fig. 4, indicate the hydrates, $SO_3 \cdot 2H_2O$, $SO_3 \cdot 3H_2O$, and $SO_3 \cdot 5H_2O$. The great stability of these hydrates renders sulfuric acid an excellent dehydrating agent. The concentrated acid will remove water from cellulose, $(C_6H_{10}O_5)_n$, and sugar, $C_{12}H_{22}O_{11}$, depositing carbon: $C_{12}H_{22}O_{11} = 12C + 11H_2O$. It, however, is not as powerful a dehydrating agent as phosphorus pentoxide, since this oxide will liberate sulfur trioxide from sulfuric acid: $P_2O_5 + H_2SO_4 = 2HPO_3 + SO_3$. The heat of solution of sulfuric acid in a large amount of water is 19.0 kcal. Sulfuric acid is dibasic; the second ionization is somewhat weak, the constant being 0.012 at 25° C. In $10M$ H_2SO_4 the percentage of SO_4^{--}, HSO_4^-, and H_2SO_4 are 2, 68 and 30 while pure sulfuric acid is 98 per cent H_2SO_4 and 2 per cent HSO_4^-. At molal concentrations the potential of the acid as an oxidizing agent is not very great (Table III), but the energy of concentration is so large that the oxidizing power of the concentrated acid becomes very strong, sufficient to dissolve copper or silver.

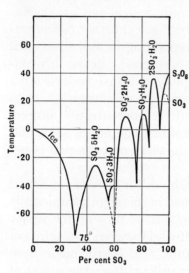

Fig. 4. The system sulfur trioxide and water.

TABLE V

CONSUMPTION OF SULFURIC ACID IN U. S. IN 1946
(Tons of 100% Acid)

Fertilizers	3,020,000
Metallurgical	755,000
Petroleum	1,000,000
Chemicals	1,780,000
Coal products	510,000
Paints and pigments	550,000
Rayon and cellulose	556,000
Explosives	105,000
Textiles	75,000

19. Applications of Sulfuric Acid.—The distribution of H_2SO_4 among the more important consuming industries is given in Table V. Sulfuric acid has played a leading role in the industrial development of the past century, due to its low cost of production and various useful chemical properties. The **high boiling point** accounts for its use in displacing more volatile acids such as hydrochloric, hydrofluoric, and nitric acids from their salts. As a **strong acid,** it is used to convert calcium phosphate to acid phosphate for fertilizer, to dissolve base metals and oxides, to clean metal surfaces prior to galvanizing and tinning, and to neutralize ammonia in its recovery from coke ovens and the packing industries. As a **dehydrating agent,** it plays an essential role in the manufacture of explosives, celluloid, pyroxaline, varnishes, ether, etc. The nitration process liberates water which is removed by the sulfuric acid thus allowing the reaction to go to completion. Many of its applications depend upon the **oxidizing power** of the concentrated acid, e.g. in removing tars and organic sulfides from petroleum. The **insolubility of many sulfates** is another factor of industrial importance, as in the manufacture of the important pigment, lithophone, a mixture of barium sulfate and zinc sulfide.

Pyrosulfuric acid, $H_2S_2O_7$, is used when the acid in its most powerful oxidizing and dehydrating form is desired. It was employed during the Great War to form "smoke screens," since it forms a very stable mist or fog composed of tiny drops of sulfuric acid.

20. Sulfates.—As a dibasic acid, sulfuric acid forms both neutral and acid salts. The acid salts may be dehydrated to form the pyrosulfates: $2NaHSO_4 = Na_2S_2O_7 + H_2O$. The normal salts of the alkali and alkaline earth metals and lead do not readily decompose upon heating, but the sulfates of the nobler metals evolve sulfur trioxide, or sulfur dioxide and oxygen if the decomposition temperature is high. The decomposition of ferric sulfate was once an important method of preparing sulfur trioxide and sulfuric acid. Sulfates are reduced by heating with carbon to form the sulfide: $Na_2SO_4 + 2C = Na_2S + 2CO_2$. Barium and lead sulfates are among the more important insoluble sulfates (Par. **32**). Though insoluble in dilute acids, their solubility is increased in concentrated sulfuric acid by the slight weakness of the HSO_4^- ion. Many of the solid sulfates crystallize with an odd number of water molecules, e.g., $CuSO_4 \cdot 5H_2O$. In this example four water molecules are attached to the copper and the fifth is attached to the

sulfate by hydrogen bonds,

$$
\begin{array}{ccc}
O & \diagdown \quad \diagup & O{-}H \\
 & S & \diagdown \\
O & \diagup \quad \diagdown & O{-}H
\end{array} \quad O.
$$

21. Selenic Acid.—Rather powerful oxidizing agents, such as PbO_2 or Cl_2, are required to oxidize selenous to selenic acid, even in dilute solution:

$$H_2O + H_2SeO_3 = SeO_4^{--} + 4H^+ + 2e^-, \; - 1.15 \text{ volts}$$

Conversely, selenic acid, when concentrated, is a very powerful oxidizing agent, liberating chlorine from chloride, and dissolving gold, but not platinum unless chloride is present. The reaction is, however, slow with many reducing agents, e.g. H_2S and SO_2, but is faster in the presence of chloride. The free acid is easily prepared by the action of bromine upon silver selenite: $Ag_2SeO_3 + H_2O + Br_2 = H_2SeO_4 + 2AgBr$. The pure acid melts at 58° and its concentrated solution is thick and sirupy. When dehydrated, it gives selenous oxide and oxygen. The solubilities of the selenates are similar to the sulfates. The soluble selenates are, however, easily distinguished from sulfates by their higher oxidizing power. In a high voltage discharge, selenium reacts with O_2 to form the very unstable SeO_3.

22. Tellurium Trioxide and Telluric Acid.—Telluric acid forms salts of the types Ag_6TeO_6 and Ag_2TeO_4. The acid, H_6TeO_6, is but sparingly soluble in water, and is but weakly acidic. Upon heating, it loses water to form H_2TeO_4 and then TeO_3. The trioxide does not react with water. The acid is a good oxidizing agent,

$$4H_2O + TeO_2(s) = H_6TeO_6(s) + 2H^+ + 2e^-, -1.02 \text{ volts}$$

The ability of tellurium to hold more than the customary four oxygen atoms, as is shown in H_6TeO_6, is interesting in connection with the same property of iodine and antimony, which occupy the neighboring position in the periodic table.

23. Other Sulfur Acids.—A very large number of complex acids of sulfur exist,

$$\begin{array}{ccc} \ddot{\ddot{O}} : \ddot{\ddot{O}} : & \ddot{\ddot{O}} : & \ddot{\ddot{S}} : \\ H : \ddot{O} : \ddot{S} : \ddot{S} : \ddot{O} : H & H : \ddot{O} : \ddot{S} : \ddot{O} : H & H : \ddot{S} : \ddot{S} : \ddot{S} : H \\ & \ddot{S} : & \ddot{S} : \end{array}$$

| Hyposulfurous acid | Thiosulfuric acid | Hydrogen polysulfide |

$$\begin{array}{ccc} \ddot{O} :: \ddot{O} : & \ddot{O} : \ddot{O} : & \ddot{O} : \ddot{O} : \\ H : \ddot{O} : \ddot{S} : \ddot{S} : \ddot{O} : H & H : \ddot{O} : \ddot{S} : \ddot{S} : \ddot{S} : \ddot{O} : H & H : \ddot{O} : \ddot{S} : \ddot{S} : \ddot{S} : \ddot{S} : \ddot{O} : H \\ \ddot{O} :: \ddot{O} : & \ddot{O} : \ddot{O} : & \ddot{O} : \ddot{O} : \end{array}$$

| Dithionic acid | Trithionic acid | Tetrathionic acid |

$$\begin{array}{cc} \ddot{O} : \quad \ddot{O} : & \ddot{O} : \\ H : \ddot{O} : \ddot{S} : \ddot{O} : \ddot{O} : \ddot{S} : \ddot{O} : H & H : \ddot{O} : \ddot{S} : \ddot{O} : \ddot{O} : H \\ \ddot{O} : \quad \ddot{O} : & \ddot{O} : \end{array}$$

| Peroxydisulfuric acid | Peroxymonosulfuric acid |

due to the ability of the sulfur atom to share electrons with oxygen and with other sulfur atoms, as is illustrated by the structural formulas of a number of these acids given above. The behavior of sulfur is somewhat comparable to carbon in this tendency to form molecules of high molecular weight with oxygen and hydrogen. A few of the more important acids will be discussed.

24. Hyposulfurous Acid.—The zinc salt of hyposulfurous acid is formed by the reduction of sulfurous acid by zinc: $2H_2SO_3 + Zn = ZnS_2O_4 + 2H_2O$. A solution of the sodium salt is prepared commercially from the zinc salt by the addition of sodium sulfite, as zinc sulfite is but moderately soluble. The salts are also prepared by the cathode reduction of bisulfite solution: $2H_2SO_3 + 2e^- = S_2O_4^{--} + 2H_2O$. The acid is too unstable to be prepared in the pure state. It is a very rapid reducing agent, reducing oxygen almost instantaneously, $2H_2O + HS_2O_4^- = 2H_2SO_3 + H^+ + 2e^-$, 0.23 volt. The sodium salt is employed commercially for the reduction of indigo to indigo white.

25. Thiosulfuric Acid.—Sulfites react with sulfur in alkaline solution to form thiosulfate: $SO_3^{--} + S = S_2O_3^{--}$. The free acid is unstable and the reaction is reversed by acid, sulfurous acid being formed and the sulfur precipitated. The reversal may be brought about even by weak acids: thus a sodium thiosulfate solution becomes turbid if exposed to the action of the carbonic acid of the air. The sulfur precipitated is amorphous and at first usually colloidal. The somewhat analogous oxidation of sulfide by sulfur in alkaline solution is discussed under the polysulfides. The product of that oxidation, SS_4^{--}, may be considered as the tetrathiosulfate.

Thiosulfate is oxidized ($2S_2O_3^{--} = S_4O_6^{--} + 2e^-, - 0.15$ volt) by iodine, ferric ion, and other moderately strong oxidizing agents to the tetrathionate. This extremely important reaction with iodine is discussed under that element (cf. **X—21**). More powerful oxidizing agents, such as chlorine and bromine, oxidize the thiosulfate to sulfate: $5H_2O + S_2O_3^{--} + 4Cl_2 = 2SO_4^{--} + 8Cl^- + 10H^+$. Thiosulfate forms complex ions and salts with many of the ions of the more noble metals, including Ag^+, Au^{+++}, Cu^+, Hg^{++}, Pb^{++}. Advantage is taken of this property in photography in the "fixing bath," to dissolve out the unchanged silver bromide.

Sodium thiosulfate, $Na_2S_2O_3 \cdot 5H_2O$, called **"hypo"** from the older name "hyposulfite," is of considerable commercial importance. Besides its use in photography, it is employed in the textile and paper industries as an "antichlor" to remove the excess chlorine used in bleaching, and in certain metallurgical processes. The very unstable sulfoxylic acid, H_2SO_2, has the same oxidation state as the average value for the sulfur in thiosulfate and decomposes to give the latter,

$$2H_2SO_2 = H_2S_2O_3 + H_2O$$

26. Polysulfides.—Soluble sulfides readily dissolve sulfur to form a series of compounds giving the ions, S_2^{--} to S_5^{--}. The alkaline solutions may be evaporated and the crystalline salts obtained, but the acids are unstable, forming hydrogen sulfide and free sulfur. These polysulfides act both as reducing and oxidizing agents. An example of the latter action is the oxidation of stannous sulfide to thiostannate. Calcium polysulfide, made by dissolving sulfur in lime, the product thereby containing some thionic salts, is used extensively as an insecticide for vineyards and orchards.

27. Thionic Acids.—The structural formulas of a number of acids of the type, $H_2S_nO_6$, have been indicated above. The subscript varies from 2 to 5. These acids are analogous to the peroxyacids. Thus tetrathionic acid may be prepared by the anodic oxidation of thiosulfate, $2HS_2O_3^- = H_2S_4O_6 + 2e^-$, similarly to the preparation of peroxydisulfuric acid, $H_2S_2O_8$, from sulfuric acid; and the structure of the tetrathionate differs from that of persulfate only by the substitution of sulfur for the peroxygen. Dithionate may be prepared by the anodic oxidation of sulfite, $2SO_3^{--} = S_2O_6^{--} + 2e^-$. Mixtures of the acids result from the interaction of sulfurous and hydrosulfuric acid in solution: $H_2S + 3SO_2 = H_2S_4O_6$; $2H_2S + 6SO_2 = H_2S_3O_6 + H_2S_5O_6$; $3H_2S + 9SO_2 = H_2S_2O_6 + 2H_2S_5O_6$. The gases themselves react to form sulfur and water. The various acids or salts are formed as intermediate products in many oxidation-reduction reactions involving sulfates and sulfites: thus, manganese dioxide reacts upon cold sulfurous acid to form manganese dithionate: $MnO_2 + 2H_2SO_3 = MnS_2O_6 + 2H_2O$. The acids are unstable in regard to decompositions giving sulfate, sulfite, and sulfur. The tetrathionate is the most important of these compounds. Its formation from thiosulfate by the action of iodine and ferric ion has been discussed.

28. Peroxysulfuric Acid.—Two important acids and an oxide of sulfur containing peroxyoxygen are known. The oxide, SO_4 or $SO_3 \cdot SO_4$, is formed in small amounts by an electrical discharge in a mixture of sulfur dioxide and oxygen: $SO_2 + O_2 = SO_4$. When dissolved in dilute sulfuric acid it does not give the ordinary peroxide reactions. Persulfuric acid, $H_2S_2O_8$ may be prepared by the reaction between cold concentrated sulfuric acid and concentrated hydrogen peroxide: $2H_2SO_4 + H_2O_2 = H_2S_2O_8 + 2H_2O$, or by the electrolysis of cold concentrated sulfuric acid: $2HSO_4^- = H_2S_2O_8 + 2e^-$. The sodium salt is prepared commercially by the electrolysis of concentrated solution of sodium acid sulfate. The sodium peroxydisulfate is but moderately soluble and crystallizes out. Peroxydisulfuric acid hydrolyzes in steps forming first the peroxymono-acid called **"Caro's acid,"** and this hydrolyzes to form sulfuric acid and hydrogen peroxide: $H_2S_2O_8 + H_2O = H_2SO_4 + H_2SO_5$; $H_2SO_5 + H_2O = H_2SO_4 + H_2O_2$. The mono-acid may be prepared by the electrolysis of cold moderately concentrated sulfuric acid. Both of the acids evolve oxygen readily, but their salts are fairly stable. The sodium peroxydisulfate is of considerable commercial importance as an oxidizing agent:

$$2SO_4^{--} = S_2O_8^{--} + 2e^-, \quad -2.05 \text{ volts}$$

In the presence of Ag^+ as a catalyst, manganous ion is oxidized to permanganate by the acid. The action of silver as a catalyst appears to involve the formation of AgO^+ and Ag^{++}.

29. Other Thio-acids.—Sulfur may be substituted for oxygen in a number of acid radicals similar to its substitution in the sulfate radical, provided the radical is not such a powerful oxidizing agent that the sulfur is rapidly oxidized to higher valences. For example, compounds are prepared in which the oxygen in phosphate is replaced by sulfur, forming the series, Na_3PO_3S to Na_3PS_4. The strong analogy between sulfur and oxygen is well illustrated by the reaction of barium sulfide and carbon disulfide to give barium thiocarbonate, $BaS + CS_2 = BaCS_3$, similar to the formation of barium carbonate from the two oxides. Mention should also be made of **thiocyanic acid,** HSCN, as many of the salts of that acid are of considerable importance (cf. **XIII—26**).

30. Sulfur Trioxide-ammonia Derivatives.—Sulfur trioxide and ammonia react to form **amidosulfonic acid** (**sulfamic acid**), NH_2SO_3H and amidodisulfonic acid, $NH(SO_3H)_2$. The former is also formed by heating urea with concentrated sulfuric acid. Sulfamic acid is used in the manufacture of dyes and cleaning compounds and in tanning. Its salts are valuable in flameproofing paper and textiles. **Sulfamide,** $SO_2(NH_2)_2$, is formed by the action of ammonia on sulfuryl chloride, SO_2Cl_2.

31. Other Acids of Selenium and Tellurium.—The tendency to form long chain complicated acids, and the tendency to substitute for oxygen, exhibited by sulfur in the thioacids, decrease with the heavier elements in the group. Both selenium and tellurium form salts of polyhydro acids, e.g. $NaSe_2$, $NaTe_3$. Selenium forms an unstable peroxyacid but tellurium does not. Selenium substitutes for oxygen in a number of acids and in many organic compounds, e.g., $NaSeCN$, sodium selenocyanate.

32. Halogen Compounds.—The halogens combine with the elements sulfur, selenium, and tellurium to form numerous compounds. These, together with a number of oxy-chlorides, compounds containing chlorine with oxygen and hydrogen, have been summarized in Table VI.

TABLE VI

HALIDE AND OXYHALIDES OF GROUP VI

	MELTING POINT ° C.	BOILING POINT ° C.		MELTING POINT ° C.	BOILING POINT ° C.
S_2F_2	− 120.5	− 38.4	S_2Br_2	− 46	decomp.
SF_4	− 124	− 40	$SeBr_2$	. . .	decomp.
S_2F_{10}	(− 53)	29	$SeBr_4$	. . .	. . .
SF_6	− 50.8	− 63.8	$TrBr_2$	280	339
SeF_4	− 13.5	93	SeI_2	. . .	. . .
SeF_6	− 34.6	− 46.6	TeI_2	. . .	. . .
TeF_4	. . .	. . .	SOF_2	− 110	− 30
Te_2F_{10}	− 14	60	$SOCl_2$	− 104.5	78.8
TeF_6	− 37.8	− 38.9	$SOBr_2$	− 50	137
S_2Cl_2	− 80	138	SO_2F_2	− 136.7	− 53.4
SCl_2	− 78	decomp.	SO_2ClF	− 124.7	7
SCL_4	− 31	decomp.	SO_2Cl_2	− 54.1	69.1
Se_2Cl_2	− 85	decomp.	$S_2O_5O_2$	− 37.5	153
$SeCl_2$	. . .	. . .	SOF_2	4.6	124
$SeCl_4$	. . .	191 Sub.	$SeOCl_2$	8.5	176
$TeCl_2$	175	324	$SeOBr_2$	41.7	. . .
$TeCl_4$	214	414			

In general, the halogen compounds hydrolyze with water to form the hydrogen halide and the acid of the positive element. The latter may, however, be unstable in respect to decomposition into compounds of higher and lower oxidation states. In some cases, as for example SF_6, the rate of hydrolysis is extremely slow.

The most important of these compounds is **sulfur mono-chloride,** S_2Cl_2. This is formed by the direct action of chlorine upon hot sulfur. It is a reddish yellow liquid and an excellent solvent for sulfur. For this reason, it is used in vulcanizing rubber. It is hydrolyzed by water: $2S_2Cl_2 + 2H_2O = SO_2 + 4HCl + 3S$. The other two chlorides may be formed by the action of chlorine upon cold mono-chloride, but are decomposed by gentle heating.

The compound S_2F_{10} is formed in small amounts together with SF_6 when sulfur is burned in fluorine. It is highly toxic while the SF_6 is essentially non-toxic. Iodine does not react with solid sulfur or selenium, but in a solution of ethylene bromide, iodine reacts with selenium to form both Se_2I_2 and SeI_4.

Sulfur dioxide reacts with chlorine, forming **sulfuryl chloride**, SO_2Cl_2. **Thionyl chloride**, $SOCl_2$, results from the reduction of phosphorus pentachloride by sulfur dioxide: $PCl_5 + SO_2 = SOCl_2 + POCl_3$. **Chlorsulfonic acid**, HSO_3Cl, is formed by the direct union of sulfur trioxide and hydrogen chloride. **Fluosulfonic** acid may be prepared by the analogous reactions or by the action of concentrated sulfuric acid upon calcium fluoride. It reacts with boric acid to form BF_3. The ammonium salt reacts with ammonia to form ammonium sulfamate, $NH_4SO_3NH_2$. **Pyrosulfuryl chloride**, $S_2O_5Cl_2$, is formed by the direct union of sulfur trioxide and sulfuryl chloride.

33. Selenium and Tellurium with Sulfur.—There appear to be no compounds containing selenium and sulfur only, and the two elements form several series of mixed crystals. The precipitate obtained by passing hydrogen sulfide into tellurous acid appears to be a mixture of the free elements and the sulfide TeS_2.

Concentrated sulfuric acid dissolves both selenium and tellurium with the formation of the compounds, $SeSO_3$ and $TeSO_3$, respectively, analogous to S_2O_3 (Par. **11**).

Selenium may be substituted for sulfur in certain of the complex sulfur acids, e.g. seleno sulfuric acid, H_2SSeO_3.

34. Analytical.—**Sulfur.** The free element may be recognized by the pungent odor of sulfur dioxide upon burning; or by dissolving in hot alkali solution and placing a drop of the solution on a silver coin, a black stain, Ag_2S, indicating the presence of sulfur. Sulfides are detected by the liberation of hydrogen sulfide by dilute acids, which may be recognized by its odor, or by its reaction with moist lead acetate paper. Sulfates are detected by the precipitation of barium sulfate, which is not soluble in dilute acids. Since sulfur in the lower valences is readily oxidized to sulfate, this also constitutes a general method for the detection and estimation of sulfur. Thus in quantitative analysis, sulfur is usually precipitated and weighed as barium sulfate. Due to the occlusion of soluble salts by the barium sulfate, it is difficult to obtain the precipitate pure. This error is decreased by precipitating from a large volume, since the occlusion is proportional to the concentration of the soluble salts, and also by digesting the precipitate for some time, which allows the more soluble small crystals to dissolve and slowly recrystallize out on the larger crystals. If precipitated from cold concentrated solution, barium sulfate is so finely dispersed that it cannot be retained by ordinary filter paper.

Selenium. The free element dissolves in concentrated sulfuric acid to form a green solution, $SeSO_3$. In the ordinary scheme of analyses, selenates are precipitated by hydrogen sulfide as elementary selenium, which is soluble in ammonium polysulfide. Red selenium is precipitated from cool selenous acid solution by strong reducing agents, hydroxylamine hydrochloride, NH_2OHHCl, being often employed. The precipitate turns black upon heating. A separation of selenium, arsenic, and germanium from the other elements may be made by distilling the material in solution with HBr and Br_2. The distillate consists of $SeBr_4$, H_3AsO_4, and $GeBr_4$.

In quantitative analysis, the selenium may be precipitated and weighed as the element, or determined volumetrically with oxidizing or reducing agents through the selenous-selenic acid couple.

Tellurium. Tellurium resembles selenium in its precipitation with hydrogen sulfide. The two elements may be separated by the hydrogen bromide treatment (cf. above) or by the reactions of the tetrapositive acids with iodide in dilute acid, selenium precipitating as the red element, and tellurium forming a back precipitate, TeI_4, soluble in excess iodide to give a red solution of TeI_6^{--}. Tellurium may be weighed quantitatively as the metal or the dioxide. Tellurous acid may be oxidized by permanganate quantitatively to telluric acid.

35. Polonium.—Isotopes of element number 84 occur in the various disintegration series (cf. **XXIII**). The name polonium was first given to the isotope of mass 210 in the uranium series which has a half-life of 138 days.

Polonium forms the hydrogen compound H_2P, but it is much less stable than the corresponding compound with the lighter elements of the family and is readily oxidized: $H_2Po = Po + 2H^+ + 2e^-$; > 1.0 volt. The ion Po^{++} appears to be stable in acid solutions although some authorities claim it is Po^{+++}. It is a moderately powerful oxidizing agent, $Po = Po^{++} + 2e$; $- 0.65$ volt. Metallic polonium plates out on a strip of tin placed in a solution of the $+ 2$ ion. Upon anodic oxidation the element is precipitated as the dioxide PoO_2, $Po^{++} + 2H_2O = PoO_2 + 4H^+ + 2e^-$; $ca - 0.8$ volt. Powerful oxidizing agents probably form PoO_3. The dioxide is somewhat acidic, dissolves in OH^- and forms salts, probably of the ion PoO_3^{--}. The complex chloride $PoCl_6^{--}$ also appears to be stable. Polonium is precipitated by hydrogen sulfide, probably as PoS.

36. Summary of Group Potentials.—The following potential diagrams are given to summarize the group.

$$\overset{-\ 1.23}{H_2O \text{———} O_2}$$

$$\overset{-\ 0.14}{H_2S \text{———} S} \overset{-\ 0.50}{\text{———} S_2O_3^{--}} \overset{-\ 0.38}{\text{———} H_2SO_3} \overset{-\ 0.20}{\text{———} SO_4^{--}}$$

$$\overset{0.35}{H_2Se \text{———} Se} \overset{-\ 0.74}{\text{———} H_2SeO_3} \overset{-\ 1.15}{\text{———} SeO_4^{--}}$$

$$\overset{0.69}{H_2Te \text{———} Te} \overset{-\ 0.53}{\text{———} TeO_{2(s)}} \overset{-\ 1.02}{\text{———} H_6TeO_{6(s)}}$$

$$\overset{>\ 1.0}{H_2Po \text{———} Po} \overset{ca\ -\ 0.65}{\text{———} Po^{++}} \overset{ca\ -\ 0.8}{\text{———} PoO_{2(s)}} \overset{-\ 1.3}{\text{———} PoO_{3(s)}}$$

Chapter XIII

CARBON

1. Several hundred thousand compounds of carbon are known, and the properties and reactions of these compounds constitute such a large portion of chemical knowledge that the whole of the science is now generally considered in respect to two great subdivisions, **organic chemistry** dealing with the carbon compounds, and **inorganic chemistry** dealing with the compounds of all the other elements.

It was once felt that the structure of the carbon compounds differed in some fundamental respect from that of the compounds of other elements, but it is now realized that their constitution can be correlated with the structure of the carbon atom and with the same general principles of compound formation which have been discussed in connection with the other periodic groups. This chapter will deal briefly with the structure of organic compounds in general and with the properties of the oxides and simpler carbon compounds. The relation of carbon to the other members of Group IV will be considered in the two subsequent chapters.

2. Structure of Carbon Compounds.—Carbon forms compounds in which the oxidation state varies from -4 to $+4$. However, the assignment of oxidation states in most of its compounds is so arbitrary as to be of little significance, that is, although we know the total number of valence electrons in the molecule, we are unable to say that a given number of electrons are definitely associated with a certain atom. The carbon atom, having four electrons, occupies a position intermediate to the elements which, on one side, lose their electrons to form positive ions, and on the other side add electrons to complete the octet and thus form negative ions. As a consequence of this position, it forms compounds in which it appears to complete the octet by sharing its electrons with other atoms. In terms of the idea that the pair of electrons constitutes a chemical bond, the behavior of carbon may be summarized by the statement: **carbon tends to form compounds in which it shares four pairs of electrons with the surrounding atoms.** The four bonds are arranged in tetrahedral symmetry, the carbon atom being at the center and the four attached atoms at the corners of the tetrahedron. As an illustration of this statement and of the non-polar character of the bonds, the electron formulas of the simple carbon, hydrogen, chlorine compounds are given below (cf. also Hildebrand, *Prin. of Chem.*, p. 90).

Oxidation State:

-4	-2	0	$+2$	$+4$
H	H	:Cl:	:Cl:	:Cl:
H : C : H	H : C : Cl :	H : C : Cl :	H : C : Cl :	:Cl : C : Cl :
H	H	H	:Cl :	:Cl :

This idea of the four bonds of carbon has been of the greatest importance in the development of organic chemistry, and it is customary to represent these bonds by lines, e.g.,

$$
\begin{array}{c}
\text{H} \\
| \\
\text{H--C--H} \\
| \\
\text{H}
\end{array}
$$

If one of the attached atoms is divalent, this is represented by drawing two bonds to it, e.g.,

$$\begin{array}{c} H \\ | \\ H-C=O \end{array}$$

All of the carbon bonds are non-polar in nature, and in general the bond energies are so large that dissociation into ions does not take place. The most important consequence of the non-polar bonds is the formation of long chain carbon molecules, e.g.,

$$\begin{array}{ccccc} H & H & H & H \\ | & | & | & | \\ H-C-&C-&C-&C-H \\ | & | & | & | \\ H & H & H & H \end{array}$$

and of complicated compounds of very high molecular weight containing hundreds of atoms. Such compounds constitute plant and animal tissues; from which fact, the term organic chemistry has arisen.

Several types of compounds are formed in which the concept of the four bonds can only be kept by placing two or more of them between adjacent carbon atoms, e.g.,

$$\begin{array}{cc} H & H \\ | & | \\ H-C=C-H \end{array} \quad \text{and} \quad H-C\equiv C-H$$

Such compounds are called "unsaturated." In terms of the "electron pairs" such compounds would be written as

$$\begin{array}{cc} \textbf{H} & \textbf{H} \\ \textbf{H:C::C:H} \end{array} \quad \text{and} \quad \textbf{H:C::C:H}$$

The tetrahedral picture postulates that, in the single bond two tetrahedra are attached by a corner, in the double bond by an edge and in the triple bond by a face. Bond angles have been determined for a number of unsaturated molecules and in most cases, the values are in approximate agreement with the tetrahedral structure.

The electron formulas preserve the idea that carbon always has four bonds, but other electron arrangements must at least be considered as possible, e.g.,

$$
\begin{array}{ccc}
\text{H} \quad \text{H} & & \text{H} \\
\text{H} : \overset{\cdot\cdot}{\underset{\cdot\cdot}{\text{C}}} : \overset{\cdot\cdot}{\underset{\cdot\cdot}{\text{C}}} : \text{H} & \text{and} & \overset{\cdot\cdot}{\text{C}} : \overset{\cdot\cdot}{\underset{\cdot\cdot}{\text{C}}} \\
& & \text{H}
\end{array}
$$

It will be observed that the fundamental difference between saturated and unsaturated carbon compounds is that the latter lack sufficient electrons to complete all of the octets, and there doubtless is resonance between the various electron structures so that no one formula can be written which completely represents the state of the molecule. In carbonates, such as calcium carbonate, $CaCO_3$, the solid is built up of a lattice of calcium and carbonate ions, and the carbonate ion has the three oxygen atoms arranged symmetrically about the carbon in the same plane:

$$
\begin{array}{c}
: \overset{\cdot\cdot}{\text{O}} : \\
: \overset{\cdot\cdot}{\text{O}} : \text{C} \\
: \overset{\cdot\cdot}{\underset{\cdot\cdot}{\text{O}}} :
\end{array}
$$

This is a definite example of a compound in which the carbon atom does not have tetrahedral symmetry and the idea of the four bonds can only be preserved by assuming a double bond between one oxygen and the carbon, and in order to give the observed triangular symmetry this double bond must resonate around the molecule.

3. Occurrence of Carbon.—Carbon occurs free in the crystalline forms of diamond and graphite. Coal is largely amorphous carbon, although it contains many complex compounds of carbon with hydrogen, as well as with oxygen and nitrogen. Methane, CH_4, is the principal constituent of natural gas; and heavier hydrocarbons constitute the mineral oils. The element is found most abundantly in the form of metal carbonates, limestone, or calcium carbonate, constituting one of the most common minerals. The occurrence of carbon in all animal and plant tissue has been mentioned.

4. Elementary Carbon.—Many of the physical properties of **diamond** and **graphite** may be correlated with their crystal structures. The diamond crystal is cubic and each carbon atom is surrounded by four other atoms located at the corners of a regular tetrahedron (Append. V). The four carbon valences are thus satisfied by carbon atoms, and the crystal is held together by bonds which are essentially the same as in the carbon compounds. As a result, diamond is the hardest known substance, and its melting point is probably higher than that of any other element. All of the electrons are doubtless held in the bonds between the atoms, and the crystal is, therefore, a nonconductor of electricity. Diamond has a very high index of refraction, 2.42; and this gives the cut gems a high brilliance, as most of the light falling upon them is totally reflected from the interior surfaces.

Graphite possesses hexagonal symmetry, and crystal structure data indicate planes of carbon atoms in hexagonal rings. Graphite is remarkably soft, and the crystal readily splits off thin flakes. The cleavage planes doubtless are identical with the planes of the carbon atoms of the crystal. Graphite is an electrical conductor, although only one thousandth as good as copper. This fact is in harmony with the crystal structure in that not all of the carbon bonds are satisfied, and some of the electrons are thus free to move through the crystal.

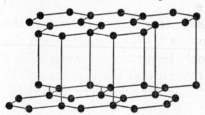

FIG. 1. Crystal structure of graphite.

All forms of carbon are somewhat volatile at 3500°, and the vapor, upon condensing, forms graphite. Although the experimental data are somewhat uncertain, the most reliable heats of combustion lead to the value: $C_D = C_G + 220$ cal.; and it may be calculated from this value that diamond at one atmosphere pressure is unstable at all temperatures in respect to graphite. However, diamond is denser than graphite and under 8000 atmospheres at 25° it would become the stable form. Experimentally, it is possible to convert diamond into graphite by heating. Moissan claimed to have prepared small diamonds by quenching solutions of carbon in molten metals. Naturally occurring diamonds have been crystallized from solutions of molten magnesium silicates under conditions of high pressure. Carbon is soluble in the basic silicates but if free SiO_2 is present, it oxidizes the carbon. This is the reason diamonds occur only in basic silicates.

The so-called **"amorphous carbon,"** such as **charcoal,** appears upon examination by X-rays to resemble graphite in structure, except that it is highly porous or cellular. Upon oxidation by hot nitric acid and potassium chlorate, both charcoal and graphite yield **mellitic acid,** $C_6(CO_2H)_6$, a derivative of benzene, thus indicating the ring structure of the carbon in these substances (Par. **16**). Charcoal possesses the property of absorbing gas, and, when cooled in liquid air, will absorb air from a sealed tube to produce a vacuum of 10^{-5} mm., or better. Highly active charcoal is used in gas masks for the absorption of poison vapors. The activation is carried out by heating for long periods in steam, which serves to remove adsorbed hydrocarbons from the surface. One cc. of active charcoal is said to have a surface of about 1,000 square meters. Bone charcoal is used in sugar refining to absorb coloring matter present in the crude sugar. Other amorphous forms of carbon are lamp black and carbon black. The former is made by the incomplete combustion of hydrocarbon oils and the latter by impinging the flame of natural gas upon a metal surface. Both are used as pigments in ink, but the carbon black is now far more important. Its largest use is in compounding rubber for automobile tires. In 1946 almost five hundred billion cubic feet of natural gas was consumed in the United States in the production of over a billion pounds of carbon black.

Graphite has long been used for the manufacture of lead pencils. It is obtained from mines in Ceylon and Madagascar, and is now made in large quantities at Niagara Falls by heating anthracite coal in an electric furnace. Because of its infusibility, it is used in making crucibles for use at high temperatures. The presence of a small portion of clay greatly increases its resistance to oxidation. Because of its high melting point, graphite is extensively used for electrodes in electric furnaces. Graphite, or gas carbon, is also used in arc lamp electrodes, cerium fluoride being often added to provide a metal vapor which increases the brilliance of the arc and also reduces its resistance. Ground in oil or water with tannin or other suspending agent, graphite forms a stable suspension, which is used in lubricating bearings. Graphite is also employed extensively in protecting metal surfaces from oxidation, e.g. in stove polish.

Liquid potassium is absorbed by graphite. The alkali atoms apparently enter the crystal between the planes of carbon atoms. Two definite compounds, C_8K and $C_{16}K$, are formed. Powerful oxidizing agents form so-called **graphitic oxide.** Here again the oxygen atoms enter the crystal between the carbon planes. The composition of the product varies from a ratio of oxygen to carbon of 1 to 2.9–3.5. In a similar manner HSO_4^- groups enter the crystal when graphite is treated with sulfuric acid in the presence of a strong oxidizing agent. The product is known as **blue graphite,** and when treated with water, graphite is again formed. A technical process for the purification of graphite is based on this fact. Fluorine also enters the graphite crystal, forming the explosive **carbon monofluoride.** As in the other absorption reactions the process results in a considerable increase in the volume of the crystal,

TABLE I

ATOMIC AND PHYSICAL PROPERTIES OF CARBON

Atomic weight..........	12.010	Ionization potential in volts,	
Atomic number.........	6	1st electron.......	11.2
Isotopes.............	12, 13	2d electron........	24.3
Electrons in various quan-		3d electron........	47.6
tum levels, 1st........	2	4th electron.......	64.2
2d........	4	Melting point, ° C......G	3500
Density..............D	3.51	Boiling point, ° C........	4830
G	2.25	Electrical resistivity,	
Heat of sublimation kcal.	170.4	ohm-cm..........D	5×10^{14}
		G	1.4×10^{-3}

The radioactive isotope of carbon with mass 14 occurs in nature as the product of the reaction between cosmic-ray neutrons and nitrogen, $N^{14} + n = C^{14} + p$. It has a half-life of 5720 years and is transformed to N^{14} by a β-emission. The isotope appears to be uniformly distributed in atmospheric carbon dioxide and the carbon in living material gives an average 12.5 β-disintegration per minute per gram of carbon. This offers a means of dating carbon containing material which was removed from the equilibrium process in ancient times. Thus wood samples from old Egyptian tombs gave a specific carbon activity of 7 counts in agreement with the age of the tombs and predicted rate of decay.

C^{14} is also produced in the high-flux neutron reactors and has become extremely important as a "tracer," used to follow the course of organic reactions.

OXIDES AND ACIDS

5. Carbon forms the monoxide, CO, which is the anhydride of carbonous or formic acid, HCO_2H, and the dioxide, CO_2, which is the anhydride of carbonic acid, H_2CO_3. In addition, several anhydrides of more complicated organic acids are known: e.g., carbon suboxide, C_3O_2, the anhydride of malonic acid, $CH_2(COOH)_2$.

Carbon monoxide is remarkably similar to nitrogen in physical properties (Table II). The two gases have the same molecular weight and also the same number (10) of

TABLE II
PROPERTIES OF CARBON MONOXIDE AND NITROGEN

	CO	N_2		CO	N_2
Melting point....	− 200°	− 210°	Critical temperature	− 140°	− 146°
Boiling point.....	− 190°	− 196°	Critical pressure, atm.	36	35
Density of liquid..	0.793	0.796	Critical volume, cc.	5.05	5.17

valence electrons. It seems probable from the similarity in properties that the arrangement of the electrons in both molecules may be the same. Probably no single electron structure should be written but rather a number of structures such as, $: C : : : O :$ or $: C : : \overset{..}{O} :$ or $: C : \overset{..}{\underset{..}{O}} :$ with resonance between them.

Carbon monoxide is but slightly soluble in water, 3 cc. per 100 cc. of water at 8°. It is more soluble in alkalies, giving formates: $CO + NaOH = HCOONa$. The gas is readily prepared in the laboratory by the action of sulfuric acid on formic or oxalic acid, or ferrocyanide: (1) $HCOOH = CO + H_2O$, (2) $H_2C_2O_4 = CO + CO_2 + H_2O$, (3) $K_4Fe(CN)_6 + 6H_2SO_4 + 6H_2O = 6CO + 2K_2SO_4 + 3(NH_4)_2SO_4 + FeSO_4$. The formation from reactions involving carbon, oxygen, and water is discussed in later paragraphs.

Carbon monoxide reacts with many metals, forming **carbonyls**, e.g., $Fe(CO)_5$, $K_6(CO)_6$, $Ni(CO)_4$, $Co_2(CO)_8$, $Cr(CO)_6$, $W(CO)_6$, $Ru(CO)_5$, $Mo(CO)_6$. The nickel compound is of especial importance (cf. **XIX—18**). Iron and cobalt form the unusual **carbonyl hydrides** $Fe(CO)_4H_2$ (cf. **XIX—15**) and $Co(CO)_4H$. The so-called potassium carbonyl appears to be a derivative of hexahydroxy benzene, $C_6(OK)_6$. The oxide enters into a number of "coordination complex ions" such as $K_3Fe(CN)_5CO$; and the gas is absorbed by both acid and ammonical solutions of cuprous chloride with the formation of rather unstable complexes, possibly $Cu(CO)Cl_2^-$, and $Cu(CO)NH_3^+$. Such solutions are employed in gas analysis in the estimation of carbon monoxide, although small amounts of the gas are more accurately determined by passing the gas over hot (160°) iodine pentoxide: $5CO + I_2O_5 = 5CO_2 + I_2$. The iodine is absorbed in iodide solution and titrated with thiosulfate.

Carbon monoxide unites directly with chlorine in the sunlight, or in the presence of active charcoal as a catalyst to form **phosgene, carbonyl chloride,** $COCl_2$. The reaction is highly exothermic, and is, therefore, favored by low temperatures (below 350°).

Carbon monoxide is extremely poisonous. Air containing 1 part in 2000 will cause death in about four hours; and 1 part in 100 will cause death in a few minutes. The physiological action is due to the formation of a bright red compound with the haemoglobin of the blood. Gas masks to protect against carbon monoxide contain a mixture of manganese and copper oxides known as "hopcalite," which acts as a catalyst for the oxidation of the gas.

6. Equilibria Involving Carbon Monoxide and Dioxide. —Around 500° C., carbon (in excess), in an atmosphere of oxygen, gives almost completely carbon dioxide: $C + O_2 = CO_2$ (1), but at 1000°, the reaction (with excess carbon) gives almost pure carbon monoxide: $2C + O_2 = 2CO$ (2). It follows that in the equilibrium: $C + CO_2 = 2CO$ (3), high temperature favors the formation of the lower oxide. Data on the equilibrium are given in Table III.

TABLE III

$C(graph) + CO_2 = 2CO$

$t°$ C.	500	600	800	1000	1200
Per cent CO_2..	95	77	7	0.6	0.06

At low temperatures, carbon monoxide is unstable with respect to the decomposition (3) above, but the rate of decomposition is extremely slow; however, around 300° platinum or nickel act as efficient catalysts.

With excess oxygen, both carbon and carbon monoxide are oxidized to the dioxide: $2CO + O_2 = 2CO_2$ (4). Only at extremely high temperatures is reaction (4) reversed and carbon dioxide dissociated (Table IV). The union of carbon monoxide and oxygen is slow at low temperatures, and even at high temperatures, if the gases are perfectly dry. Water, therefore, appears to act as a catalyst.

TABLE IV

$CO_2 = CO + \frac{1}{2}O_2$

$t°$ C.	1122	1550	2000	2600
Per cent CO_2 dissociated.	0.01	0.4	2	50

The equilibrium: $C + H_2O(g) = CO + H_2$ (5) is very important in the manufacture of artificial fuel gas (see below). At 25°, the equilibrium constant is about 10^{-16}, but at 600° it is about 1; hence there is a rapid change in the direction of the reaction with temperature.

Below 500°, steam will oxidize carbon monoxide: $CO + H_2O_{(g)} = CO_2 + H_2$ (6). This reaction is utilized in the preparation of commercial hydrogen from water gas (Par. 7). Data on the equilibrium are given in Table V.

TABLE V

$CO + H_2O_{(g)} = CO_2 + H_2$

$t°$ C.	400	500	600	800	1000
Per cent CO converted.	94	86	76	53	38

In the presence of catalysts, carbon monoxide and hydrogen will combine to form a number of hydrocarbons and alcohols, or other oxidation products of hydrocarbons, for example,

$$CO + 3H_2 = CH_4 + H_2O$$
$$CO + 2H_2 = CH_3OH$$
$$12CO + 3H_2 = C_6H_6 + 6CO_2$$

Of these reactions, the most important commercially is the formation of methyl alcohol, CH_3OH, or **methanol.** The reaction is favored by pressure (100–200 atmospheres are used), and the temperature range is between 300 and 600° C. Various mixed metal oxides are employed as catalysts. Zinc oxide favors the formation of methanol, while cobalt metal with chromium oxide yields hydrocarbons. Methanol is important as a solvent, and as a raw material for the synthesis of many organic compounds. It is a very satisfactory fuel for gas engines.

The frequent mention of carbon monoxide in metallurgical processes arises through its powerful reducing power, which enables it to remove oxygen from metal oxides: e.g., $CuO + CO = CO_2 + Cu$ (7). The more noble the metal, the greater the tendency for reaction (7) to take place. In certain cases, the reaction is complicated by the formation of carbides.

7. Carbon Monoxide Fuels.—Carbon monoxide is an important constituent of several artificial fuels. When a limited supply of air is passed through coke or anthracite coal, the resulting mixture is known as **producer gas,** and contains carbon monoxide (30 to 40 per cent), nitrogen (60 per cent), and hydrogen (2 to 5 per cent). A gas of somewhat similar composition, called **blast furnace gas,** is a product of iron smelting. The most important artificial gas, however, is **water gas,** made by passing steam over hot coal. The reaction is endothermic (see reaction (5) above) and in order to maintain the required temperature (around 600°), it is necessary to turn off the steam every few minutes and blow air in for a brief period. The resultant mixture of gases consists of carbon monoxide (40 to 50 per cent), hydrogen (45 to 50 per cent), carbon dioxide (3 to 7 per cent), and nitrogen (4 to 5 per cent). In certain localities where crude oil is cheap and coal expensive, **oil-water gas,** for cooking and heating, is made by spraying crude oil and steam upon heated bricks. The heavy hydrocarbons are "cracked" by the heat into carbon and lighter gases, such as CH_4 and C_2H_6; the former reacts with the steam to form carbon monoxide and hydrogen.

8. Formic or Carbonous Acid.—Carbon monoxide reacts with alkalies, producing formates, but does not react with water at ordinary temperatures. However, the equilibrium: $CO + H_2O = HCO_2H$ is attainable at 150° in the presence of hydrogen chloride with the system under pressure; and from measurements of this equilibrium, it may be calculated that formic acid is stable at room temperature with respect to carbon monoxide at one atmosphere. Sulfuric acid readily removes the water from formic acid and evolves carbon monoxide.

Formic acid has the formula,

$$H—C—OH \quad \text{and not} \quad H—O—C—O—H$$
$$\overset{\|}{O}$$

In this respect, it is similar to the acids of phosphorus where in the + 1 and + 3 states the H shifts to the P. The acid is monobasic, and the dissociation constant is 1.8×10^{-4}. The acid has a pungent, irritating odor, and blisters the skin like a nettle sting. All of the formates are soluble, but the silver and lead salts only moderately.

9. Carbon Dioxide.—The product of the oxidation of carbon, free or combined, with excess of oxygen is the dioxide, CO_2. This oxide is also formed by the action of acids upon carbonates: $CaCO_3 + H_2SO_4 = CaSO_4 + H_2O + CO_2$; or by the thermal decomposition of carbonates or bicarbonates: $MgCO_3 = MgO + CO_2$. An important commercial source of the oxide is the alcoholic fermentation of sugars: $C_6H_{12}O_6 = 2C_2H_5OH + 2CO_2$.

Carbon dioxide occurs in the atmosphere in amounts varying from 3 parts in 10,000 in the country, to 1 part in 100 in crowded and poorly ventilated rooms. It also occurs in effervescent mineral waters, and issues from the ground in large quantities in certain localities, as the Valley of Death, in Java.

Solid carbon dioxide has a vapor pressure of 1 atmosphere at − 78.5°, and therefore sublimes at that temperature. If heated under pressure, it melts at − 56° (5.3 atm.). The critical temperature of the liquid is 31.35°, the critical pressure, 73 atmospheres. The vapor pressure at 20° is 59 atmospheres. The oxide is usually handled commercially as the liquid in steel cylinders. If the liquid is allowed to flow from the cylinder into a heavy cloth bag, the heat of vaporization is sufficient to cool a large fraction of the oxide to the solid state, forming carbon dioxide snow. A solution of the solid in acetone under reduced pressure may be employed to obtain temperatures around − 110°.

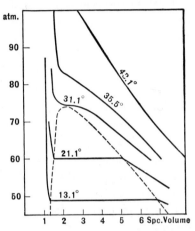

FIG. 2. Pressure-volume curves for CO_2.

The solubility of carbon dioxide in water at 1 atm. pressure and various temperatures is:

$t°$ C.	0	25	40	60
g. CO_2 per 100 g. H_2O	0.355	0.145	0.097	0.058

Up to about 5 atmospheres, the solubility is nearly proportional to the pressure, following Henry's law, but above that pressure the solubility becomes greater due to the formation of carbonic acid. Soda water contains carbon dioxide under a pressure of 3 to 4 atmospheres. The rate of the reaction, $CO_2 + H_2O = H_2CO_3$ is fairly slow requiring an activation energy of about 19 kcal. In the lungs the reaction is catalyzed by the enzyme, carbonic anhydrase.

The electron structure is generally written as
$: \overset{..}{O} :: \overset{..}{C} :: \overset{..}{O} :$ but there probably is resonance with other
structures, e.g., $: \overset{..}{O} : \overset{..}{C} :: \overset{..}{O} :$

Carbon dioxide is not poisonous; its harmful effects are due rather to suffocation through lack of oxygen. Air containing 2 to 3 per cent of the gas may be breathed without apparent ill effect, but above 5 per cent panting is produced; and 50 per cent carbon dioxide can be tolerated only for a short time. The high humidity of badly ventilated rooms is probably more harmful than the carbon dioxide content.

The principal use of carbon dioxide is in the preparation of carbonated beverages. Liquid carbon dioxide is used in refrigeration cycles; the solid is used in cold storage, in place of ice, especially in shipping fruit, as the gas liberated tends to prevent the development of aërobic bacteria. The gas is employed in the manufacture of certain carbonates, including the sodium carbonates and white lead. Carbon dioxide is generated in the soda-sulfuric acid type of fire extinguisher. In other types of extinguisher liquid carbon dioxide under pressure is employed. A few per cent of carbon dioxide in air will render it a non-supporter of combustion of most carbonaceous material. A highly electropositive element like magnesium will continue to burn in pure carbon dioxide.

Carbon dioxide is absorbed from the atmosphere by plants, and is the source of the cellulose in plant tissue: $6CO_2 + 5H_2O = C_6H_{10}O_5 + 6O_2$. This reaction (or related reactions) requires the absorption of energy; this is supplied by sunlight through the agency of the chlorophyll. The mechanism of the reaction is much more complicated than the overall equation indicates. Some carbon dioxide is absorbed in the dark but the regeneration of the active reducing agent requires light. It is this absorption of radiation by plants, that renders the sun's energy available to us through the use of plants as food, and of plant products, wood, coal, etc., as fuel. The decomposition of plant tissue, of course, returns carbon dioxide to the atmosphere, and this continuous absorption and evolution of carbon dioxide by plants is sometimes referred to as the **carbon cycle.**

10. Carbonic Acid.—The structure of carbonic acid has been discussed (Par. **2**). The acid is known only in solution, in which it doubtless exists as the meta- rather than the ortho-form. At 1 atmosphere of CO_2 and 25° C., a water solution contains $0.0338M$ H_2CO_3. The acid is weak, the dissociation constants being, respectively: $K_1 = 4.3 \times 10^{-7}$, and $K_2 = 4.7 \times 10^{-11}$. A saturated solution (1 atm.) thus contains $1.2 \times 10^{-4}M$ H^+. These constants are correctly used with the assumption that all of the CO_2 is present as H_2CO_3. However, there is evidence that less than one per cent of the CO_2 is in the acid form and K_2 for H_2CO_3 is around 2×10^{-4}. If the bonds between the carbon and oxygen are simple electron pairs the formal charge on the carbon would be $+ 1$ and the expected value of K_1 around 10^{-2} (cf. **III—7**). If there is one double bond the formal charge would be zero and K_1 less than 10^{-7}. The observed value of 2×10^{-4} therefore indicates some double bond resonance.

Because of the weakness of carbonic acid, solutions of the normal carbonates are alkaline from hydrolysis: $CO_3^{--} + H_2O = HCO_3^- + OH^-$. The concentration of OH^- in $0.5M$ Na_2CO_3 is about $0.01M$. Bicarbonate ion can either hydrolyze,

$$HCO_3^- + H_2O = H_2CO_3 + OH^-,$$

or it can ionize further,

$$HCO_3^- = CO_3^{--} + H^+.$$

The former reaction proceeds farther than the latter, as is shown by the faintly alkaline character of bicarbonate solutions; the concentration of OH^- in a molal solution is about 2×10^{-6}. However, the two reactions tend to assist each other, due to the neutralization of H^+ and OH^-; each goes farther than it would in the absence of the other, giving as the result the summation in the reaction,

$$2HCO_3^- = H_2CO_3 + CO_3^{--}$$

The equilibrium constant for this very important reaction is 1.1×10^{-4}, corresponding to about $0.01M$ CO_3^{--} and $0.01M$ H_2CO_3 in M $NaHCO_3$. Because of this equilibrium, carbonates are readily converted to bicarbonate by passing carbon dioxide into their solutions; or, if they are but slightly soluble, into a suspension in water. A very important example of such a conversion is the solution of calcium carbonate in excess carbon dioxide: $CaCO_3 + H_2CO_3 = Ca^{++} + 2HCO_3^-$. The equilibrium is displaced upon heating by the evolution of carbon dioxide, hence bicarbonates in solution form carbonates upon heating, upon evaporation, or upon neutralization of the carbonic acid. The first of these processes accounts for the formation of scale in kettles and boilers; the second for the formation of stalactites and stalagmites in caves; and the third is used in the softening of water by addition of alkaline reagents. The carbonic acid-bicarbonate equilibrium is also important in maintaining the pH of the blood.

With the exception of the alkali metals, most of the carbonates are but slightly soluble or else hydrolyze to form basic carbonates or hydroxides. The bicarbonates of the alkali metals are less soluble than the carbonates; those of other metals generally more soluble. Reference should be made to the alkali carbonates for the details of their commercial preparation.

11. Analysis of Carbonates.—Carbonates are detected in qualitative analysis by the evolution of carbon dioxide with acids, and the formation of a white precipitate when this is passed into a solution of barium or calcium hydroxide.

When only a trace of carbonate is present, the test is made more delicate by adding a small piece of zinc to the sample, so that the hydrogen evolved will carry the carbon dioxide through the lime water.

The indicator, methyl orange, changes from yellow to red at about $10^{-4} M$ H^+; hence, a dilute solution of carbonic acid gives a yellow color; but if a drop of strong acid is added, the color changes to red. Carbonates may, therefore, be titrated with a strong acid, using this indicator. An alternate method is to add an excess of standard acid,

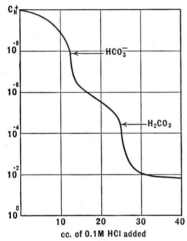

FIG. 3. Titration of carbonate with hydrochloric acid.

remove the carbonic acid by boiling, and titrate the excess of acid with alkali, using phenolphthalein as an indicator. In case hydroxide is present, the carbonate may first be removed by precipitation as barium carbonate. In a mixture of soluble carbonate and bicarbonate, the solution may first be titrated in the cold with a strong acid, using phenolphthalein as an indicator, which gives the amount of carbonate. To another portion methyl orange is added, and the titration is carried to this end-point. The second step corresponds to the sum of the moles of bicarbonate and twice the moles of carbonate. Or, the analysis may be made (1) by addition of excess of standard base, (2) precipitation of the carbonate by barium ion, (3) filtration of the carbonate and determination of total carbonate by titration, (4) titration of hydroxide in the filtrate to give the amount of bicarbonate by difference.

12. Peroxycarbonates.—Salts of the type Na_2CO_4 and $K_2C_2O_6$ are known, corresponding to the acids

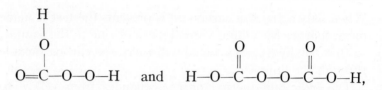

but the free acids are unstable. The monoperoxycarbonates are formed by the interaction of an alkali carbonate and hydrogen peroxide. They may be precipitated from the solution by ether. The salts of the diperoxycarbonic acid may be prepared by the anodic oxidation of solutions of alkali carbonates, cooled to $-10°$ or below. These compounds show the characteristic strong oxidizing power and strong reducing power of other peroxyacids and of hydrogen peroxide. The commercial sodium peroxycarbonate often contains hydrogen peroxide of crystallization, e.g., $Na_2CO_4 \cdot H_2O_2$.

13. Carbides.—Carbon combines directly with many metals at high temperatures to yield carbides. All the main Group I metals form carbides of the general formula, M_2C_2; and the main Group II (except beryllium), MC_2. These compounds and also Cu_2C_2 and Ag_2C_2 hydrolyze in water with the evolution of acetylene. The rare earth metals form carbides of the same general formula, MC_2, but these and other dicarbides, as UC_2, ThC_2, and MnC_2, hydrolyze to form complex mixtures of solid and liquid hydrocarbons. Beryllium carbide, Be_2C, and aluminum carbide, Al_4C_3, and a number of group four compounds, as SiC, hydrolyze to form methane and the carbides Fe_3C, Mn_3C, and Ni_3C yield chiefly methane with some hydrogen. In addition to these so-called salt-like carbides, there exists a number of comparatively non-reacting carbides as B_6C, ZrC, HfC, TaC, Cr_3C_2, W_2C, VC, Mo_2C, and MoC. These carbides are high melting and very hard. The mixed carbide $WTiC_2$, known as Kennametal, is used as a hard tool cutting edge. No carbides are formed by members of the first or the second subgroups, or by tin, lead, arsenic, antimony, or bismuth.

Commercially, the most important carbide is **calcium carbide.** This is made by heating a mixture of lime and carbon in an electric furnace (about 3000°): $CaO + 3C = CaC_2 + CO$. The reaction is highly endothermic. The formation of acetylene and cyaniamide from the carbide is discussed under those compounds.

14. Carbon and Sulfur.—The **disulfide,** CS_2, is formed by heating carbon and sulfur in an electric furnace: $C + 2S = CS_2$. It is also made commercially by the reaction of sulfur vapor and hydrocarbons, e.g., $CH_4 + 4S = CS_2 + 2H_2S$.

The compound is a heavy, colorless, volatile, highly refractive liquid. It usually has a disagreeable odor from the presence of other sulfur compounds. It has acid properties, and unites with basic sulfides forming thiocarbonate: $BaS + CS_2 = BaCS_3$. The liquid is a good solvent. The vapor is highly inflammable and poisonous. It is used in killing rodents, as a solvent for rubber and sulfur, in the preparation of carbon tetrachloride, and in the manufacture of viscose.

The **monosulfide,** CS, is prepared by the action of ozone upon carbon disulfide vapor. It may be condensed as a liquid at very low temperatures; upon heating, it polymerizes with explosive violence to a solid.

15. Carbon oxysulfide, COS, forms when carbon disulfide is treated with sulfur trioxide: $CS_2 + 3SO_3 = COS + 4SO_2$. It is a colorless gas, and resembles carbon dioxide in being rather soluble in water.

16. Carbon and Hydrogen.—The formation of heavy hydrocarbon molecules has been discussed in the introductory paragraphs of this chapter. These compounds may be considered in two main groups.

(1) The **aliphatic** compounds. The paraffin series, general formula, $C_nH_{(2n+2)}$, occurs extensively in American

mineral oils. The lighter members of the series, CH_4 to C_4H_{10}, constitute natural gas. The compounds, C_5H_{12} to C_8H_{18}, constitute the light and heavy gasolines. The members, C_9H_{20} to $C_{13}H_{28}$, are familiar as lubricating oils, and heavier molecules, up to $C_{35}H_{72}$, as paraffin wax. Various unsaturated derivatives of the paraffins (Par. 2) may be considered as separate series: such as compounds of the general type, C_nH_{2n}, the olefine series, and C_nH_{2n-2}, acetylene series.

(2) **Aromatic** compounds, consisting of benzene, C_6H_6, and its simple derivatives, such as toluene, $CH_3C_6H_5$; and more complicated double and triple ring compounds, such as naphthalene, $C_{10}H_8$ and anthracene, $C_{14}H_{10}$.

Benzene   Toluene   Naphthalene

These hydrocarbons occur in certain types of mineral oils and in the liquid condensate from the destructive distillation of coal.

17. Methane, CH_4, has been mentioned as the principal constituent of natural gas. It was formerly known as marsh gas, and was first observed as bubbles rising from the decomposition of vegetable matter in swamps. The gas has a low freezing and boiling point, and is but slightly soluble in water (5.5 cc. per 100 cc. of water at $0°$).

The gas may be formed by the direct reaction of carbon and hydrogen, at moderately high temperatures, Table VI.

TABLE VI

EQUILIBRIUM VALUES FOR THE REACTION,

$C + 2H_2 = CH_4 + 17,889$ cal.

$t°$ C.	400	600	800	1000	1200
Per cent CH_4	86	32	4	1	0.2

The reaction is obviously favored by high pressure.

Methane is also formed by the reaction of carbon monoxide and hydrogen: $CO + 3H_2 = CH_4 + H_2O$, at low temperatures, 250–300°, in the presence of certain catalysts (Par. 6). At high temperatures, the equilibrium is reversed.

The laboratory preparation of methane is usually carried out by heating a mixture of sodium acetate and soda lime, or by the action of water on aluminum carbide: $CH_3COONa + NaOH = Na_2CO_3 + CH_4$, and $Al_4C_3 + 12H_2O = 3CH_4 + 4Al(OH)_3$.

18. Acetylene, C_2H_2, is formed in small amounts by the reaction of carbon and hydrogen at very high temperatures (2500°): $2C + H_2 = C_2H_2$. It is prepared commercially by the action of water on calcium carbide: $CaC_2 + 2H_2O = C_2H_2 + Ca(OH)_2$.

The gas is colorless and odorless when pure, but usually has a pungent odor due to the presence of traces of phosphine. The vapor pressure of the liquid is about 40 atmospheres at 20°; and under these conditions it is highly explosive, as at ordinary temperatures the gas is unstable in respect to hydrogen and carbon. It is usually handled as a solution in acetone under pressure in steel cylinders.

The temperature of the oxy-acetylene torch, 2500 to 3000° C., is hotter than that of any other flame, with the possible exception of that of atomic hydrogen (cf. I—9); and this is employed extensively in cutting and welding steel and other metals. Before the introduction of the incandescent electric globe, the acetylene lamp was of considerable importance.

Acetylene acts as a very weak acid. Silver acetylide, Ag_2C_2, is formed by passing the gas through a solution of silver ammonia hydroxide. Many of the acetylides are explosive.

At high temperatures acetylene polymerizes to a number of complex products, among them being benzene, $3C_2H_2 = C_6H_6$. As an unsaturated compound, it readily adds hydrogen or halogens to form, respectively, ethane or its halogen derivatives of the type $C_2H_2X_4$.

The condensation of acetylene also yields derivatives of the **vinyl** group, $CH_2=CR^-$. Thus vinyl acetate, $CH_3COOCH=CH_2$ is made by the condensation with acetic acid, using mercuric oxide and sulfur trioxide as a catalyst. This and similar derivatives form the basis for the rapidly developing vinyl plastic industry. In the presence of mercurous sulfate acetylene adds water to form acetaldehyde, CH_3CHO. This may be reduced to ethyl alcohol or oxidized to acetic acid.

19. Oxidation Products of the Hydrocarbons.—The oxidation of methane leads to the following series of oxidation products:

$$
\begin{array}{ccccc}
\underset{\text{Methane}}{\text{H}-\overset{\displaystyle\text{H}}{\underset{\displaystyle\text{H}}{\text{C}}}-\text{H}} &
\underset{\substack{\text{Methyl}\\\text{alcohol}}}{\text{H}-\overset{\displaystyle\text{H}}{\underset{\displaystyle\text{H}}{\text{C}}}-\text{O}-\text{H}} &
\underset{\substack{\text{Formalde-}\\\text{hyde}}}{\text{H}-\overset{\displaystyle\text{H}}{\text{C}}=\text{O}} &
\underset{\substack{\text{Formic}\\\text{acid}}}{\text{H}-\overset{\displaystyle\text{O}}{\text{C}}-\text{O}-\text{H}} &
\underset{\substack{\text{Carbon}\\\text{dioxide}}}{\text{O}=\text{C}=\text{O}}
\end{array}
$$

The half reactions involved in these oxidations and their approximate potentials in water solutions are given below. The couples are not reversible at room temperature.

	VOLTS $_{25}°$
$CH_4 + H_2O = CH_3OH + 2H^+ + 2e^-$	-0.58
$CH_3OH = HCHO + 2H^+ + 2e^-$	-0.24
$HCHO + H_2O = HCOOH + 2H^+ + 2e^-$	0.01
$HCOOH = CO_2 + 2H^+ + 2e^-$	0.14

Related compounds result from the oxidation of other hydrocarbons; and these compounds are generally classified on the basis of the following characteristic groups, where R represents an organic radical formed by the removal of one hydrogen ion from a hydrocarbon, e.g. ethyl, C_2H_5, from ethane, C_2H_6.

R—OH   Alcohols—organic bases

$$\underset{R—C=O}{\overset{H}{|}}$$ Aldehydes

$$\underset{R—C—R}{\overset{O}{\overset{\|}{}}}$$ Ketones

$$\underset{RC—OH}{\overset{O}{\overset{\|}{}}}$$ Acids

R—O—R   Ethers—by removing water from two alcohol molecules

$$\underset{RC—OR}{\overset{O}{\overset{\|}{}}}$$ Esters—"salts" of an alcohol and organic acid.

20. Carbohydrates.—An important class of organic compounds contains hydrogen and oxygen in the same proportion as in water, and are termed carbohydrates. The group includes **cellulose**, $(C_6H_{10}O_5)_y$, starch, $(C_6H_{10}O_5)_x$, and the sugars. The latter are generally classified as **monosaccharides**, $C_6H_{12}O_6$, such as **glucose** or **fructose**; and as **disaccharides**, $C_{12}H_{22}O_{11}$, such as **sucrose** (cane sugar), or **lactose** (milk sugar). These compounds are really alcohol, and aldehyde or ketone derivatives of long chain hydrocarbons, e.g., glucose is $CH_2OH\cdot CHOH\cdot CHOH\cdot CHOH\cdot CHOH\cdot CHO$.

The molecular weights of cellulose and starch are not known, but the molecules are very complex. Starch may be converted to glucose by boiling in a solution containing a little hydrochloric acid: $(C_6H_{10}O_5)_x + xH_2O = xC_6H_{12}O_6$. Under similar conditions, sucrose may be hydrolyzed to a mixture of glucose and fructose.

21. Halogens and Hydrocarbons.—Any hydrogen in a hydrocarbon is capable of being replaced by a halogen atom, thus making possible thousands of halogen hydrocarbon derivatives. The replacement can often be accomplished by direct action of the halogen as a gas, or in alkaline solution upon the hydrocarbon, e.g. $C_2H_6 + Cl_2 = C_2H_5Cl + HCl$. Reactions between alcohols and halogen acids may also be employed: $C_2H_5OH + HCl = C_2H_5Cl + H_2O$. A few of the more important compounds are discussed below.

Carbon tetrachloride, CCl_4, is made by passing a mixture of carbon disulfide vapor and chlorine through a red hot tube: $CS_2 + 3Cl_2 = CCl_4 + S_2Cl_2$. The tetrachloride may be separated by fractional distillation from the sulfur chloride. Or, the reaction may be carried out by passing chlorine gas through the disulfide in the presence of a small amount of iodine. Carbon tetrachloride is a heavy, colorless liquid. It is non-inflammable, and a good solvent for non-polar substances; whence its use in dry cleaning, and in fire extinguishers, e.g. "pyrene." The vapors are slightly toxic. If partial hydrolysis to phosgene, $COCl_2$, occurs, the vapors are highly toxic.

Chloroform, $CHCl_3$, is prepared by the action of bleaching powder on alcohol. It is a heavy liquid, and is used largely as an anaesthetic.

Iodoform, CHI_3, is prepared by the action of iodine in alkaline solution on alcohol. It is a solid with a pungent characteristic odor, and finds extensive use as an antiseptic.

Ethyl chloride, C_2H_5Cl, is formed when ethane is treated with chlorine in the sunlight, or alcohol is treated with phosphorus pentachloride. It is a volatile liquid which is employed in refrigerant cycles, and as a local anaesthetic.

Ethylene dichloride, $C_2H_4Cl_2$, is used in the manufacture of the polysulfide rubbers such as **Thiokol,** through its reaction with polysulfide. The product, $C_2H_4S_2$, polymerizes in the presence of zinc oxide to a plastic. The dichlordifluormethane, CCl_2F_2, called **Freon,** has become important as a non-inflammable readily condensable gas for refrigeration cycles. Cf. also CF, Par. **4.**

Fluorocarbons are synthesized from the corresponding hydrocarbon by direct reaction with fluorine or more readily by the action of such oxidizing fluorides as cobaltic fluoride, $C_6H_{14} + 28CoF_3 = C_6F_{14} + 14HF + 28CoF_2$. These compounds are remarkably inert and are becoming important in the manufacture of chemically resistant plastics, high temperature lubricating oils and high temperature solvents.

22. Carbon and Nitrogen.—The nitride, C_2N_2, **cyanogen,** may be considered as the polymerized free cyanide radical, since it is formed by the oxidation of cyanides. The chemistry of the cyanides resembles in many respects that of the halogens, especially iodine; and the methods of preparation of cyanogen, by heating the compounds of the noble metals, and by the reaction with cupric ion, are analogous to the liberation of iodine under these conditions: $2AuCN = 2Au + C_2N_2$, $Hg(CN)_2 = Hg + C_2N_2$, $2Cu^{++} + 4CN^- = 2Cu\text{-}CN + C_2N_2$. The reaction, $C_2N_2 = 2C + N_2$, is highly exothermic (about 80,000 cal.). Many references are made in the chemical literature to the formation of cyanogen in the electric arc, but it is doubtful if, even at that high temperature, an appreciable quantity of the compound can be formed by direct union of the elements.

Cyanogen is a colorless gas, has a distinctive odor, and is extremely poisonous. It is soluble in water (4 volumes per 1 volume of water at 0°). When heated to 400° the gas polymerizes to a white solid, **paracyanogen,** $(CN)_x$. In alkaline solution, cyanogen hydrolyzes to cyanide and cyanate: $C_2N_2 + 2OH^- = CN^- + CNO^- + H_2O$ (compare $Cl_2 + 2OH^- = Cl^- + ClO^- + H_2O$). In sunlight, it decomposes, forming ammonium oxalate, ammonium formate, and urea. The potentials for the oxidation and reduction of C_2N_2 in acid solution are: $H_2O + \frac{1}{2}C_2N_2 = HCNO + H^+ + e^-$, 0.27 volt and $HCN = \frac{1}{2}C_2N_2 + H^+ + e^-$, − 0.33 volt.

23. Hydrogen Cyanide, or "prussic acid," may be prepared by the action of dilute sulfuric acid upon an alkaline cyanide, as it is a weak volatile acid. With concentrated sulfuric acid, carbon monoxide is evolved: $HCN + H_2O + H^+ = CO + NH_4^+$. The acid is also liberated by the dehydrating action of phosphorus pentoxide upon ammonium formate: $HCOONH_4 = HCN + 2H_2O$. Compounds of hydrogen cyanide with sugars (glucosides) occur in nature, e.g. in leaves and seeds of the peach tree; a solution made by boiling peach leaves in water was used by the ancient Egyptians as a poison.

A recently developed process for the manufacture of hydrogen cyanide employs CO and NH_3 as the raw materials. Methanol is reacted with carbon monoxide at high pressure to form methyl formate. This product is then treated with ammonia to give formamide and methanol, which is thus regenerated: $CH_3OH + CO = CH_3OOCH$ and $CH_3OOCH + NH_3 = HCONH_2 + CH_3OH$. The formamide is then dehydrated at 200° C. over alumina: $HCONH_2 = HCN + H_2O$.

Liquid hydrogen cyanide boils at 26.5°. The gas has the odor of bitter almonds, and is extremely poisonous. Death results in a few minutes from breathing concentrations as low as 2 mg. per liter. It is readily soluble in water, like the halogen acids; but, unlike them, it is a weak acid, $K_{18°} = 4 \times 10^{-10}$. With chlorine in solution **cyanogen chloride** is formed: $HCN + Cl_2 = HCl + CNCl$. This substance is also toxic and is one of the well known "war gases." Alkaline oxidizing agents oxidize cyanide to cyanate (see below), while acid oxidizing agents usually yield carbon dioxide and ammonia. The liquid is unstable with respect to its decomposition into the elements, and occasionally explodes. It is also difficult to keep because of the formation of solid polymers.

The arrangement of the 10 electrons in cyanide ion may be $: C :: \overset{..}{N}$ or $: C \overset{..}{:} N :$ or probably both with resonance between the structures. When the bond between the car-

bon and nitrogen is broken by hydrolysis, however, 8 of
the 10 electrons go with the nitrogen, forming ammonium:
thus,

$HCN + 2H_2O = HCOONH_4$ (ammonium formate), and C_2N_2

$$+ 4H_2O = \begin{array}{l} COONH_4, \\ | \\ COONH_4 \end{array} \quad \text{ammonium oxalate.}$$

24. The Alkali Cyanides are important commercial compounds (cf. **IV—21**). They may be prepared: (1) from
alkali ferrocyanide by fusion with sodium metal: $K_4Fe(CN)_6$
$+ 2Na = 4KCN + 2NaCN + Fe$; (2) by heating the
ferrocyanide with carbonate: $K_4Fe(CN)_6 + K_2CO_3$
$= 5KCN + KOCN + CO_2 + Fe$; (3) by the reactions:
$2NH_3 + 2Na = 2NH_2Na + H_2$ (300–400° C.) and
$2NaNH_2 + 2C = 2H_2 + 2NaCN$ (red heat); (4) from calcium cyanamide by fusion with sodium carbonate: $CaCN_2$
$+ C + Na_2CO_3 = CaCO_3 + 2NaCN$; (5) by the Bücher
process for the fixation of nitrogen, by heating a mixture of
sodium carbonate, carbon, and iron (catalyst) made into
bricks in an atmosphere of nitrogen: $Na_2CO_3 + 4C + N_2$
$= 2NaCN + 3CO$. The cyanide is extracted with liquid
ammonia.

The alkali cyanides are readily soluble in water, and the
solutions are alkaline by hydrolysis. Many complex cyanides are remarkably stable. Ions of the type $M(CN)_4^{-4+n}$
are formed by Cu^+, Cd^{++}, Ni^{++}, Hg^{++}, Pd^{++}, and Pt^{++}; of
the type $M(CN)_6^{-6+n}$ by Cr^{++}, Cr^{+++}, Co^{++}, Co^{+++}, Fe^{++},
Fe^{+++}, Mn^+, Mn^{++}, Mn^{+++}, Rh^{+++}, Ru^{++}, Os^{++}, Ir^{+++},
V^{+++}, and V^{+4}. A few complex cyanides of the type
$M(CN)_3^{-3+n}$ are known, e.g., Cu^+, Ni^+, Mn^{++}, but they
usually readily add another group. Silver forms the ion
$Ag(CN)_2^-$. W^{+4} forms $W(CN)_8^{-4}$.

25. Cyanates are readily prepared by the action of mild
oxidizing agents upon cyanides, for example, by heating
potassium cyanide with lead oxide: $KCN + PbO = KOCN$
$+ Pb$. The salt is extracted from the lead with alcohol, as

the water solution is unstable: $KOCN + 2H_2O = NH_3 + KHCO_3$. Cyanate is also formed by the action of cyanide upon copper ammonia ion: $2Cu(NH_3)_4^{++} + 3CN^- + 2OH^- = 2CuCN + OCN^- + 8NH_3 + H_2O$. The cyanide-cyanate potential

$$CN^- + 2OH^- = OCN^- + H_2O + 2e^-; \text{ is } + 0.97 \text{ volt}$$

The free acid decomposes very readily into carbon dioxide and ammonia in water solution. **Ammonium cyanate,** NH_4OCN, is isomeric with **urea:** $NH_4OCN = CO(NH_2)_2$. The rearrangement takes place upon evaporating an aqueous solution.

26. Thiocyanates may be prepared by fusing alkali cyanides with sulfur: $KCN + S = KSCN$. The ammonium salt is formed by the reaction of ammonia and carbon disulfide: $4NH_3 + CS_2 = NH_4SCN + (NH_4)_2S$. At 140°, this salt rearranges to **thiourea,** $CS(NH_2)_2$. The free acid, HSCN, is a liquid which readily polymerizes to a yellow solid.

27. Calcium Cyanamide is important in its relation to the cyanamide process for the fixation of nitrogen. Around 1000°, calcium carbide absorbs nitrogen to form cyanamide: $CaC_2 + N_2 = CaCN_2 + C$. The product is used directly as a fertilizer, or treated with superheated steam to convert the nitrogen into ammonia: $CaCN_2 + 3H_2O = CaCO_3 + 2NH_3$. At low temperatures, the hydrolysis product is cyanogenamide: $2CaCN_2 + 4H_2O = 2Ca(OH)_2 + (CNNH_2)_2$. The world's production of cyanamide in 1938 was about a million tons, but has decreased in recent years.

28. The Proteins constitute a class of extremely complicated nitrogen compounds, occurring in animal and vegetable tissue. Empirical formulas, calculated from the percentage composition, give results such as $C_{146}H_{226}N_{44}SO_{50}$, but the molecular weights appear to be much higher. The proteins are complexes of amino-acids, i.e. compounds containing the groups $\overset{|}{N}H_2C-$ and $-COOH$, such as glycine,

CH_2NH_2COOH.

THE ORGANIC CHEMICAL INDUSTRIES

Many references have been made to the use of inorganic chemicals in various organic industries. For the sake of clarifying these references, brief outlines of some of the more important industries will be given.

29. Explosives.—One of the most important explosives is **nitroglycerine** (cf. also **XII—36**). This compound is very easily detonated by shock: $4C_3H_5(NO_3)_3 = 12CO_2 + 10H_2O + 6N_2 + O_2$. Like all good explosives, the heat of the reaction is large, and the gaseous products tend to occupy a very large volume in comparison to the original compound. **Dynamite** was formerly made by absorbing nitroglycerine in a porous earth; this form is now generally replaced by solutions of guncotton in nitroglycerine, known as **blasting gelatine,** giant powder, etc. Diethylglycol dinitrate, $C_2H_4(NO_3)_2$, is now being used somewhat in place of nitroglycerine. **Guncotton,** or cellulose trinitrate, $C_6H_7O_2(NO_3)_3$, is formed by steeping cotton in a cold mixture of nitric and sulfuric acids. It explodes when detonated by another explosive. **Smokeless powder,** or **cordite,** is made by evaporating a solution, in acetone, of guncotton, nitroglycerine, and a little vaseline.

The high explosives employed in shells to produce violent shattering are **trinitrotoluene,** "TNT," $CH_3C_6H_2(NO_2)_3$, a mixture of ammonium nitrate with TNT, known as **amatol, picric acid,** $C_6H_2(OH)(NO_2)_3$ and **RDX** or **cyclonite,** $C_3N_6O_6H_6$. The development and production of the latter was an important factor in World War II. These high explosives can stand the shock of being fired from a gun and require detonators which set up high shock waves such as lead azide to cause them to explode. TNT is not readily exploded by the ordinary detonators and an explosive of intermediate sensitivity or "booster" such as tetryl is employed in addition to the detonator.

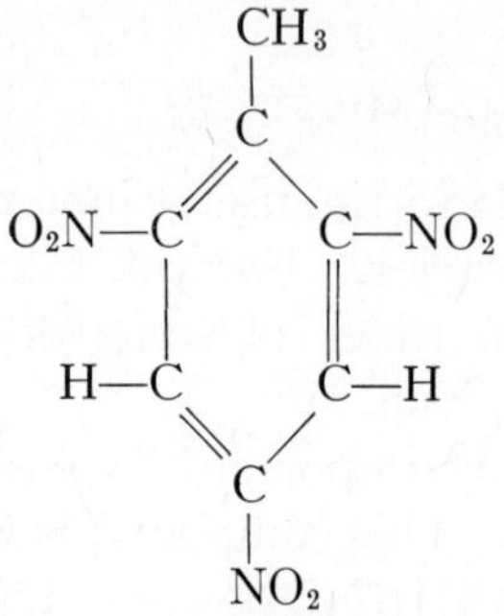

TNT

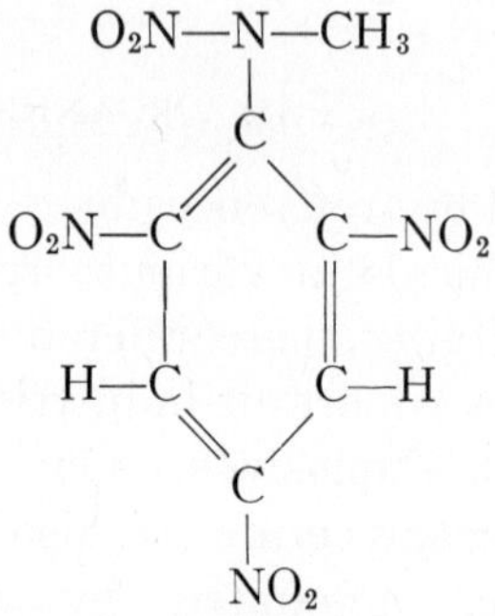

Tetryl

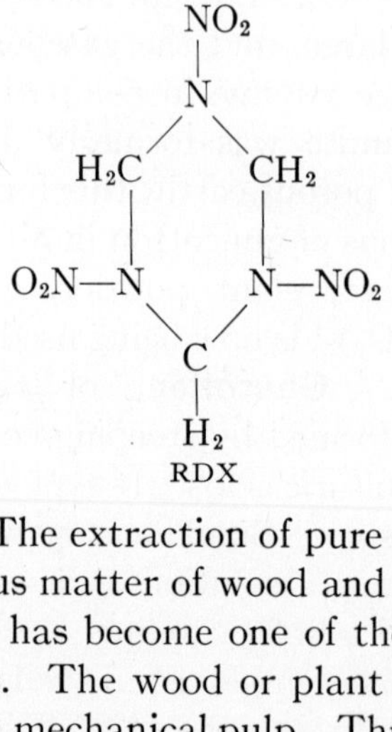

RDX

30. Cellulose.—The extraction of pure cellulose from the mineral and ligneous matter of wood and other plant fibers (especially cotton) has become one of the most important chemical industries. The wood or plant fibers are ground with water to give a mechanical pulp. Three types of chemical pulp, consisting of more or less pure cellulose are in use in America: (1) **soda pulp,** made by heating the mechanical pulp with 10 per cent NaOH under pressure, (2) **sulfite pulp,** made by digestion with a solution of calcium bisulfite and free sulfurous acid, (3) **sulfate pulp** made by treatment with sodium sulfate solution which contains some NaOH and Na_2S. Large quantities of chlorine are also employed in the bleaching of these pulps. In Europe wheat and flax straw are treated by the Pomelio process which employs chlorine gas in dilute sodium hydroxide to dissolve out the non-cellulose constituents. There are three forms of cellulose, α, β, and γ. The alpha form is insoluble in 18 per cent NaOH at 20° C. and is the most desirable. Cotton linters give a pulp which is 98 per cent alpha cellulose.

Paper is made from various mixtures of mechanical and chemical pulp, the proportion depending upon the type and grades.

For the synthetic textile and plastic industries the cellulose is dissolved by one of the following methods: (1) the cellulose is treated with CS_2 and NaOH to form a xanthate solution (**viscose** process). The cellulose is reprecipitated by acid. (2) The cellulose is nitrated and the nitrocellulose dissolved in suitable solvents. (3) The solvent is ammoniacal copper solution. The cellulose is coagulated in a caustic bath. (4) Cellulose acetate is made by dissolving the pulp in a mixture of acetic anhydride and glacial acetic acid. Cellulose acetate may be precipitated by water. The process is modified to give other esters in addition to the acetate and also cellulose ethers.

31. Rayon and other Textiles.—Any of the cellulose solutions discussed above may be employed to form threads. The liquid is forced through a small opening and coagulated. The resulting thread is gathered, washed, and wound. The 1950 production of American rayon was about a billion pounds. About 70 per cent of this was produced by the viscose process and practically none from nitrocellulose although this was the first of the artificial silks. The new **nylon** is not a cellulose but is a polymide and thus more nearly like natural silk in composition.

$$H_2N(CH_2)_6NH_2 + NH_2OC(CH_2)_4CONH_2$$

Hexamethylene   Adipamide
diamine

$$= \left[-\overset{\overset{\textstyle O}{\|}}{C} -(CH_2)_4 \overset{\overset{\textstyle O}{\|}}{C} -\overset{\overset{\textstyle H}{|}}{N}(CH_2)_6 -\overset{\overset{\textstyle H}{|}}{N} - \right]_n$$

Nylon

32. Plastics.—One of the earliest plastics was celluloid which was made by combining nitrocellulose with camphor and castor oil. Dissolved in alcohol and ether, the nitrocellulose formed a lacquer known as **collodion.** The name **Pyroxylin** is now given to this class of plastics and lacquers. The plasticizing agent camphor has now been supplemented by many others such as the organic phosphates, and derivatives of phthalic acid. This is an example of a **thermoplastic.** Such materials become soft and pliable when heated. In general, thermoplastics polymerize through carbon-carbon double bonds. The polyvinyl, polystyrene, polyacrylic esters, and cellulose acetate are examples.

Methyl methacrylate   Lucite, Plexiglass

Vinylacetate   Vinylite A

A new type of plastics made from tetrafluoroethylene and other fluorohydrocarbons has recently been introduced. **Teflon** is an example. These are very resistant to acids and alkalies even at high temperature.

The **thermosetting resins** do not soften readily when heated and are hard and tough. Their structure indicates that they have many more cross-linkages than do the thermoplastics.

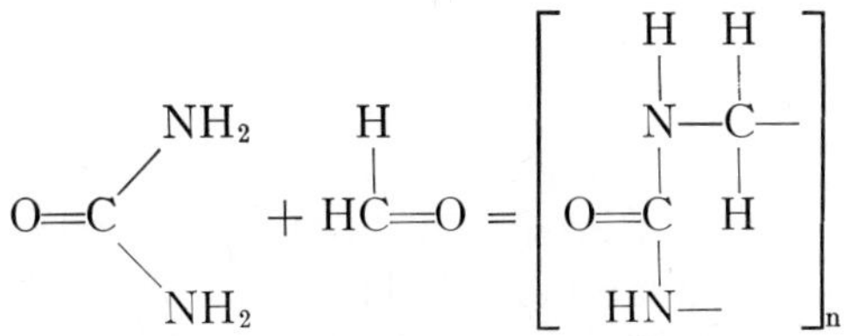

$$O=C\begin{array}{l}NH_2\\ \\ NH_2\end{array} \quad + \quad H\underset{|}{C}=O \quad = \quad \left[\begin{array}{c}H\ \ H\\ N-C-\\ O=C\ \ H\\ HN-\end{array}\right]_n$$

Urea   Formaldehyde   Plaskon

The phenol-formaldehyde resins such as **Bakelite** were among the earliest of this type. Other examples are: **plaskon** from urea and formaldehyde, **glyptal** from polyhydroxy alcohols, and polycarboxylic acids and **melmac** from melamine and formaldehyde.

33. Rubber.—Natural rubber is a type of thermoplastic made up of isoprene units, $-CH_2C\underset{\underset{CH_3}{|}}{=}CH-CH_2-$, linked together in long chains. The raw rubber as it comes from the plantation is a soft sticky substance. At the factory it is softened with steam and mixed with compounding agents (principally carbon black and zinc oxide) and with the vulcanizer, sulfur. Vulcanization requires heating to a temperature of 120 to 200° and results in cross linkage between the long carbon chains.

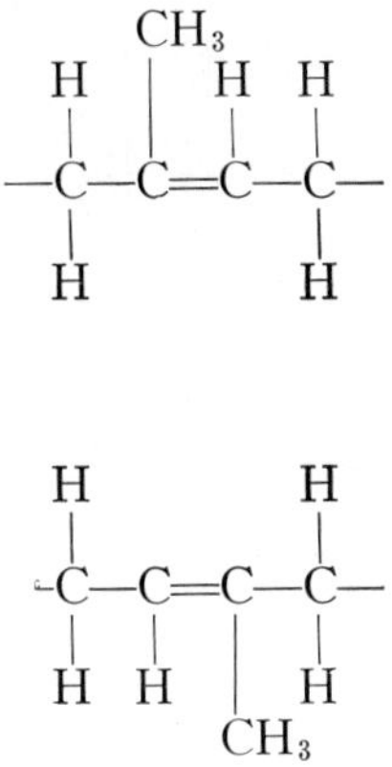

Unvulcanized chains

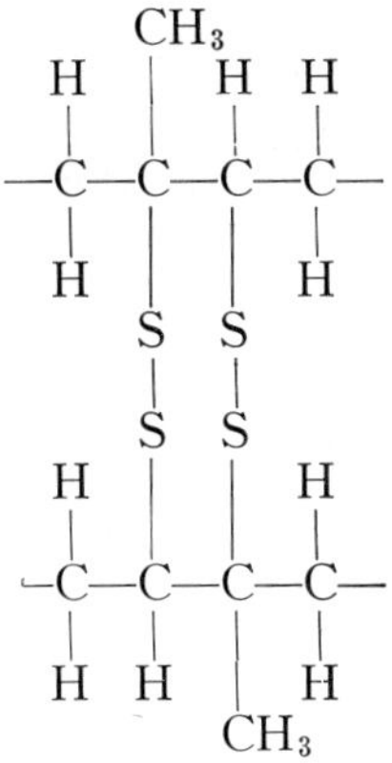

Vulcanized chains

Vulcanization decreases the plasticity and increases the resistance to abrasion. Small objects are often vulcanized by the vapor cure, using sulfur chloride. Recent developments have been the introduction of "accelerators" such as hexamethylenetetraamine, $(CH_2)_6N_4$, which lower the temperature and the time required for vulcanization and of "anti-oxidants" which retard the appearance of brittleness due to atmospheric oxidation.

The following are the more common types of the synthetic rubbers: (1) buna S, a co-polymer of butadiene, C_4H_6, and styrene, $C_2H_3C_6H_5$; (2) buna N, polymer of butadiene and vinylcyanide, C_2H_3CN; (3) neoprene, polymer of chloroprene, C_4H_5Cl; (4) butyl, polymer of isobutylene C_4H_8 and small amounts of other unsaturated hydrocarbons; (5) thiokal, made from ethylene dichloride and sodium tetrasulfide. In 1945 over 800,000 tons of GR-S, buna S type rubber, were produced, largely for the manufacture of automobile tires. In this process butadiene and styrene are emulsified and the temperature of the emulsion raised to bring about polymerization. Various catalysts have been developed to effect the polymerization at low temperatures (cold rubber).

Butadiene   Styrene   Buna S Rubber

Although the buna-S is by far the most important type of synthetic rubber, fairly large quantities of neoprene are produced for the manufacture of innertubes. The thiokals are used as material resistant to solvents and to abrasives.

34. Petroleum.—Crude oil varies greatly in composition. Some oils (the Pennsylvania) contain largely members of the paraffin series, while others (the California) consist of aromatic groups with varieties of side chains. The properties of light and heavy constituents also vary from one field to another. By distillation the crude oil is separated into (a) volatile gases, (b) gasoline, (c) solvent naphtha, (d) kerosene, (e) lubricating oil, (f) wax tar and fuel oil. The various products are agitated with sulfuric acid, and washed with water and dilute caustic soda. If the crude is high in sulfur an agitation with a solution of lead oxide in sodium hydroxide may also be used. Since the greatest demand has been for gasoline, the higher-boiling constituents are heated to a high temperature ("cracking") to cause their decomposition into lighter hydrocarbons. However, the older methods are being displaced by more efficient processes. One of these is the catalytic hydrogenation of both the heavy fractions and also of the gas oil. This tends to remove oxygen, nitrogen, and sulfur as their hydrogen compounds, to remove the unsaturated molecules which tend to condense to form gums and to give superior lubricating oils and gasolines. Another recent development has been the polymerization of the more volatile constituents, especially propane and butane. The hydrocarbons are generally cracked at relatively low temperature, cooled, and catalytically polymerized. The solvent extraction method by which a lubricating oil may be resolved into a desirable paraffinic oil and a less desirable, less heat resistant fraction by the use of selective solvents such as phenol and dichloroethyl ethers is now in general use. Modern refining methods endeavor to promote the formation of branch chain hydrocarbons, such as isooctane, which have high "anti-knock" qualities. The use of lead tetraethyl, $Pb(C_2H_5)_4$, as an "anti-knock" has also become universal.

During World War II the German chemical industry made a major portion of the gasoline required for their military needs from hydrogen and carbon monoxide by the Fischer-Tropsch process. With various catalysts the process yields products ranging from methyl alcohol to long chain hydrocarbons. This process makes available fuel oil from coal to supplement our oil reserves. The direct hydrogenation of coal at high pressures is an alternate process which may prove more efficient than the Fischer-Tropsch process.

The American petroleum industry now produces annually some 2 million tons of chemicals. These include such substances as butadiene and styrene for rubber, toluene for TNT and the dye industry, glycerine and ethyl alcohol. In 1949 about 70 per cent of the total production of ethyl alcohol was from ethylene. The ethylene is hydrated, $C_2H_4 + H_2O = C_2H_5OH$, either by direct catalytic hydration or by the hydrolysis of ethyl sulfate, formed by absorbing ethylene in sulfuric acid.

35. Dyes, Pharmaceuticals and Vitamins.—The remarkable development of synthetic organic chemistry proceeds at an accelerated pace. In 1828 Frederick Wöhler amazed the scientific world by the production of urea from ammonium cyanate. Previous to that time, it was generally believed that organic compounds could only be synthesized by living organisms. In 1930 urea sold for 80 cents a pound. In 1949 it was produced for less than 4 cents a pound by direct combination of CO_2 and NH_3. In 1856 W. H. Perkins synthesized the first dye (mauve). Now the synthetic dye industry manufactures dye worth 200 million dollars annually. During World War II the Germans converted coal to acetylene, combined this with formaldehyde (also made from coal) to get propargyl alcohol, then allyl alcohol and finally glycerol. This they combined with fatty acids from the Fischer-Tropsch process (cf. Par. **34**) to get edible fats. Each year sees the synthesis and commercial production of many new organic compounds, duplicating or improving natural products. The production of vitamins, sulfa drugs and antibiotics has been a major achievement. Examples of the structural formulas of various types of complex molecules are given below.

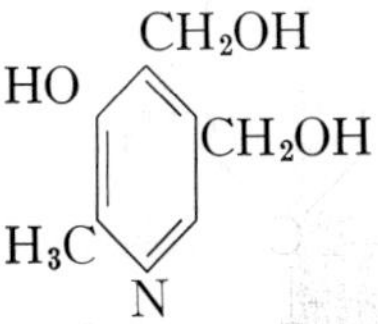

CH$_2$OH

HO

CH$_2$OH

H$_3$C

N

Vitamin B$_6$

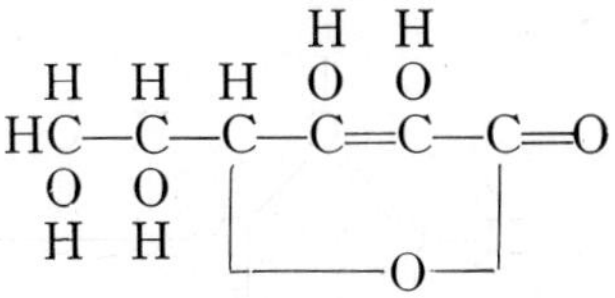

$$\begin{array}{c} \text{H} \quad \text{H} \\ \text{H} \quad \text{H} \quad \text{H} \quad \text{O} \quad \text{O} \\ \text{HC—C—C—C=C—C=O} \\ \text{O} \quad \text{O} \\ \text{H} \quad \text{H} \end{array}$$

O

Vitamin C

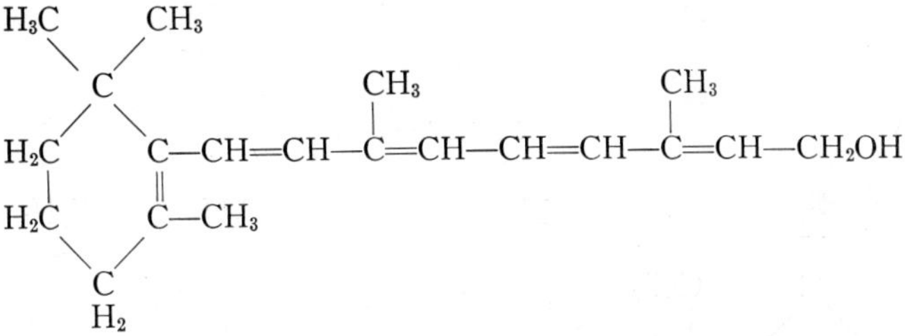

H$_3$C   CH$_3$

C

H$_2$C   C—CH=CH—C=CH—CH=CH—C=CH—CH$_2$OH

H$_2$C   C—CH$_3$

C

H$_2$

CH$_3$ CH$_3$

Vitamin A

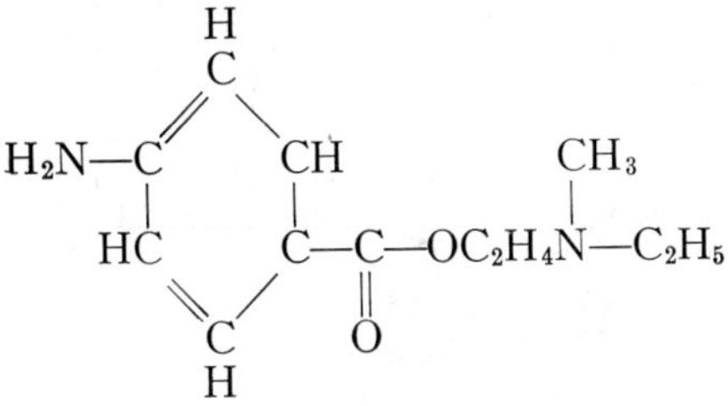

H
C

H$_2$N—C   CH   CH$_3$

HC   C—C—OC$_2$H$_4$N—C$_2$H$_5$

C   O

H

Novocaine

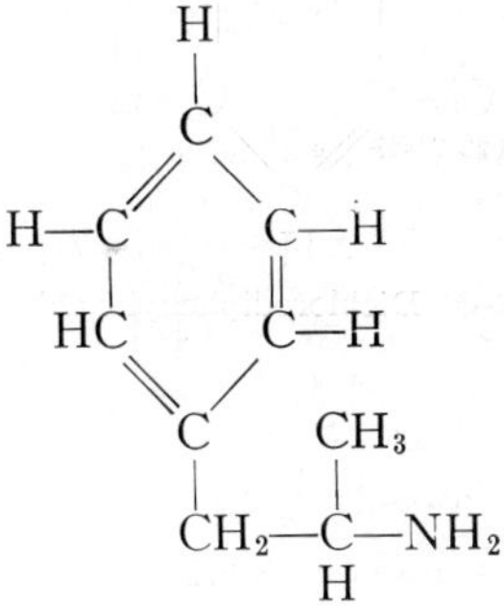

H
C

H—C   C—H

HC   C—H

C   CH$_3$

CH$_2$—C—NH$_2$

H

Benzedrine

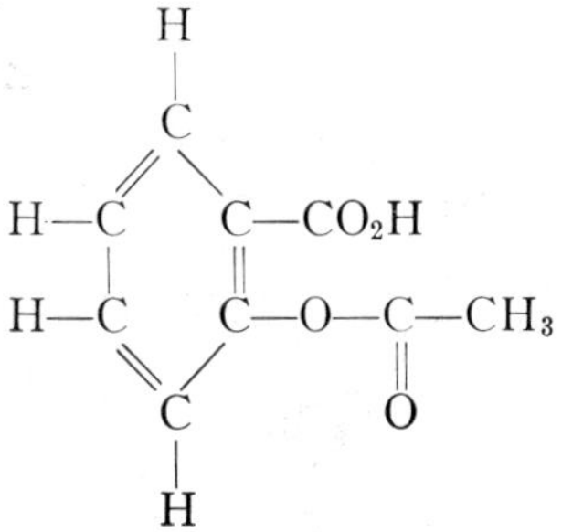

H
C

H—C   C—CO$_2$H

H—C   C—O—C—CH$_3$

C   O

H

Aspirin

NH$_3$
C

H—C   C—H

H—C   C—H

C   S———C—H

SO$_2$N—C   C—H

H   N

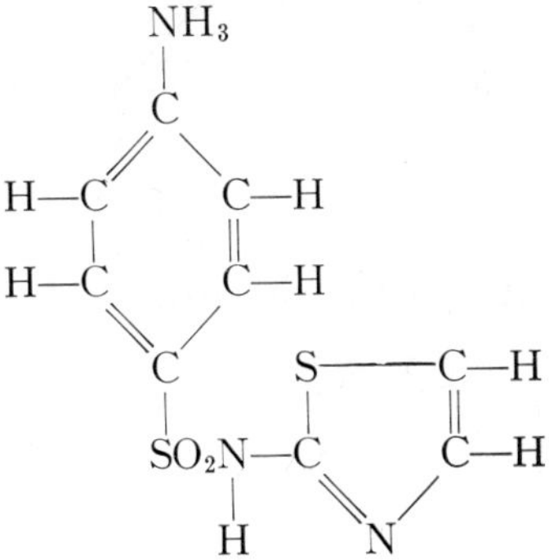

Sulfathiazole

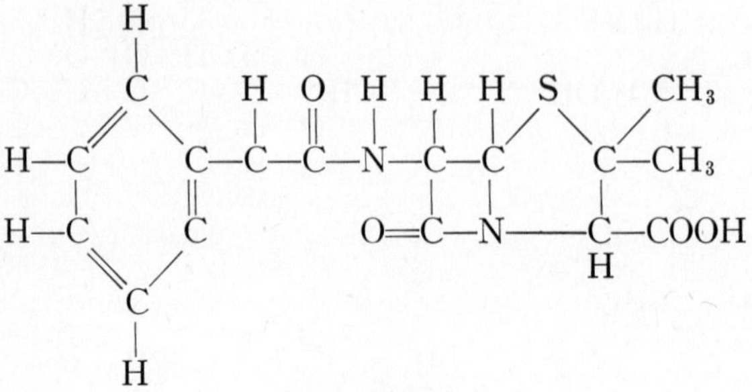

Penicillin G

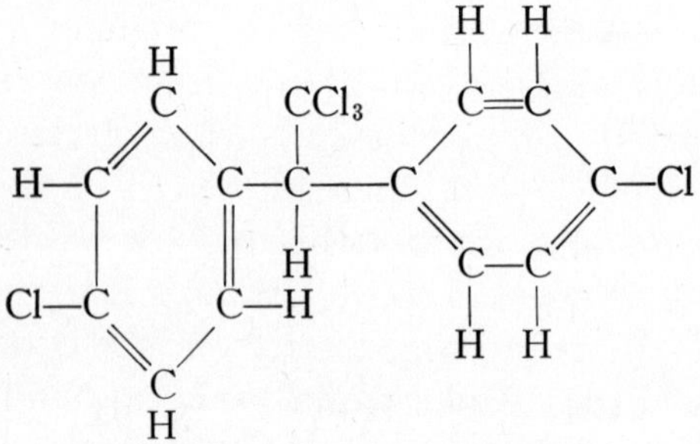

Dichlorodiphenyltrichloroethane (DDT)

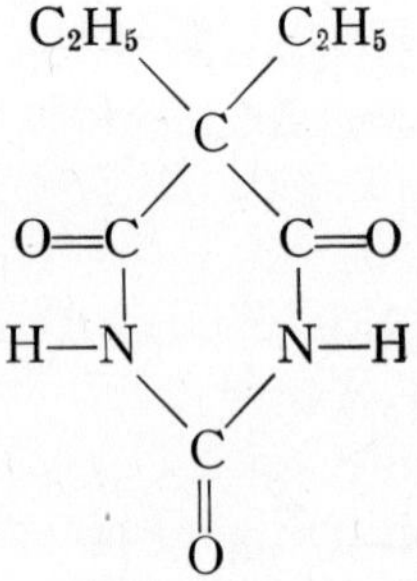

Veronal barbital

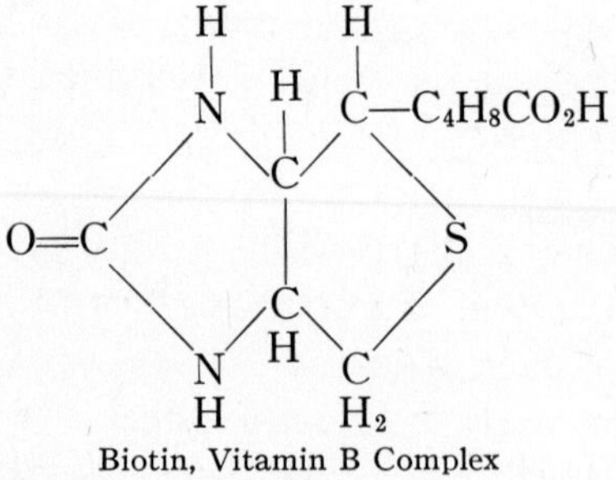

Biotin, Vitamin B Complex

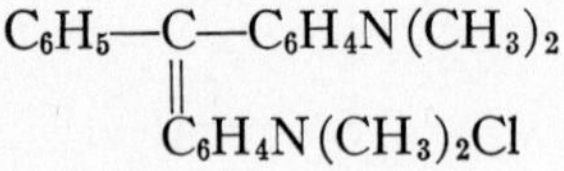

C_6H_5—C—$C_6H_4N(CH_3)_2$
$C_6H_4N(CH_3)_2Cl$

Malachite green

$C_6H_5NH_2$
N
‖
N
$C_6H_3(NH_2)_2$

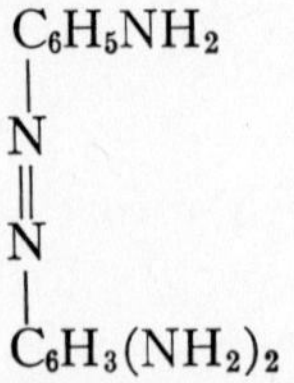

Bismarck brown

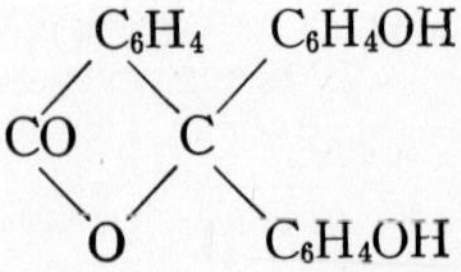

Phenolphthalein

Chapter XIV

SILICON

1. Silicon, the second element of Group IV, occupies as important a position in the mineral world as carbon does in the vegetable and animal. Its chemistry is characterized by the stability and complexity of the compounds of the dioxide, SiO_2, with basic oxides. In this respect, it resembles boron more closely than it does carbon. Although it forms hydrogen compounds similar to those of carbon, the bond between the silicons is readily broken, and the compounds do not possess the stability or importance of the corresponding carbon compounds. The oxide like that of boron is high melting and non-volatile, and many of its compounds are derivatives of polyacids, which resemble the boric acids. However, the majority of the silicates are salts of ortho or meta silicic acid, and thus contain the groups SiO_4 and SiO_3, the former having a charge of $+4$ and the latter of $+2$. Although a monoxide is known, few $+2$ or unsaturated compounds have been prepared.

In connection with the resemblance between boron and silicon, reference should be made (cf. **III—7**) to the similarity in the values for the field of force about B^{+3} and Si^{+4}.

2. Occurrence.—Silicon is never found as the free element. The dioxide and its compounds constitute about 87 per cent of the earth's crust, and the element is estimated as forming 25.8 per cent of the outer portions of the earth. Silicon thus ranks next to oxygen in abundance. The principal silicon minerals are summarized in Table VI, and the important groups, such as the feldspars, pyroxenes, amphiboles, and micas, are discussed in subsequent paragraphs.

3. Elementary Silicon has been prepared in a semi-metallic crystalline form, and also in a so-called amorphous form. The former possesses a grey luster and fair electrical conductivity (Table I). Both forms appear, from X-ray data, to have the same atomic arrangement in the crystal, the modified diamond type, hence the amorphous form is probably a mass of very small crystals.

Amorphous silicon is prepared by the high temperature reduction of silicon halides by alkali metals, or of the dioxide by magnesium: $SiCl_4 + 4Na = Si + 4NaCl$. When the dioxide, or sodium silicofluoride, Na_2SiF_6, is reduced with excess of aluminum, the silicon dissolves in the excess metal, and upon cooling, separates in the crystalline metallic form. This may be separated from the aluminum by dissolving the latter in acid. The metallic form may also be prepared by the reduction

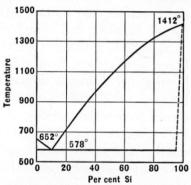

FIG. 1. Aluminum-silicon diagram.

of the dioxide with carbon in an electric furnace, although it is difficult to avoid the formation of the carbide. Amorphous silicon may be converted to the metallic form by recrystallizing from molten silver.

TABLE I

ATOMIC AND PHYSICAL PROPERTIES OF SILICON

Atomic number	14	Density (crys.)	2.4
Atomic weight	28.06	Melting point, ° C.	1410
Isotopes	28, 29, 30	Boiling point, ° C.	2193
Electrons in various quantum levels, 1st	2	Electrical resistivity, ohm-cm.	85×10^{-3}
2d	8	Radius of Si^{+4} in crystals,	
3d	4	cm. $\times 10^8$	0.41

Silicon is of considerable importance in the steel industry. It is generally prepared, however, as ferrosilicon (Par. **6**).

4. Reactions of the Element.—Silicon burns in oxygen, but not readily, as a surface layer of oxide tends to stop the reaction. It ignites spontaneously in fluorine at room temperature, in chlorine at 300–350°, in bromine at 500°; and the amorphous form reacts with iodine at red heat, but without luminosity. The oxidation reduction potential,

$$Si + 2H_2O = SiO_2 + 4H^+ + 4e^- : 0.6 \text{ volt,}$$

is not of great significance because of the slowness of the reaction. Thus, silicon is not soluble in hydrogen ion, but due to the great stability of silicates, it does dissolve in sodium hydroxide with the evolution of hydrogen. The element is also oxidized by steam. A mixture of nitric and hydrofluoric acid gives silicon tetrafluoride. Combination occurs with nitrogen and sulfur at high temperature, and with many metals to form silicides.

TABLE II

REACTIONS OF SILCON

$Si + O_2 = SiO_2$	Not rapid
$Si + 2X_2 = SiX_4$	With halogens
$Si + 2NaOH + H_2O = Na_2SiO_3 + 2H_2$	
$Si + 2H_2O = SiO_2 + 2H_2$	With steam
$3Si + 4HNO_3 + 12HF = 3SiF_4 + 4NO + 8H_2O$	
$Si + K_2CO_3 = K_2SiO_3 + C$	Fused
$3Si + 2N_2 = Si_3N_4$	
$Si + 2S = SiS_2$	
$nSi + mM = Si_nM_m$	With many metals

5. Silicides.—Silicon dissolves in many molten metals, and the temperature-composition curves indicate the formation of both solid solutions and definite compounds. Compounds of the type, M_3Si, are formed by Li and Cu; of the type, M_2Si, by Mg, Mn, Fe, Co, Ni, and Pd; of the type, MSi, by Mn, Fe, Co, Ni, Pt, and Pd; of the type, MSi_2, by Ca, Co, Sr, V, and U; and of the type, MSi_3, by Co. A few of the more important compounds are discussed below.

6. Ferrosilicon.—FeSi is made by reducing siliceous iron ore in an electric furnace. It is employed extensively in the steel industry, especially in the manufacture of silicon steels, the more important of these being (1) acid resistant steel, e.g. "duriron" (16 per cent silicon) and (2) steel of high magnetic permeability. The addition of silicon to iron also reduces the amount of iron carbide, Fe_3C; and thus converts white cast iron into grey cast iron. Silicon added to molten steel also serves as a "deoxidizing" agent.

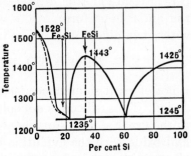

FIG. 2. Iron-silicon diagram.

Hydrogenite, a mixture of ferrosilicon and solid sodium hydroxide, evolves hydrogen upon the addition of water, and has been used as a source of hydrogen for balloons and air ships.

7. Silicon Carbide, SiC, is one of the hardest substances known. Although the data are somewhat indefinite, the arrangement of the atoms in the crystal appears to be a modified diamond type of structure. It is manufactured extensively for use as an abrasive, by heating a core of carbon packed in sand in an electric furnace: $SiO_2 + 3C = CSi + 2CO$. The furnace is of the resistance type, the carbon core serving as the heating element.

8. Calcium Silicide, $CaSi_2$, is formed by heating lime, sand, and carbon in an electric furnace: $CaO + 2SiO_2 + 5C = CaSi_2 + 5CO$. It is a powerful reducing agent, and is employed as a "deoxidizing" agent in steel manufacture, and also as a reducing agent in certain explosives.

9. Silicon and Hydrogen.—The first 7 or 8 members of the series, Si_nH_{2n+2}, corresponding to the paraffin series, are known. These hydrogen compounds resemble the hydrocarbons in physical properties, but not in stability. They inflame spontaneously in air at room temperature, or slightly above, and are decomposed by alkali with the formation of a silicate and hydrogen. A mixture of the various members of the series results from the action of acids upon magnesium silicide, Mg_2Si, while lithium silicide, Li_3Si, gives largely silicoethane, Si_2H_6. The existence of unsaturated hydrogen compounds is doubtful, with the exception of the compound SiH_2.

10. Silicon and the Halogens.—The halogens react directly with silicon, forming tetrahalides. The energy of the reaction decreases with the increasing size of the halogens; with fluorine, the reaction is spontaneous at room temperature, while with iodine the reaction occurs only at red heat. The tetrahalides hydrolyze in water to form silicic acid and the hydrogen halide, and this hydrolysis is complete with all the tetrahalides, except the **tetrafluoride.** Due to the stability of the fluoride, silicon dioxide and most of the mineral silicates dissolve in hydrogen fluoride: $SiO_2 + 4HF = SiF_4 + 2H_2O$. The solid tetrafluoride sublimes without melting; but under a pressure of 2 atmospheres it melts at $- 77°$. At room temperature the tetrafluoride is a gas with a pungent odor. With water, partial hydrolysis results in the formation of **fluosilicic acid:** $3SiF_4 + 3H_2O = 2H_2SiF_6 + H_2SiO_3$. This is a moderately strong acid, and its potassium salt is but slightly soluble. X-ray data on the solid fluosilicates show that the six fluorine atoms are arranged symmetrically at equal distances about the silicon atom. In the acid nature of the fluoride, silicon again resembles boron.

11. Silicon tetrachloride is prepared by the action of chlorine on silicon carbide, or on a hot mixture of silica and carbon: $2Cl_2 + SiC = SiCl_4 + C$; $SiO_2 + 2C + 2Cl_2 = SiCl_4 + 2CO$. The product prepared by these reactions also contains higher members of the series, Si_nCl_{2n+2}. Mixtures of the tetrachloride and ammonia have been employed for the preparation of military smoke screens, since in moist air solid silicic acid and ammonium chloride are formed. With sulfur trioxide, the oxychloride, Si_2OCl_6, and also silicon dioxide results: $2SiCl_4 + 2SO_3 = Si_2OCl_6 + S_2O_5Cl_2$, and $SiCl_4 + 3SO_3 = SiO_2 + 2S_2O_5Cl_2$.

12. By the action of hydrogen chloride upon heated silicon, chlorine hydrosilicons are formed, the most important being **silicochloroform,** $SiHCl_3$. This and other silicon hydrogen halides hydrolyze in water with the formation of oxyhydrogen compounds: $2SiH_3Cl + H_2O = 2HCl + 2(SiH_3)_2O$ (Disiloxan): $SiH_2Cl_2 + H_2O = 2HCl + (SiH_2)O$ (Prosiloxan): $Si_2Cl_6 + 4H_2O = 6HCl + (SiO_2H)_2$ (Silico-oxalic acid); $2SiHCl_3 + 3H_2O = 6HCl + H_2Si_2O_3$ (Silico-formic acid anhydride).

SILICON AND OXYGEN

13. Silicon Monoxide.—The yellowish brown monoxide, SiO, may be prepared by the reaction between carbon and excess silicon dioxide at temperatures around 2000°. $SiO_2 + C = SiO + CO$. The oxide is a solid at these temperatures, and unless rapidly cooled, decomposes: $2SiO = Si + SiO_2$. It is used commercially under the name **monox,** as a pigment, and also as an abrasive.

14. Silicon Dioxide.—Free silica, SiO_2, constitutes about 12 per cent of the earth's crust; and this, together with silica in combination with basic oxides, approximately 60 per cent. It occurs in three crystalline forms, quartz, tridymite, and cristobalite, and each of these has a number of modifications (Table III). It also exists as the supercooled liquid, or quartz glass. Sand, flint, and agate are familiar forms of silica. Kieselguhr, or diatomaceous earth, is silica resulting from the skeletons of diatoms.

Quartz belongs to the hexagonal system with threefold symmetry about its principal axis. The crystal has no plane or center of symmetry; and therefore exists in two forms called "right-handed" and "left-handed," which are mirror images of each other and rotate the plane of polarized light in opposite directions (Fig. 3). Crystals of enormous size are occasionally found in nature. Quartz has a density of 2.65, and is somewhat harder than ordinary glass. It is very transparent over a range of wave-lengths extending from the infrared far into the ultraviolet (transmission for 1 mm. thickness = 67 per cent at 0.19 μ), and therefore finds considerable application in the manufacture of optical instruments and ultraviolet lamps.

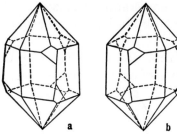

FIG. 3. Quartz crystals; a, right-handed; b, left-handed.

As indicated in Table III, tridymite and cristobalite are unstable with respect to quartz at ordinary temperatures. The transition is slow at low temperatures, however, and both forms are found in nature, especially in lavas which have cooled quickly.

TABLE III

MODIFICATIONS OF SILICA

	CRYSTAL SYSTEM	SPECIFIC GRAVITY	TRANSITION TEMPERATURE, ° C.
α-Quartz............	Hexagonal	2.65	575, to β-Quartz
β-Quartz............	Hexagonal	2.63	870, to β_2-Tridymite
α-Tridymite........	Rhombic ?	2.28	117, to β_1-Tridymite
β_1-Tridymite........	Hexagonal		163, to β_2-Tridymite
β_2-Tridymite........	Hexagonal		1470, to β-Cristobalite
α-Cristobalite........	Tetragonal	2.35	225, to β-Cristobalite
β-Cristobalite........	Cubic	2.21	1710, to liquid
Silica glass..........	Amorphous	2.21	

Liquid silica is highly viscous, and like all such liquids, readily supercools. Quartz glass has a lower density (2.2) than the crystals, and a very small coefficient of expansion, 0.0_654 (linear). Because of its low expansion, it is possible to plunge white hot quartz glass into water without having it crack. Quartz glass does not soften below 1500°, whereas ordinary glass softens around 600 to 900°. Both of these qualities make it very valuable in the construction of apparatus for high temperature measurements. It should be noted, however, that helium and hydrogen diffuse rather readily through quartz glass at temperatures as low as 300°. Quartz glass is now manufactured by fusing pure silica in a high temperature furnace.

The crystal structure of the three forms of silica may be represented as tetrahedral groups of oxygen atoms about a central silicon atom. The tetrahedra are linked at each corner so that each oxygen is attached to two silicons. The high temperature or β-modifications have a more definite structure and higher symmetry than the α-forms. β-tridymite is similar to the wurtzite structure and β-crystobalite to the sphalerite

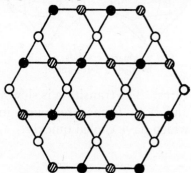

Fig. 4. Projection of silicon atoms in β-quartz.

structure, i.e., the silicon atoms are arranged like the carbon atoms of diamond. In β-quartz the tetrahedra are more closely packed. In the unit cell the silicons are located in three planes at different heights and the projection of the centers onto a single plane gives a hexagonal pattern, Fig. 4.

The various forms of silica are soluble in alkalies with the formation of silicates, but they are only slightly affected by acids, except hydrofluoric which converts silica into the tetrafluoride. The great stability of silicon dioxide is related to its high heat of formation: $Si + O_2 = SiO_2 + 200$ kcal. It is exceeded by that of the fluoride, however: $Si + 2F_2 = SiF_4 + 360$ kcal.

15. Silicic Acids.—The result of the addition of a strong acid to a soluble silicate is the formation of a colloidal solution, or hydrogel, of the general formula, $mSiO_2 \cdot nH_2O$. Upon heating, the gel may be gradually dehydrated and the dioxide formed. Partially dehydrated gels have high absorbent power, and are now used commercially in the absorption of benzene, sulfur dioxide, nitric acid, nitrogen dioxide, and other vapors. Many forms of hydrous silica occur in nature, such as opal and agate.

Salts and mineral derivatives of a large number of silicic acids are known. The nomenclature of these hypothetical acids is indicated in Table IV.

TABLE IV
SILICIC ACIDS

	Mono- $mH_2O \cdot SiO_2$	Di- $mH_2O \cdot 2SiO_2$	Tri- $mH_2O \cdot 3SiO_2$	Tetra- $mH_2O \cdot 4SiO_2$
Ortho-........	H_4SiO_4	$H_6Si_2O_7$	$H_8Si_3O_{10}$	$H_{10}Si_4O_{13}$
Meta-........	H_2SiO_3	$(H_2SiO_3)_2$	$(H_2SiO_3)_3$	$(H_2SiO_3)_4$
Meso-........	—	$H_2Si_2O_5$	$H_4Si_3O_8$	$H_6Si_4O_{11}$
Para-........	—	—	$H_2Si_3O_7$	$H_4Si_4O_{10}$
Tertero-......	—	—	—	$H_2Si_4O_9$

16. Alkali Silicates.—Commercial sodium silicate, known as **water glass,** is made by fusing sand, flint, or kieselguhr with sodium carbonate and charcoal, and extracting the glassy mass in an autoclave, or by dissolving the silica in sodium hydroxide. The product has a ratio of SiO_2 to Na_2O, between 2 and 4, and is usually sold in concentrated solution as a syrupy liquid.

Water glass is used in soaps and washing powders to provide an alkaline reaction. It is used: for fireproofing materials; in paper manufacturing as sizing; as an egg-preservative; and as a mineral glue for cementing wood, glass, porcelain, etc. Solid sodium metasilicate, $Na_2SiO_3 \cdot 5H_2O$, orthosilicate, Na_4SiO_4, and "sesqui" silicate $Na_3HSiO_4 \cdot 5H_2O$ are commercial products, used as water softeners and cleaning agents.

The other alkali silicates resemble the sodium compound.

Temperature-composition curves for the system, $K_2O \cdot SiO_2$-H_2O, show many hydrates of the salts, K_2SiO_3 and $K_2Si_2O_5$, and lithium forms the ortho salt, Li_4SiO_4. Although silica is soluble in concentrated ammonia, solid ammonium silicates cannot be prepared, as the solutions hydrolyze completely when evaporated.

17. Mineral Silicates and Rocks.—The solidification of the earth's molten magma has produced the **igneous rocks.** The action of wind and water has tended to break them up or partially dissolve them and to deposit the products as the **sedimentary rocks.** The latter have frequently been buried and subjected to considerable heat and pressure and thus changed in form. The products of this process are the **metamorphic rocks.** New flows of molten magma have occurred and these have produced changes in the adjacent rocks (contact metamorphism). The igneous rocks have generally crystallized with the separation of materials of more or less definite composition, the silicate minerals (cf. Table V) and a general classification of the igneous rocks may be made on the basis of the kinds of minerals which are present. There are so many possible combinations of the primary minerals that classification is difficult and many miscellaneous types are found outside the more common groupings. Also in any class of rocks with the same general composition there are large variations in appearance because of differences in crystal size. If the mineral grains are large enough to be seen by the unaided eye, the rocks are called **granitoid.** The fine-texture rocks are **felsitoid.**

In some cases there are large crystals in a fine-grained groundmass and the rock is known as **porphyry.** Rapid cooling may result in the formation of a non-crystalline solid or glass. Thus granite is granitoid, the felsitoid form is rhyolite, intermediate is granite porphyry and a common glass form is obsidian. The names of the common rock families given below are the names of the granitoid form followed by the name of the felsitoid, e.g., Granite—Rhyo-

TABLE V

MINERAL SILICATES

Important Primary Minerals

Feldspars	Orthoclase, $KAlSi_3O_8$ (monosymmetric) Microcline, $KAlSi_3O_8$ (anorthic) Acid plagioclase, Albite, $NaAlSi_3O_8$ Basic plagioclase, Anorthite, $CaAl_2Si_2O_8$
Feldspathoid group	Leucite, $KAl(SiO_3)_2$ Nepheline, $[Na, K]AlSiO_4$ Sodalite, $Na_8Al_6Cl_2(Si_6O_{24})$ Lazurite, $Na_5Al_3S(SiO_4)_3$
Pyroxene (Cleavage 87° and 93°)	Enstatite, $MgSiO_4$ Hypersthene, $[Mg, Fe]SiO_3$ Diopside, $Ca[Mg, Fe](SiO_3)_2$ Augite, $CaMg(SiO_3)_2 + [Mg, Fe][Al_2O_3, Fe_2O_3](SiO_3)$ Jadeite, $NaAl(SiO_3)_2$
Amphibole (Cleavage 56° and 124°)	Anthophyllite, $(OH)_2(Mg, Fe)_7Si_8O_{22}$ Tremolite, $(OH)_2Ca_2Mg_5(Si_4O_{11})_2$ Hornblende, $Ca(MgFe)_3Si_4O_{12} + NaAlSi_2O_6$
Mica	Muscovite, $(OH)_2KAl_2Si_3AlO_{10}$ Biotite, $(OH)_2K(Mg, Fe)_3AlSi_3O_{10}$ Phlogopite, $(OH)_2KMg_3Si_3AlO_{10}$ Lepidolite, $KLi_2Al(Si_4O_{10})(OH, F)_2$
Olivine group	Olivine, $(Mg, Fe)_2SiO_4$ Forsterite, Mg_2SiO_4

Minor Rock-making Minerals

Silicates of less abundant elements	Titanite, $CaTiSiO_5$ Beryl, $Be_3Al_2(SiO_3)_6$ Spodumene, $LiAl(SiO_3)_2$ Calamine, $Zn_2(OH)_2SiO_3$ Willemite, Zn_2SiO_4 Zircon, $ZrSiO_4$ Tourmaline, $(Na_2Ca)(Mg, Al)_{27}B_9Si_{18}H_xO_{93}$ Topaz, $(AlF)_2SiO_4$

Secondary Minerals

Zeolites, derived from feldspars and feldspathoids	Heulandite, $CaAl_2Si_7O_{18} \cdot 6H_2O$ Stilbite, $(Na_2Ca)Al_2Si_6O_{16} \cdot 6H_2O$ Chabazite, $[Ca, Na_2]Al_2(SiO_3)_4 \cdot 6H_2O$ Analcite, $NaAl(SiO_3)_2 \cdot H_2O$ Natrolite, $Na_2Al_2Si_3O_{10} \cdot 2H_2O$
Chlorite	Clinochlore, Al, $Mg_5Si_3Al_{10}(OH)_8$ Epidote, $Ca_2(Al, Fe)_3OH(SiO_4)_3$ Penninite, $Mg_5(Al, Fe)(Al, Si)_4O_{10}(OH)_8$ Talc, $Mg_3(Si_4O_{10})(OH)_2$
and other hydrous silicates resulting from weathering	Serpentine, $2H_2O \cdot 3MgO \cdot 2SiO_2$ Kaolinite, $Al_2(Si_2O_3)(OH)_4$ Bentonite, in part $Al_2O_3 \cdot 5SiO_3 \cdot 5H_2O$

TABLE V (*Cont'd*)

MINERAL SILICATES

Garnet	Grossularite, $Ca_3Al_2(SiO_4)_3$
	Almandite, $Fe_3Al_2(SiO_4)_3$
	Pyrope, $Mg_3Al_2(SiO_4)_3$
	Andradite, $Ca_3Fe_2(SiO_4)_3$
and	
other silicates result- ing mainly from metamorphism	Andalusite, Al_2SiO_5
	Cyanite, Al_2SiO_5
	Sillimanite, Al_2SiO_5
	Prehnite, $H_2Ca_2Al_2(SiO_4)_3$
	Scapolite, $Ca_4Al_6Si_6O_{24}(SO_4, CO_3)$ to $Na_4Al_3Si_9O_{24}Cl$
	Vesuvianite, $Ca_{10}Al_4(Mg, Fe)_2Si_9O_{34}(OH)_4$
	Wollastonite, $CaSiO_3$

lite family. In the first three families listed, the mineral quartz is present but it is absent in the others. Granite may be considered as an acidic rock because of the high percentage of the acid oxides. On the other hand peridotite is basic.

IGNEOUS ROCKS

Granite—Rhyolite. Minerals: orthoclase and quartz, with or without acid plagioclase, muscovite, biotite and hornblende. Average per cent SiO_2, 70. Glass forms: obsidian, pumice.

Granite diorite—Quartz latite. Minerals: acid plagioclase with smaller amounts of orthoclase and quartz with or without biotite hornblende, pyroxene. Average per cent SiO_2, 65.

Quartz diorite—Dacite. Minerals: plagioclase, quartz with biotite or hornblende or augite. Average per cent SiO_2, 64.

Diorite—Andesite. Minerals: plagioclase, hornblende, with or without biotite, augite, orthoclase. Average per cent SiO_2, 60. Glass forms: Andesite obsidian.

Syenite—Trachyte. Minerals: orthoclase, hornblende, plagioclase, with or without biotite. Average per cent SiO_2, 61.

Nephelite syenite—Phonolite. Minerals: orthoclase

plagioclase, nephelite, hornblende with or without biotite, sodalite, leucite, augite.   Average per cent SiO_2, 55.

Gabbro—Basalt.   Minerals: Augite, olivine, basic plagioclase biotite, hornblende.   Average per cent SiO_2, 49. Glass forms: tachylite.

Peridotite.   Minerals: pyroxene, olivine, hornblende, biotite, magnetite.   Average per cent SiO_2, 38.

Granite is the most abundant igneous rock in the earth's crust, indeed the continents appear to be slabs of granite about 20 miles thick "floating" on heavier basaltic material.   The composition of the stony meteorites is very nearly that of peridotite and it is probable that the composition of the major portion of the earth, i.e., the mantel extending down to the iron core, is similar to peridotite which consists largely of magnesium and iron orthosilicates.   There is considerable evidence to support the theory that the earth was condensed from a cold cosmic cloud.   In the initial state the outer layer was basaltic in character.   After about a billion years the radioactivity (largely K^{40}) generated sufficient heat to start the decomposition of the basalt into granite, which rose to form continents, and dunite (heavy orthosilicate) which sank. It appears probable that this process is still continuing and that the continents are growing.

TABLE VI

APPROXIMATE AVERAGE COMPOSITION OF VARIOUS IGNEOUS ROCKS

	GRANITE— RHYOLITE	SYENITE— TRACHYTE	GABBRO— BASALT	PERIDOTITE
	Acid	Intermediate	Basic	Very Basic
SiO_2.........	70	61	49	38
Al_2O_3.........	15	17	17	8
FeO, Fe_2O_3....	3	5	11	12
MgO.........	1	2	6	30
CaO.........	2	3	9	7
Na_2O.........	3	5	3	..
K_2O.........	4	5	1	..

18. Weathering.—The primary minerals disintegrate under the mechanical and chemical action of the wind and rain. Large quartz crystals are broken down into small grains of sand. The feldspars are decomposed by the action of carbon dioxide and water into sand and clay: $2KAlSi_3O_8 + H_2CO_3 + H_2O = K_2CO_3 + H_4Al_2Si_2O_9 + 4SiO_2$. Under other conditions bauxite, hydrous alumina, is formed. Another product is a fibrous type of muscovite: $3KAlSi_3O_8 + H_2CO_3 = KH_2Al_3Si_3O_{12} + 6SiO_2 + K_2CO_3$. Plagioclase alters into the zeolites and related mineral, and biotite forms chlorites. Olivine is readily attacked by carbonic acid and oxygen; the iron is oxidized and deposited as magnetite and the magnesium forms magnesite. The pyroxenes and amphiboles undergo somewhat similar changes.

Sedimentary and Metamorphic Rocks.—The common sedimentary deposited products are clay, shale, sandstone, limestone, dolomite, magnetite and gypsum. Under metamorphic conditions sandstone may become flint or quartzite. Shale may be converted to slate and limestone to marble. Contact metamorphism produces complicated changes not only in the rocks into which the intrusion takes place but also in the intruded molten mass.

19. Uses of Common Minerals.—The **micas,** muscovite (white mica) and phlogopite (amber mica), are used extensively in the electrical industries as insulating materials. A striking characteristic of these minerals is their cleavage into very thin elastic transparent sheets. Mica is used in making windows for stoves, in lamp chimneys, as Christmas tree "snow," as a decorative material for wall paper, and in many special paints. The term **asbestos** includes all minerals having a fibrous structure. The most important are some of the amphibole minerals, e.g., anthophyllite and fibrous serpentine. These minerals have a fibrous structure, silky luster, and are difficultly fusible. Asbestos is important commercially as a thermal insulator. The long fibers permit the manufacture of asbestos yarn, cloth, and paper, and from these innumerable fireproof objects. Mixtures of asbestos and Portland cement are used in fireproof shingles.

Kaolin, impure kaolinite, or **clay,** is a hydrated aluminum silicate, and **talc,** or **soapstone,** is a hydrated magnesium silicate. Clay is further discussed under pottery. Talc is used in soap, French chalk, talcum powder; and in paint, roofing, and rubber. A fibrous form is used extensively in paper. Soapstone is used as a refractory material. The bentonites and the pyrophillites are forms of aluminum silicates or the clay minerals. Both are important as commercial fillers for rubber, paper, and soaps. **Feldspar** is employed most extensively in the glass and ceramics industries. It is also used to cover cement and tarred surfaces to give them the appearance of granite.

20. Structure of Silicate Minerals.—The tetrahedron of oxygen atoms with a silicon at the center, which occurs in silica (Par. **14**), is a general characteristic of all silicate minerals. In the orthosilicates such as zircon, $ZrSiO_4$, and olivine, $(Mg, Fe)_2SiO_4$, the crystal is a lattice of SiO_4 tetrahedra and the positive ions; and the same is true of the orthodisilicates, the negative ion, $Si_2O_7^{-6}$, consisting of two tetrahedra linked by a corner. The metasilicates (SiO_3^{--} radical) may complete the tetrahedron of oxygen atoms by forming rings in which two corners of each tetrahedron are shared. The most common ring contains six tetrahedra, for example beryl, $Be_3Al_2Si_6O_{18}$, consists of a lattice of the positive ions with the ring-like negative ions $Si_6O_{18}^{-12}$. A three membered ring is also known in benitoite, $BaTiSi_3O_9$. In the pyroxenes, e.g., $CaMg(SiO_3)_2$, which are also metasilicates, the SiO_3 groups form infinite chains instead of rings, and the positive ions serve to bind the chains together. The amphiboles contain infinite double chains formed from the $Si_4O_{11}^{-6}$ groups. These are illustrated in Fig. 5. In the various types of asbestos these chains are in bundles of parallel fibers. In other cases they form sheets of matted fibers. Jade appears to be a mineral in which the fibers are matted in all directions.

Silicates containing the $Si_4O_{10}^{-4}$ group (or $AlSi_3O_{10}^{-5}$ if one Si is replaced by Al) form infinite sheets of silicon oxygen tetrahedra. These may be looked upon as two dimensional extensions of the arrangement shown in Fig. 5 to give a

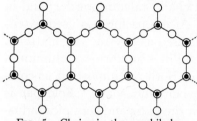

FIG. 5.   Chains in the amphiboles.

sheet with the appearance of a wire netting. Such sheets held together by positive ions are found in the clay minerals. Double sheets with the vertices of the tetrahedra pointing toward each other occur in the mica minerals and talc. In the former the sheets are held together by alkali or alkaline earth ions, but the latter contains no intermediate atoms. In the chlorite the mica-like sheets are separated by intermediate magnesium-aluminum oxide layers.

Silica has been given as an example of a three-dimensional network of silicon-oxygen tetrahedra. If one out of every four silicons in the structure is replaced by KAl, the resulting feldspar, e.g., $KAlSi_3O_8$, is a network of SiO_4 and AlO_4 tetrahedra. The negative charge is neutralized by the potassium ions which occupy holes in the structure. In addition to the feldspar group the zeolite minerals have a three-dimensional framework. These structures are, however, more open with large cavities and channels. They are capable of holding large amounts of water which may be driven off readily, and the positive ions which are contained in the cavities and balance the negative charge on the framework are readily replaceable by other ions.

21. Pottery and Porcelain.—Mixtures of clay (kaolinite), quartz, and feldspar, in various proportions and baked at various temperatures, form an extensive series of ceramic products. Most types of pottery or bricks are made from naturally occurring clays, which contain sand and feldspar. They are usually colored buff or red by iron oxide, the white porcelain clays being relatively scarce. Upon heating, kaolin is altered, probably losing water, according to the equation: $H_4Al_2Si_2O_9 = Al_2SiO_5 + SiO_2 + 2H_2O$; and around 1200° the feldspar fuses and serves to bind the clay and quartz together. The properties of the earthenware depend to a great extent upon the temperature at which it is baked, and there is often but slight variation in composition between different types of products. Soft porcelain contains a high per cent of calcium phosphate. Glaze is imparted to the cheaper grades of pottery by the introduction of sodium chloride near the end of the firing. Other glazes used are fusible lead calcium alumino-borosilicates, or, in many cases, simple feldspar.

22. Glass.—Glass is a fused non-crystalline mixture of basic oxides and silicon dioxide. The basic oxides are usually the alkalies and alkaline earths, but they may be substituted in whole or in part by oxides of lead, zinc, arsenic, antimony, aluminum, etc.; and the silicon dioxide by boric or phosphoric oxides. Like all super-cooled liquids, glass does not have a definite melting point, but softens gradually over a range of temperatures. In this viscous state, glass may be blown or rolled into almost any desired shape or form. The raw materials which are fused together to form glass are sand, or the other acid oxides, and generally the carbonates of the basic constituents.

The manufacture of common **soda glass** is often represented by the equation, $2Na_2CO_3 + CaCO_3 + 6SiO_2 = Na_4CaSi_6O_{15} + 3CO_2$, but the product cannot be considered as a definite compound. It is used in making bottles, window glass, glass tubing, etc. The percentage composition of soda glass is approximately: SiO_2, 71–78; Na_2O, 12–17; CaO, 5–15; Al_2O_3, 1–4. The corresponding **potash glass,** also called **hard glass,** or **Bohemian glass,** has a

TABLE VII

PERCENTAGE COMPOSITION OF VARIOUS GLASSES

OXIDE	EGYPTIAN 1500 BC	BOTTLE GLASS	WINDOW GLASS	POTASH GLASS	FLINT GLASS	PYREX GLASS	JENA GLASS
SiO₂	67.8	74.1	71.7	80.0	45.5	80.7	64.7
B₂O₃	...	...	...	...	...	12.0	10.9
Na₂O	13.7	15.1	12.6	0.7	1.7	4.1	7.5
K₂O	2.1	...	...	11.6	8.7	0.1	0.4
CaO	4.0	4.6	11.5	7.8	0.5	0.3	0.6
MgO	2.3	3.4	2.4	0.1	...	...	0.2
ZnO	...	...	...	...	...	...	10.9
PbO	...	...	...	...	43.5	...	...
Al₂O₃	4.4	1.2	1.0	0.3	0.3	2.2	4.2
Fe₂O₃	1.0		0.1	0.5	...		0.2
SO₃	1.0	...	0.5	...	...	...	...

higher fusing temperature. **Potash-lead glass,** or **flint glass,** has a high density and index of refraction, and is used in making cut glass articles. **Pyrex glass** is very high in the acid oxides: SiO_2, 80 per cent, B_2O_3, 12 per cent, with the balance Na_2O and Al_2O_3. It has a low coefficient of expansion, and is, therefore, very suitable for articles subject to sudden changes in temperature. It is also resistant to chemical action. **Jena glass** is a zinc-barium borosilicate.

Two Si^{+4} ions in a crystal may be replaced by the combinations $Al^{+3}P^{+5}$ or $B^{+3}P^{+5}$. Thus $AlPO_4$ has a crystal structure which resembles that of cristobalite. This principle has been utilized in the development of **phosphate** glasses which are chemically resistant to the action of hydrofluoric acid.

Glass may be colored by the presence of small amounts of metal oxides: chromium or copper giving green; cobalt, blue; manganese, violet. A colloidal metal suspension of gold gives ruby glass. "Milk glass" usually contains stannic oxide or calcium fluoride.

If glass is held at a high temperature for a long time, a certain amount of crystallization may occur (called devitrification). Thick glass objects must be carefully annealed, i.e. cooled very slowly, as the cooling of the outer portions more rapidly than the interior will result in great strains and the subsequent cracking of the object.

23. Portland Cement.—Although lime mortars have been used for centuries, the modern hydraulic cement dates back only to about 1825, and its extensive use to about 1900. The approximate composition of Portland cement is given in Table VIII.

TABLE VIII

COMPOSITION OF PORTLAND CEMENT

Oxide..........	CaO	SiO_2	Al_2O_2	Fe_2O_3	MgO	SO_3	Na_2O, K_2O
Per cent.......	58–67	19–26	4–11	2–5	0–5	0–2.5	0–3

Cement is made by heating a mixture of limestone and clay, or material of equivalent composition, to the point of incipient fusion (about 1450° C.). The product, termed clinker, is ground with 2–3 per cent of gypsum, added to decrease the time of setting, to give the cement.

The chemical composition appears to be a solid solution of approximately two moles of Ca_2SiO_4 and one of $Ca_3(AlO_3)_2$ although considerable Ca_3SiO_5 may also be present. The Ca_2SiO_4 and Ca_3SiO_5 hydrolyze with water, $Ca_2SiO_4 + H_2O = CaSiO_3 + Ca(OH)_2$, and the strength of the set cement is due to the —Si—O—Si— bonds of the $CaSiO_3$ chain structure. The initial setting is aided by the conversion of the $Ca(OH)_2$ into $CaCO_3$. The principal function of the calcium aluminate appears to be the lowering of the point of incipient fusion.

The production of cement in the United States in 1948 was about 175 million barrels. The major portion of this was used in mixture with crushed rock and sand to make **concrete.**

24. Organo-silicon Polymers.—The bond between carbon and silicon is relatively strong. Thus silicon tetraphenyl, $Si(C_6H_5)_4$, is a crystalline substance which distills at red heat without decomposition and silicon tetramethyl, $Si(CH_3)_4$, can be shaken with concentrated sulfuric acid without reaction. Organo-derivatives of $Si(OH)_4$ can be prepared by the hydrolysis of the organo-silicon chlorides. Thus dimethyldichlorsilicomethane hydrolyzes, $(CH_3)_2SiCl_2 + 2H_2O = (CH_3)_2Si(OH)_2$. This ester polymerizes to give chains having the structure,

$$
\begin{array}{ccc}
CH_3 & CH_3 & CH_3 \\
| & | & | \\
-Si-O-Si-O-Si-O- \\
| & | & | \\
CH_3 & CH_3 & CH_3
\end{array}
$$

These organo-silicon polymers are called **silicones** from analogy of the $(CH_3)_2SiO$ group to acetone, and the general name is now used for all materials having C—Si—O bonds.

Cross linkage of linear chains may be obtained by the simultaneous hydrolysis of a disubstituted silicon chloride with a monosubstituted compound or with carbon tetrachloride.

$$
RSi(OH)_3 + R_2Si(OH)_2 = \left[
\begin{array}{cc}
R & R \\
| & | \\
-Si-O-Si-O- \\
| & | \\
O & R \\
|
\end{array}
\right]_n
$$

$$
Si(OH)_4 + R_2Si(OH)_2 = \left[
\begin{array}{cc}
| & \\
O & R \\
| & | \\
-Si-O-Si-Si-O- \\
| & | \\
O & R \\
|
\end{array}
\right]_n
$$

The methyl silicones may be obtained as short chain oils or "rubber"-like plastics. The oils have very small variations of viscosity with temperature and remain fluid to temperatures as low as − 80° C. Their uses include high temperature electrical insulations, low temperature lubrication and heat-resisting greases. The elastomers may be compounded to "rubbers" that do not decompose at 300° C. nor harden at − 55° C. They are employed as gasket materials for high temperature operation. In addition to the methyl derivatives, polymers of ethyl and phenyl radicals are also prepared.

The methylchlorosilicones as vapors react with hydrophilic surfaces to give a film which is essentially a thin coating of a silicone. Such surfaces are highly water-repellent. Wood, cotton and glass surfaces are readily coated and by special treatment certain metallic surfaces may also be coated. This process for metals is the basis for the development of cooking utensils which require no grease.

25. Silicon and Sulfur.—Silicon burns in sulfur vapor to form the **disulfide,** SiS_2. The structure of the solid is infinite chains of SiS_4 tetrahedra sharing opposite edges:

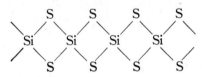

The sulfide hydrolyzes in water to silicic acid and hydrogen sulfide. When the sulfide is fused with alkali sulfides, **thiosilicates** are formed, e.g., Na_2SiS_3.

26. Silicate Analysis.—In detecting the presence of silicon, advantage is taken of the volatility of silicon tetrafluoride. The sample is heated with hydrofluoric acid in a lead or platinum dish. If silicon is present, a drop of water in a wire loop, placed in the fumes, becomes cloudy owing to the formation of silicic acid: $3SiF_4 + 3H_2O = H_2SiO_3 + 2H_2SiF_6$.

Silicates are determined quantitatively by gravimetric methods, generally separating silicon dioxide and weighing as such. In this process, decomposition of the silicate may often be accomplished by digesting with concentrated hydrochloric acid, leaving a residue of silica. Other silicates must first be fused with sodium carbonate before they can be decomposed by acid. The silica residue may be contaminated with $BaSO_4$, Al_2O_3, Fe_2O_3, TiO_2, and oxides of certain rare elements; the amount in the mixture is often determined by heating with hydrofluoric acid, obtaining the silica by loss of weight, due to the volatilization of the tetrafluoride.

Chapter XV

THE METALS OF GROUP IV. TITANIUM, ZIRCONIUM, HAFNIUM, AND GERMANIUM, TIN, LEAD

1. The first and second elements of Group IV, carbon and silicon, have been discussed in the two preceding chapters. The remaining elements of the main group are titanium, zirconium, and hafnium, and of the subgroup, germanium, tin, and lead. All of the free elements are metals, but both branches of the group show many similarities to silicon in their chemical properties.

Titanium and the heavier elements of the main group are each the second elements of a transition series in which the kernel is being transformed from the noble gas structure to the eighteen electron type (Append. XVIII). However, the two d electrons are easily removed so that all members of the group show the characteristic $+4$ oxidation state. Titanium has also a fairly stable $+3$ and a less stable $+2$ state.

The subgroup elements form compounds of both the $+2$ and $+4$ states, the former becoming increasingly stable with respect to the latter with increasing atomic weight.

The tetroxides of all the elements, are amphoteric, and those of the main group are, in general, somewhat more basic than the oxides of the corresponding elements of the subgroup, which is in agreement with a slightly larger size of the main group ions, and in both groups the basic character increases with increasing size. Like silicon, all of the members of the group form complex fluorides, and all the tetrachlorides, except thorium, are volatile liquids.

One of the most striking differences between the two branches of the group is the much greater stability of the sulfides of germanium, tin, and lead. This stability of the sulfides is a general characteristic of the ions with eighteen electrons in the outer shell of the kernel (cf. **VII—2**). The elements of Subgroup IV resemble those of Subgroup III in not forming complex ions with ammonia.

Cerium and thorium are often discussed in connection with Group IV, but the former should be included in the rare earths, the latter with the actinide series although in many respects their chemistry resembles that of zirconium and hafnium.

TITANIUM, ZIRCONIUM, AND HAFNIUM

2. Occurrence.—The elements of this group are by no means as rare as they have commonly been considered. Titanium ranks eighth among the metals in order of abundance in the igneous rocks, the per cent of the element present in the earth's crust being estimated at 0.43, and is the fourth most abundant metallic element. The values for the other elements of the group are: zirconium, 0.026; and hafnium, 3×10^{-5}. Zirconium is more abundant than copper, zinc and lead combined.

The elements do not occur free, but their compounds are widely distributed in nature. Because of the similarity in chemical behavior between these elements and silicon, their presence in rocks is often overlooked.

The most important titanium ores are **ilmenite,** $FeTiO_3$, and **rutile,** TiO_2. There are various related ores such as **arizonite,** $Fe_2O_3 \cdot 3TiO_2$. Metatitanates of ferric iron, calcium, magnesium, manganese, and lead, also occur. Titanosilicates such as **sphene,** $CaTiSiO_5$, are common, and less frequently borotitanates and titanoantimonates. The

American production of the oxide is around 150,000 tons, largely from the deposits of ilmenite in New York, and an additional 250,000 tons are imported. The sand of certain beaches in India is the principal foreign source. The major portion is consumed in the manufacture of white pigments.

Zirconium occurs principally as **baddeleyite,** ZrO_2, and **zircon,** $ZrSiO_4$. The domestic consumption of the dioxide is around 30,000 tons. Of this, 3,000 tons are obtained from Florida sand dunes and the balance imported from Brazil and Australia. Hafnium is present to the extent of 1 or 2 per cent in practically all primary zirconium minerals.

3. The Metals.—The electro-positive nature of the elements, together with the high melting point of the oxides and the tendency to form carbides, nitrides, and silicides at high temperatures, renders the preparation of the metals difficult. The Goldschmidt reduction with aluminum gives aluminum alloys. In the case of titanium, the alloy contains 5 or 6 per cent aluminum, but if iron is present, the product is largely ferro-titanium. Zirconium may be separated from the aluminum alloy by distillation. The reduction of titanium dioxide by carbon in an electric furnace yields a mixture of the metal and carbide. Ferro-carbontitanium is made by the reduction of mixtures of iron and titanium oxides. Both titanium and zirconium are produced commercially by the reduction of the tetrachloride by magnesium in an atmosphere of helium around 800–900° C. In the case of titanium, the excess magnesium metal and chloride is removed by dilute acid while with zirconium these products are volatilized out under vacuum at 900° C. The metals are ground, the powder highly compressed and cintered at about 1000° C.

Titanium metal is silver white. It may be rolled and cold worked, is lighter and stronger than steel, and has excellent corrosion resistance. The metal surface oxidizes or nitrides with ease and may thus be surface hardened. The properties of zirconium are similar and in addition the metal is highly resistant to corrosion by concentrated HCl, HNO_3 or H_2SO_4. The metals titanium, zirconium, and hafnium appear to have the hexagonal close packed form of crystal lattice, but titanium changes to a body centered cubic above 880° C.

TABLE I

ATOMS AND PHYSICAL PROPERTIES

	Ti	Zr	Hf
Atomic weight	47.90	91.22	178.6
Atomic number	22	40	72
Isotopes	46, 47, 48, 49, 50	90, 91, 92, 94, 96	176, 177, 178, 179, 180
Melting point, ° C	1,812	1,852	2,130
Boiling point, ° C	3,130	3,580	5,230
Density	4.5	6.5	13.3
Electrical resistivity, ohm-cm	3×10^{-6}	49×10^{-6}	30×10^{-6}
Radius of M^{+4} ion in crystals, cm. $\times 10^8$	0.68	0.80	—
Tensile strength, cold worked, lb/sq. in	120,000	130,000	—

If the price of titanium can be reduced, it promises to become most important as a structural material. At the present price of $4 per pound it can replace many special steels and aluminum bronze for light objects. Ferrotitanium is used extensively in the steel industry; the titanium is considered extremely valuable in removing nitrogen (by forming nitride) from, and in imparting toughness to, steel. Ferrozirconium is an excellent scavenger for oxygen and sulfur and also improves the grain size in steel. Zirconium should replace tantalum in radio tubes, electric condensers and as a non-corrosive metal for pipes, tank linings and chemical uses.

4. Reactions of the Metals.—The reactions of the metals are summarized in Table II. At ordinary temperatures, they are not very reactive, being oxidized but slowly by oxygen or by hydrogen ion. Measurements of the electrode

potentials of the group are unreliable because of the difficulties in obtaining equilibrium conditions. In spite of its

TABLE II

REACTIONS OF Ti, Zr, AND Hf

$M + O_2 = MO_2$	Burn when heated
$M + 2X_2 = MX_4$	With halogens when heated
$M + 2H_2O = MO_2 + 2H_2$	With steam
$M + 4HF = MF_4 + 2H_2$	
$M + 4HCl = MCl_4 + 2H_2$	With hot concentrated acid, but Ti gives $TiCl_3$
$M + H_2 = MH_2$	TiH_2 doubtful. Slow with Zr and Hf
$M + 2S = MS_2$	Also react with P, C, B, and Si at high temperatures
$3M + 2N_2 = M_3N_4$	Also MN
$M + 2H_2O = MO_2 + 4H^+ + 4e^-$	Potential in volts, Ti, 0.86; Zr, 1.43; Hf, 1.57

highly electropositive character zirconium is not readily
soluble in nitric acid.

TITANIUM COMPOUNDS

5. Oxidation States.—Titanium forms compounds in
which it has the oxidation states of $+ 2$, $+ 3$, and $+ 4$.
Important oxidation-reduction potentials relating the states
are given below:

	VOLTS
$Ti = Ti^{++} + 2e^-$	1.63
$Ti^{++} = Ti^{+++} + e^-$	0.37
$H_2O + Ti^{+++} = TiO^{++} + 2H^+ + e^-$	$ca -0.1$
$6F^- + Ti = TiF_6^{--} + 4e^-$	1.19

6. The $+ 2$ State.—The **oxide,** TiO, is prepared by the
high temperature reduction of the dioxide by carbon,
magnesium, or titanium. It is basic, but its salts are readily
oxidized in solution by hydrogen ion unless the acid concentration is very low. The **dichloride** may be formed at
high temperatures by the decomposition of the trichloride:
$2TiCl_3 = TiCl_2 + TiCl_4$.

7. Compounds of the $+3$ State.—The **sesquioxide** is formed in the reaction: $2TiO_2 + H_2 = Ti_2O_3 + H_2O$. It also is basic. The corresponding **titanous hydroxide,** $Ti(OH)_3$, is precipitated upon the addition of alkalies to titanous salts in solution. This hydroxide is a very powerful reducing agent (Par. **5**). It evolves hydrogen to form the dioxide: $Ti(OH)_3 = TiO_2 + H_2O + \frac{1}{2}H_2$; and reduces nitrate in alkaline solution to ammonia: $8Ti(OH)_3 + NO_3^-$ $= NH_3 + 8TiO_2 + OH^- + 10H_2O$. Anhydrous **trihalides** may be prepared by reducing the tetrahalides at moderately high temperatures, e.g., $TiCl_4 + Ag = TiCl_3 + AgCl$.

Solutions of titanous ion, Ti^{+++}, are readily prepared from solutions of titanic salts by electrolytic reduction, or by the reducing action of zinc upon the hot solution. Titanous solutions are violet. Titanous solutions are important as volumetric reagents, as they are oxidized quantitatively by many oxidizing agents, e.g., Fe^{+++} and MnO_4^-. Titanous ion is much less hydrolyzed than the titanic ion. The formation of the slightly soluble hydroxide has been discussed above. The cesium titanous alum, $CsTi(SO_4)_2$ $\cdot 12H_2O$, is but sparingly soluble.

8. Compounds of the $+4$ State.—The **dioxide** occurs in nature in two tetragonal forms, **rutile** and **anatase,** and also in a rhombic form called brookite. The pure oxide is white, but natural rutile is usually brown or black. The arrangement of the atoms in the rutile crystal lattice is given in Appendix V. This is the common crystal form of compounds MX_2 when the ratio of the diameter of M to X is < 0.6. When this ratio is greater the arrangement is generally that of fluorite.

The fused oxide is difficult to dissolve, but the hydrated forms dissolve readily in acids and slightly in alkalies. However, the chemistry of the titanium minerals is essentially that of an acid oxide. The oxide fused with metal oxides or carbonates yields **titanates,** e.g., $CaTiO_3$, $Ba_2Ti_3O_8$, $ZnTiO_3$, Zn_2TiO_3, $PbTiO_3$, Mn_2TiO_4. The potassium metatitanate, K_2TiO_3, is soluble in cold water, but upon boiling, the titanium is completely precipitated as the dioxide. The dioxide has become one of the most important white pigments, the annual domestic consumption for this purpose being close to 400,000 tons. The pigment is made by hydrolysis of $Ti(SO_4)_2$ and possesses both good covering power and chemical inertness. The dioxide is used in ceramics to make a yellow glassware. The hydrous oxide made by hydrolysis of the tetrachloride is an important mordant.

When an acid solution of a titanium salt is made alkaline, a hydrogel is formed. Upon aging, the gel gives an X-ray pattern corresponding to that of anatase. Hydrous oxide formed by the hydrolysis of $TiCl_4$ appears to be the rutile modification. The precipitated gel, often referred to as ortho- or α-titanic acid, is readily soluble in acids. So-called meta- or β-titanic acid, an insoluble form, is obtained by the action of nitric acid upon the metal. (Cf. similar stannic acids.)

Rutile is also of considerable importance in the manufacture of welding rods, in the production of titanium carbide for cutting tools and as a high dielectric material. The dielectric constant of rutile is 173 parallel to the principal axis and 89 perpendicular to the axis. The dielectric constant of preparations of $CaTiO_3$ is as high as 20,000.

The addition of hydrogen peroxide to a solution of the sulfate yields the complex orange peroxy ion $TiO_2(SO_4)_2^{--}$. The peroxy-acid, H_4TiO_5 has been precipitated from ammonia solutions and the salt K_4TiO_8 is known.

9. The anhydrous **halides** are prepared by direct reaction of the elements, or by the action of the halogen upon heated mixtures of the oxide and carbon, e.g., $TiO_2 + C + 2Cl_2 = TiCl_4 + CO_2$. Water solutions are prepared by dissolving the hydrated oxide in concentrated hydrohalic acid, but in dilute acid the halides readily hydrolyze to the dioxide. The tetrachloride is employed for producing smoke screens. The smoke particles are largely $TiCl_4 \cdot 5H_2O$. The lighter halides form complex ions, e.g., TiF_6^{--} and $TiCl_6^{--}$. **Potassium fluorotitanate,** K_2TiF_6, is but slightly soluble.

10. The hydrated **dioxide** dissolves in sulfuric acid solutions. In dilute acid, the sulfate hydrolyzes to form **basic sulfates,** e.g., $Ti_2O(SO_4)_3 \cdot 3H_2O$ and $TiO \cdot SO_4 \cdot nH_2O$. Similarly **basic nitrates** and **phosphates** exist, and the phosphates form a number of double basic compounds, e.g., potassium titanyl phosphate, $K(TiO)PO_4$.

The addition of soluble sulfides to titanium solutions results in the precipitation of the dioxide, but the **sulfide** may be formed by heating chloride and hydrogen sulfide vapors together: $TiCl_4 + 2H_2S = TiS_2 + 4HCl$. The sulfide does not form polysulfides with alkali sulfides. At high temperatures, the element unites with sulfur, forming TiS and Ti_2S_3.

ZIRCONIUM COMPOUNDS

11. Zirconium forms the **dioxide** and possibly two oxides of lower oxidation states, but the evidence in favor of these is of doubtful nature. The dioxide occurs in nature as the mineral baddeleyite. Like titania, it reacts with fused hydroxides and carbonates, forming insoluble **zirconates,** e.g., Na_2ZrO_3, $CaZrO_3$, $PbZrO_3$. The oxide is widely used in ceramics as a constituent of enamels. Zircon refractories are finding increasing use in steel mills since zirconium oxide has a melting point of 2950° C. or about twice that of steel. The hydrated oxide, usually regarded as **zirconium hydroxide,** $Zr(OH)_4$, is formed as a **hydrogel** upon the addition of alkali to solutions of zirconium salts. The hydroxide is readily soluble in acids and somewhat soluble in cold concentrated alkali, with which it reacts mainly to form insoluble zirconate. Hydrogen peroxide reacts with the hydroxide to form the **hydrated peroxide,** probably H_4ZrO_5. In sulfuric acid solution the complex peroxysulfate, $O_2ZrO_2SO_4ZrO_2$, appears to be formed.

The **tetrahalides** resemble those of titanium in properties and methods of formation. Basic halides are obtained upon evaporation of the water solutions of the halides, e.g., **zirconyl chloride**, $ZrOCl_2$. The latter is employed in tanning. Many slightly soluble **fluorozirconates** are known, e.g., K_2ZrF_6, $BaZrF_6$, and also less stable **chlorozirconates**.

Reduction of the tetrachloride with aluminum at 300° yields the **trichloride**, $ZrCl_3$, and at higher temperatures, the **dichloride**, $ZrCl_2$, but these compounds cannot be formed in water solutions.

Zirconium sulfides, sulfates, nitrates, and **phosphates** resemble closely the corresponding titanic compounds. The normal sulfate may be crystallized from concentrated sulfuric acid solutions, and many basic and double sulfates are known. Hydrogen reacts with zirconium at red heat, apparently forming the unstable **hydride**, ZrH_2.

The naturally occurring **silicate**, $ZrSiO_4$, known as **zircon** or **jargon,** is valued as a jewel. On account of their luster and hardness (7.5) zircons are employed as substitutes for diamonds. They occur in a great variety of colors, red, green, blue, and white.

Hafnium Compounds

12. Hafnium resembles zirconium so closely that the presence of several per cent of hafnium in the zirconium compounds was not discovered until 1923, although the chemistry of zirconium was carefully investigated during the preceding century. Any compound formed by the one element appears to be formed by the other, and, as a rule, the melting points, boiling points, and solubilities of the two compounds are very similar. Hafnium dioxide and hydroxide appear to be slightly more basic than the zirconium compounds.

13. Analytical.—Titanium may be extracted from its ores by alkaline fusion, followed by digestion in acid, or by fusion with potassium acid sulfate and extraction with water.

The addition of hydrogen peroxide to a sulfuric acid solution of titanium produces the characteristic yellow or orange color of the peroxy-acid. Titanic solutions may be reduced to the violet $+ 3$ state by zinc in hot acid solution, and the titanium may be determined quantitatively by titrating this solution with permanganate. Titanium hydroxide is precipitated by the addition of alkalies, ammonia, and soluble carbonates and sulfides to solutions of titanium salts. If formed in cold solution, it is readily soluble in acids, and somewhat soluble in excess alkali. Precipitated from hot solution, it is not rapidly soluble in acid.

Zirconium and hafnium ores may be got into solution by methods similar to those given for titanium. The two elements may be separated from iron, aluminum, beryllium, titanium, and thorium by precipitation from highly acid solutions, as the very slightly soluble zirconyl and hafnyl phosphates, $ZrO(H_2PO_4)_2$. Alkalies precipitate zirconium and hafnium hydroxides, which are not soluble in excess of the reagent. Ammonium oxalate or oxalic acid precipitate the oxalates, soluble in excess of the reagents. Separation from iron may be accomplished through the slight solubility of the potassium complex fluorides.

The per cent of hafnia and zirconia in a sample may be estimated by determination of the density of the oxide mixture. The values for the pure oxides are ZrO_2, 5.73, and HfO_2, 9.68. Hafnium and zirconium are extremely difficult to separate from each other. The greatest difference in the solubilities of their compounds appear to exist in the citrates, the hafnium salt being the more soluble. Separation may also be carried out through the fractional precipitation of the phosphates, oxychlorides, and the ammonium and potassium complex fluorides. Separation may also be attained by use of the cation exchange resins and by solvent extraction of organic complexes. The complex of hafnium with certain diketones is more soluble in benzene than the corresponding zirconium complex.

GERMANIUM, TIN, AND LEAD

14. Occurrence.—The elements of this group constitute but a very small portion of the igneous rocks, the estimated percentages being germanium, 10^{-11}, tin, 10^{-6}, and lead, 2×10^{-5}. They do, however, occur frequently in workable deposits.

Germanium is found in many sulfide ores, especially those of silver, lead, tin, antimony, and zinc. In a number of ores definite sulfide complexes appear to be present, such as Ag_4GeS_4 and Pb_2GeS_4. An English coal ash has been reported which contains 1.6 per cent GeO_2. The small domestic supply comes largely from the cadmium fume dust obtained in sintering zinc concentrates.

The most important tin mineral is the oxide, SnO_2, called **cassiterite.** Deposits of cassiterite in Cornwall, England, were worked as early as 1000 B.C. by the Phoenicians. The principal sources of the metal at present are mines in the Malay States, Bolivia, and the Dutch East Indies. Tin also occurs as complex sulfides, e.g., $SnCu_2 \cdot FeS_4$, $Pb_5Sn_2 \cdot Sb_2S_{12}$,

TABLE III

ATOMIC AND PHYSICAL PROPERTIES OF GERMANIUM, TIN, AND LEAD

	GE	SN	PB
Atomic weight	72.60	118.70	207.22
Atomic number	32	50	82
Stable Isotopes	70, 72, 73, 74, 76	112, 114, 115, 116, 117, 118, 119, 120, 122, 124	204, 206, 207, 208
Melting point, ° C	958	231.9	327.5
Boiling point, ° C	2700	2,337	1,750
Density, g.c/c	5.36	W 7.31 G 5.75	11.34
Electrical resistivity, ohm-cm. at 20° C	ca 0.2	11.4×10^{-6}	21.9×10^{-6}
Size of M^{+4} ion in crystal, cm. $\times 10^8$ (if $Cl^- = 1.81$)	0.53	0.71	0.84
Ionization Potentials, 1st electron	8.09	7.30	7.38
2d electron	15.86	ca 14.5	14.96

and Ag_8SnS_6, and as complex oxides, e.g., $CaSnO_4(BO)_2$ and $CaO \cdot SnO_2 \cdot 3SiO_2 \cdot 2H_2O$, but these minerals are of slight importance.

The principal lead ore is the sulfide or **galena,** PbS, and this is generally associated with sulfides of silver, copper, arsenic, antimony, bismuth, and tin. Other common ores are **cerussite,** $PbCO_3$, and **anglesite,** $PbSO_4$, which appear to have been formed by the weathering of sulfide ores. Complex oxides and oxychlorides of the metals of Groups V and VI also occur.

15. Metallic Germanium.—The metal may be prepared by reduction of the dioxide with carbon at red heat, or by the reduction of the oxide or sulfide by heating with potassium cyanide. A metallic copper compound, Cu_3Ge, may be electro deposited from aqueous alkaline cyanide solutions, and the metal may be deposited from solutions of GeI_4 in ethylene glycol and from a fused borax electrolyte in which the dioxide is dissolved. Germanium is a greyish-white metal, rather hard and brittle. It forms good tarnish resisting mirrors. X-ray data for the solid indicate that the atoms are arranged in a modified diamond structure. The metal is a "semi-conductor" and is employed in radar for the rectification of microwaves. The copper compound has high chemical resistance and may become a useful bronze.

16. Tin.—Cassiterite is easily reduced to the metal by smelting with carbon in a reverberatory furnace: $SnO_2 + C = Sn + CO_2$. The liquid metal is drawn off from the furnace and cast into molds. The greatest difficulty in the metallurgy is the purification of the ore before smelting. This is carried out by roasting, to remove sulfur and arsenic, and if tungsten is present, the ore is fused with sodium carbonate and the tungsten extracted with water. The crude metal usually contains some compounds of iron and arsenic, which may be removed by carefully melting the ingots (liquation), as the compounds melt at temperatures somewhat higher than the pure metal. The annual production of tin is about 170,000 tons. Considerable tin is recovered from scrap metal. In the case of tin cans, the recovery is effected by boiling the scrap in a solution of NaOH and NaNO₃. The sodium stannate obtained is then reduced electrolytically to the metal.

Tin exists in three solid forms, with definite transitions as summarized in the following scheme:

$$\overset{18°\quad 161°\quad 232°}{Sn\alpha = Sn\beta = Sn\gamma = Sn \text{ (liquid)}}$$

The α-form is the ordinary white tin. The transition of white tin to β or grey tin is slow at the transition temperature, but at $-50°$ the transformation is complete in a few days if a little of the latter form is present to start the reaction. The transition is accompanied by an increase in volume, and the product is a brittle substance which is readily powdered. The phenomenon was first observed in cold countries in the disintegration of organ pipes and other tin objects, and was called **"tin disease."** Grey tin is cubic, with the diamond lattice structure, while white tin is tetragonal with a ditetragonal-bipyramidal lattice. Γ-Tin belongs to the rhombic system.

White tin is very malleable, and may be rolled into thin sheets called tinfoil, which has been used extensively for wrapping, but is now largely replaced by aluminum foil and by plastics. It is very resistant to corrosion, whence its use in tinning iron and copper surfaces. Tin does not, however, give the galvanic protection afforded by zinc (cf. **VII—4**), since tin is not a more powerful reducing agent than iron. Tin forms many useful alloys. (See Table VI and also Copper and Bismuth.) The approximate percentage consumption of tin in America by various industries is: tinplate, 33; bronze, 27; solder, 21; and babbitt, 9. A great saving in tin has been accomplished through the replacement of the old dipping methods for the manufacture of tinplate by electrolytic deposition. The most widely used electrolyte is a bath containing phenylsulfonic acid and glue.

17. Lead.—The metallurgy of lead is concerned largely with the reduction of the sulfide, and this may be brought about in several ways. (1) Part of the sulfide may be roasted to the oxide, PbO, or sulfate, $PbSO_4$, and the oxidized ore

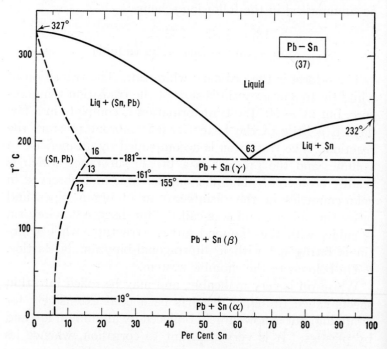

FIG. 1.   Lead-tin temperature-composition curves.

heated with more of the sulfide: $2PbO + PbS = 3Pb + SO_2$; and $PbSO_4 + PbS = 2Pb + 2SO_2$. (2) The ore may be roasted to the oxide and this reduced with carbon or carbon monoxide: $PbO + CO = Pb + CO_2$. (3) The sulfide may be reduced by heating with scrap iron: $PbS + Fe = Pb + FeS$. The iron may be added as such, or it may be produced in the furnace from a mixture of iron oxides and carbon. In the United States, the ore is generally first concentrated by "flotation" (cf. **VII—5**), and the smelting process is a combination of the three methods outlined above. A mixture of part roasted and part unroasted ore with iron oxide and carbon is heated in a blast furnace. Copper present collects in the iron sulfide matte, while silver and gold dissolve in the molten lead. In the refinement of the crude blast furnace lead, the more electropositive impurities are generally removed by melting the

TABLE IV
ALLOYS OF TIN AND LEAD

Britannia	Sn 90, Sb 10	Hard metal, Pb 90, Sb 10
Babbitt	Sn 90, Sb 7, Cu 3	Frary metal, Pb 90, Ca 10
Antifriction	Sn 75, Sb 12.5, Cu 17.5	Type metal, Pb 82, Sb 15, Sn 3
Solder	Sn 50, Pb 50	White metal, Pb 75, Sb 14, Sn 10, Cu 1
Pewter	Sn 85, Cu 6.8, Bi 6, Sb 1.7	Rose metal, Bi 50, Pb 27.1, Sn 22.9
Aluminum		Battery plate, Pb 94, Sb 6
solder	Sn 86, Zn 9, Al 5	

metal and keeping it molten for several hours with frequent stirring. The impurities, when oxidized, rise to the surface and are skimmed off. Some lead, especially if high in bismuth, is now refined electrolytically, using as an electrolyte a solution of lead fluosilicate. The crude lead serves as the anode, and a bag about the anode collects the "mud" from which bismuth and the noble metals are recovered. The annual production of lead is about 1,500,000 tons, of which about one fourth is produced in the United States.

Ordinary lead is very largely a mixture of the two isotopes, 208 and 206. Lead extracted from uranium ores is largely the lower isotope, and has a density of 11.27 as compared with 11.34 for ordinary lead. The crystal lattice of the metal is of the face centered type. The metal is so soft that it can be squirted, under pressure, into pipes and even into fine wire or rolled into thin sheets, but it lacks tensile strength. Lead may be hardened by the addition of antimony or the alkaline earth metals. The most important industrial uses of lead are in the manufacture of storage batteries, preparation of white lead and other pigments, manufacture of cable coverings, in plumbing, and in acid works. Important alloys of lead are listed in Table IV.

18. Reactions of the Metals.—The metals are powerful reducing agents in the presence of an alkaline solution and fairly strong in acid solutions. Pure tin and lead do not

TABLE V

REACTIONS OF Ge, Sn, AND Pb

$M + O_2 = MO_2$	Lead forms PbO or Pb_3O_4
$M + 2H^+ = M^{++} + H_2$	Not with Ge. Slowly with Sn and Pb
$M + 2S = MS_2$	Lead forms only PbS
$M + 2X_2 = MX_4$	With halogens, except PbI_4
$M + 2OH^- = MO_2^{--} + H_2$	Slowly with Sn and Pb. Ge forms GeO_3^{--}
$M = M^{++} + 2e^-$	Ge $ca.$ 0.0, Sn 0.14, Pb 0.13 (values in volts)
$3Ge + 4HNO_3 = 3GeO_2 + 4NO + 2H_2O$	
$3Sn + 4HNO_3 = 3SnO_2 + 4NO + 2H_2O$	Forms slightly soluble metastannic acid
$3Pb + 8HNO_3 = 3Pb(NO_3)_2 + 2NO + 4H_2O$	
$Pb + 2CH_3CO_2H + \frac{1}{2}O_2 = Pb(CH_3CO_2)_2 + H_2O$	Also with other acids
$Pb + 2H_2O + O_2 = Pb(OH)_2 + H_2O_2$	Slowly at moderate temperatures

evolve hydrogen readily with acids due to high over-voltage effects (Append. I). Lead is quite resistant to the action of even moderately concentrated sulfuric acid, but is readily oxidized by oxygen in the presence of various weak organic acids, e.g., acetic acid.

GERMANIUM COMPOUNDS

19. Germanium dioxide, GeO_2, is readily formed by roasting the sulfide minerals. The oxide is somewhat soluble in water with the formation of the acid. It is not more soluble in nitric or sulfuric acids, but is dissolved when heated with concentrated hydrofluoric or hydrochloric acids with the formation of volatile **tetrahalides.** The oxide is readily soluble in a mixture of oxalic acid and ammonium oxalate; and also in triethanolamine. The halides are hydrolyzed in water with the precipitation of the hydrated dioxide, except the fluoride, which forms a mixture of the dioxide and **fluogermanic** acid, H_2GeF_6. The potassium salt, K_2GeF_6, is but slightly soluble. The dioxide is soluble in alkalies forming **germanates,** e.g., Na_2GeO_3.

Germanium **disulfide,** GeS_2, may be precipitated in strong sulfuric acid by hydrogen sulfide, but yields a colloidal suspension in dilute acid. It is soluble in alkali sulfide, forming **thiogermanates.**

Germanium resembles silicon in the formation of an unstable **hydride,** GeH_4, and also traces of the heavier compounds, Ge_2H_6 and Ge_3H_8, when germanium compounds are reduced with aluminum in alkaline solution. The metal heated in a stream of hydrogen chloride forms **germanium chloroform,** $GeHCl_3$. This compound hydrolyzes to form **germanous acid,** which appears to resemble formic acid in structure: $GeHCl_3 + 2H_2O = 3HCl + HGeO(OH)$. The acid is soluble in alkalies, forming **germanites,** and upon heating forms **germanous oxide,** GeO, which possesses basic properties in that it is soluble in acids. The monoxide sublimes at 710° C. and has been one of the principal difficulties in the electrolytes reduction of the element in molten electrolytes. **Germanous halides** and the **sulfides** may be prepared by igniting strongly the $+ 4$ compounds, e.g. $GeI_4 = GeI_2 + I_2$. The germanous ion is readily oxidized, $2H_2O + Ge^{++} = GeO_2 + 4H^+ + 2e^-$, ca 0.3 volt. Germanous ion appears to be unstable with respect to its own oxidation and reduction but halide complexes may be formed in solution by reduction of the $+ 4$ ion with hypophosphite. The compound $(GeOOH)_2$

analogous to oxalic acid is known.   Germanite ion is probably unstable.

Compounds of Tin

20. Oxidation States.—The stability of the two oxidation states of tin in respect to oxidizing and reducing agents is indicated by the following potentials:

	VOLTS
$Sn = Sn^{++} + 2e^-$	$+ 0.13$
$Sn^{++} = Sn^{++++} + 2e^-$	$- 0.13$
$3OH^- + Sn = HSnO_2^- + H_2O + 2e^-$	0.91
$H_2O + 3OH^- + HSnO_2^- = Sn(OH)_6^{--} + 2e^-$	0.96

It follows from these values that the equilibrium, $Sn + Sn^{++++} = 2Sn^{++}$, favors the reaction as written, that is, soluble stannic compounds may be reduced to stannous by the metal. The equilibrium is reversed in alkaline solutions: $2H_2O + 2HSnO_2^- = Sn + Sn(OH)_6^{--}$.

21. Oxides and Hydroxides.—The **dioxide,** SnO_2, is the principal tin ore. The crystal lattice is similar to rutile. When fused with alkalies, the oxide forms **stannates,** e.g., Na_2SnO_3. The alkali stannates are soluble in water, and upon the addition of acid to the solution precipitate "α-stannic acid" or α-hydrous oxide. This acid or hydrous oxide is amphoteric, and readily dissolves in excess of either base or acid.

Another hydrous oxide, β-oxide (also called metastannic acid) is formed by the action of nitric acid upon tin or by the hydrolysis of stannic salts in hot solutions. This compound is not soluble in excess of any acid, but is peptized by concentrated hydrochloric acid to form a sol which may be dissolved in dilute acid. The composition of the two "acids" appears to be the same, the different behavior being due to differences in physical state. X-ray diffraction patterns of both are identical with cassiterite. Sodium hydroxide dissolves the β-oxide.

22. Stannous oxide, SnO, may be prepared by heating stannous hydroxide or oxalate, or by heating the metal in a limited supply of oxygen. It burns when heated in air to form the dioxide. Hydrous hydrated stannous oxide, probably $SnO \cdot \frac{1}{2}H_2O$, is precipitated by the addition of alkalies to stannous solutions. It is also amphoteric, dissolving in alkali hydroxides, but not in ammonia or soluble carbonates. Solutions of **stannites** are powerful reducing agents.

23. Peroxystannic acids, $H_2Sn_2O_7$ and $HSnO_4$, and their salts, are formed by the action of peroxides on stannic solutions, or by the anodic oxidation of cold solutions of alkali stannates.

24. Halides.—The anhydrous **stannic halides** may be prepared by the action of the halogens on the metal and aqueous solutions of the salts by dissolving stannic oxide in the hydrohalic acid. Complex halidostannates are formed in solution and a number of these soluble salts may be obtained upon crystallization, e.g., K_2SnF_6. **Stannic chloride** is important commercially as a mordanting agent. It crystallizes from an acid solution as $SnCl_4 \cdot 5H_2O$ although the anhydrous compound is a liquid. The **ammonium chlorostannate,** $(NH_4)_2SnCl_6$, is also used in dyeing under the name "pink salt."

Stannous halides are readily prepared from the stannic by reduction with tin, or by dissolving the metal in the halogen acid. The solutions are readily oxidized by air. **Stannous chloride** is also important as a mordant. The salt is very soluble in water, but forms the basic salt, $Sn(OH)Cl$, unless acid is present to prevent hydrolysis.

25. Sulfides.—**Stannous** and **stannic sulfides** may be prepared by fusing the elements together, but the latter is unstable at high temperatures: $SnS_2 = SnS + S$. Hydrogen sulfide precipitates brown stannous and yellow stannic sulfide from dilute acid solutions of stannous and stannic salts respectively. Both sulfides are soluble in concentrated hydrochloric acid but stannic sulfide, being the more acid in nature, is the less soluble of the two. The disulfide is amphoteric and dissolves in excess of sulfide to form **thiostannates**: $SnS_2 + S^{--} = SnS_3^{--}$. The stannous sulfide is not soluble in excess sulfide unless polysulfide is present, in which case it is oxidized to thiostannate: $SnS + S_2^{--} = SnS_3^{--}$. The thiostannates are not stable in acid solution: $SnS_3^{--} + 2H^+ = H_2SnS_3 = H_2S + SnS_2$.

Stannic sulfide has long been used as a gilding pigment under the name of **mosaic gold**. The preparation is carried out by heating together a mixture of tin, sulfur, ammonium chloride, and mercury. The exact action of the two latter substances is uncertain, but they volatilize and leave the sulfide as brilliant yellow crystals.

26. Other Tin Compounds.—Small amounts of the **hydride,** SnH_4, are formed by the cathodic reduction of tin in dilute acid solution, and by the action of acid upon tin-magnesium alloy. Both stannous and stannic **carbonates** are completely hydrolyzed to the hydroxides. Both of the **nitrates** and the **sulfates** are formed in solution by the action of the acids upon the hydroxides, but they are difficult to crystallize without the formation of basic salts. Slightly soluble **stannous phosphate,** $Sn_5H_2(PO_4)_4 \cdot 3H_2O$, may be precipitated from slightly acid stannous chloride by sodium acid phosphate, and a number of slightly soluble basic and double stannic phosphates are known.

Lead Compounds

27. Oxidation States.—The most important oxidation reduction potentials for lead are given below:

	Volts
$Pb = Pb^{++} + 2e^-$	$+ 0.126$
$Pb + SO_4^{--} = PbSO_4 + 2e^-$	$+ 0.355$
$Pb + 3OH^- = HPbO_2^- + H_2O + 2e^-$	$+ 0.54$
$Pb^{++} + 2H_2O = PbO_2 + 4H^+ + 2e^-$	$- 1.456$
$PbSO_4 + 2H_2O = PbO_2 + 4H^+ + SO_4^{--} + 2e^-$	$- 1.685$
$PbO + 2OH^- = PbO_2 + H_2O + 2e^-$	$- 0.25$

It follows that lead is a fair reducing agent in acid solutions, and a strong reducing agent in alkaline solutions, and that the dioxide is an extremely powerful oxidizing agent in acid solutions but much weaker in alkaline solutions.

28. Oxides and Hydroxides.—Lead forms the **monoxide,** PbO, and the **dioxide,** PbO_2. Two additional oxides appear to be plumbous plumbate salts, the **trioxide,** Pb_2O_3 being $PbPbO_3$, and **red lead,** Pb_3O_4, being Pb_2PbO_4. The existence of a so-called suboxide or its salts is extremely doubtful.

The monoxide, or **litharge,** orange-yellow, is prepared by heating the metal in air; and around 550° C. the other oxides evolve oxygen to form the monoxide. The oxide is soluble in acids and alkalies, forming respectively **plumbous,** Pb^{++}, and **plumbite,** $HPbO_2^-$, ions, and the addition of alkalies and acid, respectively, to these solutions, precipitates the "hydroxide," or hydrous hydrated oxide, possibly PbO $\cdot\frac{1}{2}H_2O$, which is soluble in excess of either reagent. The "hydroxide" is more basic than stannous "hydroxide" as is indicated by the formation of a carbonate.

Litharge is used in glazing pottery and in making glass. A mixture with glycerine is sometimes used as a cement, since it sets to a solid lead glyceride.

Red lead or **minium** is made by carefully heating the monoxide at temperatures below 500°. The composition of the product varies with the temperature of roasting, a maximum of PbO_2 (33 per cent) is obtained at about 430°. When treated with nitric acid, it is decomposed: $Pb_3O_4 + 4HNO_3 = 2Pb(NO_3)_2 + PbO_2 + 2H_2O$. Red lead is used in making flint glass, and as a red pigment. Structural iron is often given a first coat of red lead paint as it serves very effectively to protect the iron from corrosion, due possibly to the iron becoming passive.

29. Lead dioxide may be prepared from red lead as indicated above, but it is most readily formed by the oxidation of lead monoxide or plumbites in dilute alkali solutions, e.g., $PbO + ClO^- = PbO_2 + Cl^-$. The oxide is also readily prepared by the anodic oxidation of solutions of plumbous ion. The dioxide has the rutile type of crystal lattice, and is a fair electrical conductor. It is only slightly soluble in water and is comparatively inert toward hydrogen and hydroxide ions. Concentrated alkalies do, however, dissolve the oxide forming **plumbates,** and soluble metaplumbates may be formed by fusing the oxide with alkalies. Many plumbates, both ortho and meta, of the more basic + 2 oxides have also been prepared. The oxide is slowly soluble in dilute nitric acid, but the tetrapositive lead ion oxidizes water with the evolution of oxygen. Cold concentrated hydrochloric acid forms liquid tetrachloride, but at ordinary temperatures chlorine is evolved. For the use of the dioxide in the lead storage battery, see Paragraph **39.**

30. Lead Halides.—Lead **tetrafluoride** is formed upon heating the dioxide with potassium acid fluoride, although the product does not appear to be the pure compound. The formation of the **tetrachloride** is discussed in the preceding paragraph. In dilute acid, both halides are hydrolyzed to the dioxide; in the concentrated halogen acids, the **fluoplumbic acid,** H_2PbF_6, and **chloroplumbic acid,** H_2PbCl_6, are formed. Alkali salts of both of these acids have been prepared.

The plumbous halides are but sparingly soluble in cold water, but the chloride and bromide are readily soluble in hot water, and the iodide partially soluble. The solubility of the halide is decreased in dilute solutions containing the halogen ion but is increased in concentrated solutions, doubtless with the formation of complex ions, such as $PbCl_4^{--}$.

31. Nitrate.—The nitrate, $Pb(NO_3)_2$, is readily soluble, but unless a slight excess of acid is present to prevent hydrolysis, basic nitrates are precipitated.

32. Acetate.—The acetate, $Pb(C_2H_3O_2)_2 \cdot 3H_2O$, called **sugar of lead,** is one of the few soluble lead salts, and it appears to form a complex ion with excess acetate. Like the nitrate, the solution tends to form basic salts, but the basic compound, $Pb(OH)C_2H_3O_2$, is soluble. Both the acetate and nitrate are extremely poisonous.

The dioxide is soluble in glacial acetic acid with the formation of the tetra-acetate, but this compound is completely hydrolyzed in water.

33. Sulfate.—The sulfate, $PbSO_4$, resembles the alkaline earth sulfates in being slightly soluble in water. It is soluble in excess acetate (see above), and in excess alkali it dissolves to form plumbite. The basic sulfate, Pb_2OSO_4, known as the pigment "sublimed white lead," is made by roasting lead sulfide with carbon. The product sublimes and is condensed to a pure white powder. The commercial pigment usually contains excess of $PbSO_4$ and some zinc oxide.

34. Chromate.—The chromate, $PbCrO_4$, is very slightly soluble in water, but dissolves somewhat in acids with the formation of dichromate, and in bases with the formation of plumbite. It is an important yellow pigment, **chrome-yellow.** The stable yellow modification of lead chromate is monoclinic. A red tetragonal modification may be stabilized by the addition of lead molybdate. This pigment is known as **molybdenum orange.**

35. Sulfide.—The occurrence of the sulfide in the mineral galena and its metallurgy has been discussed. The sulfide is precipitated from dilute acid solutions by hydrogen sulfide, but is soluble in concentrated hydrochloric acid and in hot $2N$ nitric acid. It is not soluble in excess sulfide. The crystal has the sodium chloride type of lattice. It acts as a rectifier for oscillating electric currents.

36. Lead Carbonate.—Normal lead carbonate, $PbCO_3$, may be prepared by the action of sodium bicarbonate solution upon lead chloride or sulfate. When soluble carbonates are added to a solution of lead ion, the **basic carbonate,** $Pb_3(OH)_2(CO_3)_2$, is formed. This compound is extremely important as the pigment **white lead.** The annual consumption in the United States is about 100,000 tons. It is prepared commercially by the action of air, carbon dioxide, and acetic acid upon the metal. A small amount of acetic acid serves to convert a large quantity of lead into the carbonate. The following reactions may represent the mechanism of the process: $2Pb + O_2 + 2HAc = 2Pb(OH)$-$Ac$; $6Pb(OH)Ac + 2CO_2 = Pb_3(OH)_2(CO_3)_2 + 3PbAc_2 + 2H_2O$; and $2Pb + O_2 + 2PbAc_2 + 2H_2O = 4Pb(OH)Ac$. In the older forms of the process, perforated lead disks were placed over pots containing acetic acid. Tiers of these pots were stacked with tan bark which decomposed under bacterial action, liberating carbon dioxide and also providing heat. This process required about three months for completion, and more rapid methods are now being used to some extent, as for example, the churning of lead dust with acetic acid, air, and carbon dioxide.

The covering power of white lead is excellent, but it has the disadvantage of darkening due to the formation of the sulfide, and its poisonous nature is also objectional.

37. Other Lead Compounds.—Lead **orthophosphate,** $Pb_3(PO_4)_2$, may be precipitated from dilute acid plumbous solutions by disodium phosphate. Many basic and double phosphates are also known. Lead **silicate,** $PbSiO_3$, is formed by fusing lead monoxide and silica. It is a constituent of lead glass and of certain glazes used on earthenware.

38. Lead Storage Battery.—The ordinary lead accumulator depends upon the reversibility of the reaction: $Pb + PbO_2 + 4H^+ + 2SO_4^{--} = 2PbSO_4 + 2H_2O$. When fully charged, one electrode consists of a plate of spongy lead, the other electrode a plate impregnated with lead dioxide, and the electrolyte is sulfuric acid. The half reactions for discharge are: $Pb + SO_4^{--} = PbSO_4 + 2e^-$ and $PbO_2 + 4H^+ + SO_4^{--} + 2e^- = PbSO_4 + 2H_2O$. Lead sulfate thus forms on each plate upon discharge, and the concentration of sulfuric acid decreases. The density of the acid under normal conditions is 1.20 at 2.05 volts (charged) and 1.05 at 1.91 volts (discharged). The cell is not completely reversible as is evident from the higher voltage required to reverse the reaction and recharge the cell (Fig. 2). The final rapid increase in the charging voltage curve occurs when all the solid sulfate is used up and the concentration of the lead ion diminishes.

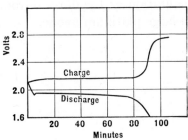

Fig. 2. Charge and discharge curves for the lead storage battery at 15° C.

39. Analytical. —Advantage is taken of the slight solubility of the sulfides of the group in qualitative analysis. The reactions of these compounds with acids and bases have been discussed, and reference should be made to Appendix VI for the treatment of tin and lead in the systematic separation of the positive ions. The reduction of mercuric chloride, first to mercurous and then to grey metallic mercury by stannous ion, is used as a confirmatory test for tin, and the slight solubilities of $PbSO_4$ and $PbCrO_4$ are used in the confirmation of lead.

Germanium is determined quantitatively by precipitating as the disulfide and weighing as the dioxide.

Tin is sometimes determined gravimetrically as the dioxide, but it is most readily determined by the volumetric titration of stannous ion by iodine: $Sn^{++} + I_3^-$ $= Sn^{++++} + 3I^-$. The reduction of any stannic salts prior to the titration is accomplished with aluminum foil in acid solution, or by nickel in hydrochloric acid.

In gravimetric analyses, lead is often precipitated and weighed as the sulfate, $PbSO_4$, chromate, $PbCrO_4$, or molybdate, $PbMoO_4$. In the precipitation as the sulfate, separation from barium is secured by dissolving out the lead in

ammonium acetate and dilute sulfuric acid, and reprecipi-
tating. The molybdate method has the advantage that
the barium salt is soluble.

Lead is often determined electrolytically by anodic precipitation as the dioxide from a nitric acid solution, using
a large platinum anode.

Chapter XVI

SUBGROUP V. VANADIUM, NIOBIUM, TANTALUM

1. The elements of Subgroup V occur in transition series resulting from the building up of the number of electrons in the outer shell of the kernel from eight to eighteen (Append. XVIII). Spectral data indicate that the normal gaseous atoms have two electrons in the outer s orbital, so that three additional valence electrons must, in the normal atom, be located in lower d orbitals. However, all five valence electrons are removable, and all members of the group form compounds of the $+ 5$ oxidation state.

The elements are semi-noble, steel-like metals with high melting points. Vanadium forms compounds of all its possible positive oxidation states except $+ 1$. Unlike the main Group V, the $+ 5$ state becomes more stable with increasing atomic weight; and the pentoxide, which is amphoteric in the case of vanadium, becomes more inert to the action of both acids and bases.

2. Occurrence.—Vanadium is estimated as present in igneous rocks to the extent of 1.7×10^{-4} per cent, and columbium and tantalum together as 3×10^{-5} per cent.

The principal vanadium minerals are **vanadinite,** $Pb_2(VO_4)Cl$ (analogous to apatite); dechenite, $[Pb, Zn](VO_3)_2$; pucherite, $BiVO_4$; volborthite, $[Cu, Ca]_3(VO_4)_2H_2O$; and roscoelite, a vanadium mica containing V_2O_3. **Carnotite,** $K(UO_2)VO_4 \cdot 3/2H_2O$, is also important as a source of uranium.

Columbium (also called niobium) and tantalum usually occur together, the principal minerals are columbite, $FeCb_2O_6$, and tantalite, $FeTa_2O_6$. Other minerals are: pyrochlor, calcium columbate, containing titanium, thorium and rare earths; yttrotantalite and fugersonite, complex oxide mixtures containing largely Ta_2O_5, Cb_2O_5, Yt_2O_3, and Er_2O_3.

3. Metallurgy.—**Vanadium** is extracted from its ores by leaching out the ore with strong hydrochloric acid, and is precipitated from this solution as ammonium vanadate by evaporation of the solution with excess of ammonium chloride. Ammonium vanadate, when roasted, yields the oxide.

The preparation of the pure metal is a difficult operation. The reduction of the pentoxide with carbon in an electric furnace yields mostly carbide; and the reduction with aluminum gives a mixture of the metal and dioxide. The reduction of the dichloride with hydrogen is a satisfactory method of preparing the metal on a small scale. Very little of the pure metal is prepared commercially, however, as the steel industry, which is the principal consumer, employs ferrovanadium. This is manufactured by the reduction of the mixed oxides with carbon in an electric furnace. A small amount of vanadium is consumed in making metavanadate for use as a catalyst in the manufacture of sulfuric acid.

The separation of pure **columbium** and **tantalum** oxides from their ores is largely an analytical problem (Par. **17**). The metals may be prepared by the reduction of the complex alkali fluorides with sodium, or the oxide with metallic calcium or aluminum. Tantalum may be electroplated from the fused complex potassium fluoride, but the electrodeposition of niobium is not very satisfactory and the metal is generally prepared by heating a mixture of the oxide and carbide at 1600° C.

4. The Metals.—The more important physical properties are given in Table I. The metals are grey or silver white

TABLE I

ATOMIC AND PHYSICAL PROPERTIES

	V	Cb	Ta
Atomic weight	50.95	92.91	180.88
Atomic numbers	23	41	73
Isotopes	51	93	181
Melting point, ° C.	1,730	2,497	2,997
Boiling point, ° C.	3,530	5,130	6,000
Density	5.9	8.4	16.6
Electrical resistivity, ohms-cm. at 25° C.			15×10^{-6}
Ionization potential of gaseous atom, volts	6.71		
Tensile strength, lb. sq. in.			130,000
Radius of metal ions M^{+5} in crystals, cm. $\times 10^8$	0.59	0.70	

in color, and do not tarnish readily. Though very hard, they may be rolled or hammered, and drawn into wire. Vanadium is used extensively in the steel industry (cf. **XIX**—**7**), to add tensile strength to steel. Columbium in the form of ferrocolumbium is employed in the manufacture of chromium steels to render them more weldable. Tantalum was formerly employed in electric light filaments, but has been replaced by tungsten. The metal, in spite of its electropositive character, is extremely resistant to chemical action at ordinary temperatures and is being employed as pipes, kettles, and containers in many chemical manufacturing processes, displacing platinum, and other expensive metals. Due to the passive nature of tantalum, it exhibits, to a high degree, an electrolytic valve action (see Aluminum, **VI**—**17**) and is employed in cells to act as current rectifiers. Tantalum absorbs gases readily at high temperatures; and becomes hard and brittle. For this reason, the metal must be worked cold or in a vacuum. Because of its hardness tantalum carbide is employed as a constituent of hard cutting-tool mixtures.

5. Reactions of the Metals.—The metals are attacked by oxygen only when heated. Vanadium and niobium are dissolved by nitric acid and other powerful oxidizing agents (Par. **6**); but tantalum is attacked readily only by a mixture of nitric and hydrofluoric acids. The general reactions of the group are summarized in Table II.

TABLE II

REACTIONS OF VANADIUM, NIOBIUM, AND TANTALUM

$4M + 5O_2 = 2M_2O_5$	Heated. V also forms VO_2
$2M + 5X_2 = 2MX_5$	Heated. Ta and Nb with F, Cl, and
	Br. V and Nb form only VCl_4 and VBr_3.
$6M + 5N_2 = 2M_3N_5$	Heated. V forms VN
$M + C = MC$	High temperature
$M + 2S = MS_2$	Heated. V forms V_2S_5 also
$M + 5NaOH = NaMO_3 + \frac{5}{2}H_2$	
$+ 2Na_2O$	Fused. Ta and Nb form $Na_8M_6O_{19}$
$3M + 15HF + 5HNO_3$	
$= 3H_2MOF_5 + 5NO + 7H_2O$	Also other complex fluo-acids
$2V + Si = V_2Si$	High temperature
$2Cb + H_2 = 2CbH$	

VANADIUM COMPOUNDS

6. Oxidation States.—Vanadium forms compounds possessing the oxidation states 2, 3, 4, and 5. The two lower valences are basic; but the two higher are amphoteric, though in the aqueous solutions, the positive ions exist only as vanadyl, VO^{++}, and pervanadyl, $V(OH)_4^+$.

Oxidation-reduction potentials involving the various states are summarized below:

	VOLTS
$V = V^{++} + 2e^-$	$+ 1.5$
$V^{++} = V^{+++} + e^-$	$+ 0.2$
$V^{+++} + H_2O = VO^{++} + 2H^+ + e^-$	$- 0.314$
$VO^{++} + 3H_2O = V(OH)_4^+ + 2H^+ + e^-$	$- 1.00$

From these values, it follows that vanadic acid in concentrated hydrogen ion, i.e. $V(OH)_4^+$ is a moderately powerful oxidizing agent; but the hydrogen ion is involved to such a high power that the potential decreases markedly in dilute acid, so that vanadate in neutral solution is not easily reduced. As the potentials indicated, the reduction products depend upon the strength of the reducing agent, e.g. Fe^{++} gives VO^{++}, Sn^{++} gives V^{+++}, and Zn gives V^{++}. Vanadous ion, V^{++}, is a strong reducing agent, and vanadic ion is fairly strong. The metal is oxidized by moderate oxidizing agents in acid solution to the $+ 4$ state and by powerful agents to vanadate.

7. The $+ 2$ State.—The monoxide, VO, is prepared by the reduction of vanadyl chloride, $VOCl_2$, by carbon, zinc, or hydrogen at red heat. The oxide is semi-metallic in appearance and was considered by Berzelius to be the metal. The **hydroxide**, $V(OH)_2$, is but slightly soluble. Its salts in solution have a deep violet color. The **sulfate,** VSO_4, is prepared in solution by the reduction of sulfuric acid solutions of vanadates by zinc, or by cathodic reduction in an atmosphere of carbon dioxide. The solid hydrate, $VSO_4 \cdot 7H_2O$, may be obtained upon evaporation, and **double sulfates** are formed with the alkali sulfates, $M_2V(SO_4)_2 \cdot 6H_2O$. The sulfate solution absorbs nitric oxide, similar to ferrous ion, and the **complex cyanide,** $V(CN)_6^{-4}$, is similar to ferrocyanide in the solubilities of its salts. The anhydrous **chloride** and the **sulfide** are prepared, respectively, by the reactions: $VCl_4 + H_2 = VCl_2 + 2HCl$, and $V_2S_3 + H_2 = 2VS + H_2S$. The latter is not soluble in dilute hydrogen ion or in sulfide ion.

8. The $+ 3$ State.—In formulas and solubilities, the vanadic compounds resemble ferric, but unlike the latter, they are readily oxidized. The salts in solution are green; and the green **hydroxide,** $V(OH)_3$, is precipitated from solutions of its salts by ammonia or alkali hydroxides. It is rapidly oxidized by air to form the dioxide. The **sesquioxide,** V_2O_3, may be obtained by reducing the pentoxide with hydrogen or carbon, and the product is insoluble in most acids. Solutions of the **halides** may be prepared by dissolving the hydroxide in the halogen acid. The anhydrous compounds may be prepared by reactions analogous to the following: $2VCl_4 = 2VCl_3 + Cl_2$, and $V_2O_3 + 3Br_2 + C = 2VBr_3 + 3CO$. The **oxychloride,** VOCl, is but slightly soluble. Reduction of sulfuric acid solutions of the pentoxide gives **vanadic sulfate,** $V_2(SO_4)_3$, in solution; this salt readily forms alums. The oxide reacts when heated with ammonia, and with hydrogen sulfide, to give the **nitride,** VN, and the **sulfide,** V_2S_3, respectively. The latter is soluble in dilute acids.

Vanadic ion forms many complex and double salts, the most important being **double fluorides,** as $(NH_4)_3VF_6$, or $(NH_4)_2VF_5$; **double oxalates** as, $K_3V(C_2O_4)_3\cdot3H_2O$; complex cyanides as $K_3V(CN)_6$; and sulfocyanides, $K_3V(CNS)_6$.

9. The + 4 State.—The **dioxide,** VO_2, may be obtained by partial reduction of the pentoxide; the **hydrous oxide,** is precipitated by the addition of sodium carbonate to vanadyl salts in solution. The hydrous oxide is oxidized in air. It is soluble in the alkali hydroxide and in ammonia, forming **vanadites,** e.g. $K_2V_4O_9\cdot7H_2O$. These compounds in solution have a deep black color, are not readily oxidized, and form slightly soluble vanadites with the heavy metals.

The dioxide dissolves in acid to form the blue vanadyl ion, VO^{++}, and many salts of this ion are known, e.g., $VOCl_2$, $VOSO_4$. The **anhydrous chloride** is formed by the reactions: $V + 2Cl_2 = VCl_4$, and $VOCl_3 + 1/2Cl_2 + C = VCl_4 + CO$. It is a heavy liquid with an extremely low melting point. The water solutions hydrolyze to vanadyl chloride. The addition of sulfide to an acid vanadyl solution precipitates the **sulfide,** VS_2, which is soluble in excess sulfide to form **thiovanadites.**

10. The + 5 State.—The **oxide,** V_2O_5, may be prepared by roasting ammonium metavanadate, NH_4VO_3; or by the hydrolysis of pervanadyl chloride, $VOCl_3$. It is somewhat soluble in water to give a slightly acid solution, but with excess of hydrogen ion the acid forms pervanadyl ion, $V(OH)_4^+$ (or VO_2^+). **Metavanadic** acid, HVO_3, may be precipitated as golden yellow solid by the action of sulfurous acid upon copper vanadate. The acid is sometimes employed as gold bronze. **Pyrovanadic acid,** $H_4V_2O_7$,

is precipitated by the addition of nitric acid to vanadate solutions.

The addition of alkali to vanadic acid results in the formation of complicated poly-anions.

Sodium salts of the **meta-, ortho-, pyro-,** and **hexa-vanadic** acids are known: $NaVO_3$, Na_3VO_4, $Na_4V_2O_7$, $Na_2H_2V_6O_{17}$. The metavanadates of sodium, potassium, ammonium, barium, and lead are but slightly soluble in cold water; but salts of other positive ions are soluble, and the color is generally yellow. The alkali pyrovanadates are soluble. In solution orthovanadate is readily hydrolyzed: $2VO_4^{---}$ $+ H_2O = V_2O_7^{----} + 2OH^-$. At high temperatures, the ortho salts are stable, however, and constitute many of the vanadium minerals. The most important compound is probably ammonium metavanadate, NH_4VO_3, which is precipitated by excess ammonium chloride from meta- and pyrovanadate solutions. In recent years large quantities of the salt have been used in the preparation of the vanadium catalysts for the manufacture of sulfuric acid.

The alkali metavanadates are readily converted to **per-oxyvanadates**, MVO_4, by hydrogen peroxide; and peroxy-vanadic acid, HVO_4, is formed when the pentoxide is added to a solution of hydrogen peroxide in sulfuric acid. The solution has a deep red color.

Of the pervanadyl compounds, the most important is probably the **pervanadyl sulfate**, $(VO)_2(SO_4)_3$. This may be obtained as a red-brown solid upon evaporating the acid solution, and basic salts as, $VO(OH)SO_4$, are also formed. With concentrated hydrochloric acid, chlorine is evolved and the dioxide formed. However, the **pervanadyl chloride** may be made by the action of chlorine upon VO or V_2O_3, or upon a heated mixture of the pentoxide and carbon. The chloride is a heavy low melting liquid with a lemon-yellow color. It fumes in moist air and is hydrolyzed by water to vanadic acid. **Complex oxyfluovanadates,** as K_2VOF_5 and $K_2VO_2F_3$, are precipitated by the addition of potassium fluoride to the pervanadyl fluoride solutions.

Ammonium sulfide acts upon vanadate solutions to form **thiovanadate, VS$_4$$^{---}$**. The addition of acid to this solution precipitates the **sulfide, V$_2$S$_5$**, or possibly a mixture of V$_2$S$_5$ and VS$_2$.

COLUMBIUM COMPOUNDS

11. Oxidation States.—The compounds of lower states are much less stable than in the case of vanadium. The only + 5 compounds which may be obtained in acid solution are the complex fluoride and chloride, and these solutions may be reduced quantitatively by zinc in the cold to a blue solution of the + 3 columbium; but, if the solution is heated, a precipitate of mixed oxides, possibly CbO$_2$ and Cb$_2$O$_3$, is formed. The + 3 compounds in solution are oxidized very rapidly by oxygen. The oxychloride, CbOCl$_3$, may be reduced by sodium to the monoxide, CbO, which dissolves in acid with the liberation of hydrogen. The pentoxide may be reduced by magnesium to the dioxide, CbO$_2$, which is not attacked by acids, but burns in air when heated.

Due to the passivity of the metal and the inertness of the oxide, very little is known about the true oxidation-reduction potentials of columbium, and the following values are calculated from thermal data.

VOLTS

$$2Cb + 5H_2O = Cb_2O_5 + 10H^+ + 10e^-$$ 0.62
$$Cb = Cb^{+++} + 3e^-$$ .... *ca.* 1.1

12. Pentoxide and Columbates.—The pentoxide, Cb$_2$O$_5$, may be prepared by decomposing the potassium oxyfluoride with sulfuric acid. With concentrated acid the oxide dissolves with the formation of some complex ion, possibly Cb(SO$_4$)$_3$$^-$. The pentachloride hydrolyzes in water to give the **meta-acid, HCbO$_3$**. The oxide and acid when fused with alkalies or alkali carbonates yield complex columbates. **Potassium hexacolumbate,** $K_8Cb_6O_{19}\cdot15H_2O$, is readily soluble in water, and with excess of alkali forms a number of other salts, such as $K_4Cb_2O_7\cdot11H_2O$.

Peroxycolumbates are formed by the action of peroxides upon columbates; and the **peroxy-acid,** $HCbO_4$, is obtained as a yellow solid when columbic acid is warmed with hydrogen peroxide.

Halogen Compounds.—Columbic acid is soluble in hydrofluoric acid; the addition of potassium fluoride to the solution yields **fluocolumbate,** K_2CbF_7, and in less concentrated acid double salts of the oxyfluoride, such as K_2CbOF_5.

The **pentachloride,** $CbCl_5$, is formed by passing chlorine over a heated mixture of the oxide and carbon; or sulfur chloride, S_2Cl_2, over the oxide. The pentachloride is soluble in hydrochloric acid. The **oxychloride** is a volatile solid, and like the chloride, is completely hydrolyzed in water. Corresponding compounds of fluorine and bromine have also been prepared, which have rather similar properties.

At red heat, the pentachloride decomposes into the **trichloride,** $CbCl_3$. This anhydrous chloride is not decomposed by water, but is readily oxidized with nitric acid, and when heated reacts with carbon dioxide: $CbCl_3 + CO_2 = CbOCl_3 + CO$.

Other Compounds.—The metal heated in nitrogen at 1200° forms the **nitride,** Cb_3N_5. Mixed oxide-nitride compounds result from the action of ammonia upon the oxide at red heat, but the nitride NbN is formed by the action of ammonia upon the metal at red heat.

The metal unites with hydrogen when heated to form the **hydride,** NbH, which is not attacked by acids, but readily burns in air. The oxide is not converted into sulfide by ammonium sulfide, but oxysulfides, e.g., $Nb_2O_2S_3$, $NbOS_3$, form when the oxide is heated in an atmosphere of carbon dioxide and carbon disulfide.

TANTALUM COMPOUNDS

13. Although there is very little experimental work on the oxidation-reduction potentials of tantalum, the value for the heat of formation of the pentoxide, $-484,500$ cal., leads to the following approximate potential:

$$2Ta + 5H_2O = Ta_2O_5 + 10H^+ + 10e^- \dots\dots\dots\dots\dots\dots \quad 0.71 \text{ volt}$$

No compounds of lower oxidation states are stable in aqueous solution. The $+2$ chloride has been prepared at high temperatures, but the water solution evolves hydrogen rapidly.

14. Pentoxide and Tantalates.—The pentoxide, Ta_2O_5, is formed when the metal burns in air. It is left as a residue when tantalates are fused with potassium acid sulfate, and the product extracted with hydrochloric acid. The oxide is very inert, but when fused with alkali hydroxides forms **hexatantalates,** e.g. $Na_8Ta_6O_{19}\cdot25H_2O$. These compounds are soluble in water. When ignited with ammonium chloride, **metatantalates,** e.g. $NaTaO_3$, are formed; these are not soluble. The **meta-acid,** $HTaO_3$, is precipitated when the pentachloride is added to water.

A solution of potassium hexatantalate gives with peroxide a **peroxytantalate,** $K_3TaO_8\cdot1/2H_2O$, which may be precipitated from the solution by the addition of alcohol. The compound is decomposed by sulfuric acid to give the acid, $HTaO_4$, which is fairly stable.

The pentoxide reduced with magnesium yields a **monoxide,** TaO, which is not soluble in acids, and burns in air to the pentoxide.

The ignited pentoxide is not soluble in any acid, but the hydrated oxide dissolves in hydrofluoric acid, and either dissolves slightly, or is peptized by other acids.

15. Compounds with the Halogens.—The **pentafluoride, chloride,** and **bromide,** form when the metal is heated in the corresponding halogen. Alkali **fluotantalates,** e.g.

K_2TaF_7, are obtained by dissolving the hydrated pentoxide in hydrofluoric acid, and adding alkali fluoride. These compounds are easily soluble in hot water, but much less soluble in cold. When the solution of the potassium salts is boiled, an **oxyfluoride**, $K_4Ta_4O_5F_{14}$, precipitates.

The pentachloride and bromide are most readily prepared by heating a mixture of the oxide and carbon in a stream of chlorine. These compounds are readily volatile around 150°, and are completely hydrolyzed by water.

16. Other Compounds.—The **sulfide**, TaS_2, is said to be formed by the action of hydrogen and carbon disulfide upon the heated oxide. It is not soluble in hydrogen ion. When the chloride is heated in ammonia at not too high a temperature, a bright red **nitride**, Ta_3N_5, is formed. At higher temperatures, the compound TaN is produced. The pentanitride is also formed when the metal is heated in nitrogen at 1000° C.

The **carbide**, TaC, forms when the oxide is reduced with carbon at high temperatures.

17. Analytical.—The slight solubility of the oxides of vanadium, columbium, and tantalum in dilute hydrogen ion, and in oxidizing agents, and their ready solubility in hydrofluoric acid, places them analytically in a group consisting of Sb_2O_5, SnO_2, WO_3, MoO_3, TeO_2, V_2O_4, TiO_2, Ta_2O_5, Cb_2O_5, and Bi_2O_3, together with phosphates of Sn, Ti, and Zr. When these oxides are dissolved in hydrofluoric acid and treated with ammonium sulfide, a separation is obtained, giving in the filtrate, the thio-salts of Sb, Sn, W, Mo, Te, V, and a residue of TiO_2, Ta_2O_5, Cb_2O_5, Bi_2O_3, and Ti and Zr phosphate or vanadate. The presence of vanadium in the thio-salt solution is recognized by the violet-red color of $(NH_4)_3VS_4$.

When the TiO_2, Ta_2O_5, etc. residue above is boiled with sodium salicylate solution, the titanium and vanadium are extracted. The residue is fused with K_2CO_3; and $K_8Ta_3O_{18}$ and $K_8Cb_3O_{18}$ are obtained in solution by extracting with cold water. The tantalum is separated from the niobium by the smaller solubility of the potassium oxyfluotantalate, and the niobium recognized by reduction to $NbCl_3$, blue, with zinc, and the reaction of this solution with mercuric chloride to give mercurous chloride. The fractional crystallization of the complex fluorides with excess HF may also be employed. The solubility data in grams per liter are: K_2TaF_7, 5; $K_2TiF_6 \cdot H_2O$, 12; and $K_2NbOF_5 \cdot H_2O$, 77.

In gravimetric determinations, these elements are usually separated and weighed as the pentoxides. Vanadium and niobium are determined volumetrically by reduction to vanadyl and to the $+3$ niobium, and titration with permanganate.

18. Summary of Potential Values.—The variation in the oxidation reduction potentials for the members of the group are indicated in the following potential diagrams.

$$
\begin{array}{c}
\text{(1.5)} \qquad 0.25 \qquad\quad -0.36 \qquad\quad -1.0 \\
V\text{———}V^{+2}\text{————}V^{+3}\text{————}VO^{++}\text{————}V(OH)_4{}^+
\end{array}
$$

$$
\begin{array}{c}
\qquad\quad \text{(1.1)} \qquad\qquad\qquad \text{(0.1)} \\
Nb\text{———————}Nb^{+3}\text{————}Nb_2O_5 \\
\lfloor\text{————————}0.62\text{————————————}\rfloor
\end{array}
$$

$$
\begin{array}{c}
\qquad\qquad\qquad 0.71 \\
Ta\text{——————————————————}Ta_2O_5
\end{array}
$$

Chapter XVII

SUBGROUP VI. CHROMIUM, MOLYBDENUM, TUNGSTEN (WOLFRAM)

1. The elements of Subgroup VI have 6 as the maximum positive oxidation state and in this state show many properties common to each other, as well as to sulfur in the sulfates. In addition, the elements of the group have a variety of lower oxidation states, in which they do not resemble each other as much as they do the elements of higher and lower atomic numbers; especially is this true of chromium, whose lower states are similar to the corresponding ones of vanadium and manganese. This fact is to be correlated with the position of the elements in transition series in which an eight electron shell is being converted to an eighteen electron shell (Append. XVIII). One of the most striking properties of the + 6 compounds is the tendency to form poly-acids. This tendency reaches a maximum in molybdenum, which forms acids containing many molecules of the trioxide. The acidic nature of the oxides decreases with increasing size of the ions.

The metals have very high melting points, that of tungsten being higher than that of any other metal. They are also very tough, and advantage is taken of this in forming many important alloys with iron.

Uranium was formerly included in Subgroup VI, but the evidence is now definite that it contains electrons in the 5*f* shell and its chemistry is discussed with the element of the Actinide series. Tungsten is also known as **wolfram.**

2. Occurrence.—The metals do not occur free in nature. Chromium is the most abundant of the group, and is present to the average extent of about 0.037 per cent in igneous rocks, usually as Cr_2O_3, replacing Al_2O_3 in aluminates. The estimated percentages of the others are: molybdenum 10^{-6}, and tungsten 5×10^{-5}. The most important chromium ore is **chromite**, $Fe(Cr_2O_4)$, or $FeO \cdot Cr_2O_3$. Lead chromate, $PbCrO_4$, and other chromates of the heavy metals also occur. The major chromite-producing countries are: New Caledonia, Rhodesia, South Africa, Russia, Turkey and Cuba. The domestic deposits are very limited.

Molybdenum is most frequently found as the sulfide, **molybdenite**, MoS_2, which resembles graphite in appearance. It also occurs as molybdates, especially $PbMoO_4$ and $Fe_2(MoO_4)_3 \cdot 7.5H_2O$. Extensive deposits of molybdenite occur in Colorado. It is estimated that the known reserves of "proved ore" in this state are around one million tons of molybdenum.

The most important tungsten ore is **wolframite**, an isomorphous ferrous-manganous tungstate, $[Fe, Mn] WO_4$. Other tungstates, as $CaWO_4$, $PbWO_4$, and $CuWO_4$, and the trioxide, WO_3, or wolfram ocher, are also found. China and Burma have been the leading producers of tungsten. Domestic production is largely from Nevada.

METALS AND METALLURGY

3. Chromium.—The greater portion of metallic chromium is utilized in chrome steel, and for this use ferrochrome is prepared by the direct reduction of chromite by carbon: $FeCr_2O_4 + 4C = Fe + 2Cr + 4CO$. For the preparation of chromium compounds, the ore is usually fused with sodium carbonate in air: $4FeCr_2O_4 + 8Na_2CO_3 + 7O_2 = 2Fe_2O_3 + 8Na_2CrO_4 + 8CO_2$; the sodium chromate is then extracted with water. The pure metal is conveniently prepared by reducing chromic oxide with aluminum (Goldschmidt reaction), or with carbon in an electric furnace. The electrolytic deposition of chromium on iron or copper has recently assumed importance. The electrolyte used is an acid chromic chromate solution containing sulfate, phosphate, borate, or other acid radicals.

Chromium is similar to platinum in luster, and this together with its high resistance to corrosion, has resulted in the use of the electroplated metal on motor cars and miscellaneous domestic appliances.

Chrome steel (0.5 to 1.0 per cent Cr, 0.75 per cent Si, and 0.5–1.25 per cent Mn) is very hard and tough. **Stainless steel** (14 per cent Cr) is used in the manufacture of cutlery, valves, turbine blades, etc. **Nichrome** (60 per cent Ni, 15 per cent Cr, and 25 per cent Fe) is used as resistance wire in electrical heaters. Chromium, with cobalt and tungsten, or molybdenum, forms an alloy known as **stellite,** suitable for high-speed tools (cf. **XIX—19**).

It is estimated that 50 per cent of the American consumption of chromate is for metallurgical industries, 40 per cent for the manufacture of refractory chrome-brick for furnace lining, and 10 per cent for the chemical industries.

4. Molybdenum.—The sulfide ore is now generally roasted to the oxide and converted into calcium molybdate by the addition of lime. This product is then used directly in the production of alloy steels or made into ferromolybdenum by reduction with carbon in an electric furnace. The pure metal may be prepared by reduction of the oxide with aluminum or hydrogen, and also by the electrolytic reduction of molybdic acid. Molybdenum is silver white in color, tough, and ductile. It is added to low carbon steel as a toughener; the addition of 1 per cent of molybdenum doubles the strength of low carbon steels at temperatures above 475° C. Such steels are used, for example, in superheated steam plants. The addition of molybdenum to chrome (stainless) steel increases the resistance to chemical action.   High molybdenum   steels are finding increasing use as high-speed tools.

5. Tungsten.—Tungsten is generally obtained from wolframite ores by fusion with sodium carbonate, to convert to sodium tungstate, which is then extracted with water, and the solution digested with hydrochloric acid to precipitate tungstic acid.   The acid is reduced by heating strongly with carbon, but the product is a powder, as the temperature is far below the melting point of the metal.   Rods of the metal are formed by sintering the particles together by passing a strong electric current through the compressed powder. Tungsten has become one of the most important industrial metals.   In 1950 a billion and a quarter of tungsten filament electric lamps were sold in the United States.   In

TABLE I

ATOMIC AND PHYSICAL PROPERTIES

	Cr	Mo	W
Atomic weight................	52.01	95.95	183.92
Atomic number...............	24	42	74
Stable isotopes................	50, 52, 53, 54	92, 94, 95, 96, 97, 98, 100	182, 183, 184, 186
Density......................	7.1	10.2	19.3
Melting point, ° C.............	1,530	2,610	3,380
Boiling point, ° C.............	2,475	4,800	5,630
Tensile strength, lbs. per sq. in....			590,000
Electrical resistivity, ohm-cm.....	2.6×10^{-6}	4.8×10^{-6}	5.5×10^{-6}
Ionization potential, volts........	6.74	7.35	
Radius of M^{+6} ion in crystals, cm. $\times 10^8$......................	0.52	0.62	

order to draw the metal into wire, it is necessary to subject the rod to severe working at a low temperature to break up the large crystals which form when the metal is heated and render it brittle.   The tensile strength of the drawn wire exceeds that of any other metallic substance.   The metal is also used as contact joints for making and breaking electrical circuits, for internal combustion engine valves, X-ray apparatus and utensils. The metal may be electroplated from solutions of sodium tungstate, but the best coatings are secured by deposition with nickel (or other metals). The nickel-tungsten (35–50 per cent W) alloy surfaces have remarkable resistance to chemical action.

Ferro-tungsten can be prepared by the reduction of the purer forms of iron tungstate ore with carbon. It is employed in the manufacture of "high-speed" steels and cobalt alloys such as stellite (cf. **XIX—19**).

In recent years, tungsten carbide, WC, has assumed great importance as a cutting material. Tungsten carbide is extremely hard but quite brittle. To overcome the brittleness it is imbedded in a matrix of some tough metal, frequently cobalt. These cemented carbides are the hardest metals so far produced.

TABLE II

REACTION PRODUCTS OF THE ELEMENTS

REACTION WITH	Cr	Mo	W
O_2	Cr_2O_3	MoO_3	WO_3
F_2	CrF_3	MoF_6	WF_6
Cl_2	$CrCl_3$	$MoCl_5$	WCl_6
Br_2	$CrBr_3$	$MoBr_4$	WBr_6
I_2	CrI_2	No action at 500°	WI_2
H^+	Cr^{++}, Cr^{+++}(slow)	No action	No action
OH^-	CrO_2^- (slow)	No action	WO_4^{--}
HNO_3	Cr^{+++}	MoO_3	WO_3
C	Cr_2C_3	Mo_2C, MoC	W_2C, WC
N_2	CrN	No action at 1000°	No action at 2000°, WN_2 at 2500°
S	CrS	MoS_2, Mo_2S_3	WS_2
B	CrB, Cr_3B	Mo_3B_4	WB_2

6. Reactions of the Metals.—The reactions of the metals with common reagents are so varied in nature as to render them difficult to summarize in the form of general group reactions; however, the principal reaction products have been summarized in Table II. The lighter members of the group exhibit to a high degree the property of passivity, and their reactions with powerful oxidizing agents are thus often extremely slow.

Compounds of Chromium

7. Oxidation States.—Chromium forms compounds in which it has the oxidation numbers + 2 (chromous), + 3 (chromic), and + 6 (chromate). The + 2 state is basic, the + 3 state is amphoteric, and the + 6 state is acidic. The potential relations between the states are summarized in the following half reactions:

$$
\begin{array}{lr}
 & \text{VOLTS} \\
\mathrm{Cr} = \mathrm{Cr}^{++} + 2e^{-}\dotfill & + 0.86 \\
\mathrm{Cr}^{++} = \mathrm{Cr}^{+++} + e^{-}\dotfill & + 0.41 \\
2\mathrm{Cr}^{+++} + 7\mathrm{H_2O} = \mathrm{Cr_2O_7}^{--} + 14\mathrm{H}^+ + 6e^{-}\dotfill & - 1.36
\end{array}
$$

It is evident from these values that the chromate in acid solution is a powerful oxidizing agent. The equilibrium, $\mathrm{Cr} + 2\mathrm{Cr}^{+++} = 3\mathrm{Cr}^{++}$, favors the formation of chromous ion, but the latter is such a powerful reducing agent that its solutions are oxidized even by very weak oxidizing agents to chromic ion.

8. Chromous Compounds.—Chromous compounds are somewhat similar to ferrous. **Chromous hydroxide,** $\mathrm{Cr(OH)_2}$, is a slightly soluble, brownish yellow substance, which is oxidized readily in air and when heated liberates hydrogen: $2\mathrm{Cr(OH)_2} = \mathrm{Cr_2O_3} + \mathrm{H_2O} + \mathrm{H_2}$. Solutions of chromous ion are blue, and may be prepared by the reduction of chromic solutions by the metal or by zinc (see above). The **chloride** and **sulfate** are soluble. The former may be prepared as an anhydrous salt, by heating the metal in hydrogen chloride. The **sulfide,** CrS, and **carbonate,** $\mathrm{CrCO_3}$, are but slightly soluble, and the **acetate,** $\mathrm{Cr(C_2H_3O_2)_2}$, but moderately so.

9. Chromic Compounds.—The **oxide,** $\mathrm{Cr_2O_3}$, is the most stable of the chromium oxides, and is formed by heating the metal or other oxides in air. Due to its fine green color it is used as a pigment, **chrome oxide green.** This is generally prepared by igniting sodium dichromate with sulfur or ammonium chloride: $Na_2Cr_2O_7 + S = Cr_2O_3 + Na_2SO_4$ and $Na_2Cr_2O_7 + 2NH_4Cl = Cr_2O_3 + 2NaCl + N_2 + 4H_2O$. The oxide is isomorphous with corundum, Al_2O_3. A **hydrated oxide,** $Cr_2O_3 \cdot H_2O$, may be formed by hydrolysis under pressure, but there is no evidence for the existence of $Cr(OH)_3$. The so-called "hydroxide" which is precipitated from chromic solution, may best be described as a **hydrous oxide.**

In its amphoteric properties the hydrous oxide, $Cr_2O_3 \cdot nH_2O$, resembles aluminum hydroxide, and like the latter is precipitated by ammonium hydroxide, and by solutions of alkali sulfides and carbonates. Excess of alkali hydroxide dissolves the precipitate with the formation of **chromites,** but the hydroxide or hydrated oxide is precipitated upon boiling. Chromites are readily formed by fusing the oxide with metal oxides, and such compounds constitute the common chromium minerals, the most important being **ferrous chromite,** $FeCr_2O_4$. Chromite is used extensively as a refractory, especially in lining open-hearth furnaces used in the manufacture of steel.

10. Chromic ion forms numerous coordination complexes, especially with ammonia, water, halides, cyanide, and thiocyanate. A number of these are tabulated below. The coordination number of chromium is six. In solution these compounds dissociate into the complex ion and the ions placed outside the bracket.

$[Cr(NH_3)_6]Cl_3$ $[Cr(NH_3)_6](CNS)_3$ $[Cr(NH_3)_5(H_2O)]Cl_3$
$[Cr(NH_3)_5Cl]Cl_2$ $[Cr(NH_3)_3(CNS)_3]$ $[Cr(NH_3)_5NO_2]Cl_2$
$[Cr(H_2O)_6]Cl_3$ $[Cr(CNS)_6]K_3$ $[Cr_4O(SO_4)_4]SO_4$
$[Cr(H_2O)_4Cl_2]Cl$ $[Cr(CN)_6]K_3$ $[Cr(OH)(NH_3)_5]Br_2$

The two water-chloride complexes are of especial interest. The complex ion, $[Cr(H_2O)_6]^{+++}$, has a violet color, and is present largely in dilute chromic ion solutions, while the complex, $[Cr(H_2O)_4Cl_2]^+$, is green and forms in more concentrated solutions in presence of excess chloride. The rates of transition are slow, however, and the two ions may be obtained in the same solution. Only one third of the chloride may be precipitated from the green solution by silver ion.

11. **Chromic sulfate,** $Cr_2(SO_4)_3 \cdot 18H_2O$, may be precipitated by the addition of alcohol to a solution made by dissolving the oxide in sulfuric acid. This solution is violet, probably $Cr(H_2O)_6^{+++}$, *vide supra*, but upon heating a green sulfate solution is formed, which does not form a precipitate upon the addition of alcohol, and in which only one third of the sulfate is ionized. Upon standing, the green solution reverts to the blue. Chromic sulfate readily forms **alums,** e.g., $KCr(SO_4)_2 \cdot 12H_2O$.

Chromic phosphate, $CrPO_4 \cdot 6H_2O$, precipitates when sodium hydrogen phosphate is added to a chromic solution. Several other hydrates are formed by carrying out the precipitation at higher temperatures.

12. **Chromic Acid and Derivatives.**—**Chromic anhydride,** or chromium trioxide, separates as a mass of scarlet needles when a cold concentrated solution of potassium dichromate is treated with concentrated sulfuric acid. It melts without decomposition, but loses oxygen around 250° to form the oxide, $Cr_2O_3 \cdot CrO_3$, or CrO_2, and at higher temperatures, Cr_2O_3. The trioxide is very soluble in water, forming **chromic** and **dichromic acids,** H_2CrO_4 and $H_2Cr_2O_7$. The former may be crystallized from warm concentrated solutions. A solution of chromic acid, formed by adding sulfuric acid to sodium dichromate, is frequently used in the laboratory as **"cleaning solution."**

Like the other members of the sixth periodic group, chromate forms complexes containing varying amounts of the trioxide; and the potassium salts, K_2CrO_4, $K_2Cr_2O_7$, $K_2Cr_3O_{10}$, and $K_2Cr_4O_{13}$ are known. However, only the first two are important, the chromate existing in alkaline solution, and the dichromate in acid solutions. The equilibrium between the two ions is represented by the equation: $2CrO_4^{--} + 2H^+ = Cr_2O_7^{--} + H_2O$, $K = 4.2 \times 10^{14}$. The mechanism of the equilibrium involves the two equilibria: $HCrO_4^- = CrO_4^{--} + H^+$, $K = 3.2 \times 10^{-7}$, and $2HCrO_4^- = H_2O + Cr_2O_7^{--}$, $K = 43$.

The **alkali chromates** are prepared from chromite by roasting the ore with the alkali carbonate, or mixtures of limestone and alkali sulfate: $4FeCr_2O_4 + 8Na_2CO_3 + 7O_2 = 2Fe_2O_3 + 8Na_2CrO_4 + 8CO_2$. The cinder is then crushed and extracted with water to obtain the chromate. **Sodium chromate** crystallizes as $Na_2CrO_4 \cdot 10H_2O$, isomorphous with the sulfate, and changes to the hexahydrate at 79.5°. **Potassium chromate,** K_2CrO_4, is isomorphous with potassium sulfate.

Sodium dichromate, $Na_2Cr_2O_7 \cdot 2H_2O$, is obtained from the chromate by adding acid and crystallizing from the acid solution. Above 82°, the anhydrous salt separates. **Potassium dichromate** is prepared in a similar way. It is not very soluble in cold water, but readily soluble in hot. **Ammonium dichromate,** $(NH_4)_2Cr_2O_7$, is generally made from chromic acid and ammonia. Upon heating, it decomposes according to the equation: $(NH_4)_2Cr_2O_7 = Cr_2O_3 + N_2 + 4H_2O$.

Dichromates are employed extensively in processes requiring a strong oxidizing agent. In the chrome-tanning process, the hide is treated with sodium dichromate, which is then reduced, and chromic hydroxide precipitated in the pores of the leather. Dichromate forms with gelatine, when exposed to the light, an insoluble product, and advantage is taken of this fact in a number of photographic processes. Potassium dichromate is important in analytical chemistry in the titration of reducing agents, especially ferrous salts (cf. **XIX—16**).

A number of slightly soluble chromates are important pigments: e.g. **chrome yellow,** $PbCrO_4$; **chrome orange,** Pb_2,

$OCrO_4$; **zinc yellow** approximately $K_2O \cdot 4ZnCrO_4 \cdot 3H_2O$. In general, the solubilities of the chromates are very similar to those of the sulfates.

13. Chromyl Compounds.—**Chromyl chloride,** CrO_2Cl_2, and **fluoride,** CrO_2F_2, may be prepared by distilling dichromate with the alkali halide and sulfuric acid. The chloride is a blood-red liquid, which is hydrolyzed by water to chromic and hydrochloric acids. Intermediate **chlorchromates** also exist, e.g. $KCrO_3Cl$, and the halides may be replaced from the chromyl compounds with ammonia to form **chromyl diamide,** $CrO_2(NH_2)_2$.

14. Peroxychromates.—Hydrogen peroxide gives with chromate in acid a deep blue solution of peroxychromate. If this solution is shaken with ether, the peroxy-acid is extracted. This constitutes a very delicate test for chromate or for hydrogen peroxide. The exact composition of the acid is uncertain but appears to be CrO_5. With alkalies it gives salts which are thought to have formulas such as $K_2Cr_2O_{12}$. At low temperatures in alkaline solution red peroxy-salts such as $K_6Cr_2O_{16}$ are formed. From ammoniacal solutions the compound $CrO_4 \cdot 3NH_3$ has been prepared.

COMPOUNDS OF MOLYBDENUM

15. Oxidation States.—Molybdenum forms compounds having the positive oxidation states 2, 3, 4, 5, and 6; however, the $+ 2$ and $+ 4$ compounds exist in water solutions only in the form of a few relatively unstable complex ions. Approximate values of the oxidation-reduction potentials for the other states in acid solution are given below.

	VOLTS
$Mo + 3H_2O = MoO_3 + 6H^+ + 6e^-$	$- 0.1$
$MoO_2^+ + 2H_2O = H_2MoO_4 \text{ (aq)} + 2H^+ + 2e^-$ .... $ca.$	$- 0.4$
$Mo^{+++} + H_2O = MoO_2^+ + 4H^+ + 2e^-$ .... $ca.$	0.0
$Mo = Mo^{+++} + 3e^-$ .... $ca.$	0.2

16. The $+ 2$ State.—The **dichloride,** $MoCl_2$, is formed by heating the trichloride: $2MoCl_3 = MoCl_2 + MoCl_4$.

The **bromide** may be prepared in a similar manner, and the iodide by heating the pentachloride in hydrogen iodide. These halides are insoluble in water but dissolve in alkalies, and upon acidifying the solution, precipitate the complex bases $(Mo_3X_4)(OH)_2$. The halides appear to be derivative of the same complex having the formula Mo_3X_6, or $[Mo_3X_4]$-X_2. They are slowly oxidized by water.

17. The + 3 State.—Solutions of + 3 molybdenum are prepared by the reduction of molybdic acid by powerful reducing agents. The color of the solutions is generally an olive green. The **hydroxide**, $Mo(OH)_3$, (or hydrous oxide) is black, and insoluble in water or excess hydroxide. Upon ignition, it gives the **oxide**, Mo_2O_3. Ammonium sulfide precipitates the **sulfide**, Mo_2S_3, soluble in excess of the reagent. The **phosphate** is also but slightly soluble. Complex ions are formed with halides, and with thiocyanate, e.g. K_3MoCl_6 and $K_3Mo(CNS)_6$; and the colors of these solutions vary from red to violet.

18. The + 4 State.—The **sulfide**, MoS_2, is the principal ore of the element. The **oxide**, MoO_2, forms when the sesquioxide is heated in air, or the trioxide is reduced with hydrogen (500°) or carbon (700°). The chloride, bromide, and iodide may be prepared mixed with the dihalide, by heating the trihalide. These compounds are not soluble in water, and the + 4 ion is not stable, probably being oxidized and reduced to MoO^{+++} and Mo^{+++}. However, a number of water soluble complex cyanide and halide compounds have been prepared, e.g., $K_4Mo(CN)_8$, $K_4MoO_2(CN)_4$, and H_nMoI_{4+n}.

19. The + 5 State.—The **pentachloride**, $MoCl_5$, is made by heating the metal or lower chloride in chlorine. It is the only known oxygen-free compound of this state. In water, it hydrolyzes to the molybdenyl compound: $MoCl_5 + H_2O = MoOCl_3 + 2HCl$. Compounds of the common acids, with MoO^{+++} or MoO_2^+, are prepared by the reduction of molybdate in acid solution with moderately strong reducing agents, e.g. $SnCl_2$. The addition of hydroxide to the solutions precipitates the **hydroxide,** $MoO(OH)_3$, which may be decomposed to the **pentoxide,** Mo_2O_5. A delicate test for $+ 5$ molybdenum is the formation of a deep red colored solution upon the addition of thiocyanate, probably $Mo(OH)_2(CNS)_3$. Mild reducing agents act upon an excess of molybdic acid with the production of a deep blue precipitate, **molybdenum blue,** which appears to be a molybdenyl molybdate, $(MoO)_3(MoO_4)_2$, or $(MoO_2)_2MoO_4$. In high acid concentration the reduction forms an ion, probably MoO_2^+. A number of complex chlorides, e.g. $MoOCl_5^{--}$ and $MoOCl_4^-$ are known.

20. The + 6 State.—The **trioxide,** MoO_3, is a white solid which is soluble, one part in 500 parts of cold water, forming a slightly acid solution. The oxide is formed by roasting the disulfide in air, by the igniting of ammonium molybdate, or by the decomposition of a molybdate with hot nitric acid. In the latter case, if the solution is allowed to crystallize in the cold, yellow **molybdic acid,** $H_2MoO_4 \cdot H_2O$, separates.

The oxide forms normal **molybdates,** e.g. Na_2MoO_4, especially if fused with basic oxides or carbonates; but these normal salts are in general unstable, if soluble in water, and tend to form **polymolybdates.** The complexity of the polyion depends upon the hydrogen ion concentration and the following values have been given: pH, 14–6.5, MoO_4^{-2}; pH, 6.3–4.5, $(Mo_3O_{11})^{-4}$; pH 4.5–1.5, $(Mo_6O_{21})^{-6}$; pH, 1.25, $(Mo_{12}O_{41})^{-10}$; and pH 1.0, $(Mo_{24}O_{78})^{-12}$. Commercial **ammonium molybdate** has a composition which is approximately $(NH_4)_6Mo_7O_{24} \cdot 4H_2O$, but it may not be a definite compound. Lead and the alkaline earth normal molybdates are but slightly soluble, similar to the sulfates and chromates. (Cf. molybdenum orange, **XVII—35.**) The slightly soluble molybdenyl molybdate has been mentioned above.

A compound of analytical importance is the **ammonium phospho-molybdate,** $(NH_4)_3PO_4 \cdot 12MoO_3$. It forms as a yellow precipitate, when a solution of ammonium molybdate is added to a solution of orthophosphate in nitric acid. It is readily soluble in ammonia or alkalies and in phosphoric acid, and its solubility is increased in the presence of chloride and many organic acids. Its importance in analytical work lies in its use in separating phosphate from iron and other ions which form slightly soluble phosphates. The composition of the precipitate is approximately as written, but may contain slightly less MoO_3, depending on the conditions of precipitation.

Rubidium and thallium phosphomolybdates are likewise insoluble in nitric acid, as are also salts of many of the heavy metals, if the solutions are not too acid. A number of other phosphomolybdate complexes also exist: for example, the compound, $(NH_4)_6(PO_4)_2 \cdot 5MoO_3 \cdot 7H_2O$, crystallizes from the solution formed by dissolving the ordinary precipitate in excess ammonia.

21. Normal molybdates form with hydrogen peroxide the red **peroxy-acid,** H_2MoO_8, and salts of this peroxy-acid have been prepared. With the polymolybdates more complicated peroxy-acids are formed.

The trioxide acts toward strong acids as a basic oxide; with hydrochloric acid it forms the somewhat volatile **oxychloride,** $MoO(OH)_2Cl_2$; and with sulfuric acid the **oxysulfate,** MoO_2SO_4. **Oxybrom** compounds also form, but the iodine compounds are not stable. Fluorine forms a **hexahalide,** MoF_6, when the metal is heated in the halogen.

Hydrogen sulfide gives with an acid solution of molybdates a precipitate of the **sulfide,** MoS_3. This compound is soluble in excess ammonium sulfide with the formation of **thiomolybdate.**

COMPOUNDS OF TUNGSTEN

22. Oxidation States.—Compounds are known containing tungsten with the positive oxidation numbers 2, 3, 4, 5, and 6. The + 6 compounds alone are of importance. In alkaline solution the tungstates $(+6)$ are very stable, but tungstic acid in the presence of hydrochloric acid is reduced by stannous chloride to a blue compound, probably $(WO_2)_2(WO_4)$; and stronger reducing agents, e.g. tin, will reduce the solution to WO^{+++} (green), and upon further action to complex ions of W^{+4}, probably $W(OH)Cl_4^-$ (red brown color), and of W^{+3}, probably $W_2Cl_9^{---}$ (reddish blue). The following potentials are only approximate and are considerably modified in the presence of halide ions.

	VOLTS $_{25°}$
$W = W^{+++} + 3e^-$	< 0.05
$W^{+++} + 2H_2O = WO_2 + 4H^+ + e^-$	> 0.05
$2WO_2 + H_2O = W_2O_5 + 2H^+ + 2e^-$	0.0
$W_2O_5 + H_2O = 2WO_3 + 2H^+ + 2e^-$	-0.15
$WOCl_4^- + H_2O = WO_2Cl_3^- + Cl^- + 2H^+ + e^-$	-0.26

23. The + 2 Compounds.—The **halides,** WCl_2, WBr_2, WI_2, have been prepared by the action of reducing agents upon higher halides at high temperatures. The chloride is somewhat soluble in water, but the solution hydrolyzes to some complex substance; the compound $HW_3Cl_7 \cdot 4\frac{1}{2}H_2O$ has been obtained from alcoholic solutions.

24. The + 3 Compounds.—Alkali and ammonia salts, of the general formula, $R_3W_2Cl_9$, have been prepared by the reduction of tungstic acid with tin, but no simple compounds of this valence are known. Crystal structure data indicate that the ion $(W_2Cl_9)^{-3}$ has an interesting structure. Six chloride ions form an octahedron about the tungsten as indicated in the following diagram:

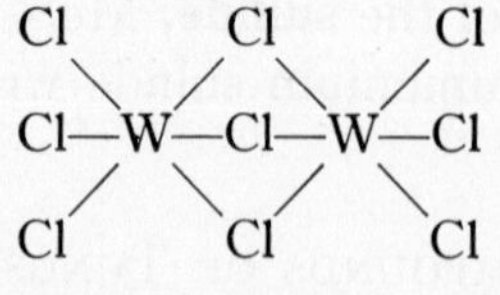

$$
\begin{array}{ccccc}
Cl & & Cl & & Cl \\
\diagdown & \diagup & \diagdown & \diagup & \\
Cl & \!\!-W- & Cl & \!\!-W- & Cl \\
\diagup & \diagdown & \diagup & \diagdown & \\
Cl & & Cl & & Cl
\end{array}
$$

25. The + 4 Compounds.—The **dioxide,** WO_2, is formed by heating the trioxide in hydrogen, but if too high a temperature is employed the oxide is reduced to the metal.

The oxide is also a product of the hydrolysis of the tetrachloride, or of tetravalent solutions. It is readily oxidized, and with alkali evolves hydrogen and forms tungstate. It is only slightly soluble in acids. Anhydrous **tetrachloride** and **iodide** may be prepared at high temperatures, but they are readily hydrolyzed by water. The **complex cyanide** ion, $W(CN)_8^{-4}$, is stable in water solution, and many of its salts have been prepared. The **sulfide**, WS_2, forms when the trisulfide is ignited. The compound is not soluble in water or dilute hydrogen ion.

26. The + 5 Compounds.—The **chloride**, WCl_5, and **bromide**, WBr_5, are formed by carefully reducing the hexahalides in hydrogen. The compounds are readily soluble in water, forming light green solutions which contain the ions WO^{+++} or WO_2^+; with excess halide the solution appears to form **complex halides** such as $WOCl_5^{--}$.

Similar solutions are formed by the cathodic reduction, or reduction by tin of alcoholic solutions of tungstic acid in hydrochloric acid. When oxalic acid is used, **complex oxalates** are formed, e.g. $Na_3WO_2(C_2O_4)_2$. Compounds of the complex cyanide ion $W(CN)_8^{-3}$ are known.

The addition of ammonia to solutions of the complex chlorides precipitates the hydroxide $W(OH)_5$. The sulfide is not known.

Stannous chloride gives with tungstic acid a blue precipitate, **tungsten blue**, which probably has the composition $(WO_2)_2WO_4$.

27. The + 6 Compounds.—The yellow trioxide, WO_3, occurs as the mineral wolframocher. It is readily prepared by gently igniting the acid, which is obtained from its salts by digestion with hydrochloric acid. In the cold, the hydrated acid, $H_2WO_4 \cdot H_2O$, separates, while in hot solutions, the anhydrous acid precipitates. The former is somewhat soluble in water, but the latter neither dissolves in water nor any acid, except hydrofluoric.

The trioxide also forms many **polytungstates.** Thus,

compounds with sodium oxide of the general formula $(Na_2O)_n(WO_3)_m$ are known, in which, when $n = 1$, m may vary from 1 to 6; and more complicated compounds in which both n and m are large numbers. Except for a few of the alkali compounds, the tungstates are not soluble in water. Although the normal sodium salt, $Na_2WO_4 \cdot 2H_2O$, is readily prepared, the commercial "tungstate of soda" is the paratungstate, $Na_{10}W_{12}O_{41} \cdot 28H_2O$. This salt is employed as a mordant in dyeing.

Like molybdenum, the trioxide forms a number of **phosphotungstic** acids. The acid, $H_3PO_4 \cdot 12WO_3$, is used as a reagent to precipitate alkaloids and proteins. The oxide also forms **silicotungstic** acids: e.g. by boiling silica with ammonium polytungstate, the compound, $(NH_4)_8SiW_{10}O_{36}$ $\cdot 8H_2O$, is obtained.

When a solution of sodium paratungstate is boiled with hydrogen peroxide, the solution is found to contain the **peroxytungstate,** $NaWO_4 \cdot H_2O$, and many complicated compounds have been obtained.

Tungstates are converted by alkali sulfides into **thiotungstates,** e.g. $(NH_4)_2WS_4$; when these solutions are acidified, the **trisulfide,** WS_3, is precipitated.

The **hexahalides,** WF_6, WCl_6, and WBr_6 result from the action of the halogens upon the heated metal. The fluoride is also formed by the reaction: $WCl_6 + 6HF = WF_6 + 6HCl$. The **oxyhalides,** WO_2X_2 and WOX_4, may also be prepared. The fluorides, and also the trioxide, are soluble in excess of fluoride to form complex ions, e.g. $WO_2F_4^{--}$.

28. Analytical.—In the systematic separation of the metallic elements, chromium is associated with the aluminum group in that it is not precipitated by H_2S in $0.3N$ H^+, but is precipitated by NH_4OH and $(NH_4)_2S$ as $Cr(OH)_3$. When this precipitate is dissolved in nitric acid and treated with sodium peroxide, the chromium remains in solution as Na_2CrO_4. Chromium may be identified by the precipitation of lead chromate from dilute nitric acid solution.

Molybdenum resembles antimony in that it is precipitated by H_2S in $0.3N$ H^+, and the sulfide is soluble in ammonium sulfide to form the thio-salt. The filtrate from the hydrogen sulfide precipitation, however, is colored blue through the reduction of some of the molybdenum.

In the absence of phosphate, MoO_3 remain as a residue when molybdenum compounds are evaporated with the acids, $HNO_3 + HClO_4$, and the product washed with water. The oxide is soluble in hydrogen fluoride, and the hydrated oxide, H_2MoO_4 is soluble in $2N$ HCl.

Tungstate gives a precipitate of tungsten blue with stannous chloride in dilute HCl; and molybdate gives a precipitate of molybdenum blue with stannous chloride in $12N$ HCl, and an orange color (Mo^{+5}) in dilute acid. The Mo^{+5} solution forms, with KCNS, a deep red color of $MoO(CNS)_3$.

In **gravimetric analysis,** the following pure compounds may be separated and weighed: Cr_2O_3, $BaCrO_4$, MoO_3, $PbMoO_4$, and WO_3. The trioxides of molybdenum and tungsten may be separated by precipitating the mercurous salts, which are then ignited to the oxide.

In **volumetric analysis** dichromate may be titrated against ferrous ion, or an excess of iodide may be added to dichromate in acid, and the iodine titrated with thiosulfate.

Molybdates may be reduced to MoO_2^+ with hydrogen iodide, and the iodine determined with thiosulfate, or the molybdate may be reduced to Mo^{+++} by zinc, and the product titrated with permanganate.

29. Potential Diagrams.—In order to compare the trends in the oxidation-reduction potentials of the elements of this group, the following diagrams are given.

$$
\begin{array}{l}
\quad 0.86 \qquad\quad 0.41 \qquad\qquad\qquad -1.36 \\
Cr\text{———}Cr^{++}\text{———}Cr^{+++}\text{———————————————}Cr_2O_7^{--} \\
\qquad (0.2) \qquad\qquad\qquad (0.0) \qquad\qquad (-0.4) \\
Mo\text{————————}Mo^{+3}\text{—————————}MoO_2^+\text{———}MoO_3(aq) \\
\quad <0.05 \qquad\quad >0.05 \qquad 0.0 \qquad -0.03 \\
W\text{———————————}W^{+3}\text{————}WO_2\text{——}W_2O_5\text{———}WO_3(S)
\end{array}
$$

Chapter XVIII

SUBGROUP VII. MANGANESE, TECHNETIUM, AND RHENIUM

1. The elements of Subgroup VII are manganese, technetium, and rhenium. The discussion of the relation of atomic structure and oxidation states of the elements of Subgroup VI is also applicable to Subgroup VII except, of course, that these elements possess one more electron. In the + 7 state they show certain resemblances to the perhalates, but in the lower states they are more closely related to the elements of neighboring atomic numbers. These latter relations are further discussed in Chapter **XIX**. Rhenium may be reduced to the − 1 state. This seems most remarkable, since octet formation is otherwise restricted to s-p electron groups.

2. Occurrence.—Manganese is ranked 9th among the metals in order of abundance, the estimated percentage in igneous rocks being 0.10. The principal ore is pyrolusite, MnO_2. Other minerals are braunite, $3Mn_2O_3 \cdot MnSiO_3$; manganite, $Mn_2O_3 \cdot H_2O$; hausmannite, Mn_3O_4; rhodochrosite, $MnCO_3$; alabandite, MnS; hauerite, MnS_2. The manganese ores are generally associated with iron.

The evidence is fairly definite that there is no isotope of element number 43 of sufficient stability to exist in nature. Radioactive isotopes were first prepared in 1937 by the bombardment of molybdenum with deuterons accelerated in a cyclotron. The previously suggested name of masurium has now been replaced by technetium, derived from the

Greek word for "technical" in recognition of the fact that this was the first new element to be produced by technical means. The most stable isotope Tc^{99} (half-life 9.4×10^5 years) is a product of the slow neutron fission of uranium and the fission yield is 6.2 per cent. A uranium pile operating at a power level of 10^5 kw produces about 4 grams of Tc^{99} per day.

The abundance of rhenium is quite low. The first commercial production, around 1935, came from the potash residues (now exhausted) in Germany. A small domestic production has been developed from "flue dust" containing molybdenum sulfide in an Arizona copper smelter.

3. The Metals.—Manganese is difficult to prepare in the pure state by reduction with carbon, as it forms a series of solid solutions with the carbide, Mn_3C. It may be prepared by the reduction of the oxide by aluminum. The production of the metal by electrolytic reduction has developed rapidly in recent years. The electrolyte is manganous sulfate with a high concentration of ammonium sulfate. Manganese is an essential constituent of most of the domestic steels; the average consumption is 12 pounds of manganese per ton of steel. It is used to deoxidize the molten metal. This property depends in part upon the very slight solubility of the manganous oxide and sulfide in molten iron. It also improves the rolling and forging qualities of the steel and contributes toughness. For this purpose ferromanganese (70–80 per cent Mn) and, to a lesser extent, Spiegel iron (15–25 per cent Mn) are employed. These iron alloys are prepared by reducing the mixed ores in a blast furnace. The annual consumption of manganese in the steel industry is around a million tons of 35 per cent ore and about 90 per cent of this is imported, principally from India, Brazil and Africa.

The pure metal is reddish-gray, and relatively soft compared to iron, but if it contains carbon, it is very hard and brittle. The melting point is lower than those of either

TABLE I

ATOMIC AND PHYSICAL PROPERTIES OF ELEMENTS OF SUBGROUP VII

	Mn	Tc	Re
Atomic weight................	54.93	98–99	186.31
Atomic number................	25	43	75
Isotopes......................	55	None stable	185, 187
Density......................	7.2	11.5	21.4
Melting point, ° C.............	1,244	—	3,147
Boiling point, ° C.............	2,087	—	5,530
Electrical resistivity, ohm-cm.....	5×10^{-6}	—	2×10^{-5}
Ionization potential of gas atom, volts......................	7.4	—	—

iron or chromium. The metal tarnishes readily in moist air, especially if it contains the carbide, Mn_3C, which evolves methane and hydrogen with water.

Manganese bronze contains about 34 per cent Mn, 60 per cent Cu, and 35 per cent Zn. The alloy **manganin** (Cu 84, Mn 12, Ni 4) has a very low temperature coefficient of resistance and is used in electrical instruments. Small amounts of manganese are added to many aluminum alloys.

Technetium metal may be precipitated from solutions of TcO_4^- electrolytically or by the action of Fe or Cu. It has also been prepared by the reduction of the sulfide by H_2 at 1000° C.

Rhenium metal may be prepared by electrolytic precipitation from water solution of the perrhenate. In contact with water it is readily oxidized back to the perrhenate. The metal is somewhat soft and ductile in spite of the extremely high melting point. There are no commercial uses at present.

4. Reactions of the Metals.—The electropositive nature (Par. **5**) of manganese renders it highly reactive toward oxidizing agents. The principal reactions are given in Table II. Rhenium is less electropositive than manganese and is not oxidized as readily by weak oxidizing agents, but moderately strong oxidizing agents will carry it all the way up to the perrhenate. By direct reaction with the elements metallic rhenium forms Re_2O_7, ReF_6, $ReCl_4$, $ReBr_3$, and ReS_2. Technetium is not oxidized by HCl.

TABLE II

REACTIONS OF MANGANESE

$3Mn + 2O_2 = Mn_3O_4$	Heated in air
$Mn + 2H^+ = Mn^{++} + H_2$	
$Mn + 2H_2O = Mn(OH)_2 + H_2$	Slowly in cold
$Mn + X_2 = MnX_2$	X = halogen. F_2 also gives MnF_3
$Mn + S = MnS$	Heated together
$3Mn + C = Mn_3C$	High temperature. With Si forms MnSi and Mn_2Si
$10Mn + 3N_2 = 2Mn_5N_3$	Burns in N_2 at 1200°. With P forms Mn_5P_2 and MnP
$2Mn + 4KOH + 3O_2 = 2K_2MnO_4 + 2H_2O$	

COMPOUNDS OF MANGANESE

5. Oxidation States.—Manganese forms compounds having the positive oxidation states 2, 3, 4, 5, 6, and 7. The two lower states are basic, the + 4 amphoteric, and the three higher states acidic. There is evidence for the + 1 complex cyanide, e.g., $K_5Mn(CN)_6$. The oxidation-reduction potentials relating to the various states are summarized in the following potential diagrams:

Acid Solution

$$\text{Mn} \overset{1.18}{\rule{1cm}{0.4pt}} \text{Mn}^{++} \overset{-1.51}{\underset{-1.23}{\rule{1cm}{0.4pt}}} \text{Mn}^{+++} \overset{-0.95}{\rule{1cm}{0.4pt}} \text{MnO}_2 \overset{-2.26}{\underset{-1.70}{\rule{1cm}{0.4pt}}} \text{MnO}^{-}_4 \overset{-0.56}{\rule{1cm}{0.4pt}} \text{MnO}_4^{-}$$

Basic Solution

$$\text{Mn} \overset{1.57}{\rule{1cm}{0.4pt}} \text{Mn(OH)}_2 \overset{-0.1}{\underset{0.04}{\rule{1cm}{0.4pt}}} \text{Mn(OH)}_3 \overset{-0.2}{\rule{1cm}{0.4pt}} \text{MnO}_2 \overset{-0.8}{\underset{-0.60}{\rule{1cm}{0.4pt}}} \text{MnO}_3^{-} \overset{\overset{-0.59}{-0.3}}{\rule{1cm}{0.4pt}} \text{MnO}_4^{--} \overset{-0.56}{\rule{1cm}{0.4pt}} \text{MnO}_4^{-}$$

A number of very important relations in the chemistry of manganese may be correlated with these values:

Manganic ion, Mn^{+++}, is unstable even at very low concentrations in respect to the decomposition: $2Mn^{+++} + 2H_2O = Mn^{++} + MnO_2 + 4H^+$.

Manganate, MnO_4^{--}, when acidified, decomposes to the dioxide and permanganate: $3MnO_4^{--} + 4H^+ = MnO_2 + 2MnO_4^- + 2H_2O$. For the equilibrium in alkaline solution, $3MnO_4^{--} + 2H_2O = MnO_2 + 2MnO_4^- + 4OH$, $K = 16$. Hence at high concentrations of OH^-, the ratio of MnO_4^{--} to MnO_4^- may be large.

Permanganate in acid solution will oxidize manganous ion to the dioxide, and in alkaline solution will oxidize the dioxide to manganate.

Manganese dioxide in concentrated acid, and permanganate in both acid and alkali, will slowly evolve oxygen from water. With concentrated acid the reaction of permanganate is explosive.

Oxygen in normal alkali is not capable of oxidizing the dioxide to manganate, but the reaction does occur in fused potassium hydroxide. $Mn(OH)_2$ is readily oxidized by O_2 to $Mn(OH)_3$.

Excess of a reducing agent upon permanganate in acid solution yields manganous ion; but in alkaline or neutral solution the product is the dioxide. Partial reduction of permanganate in alkaline solution gives manganate. Reduction of MnO_4^{--} first forms a compound of the + 5 state, probably MnO_3^-, but this state is relatively unstable even in high OH^- and the reduction proceeds to MnO_2.

6. Manganous Ion.—Compounds of the + 2 state are known as manganous. They resemble magnesium and ferrous iron in their solubility relations, and are in general characterized by a delicate pink color. The **hydroxide**, $Mn(OH)_2$, forms when alkali or ammonium hydroxides are added to a manganous solution. Like magnesium hydroxide, it is soluble in ammonium salts. In the air, it quickly darkens through the oxidation to manganic hydroxide, $Mn(OH)_3$, or possibly $MnO \cdot MnO_2 \cdot nH_2O$. When heated in the absence of air, the hydroxide forms the **oxide**, MnO; and this, heated in air, is oxidized to Mn_3O_4.

Alkali and ammonium carbonates precipitate the **car-**

bonate, $MnCO_3$. This, like the hydroxide, is soluble in excess ammonium ion.

The pink **sulfide**, MnS, though precipitated by soluble sulfides, is readily soluble in dilute acids. The moist solid oxidizes, upon standing in the air, to the sulfate.

The **sulfate, nitrate, halides,** and **cyanide** are soluble; and the last forms the complex ions $Mn(CN)_3^-$ and $Mn(CN)_6^{----}$. The sulfate crystallizes in a number of hydrated forms, a transition from the penta-hydrate to the tetra-hydrate occurring at about 26°. It forms double salts, such as $K_2SO_4 \cdot MnSO_4 \cdot 6H_2O$, isomorphous with the corresponding salts of magnesium.

The **ammonium phosphate,** NH_4MnPO_4, **ferrocyanide,** $Mn_2Fe(CN)_6$, and **oxalate,** $MnC_2O_4 \cdot 2H_2O$, are but slightly soluble, and are of importance in analytical work.

7. Manganese in the $+3$ State.—Reference has been made in the preceding paragraph to the formation of the **hydroxide,** $Mn(OH)_3$ (probably hydrous oxide), by oxidation of manganous hydroxide. Due to the instability of the manganic ion, Mn^{+++} (Par. **5**), the only compounds which can be prepared from water solutions are slightly soluble, or slightly dissociated.

The **trifluoride** may be prepared by the action of fluorine upon the metal, and the **trichloride** by the decomposition of the tetrachloride. In water, they decompose, e.g. $2MnF_3 + 2H_2O = Mn^{++} + 6F^- + MnO_2 + 4H^+$, but a deep red solution containing the complex fluoride, K_2MnF_5, may be prepared by dissolving the hydroxide in excess of potassium acid fluoride. There is evidence of the formation of some H_2MnCl_5 when the dioxide is treated with concentrated hydrochloric acid. Powerful oxidizing agents in concentrated hydrochloric acid oxidize manganous ion to the complex chloride. The hydroxide in sulfuric acid forms an unstable **sulfate,** and **alums** have been prepared. Powerful oxidizing agents, e.g., $KMnO_4$, convert manganous ion, in excess acetic acid, into manganic **acetate.**

8. Manganese Dioxide.—The chemistry of $+4$ manganese deals largely with the **dioxide,** MnO_2. As the mineral, pyrolusite, it is the most important source of the element. In many respects, the dioxide resembles lead dioxide; and like the latter, although essentially amphoteric, it is comparatively inert toward both acids and bases. In cold concentrated hydrochloric acid, the oxide dissolves slowly to form a green solution of the **tetrachloride,** and the hydrous dioxide may be reprecipitated from this solution; but upon heating, chlorine is evolved and manganous chloride formed. The sulfate may also be obtained in solution, but it is very unstable toward the evolution of oxygen. A **complex fluoride,** K_2MnF_6, however, is more stable.

The oxide does not dissolve readily in alkali, but **manganites** are formed by fusing the oxide with certain basic oxides. Calcium manganite, $CaMn_2O_5$, is prepared by oxidizing manganous oxide with bleaching powder, and potassium manganite, $K_2Mn_5O_{11}$, by passing carbon dioxide into potassium manganate solution. The oxides, Mn_2O_3 and Mn_3O_4, may be considered as manganous manganites; upon heating, the dioxide loses oxygen to form these oxides or possibly solid solutions of the type $(MnO)_n(MnO_2)_m$.

The oxidation-reduction potentials of the dioxide have been discussed in Paragraph **5.**

Manganese dioxide is employed in the paint and varnish industry to catalyze the oxidation of oils by oxygen, i.e. the drying process. The glass industry employs the dioxide to neutralize the green color of ferrous silicate impurities. The largest use (about 30,000 tons in U. S. annually) of the dioxide is as the oxidizing constituent of the ordinary dry cell.

9. "Dry Cells."—The dry Leclanché battery, generally called the "dry cell," consists of a zinc anode, a cathode of carbon packed in manganese dioxide, and an electrolyte of ammonium chloride solution, containing a little zinc chloride, which is held in a porous solid (kieselguhr). The anode reaction is $Zn + 2Cl^- = ZnCl_2(s) + 2e^-$; and the cathode reaction, $MnO_2 + NH_4^+ + 2H_2O + e^- = NH_4OH + Mn(OH)_3$. The voltage is 1.48. Large currents cannot be drawn from the cell, owing to the polarization of the cathode, possibly due to the slow diffusion of the electrolyte. The ordinary dry cell does not function below $- 20°$ C., but the addition of LiCl or $CaCl_2$ to the electrolyte extends the range to $- 40°$ C.

Several other types of "dry" batteries are in use. A Mg-AgCl on Ag cell employs the reaction, $Mg + 2AgCl = MgCl_2 + 2Ag$. The electrodes are separated by a sheet of filter paper and the cell is activated by moistening the paper with salt water. The potential is 1.3 to 1.5 volts. The reaction, $AgO + Zn + KOH = Ag + KHZnO_2$, is used in a cell which is stored dry and is activated by the addition of KOH. The voltage is 1.5. Cells employing atmospheric oxygen on activated charcoal as the cathodes are increasing in importance. The anode is generally amalgamated zinc and the electrolyte, NaOH or $Ca(OH)_2$. The anode reaction is $Zn + 3OH^- = HZnO_2^- + H_2O + 2e^-$ and the cathode reaction, $O_2 + H_2O + 2e^- = HO_2^- + OH^-$, followed by the catalytic decomposition of the HO_2^-. The potential is around 1.3 volts.

10. The $+ 5$ State.—Manganese dioxide in fused KOH absorbs oxygen to give a ratio of 2.5 oxygens per manganese, i.e., Mn_2O_5. The careful electrolytic reduction of manganate in $0.1M$ OH^- gives a blue solution which disproportionates in a few minutes into the dioxide and manganate. The reduction of manganate in $0.01M$ OH^- goes directly to the dioxide.

11. Manganate.—When manganese dioxide is fused with potassium hydroxide, some decomposition occurs: $3MnO_2 + 2KOH = Mn_2O_3 + K_2MnO_4 + H_2O$. In the presence of air or other oxidizing agents, as potassium chlorate, the manganese is all oxidized to manganate: $2MnO_2 + 4KOH + O_2 = 2K_2MnO_4 + 2H_2O$. The potassium compound is soluble in water, giving a green solution, from which the salt may be crystallized. Manganates are somewhat similar in solubility to sulfates. The free acid cannot be prepared because of the decomposition into the dioxide and permanganate: $3MnO_4^{--} + 4H^+ = MnO_2 + 2MnO_4^-$ $+ 2H_2O$; but the very unstable trioxide has been prepared by the reaction: $(MnO_3)_2SO_4 + Na_2CO_3 = Na_2SO_4$ $+ 2MnO_3 + CO_2 + \frac{1}{2}O_2$. Reference should be made to Paragraph 5 for the oxidation-reduction relations of manganate.

12. Permanganate.—When the concentration of hydroxide in a manganate solution is decreased, the color changes from green to purple with the formation of permanganate and the dioxide: $3MnO_4^{--} + 2H_2O = 2MnO_4^- + MnO_2$ $+ 4OH^-$. The conversion of manganate into permanganate may also be carried out by powerful oxidizing agents in alkaline solution: e.g. $2MnO_4^{--} + ClO^- + H_2O = 2MnO_4^-$ $+ Cl^- + 2OH^-$.

A solution of **permanganic acid,** $HMnO_4$, may be prepared by the reaction of dilute sulfuric acid and barium permanganate, or by the oxidation of manganous sulfate by lead dioxide: $2MnSO_4 + 5PbO_2 + 3H_2SO_4 = 2HMnO_4$ $+ 5PbSO_4 + 2H_2O$. The solution decomposes upon boiling, or in the sunlight. When potassium permanganate is treated with cold concentrated sulfuric acid, the solution turns green through the formation of the sulfate, $(MnO_3)_2$-SO_4; and upon the careful addition of cold water, the **heptoxide,** Mn_2O_7, separates as a dark brown, highly explosive liquid

Alkali permanganates are usually prepared commercially by fusing the dioxide with alkali hydroxide in air to form the manganate, followed by oxidation with chlorine in the alkaline solution. They may also be prepared by the anodic oxidation of manganate.

If a pure permanganate is desired, the potassium salt is generally employed instead of the sodium salt, as the great solubility of the latter renders it difficult to prepare free from impurities. Alkali permanganates are used as disinfectants (Condy's Liquid), as oxidizing agents in industrial processes, and as volumetric reagents (Par. **15**).

COMPOUNDS OF TECHNETIUM

13. Oxidation States.—Detailed information on the chemistry of technetium is still lacking. In general the chemistry is intermediate between that of manganese and rhenium but it appears to resemble the rhenium more than manganese. The ion TcO_4^- in acid is a fair oxidizing agent and is reduced to the metal by Sn or Cu: $Tc + 4H_2O = TcO_4^- + 8H^+ + 7e^-$ $E° = ca. -0.5$. There is no evidence for a -1 state. Tc^{++} appears to be stable in water solution and the dioxide TcO_2 is a much weaker oxidizing agent than MnO_2.

COMPOUNDS OF RHENIUM

14. Oxidation States.—Rhenium forms the oxides Re_2O_3, ReO_2, ReO_3, Re_2O_7 and claims have been made for the formation of Re_2O. Halides or complex halides are known corresponding to the oxidation states $+ 3$, $+ 4$, $+ 5$, $+ 6$, and $+ 7$. When perrhenate is reduced in acid solution with zinc, eight equivalents of oxidizing agent are required to oxidize the solution, and this constitutes evidence for the existence of rhenide ion, Re^-. The following potentials are only approximate:

	VOLTS 25°
$Re + H_2O = ReO_4^- + 8H^+ + 7e^-$	$- 0.365$
$Re + 2H_2O = ReO_2 + 4H^+ + 4e^-$	$- 0.25$
$ReCl_6^{--} + 4H_2O = ReO_4^- + 6Cl^- + 8H^+ + 3e^-$ ......$ca.$	$- 0.5$
$Re^- = Re + e^-$ ......$ca.$	0.4
$ReO_2 + 2H_2O = ReO_4^- + 4H^+ + 3e^-$	$- 0.51$

15. Perrhenate.—The oxide, Re_2O_7, is colorless and dissolves readily in water to give the solution of **perrhenic acid,** $HReO_4$. The potassium, silver, and thallous salts are but slightly soluble. So-called "mesoperrhenates," e.g., Ba_3-

$(ReO_5)_2$, are formed with excess base. The acid is a poor oxidizing agent (Par. **12**) but in the presence of hydrochloric acid it is somewhat more powerful because of the formation of the complex ion $ReCl_6^{--}$, and will oxidize iodide. The sulfide, Re_2S_7, is precipitated by H_2S in ammonia solution and is soluble in excess sulfide with the formation of thio-perrhenate, ReS_4^-.

16. The Lower Oxidation States.—The complex chloride ions, $ReCl_6^-$ and $ReCl_6^{--}$, may be prepared by the reduction of perrhenate in hydrochloric acid. The former is green in color and the latter a yellow brown. The $+5$ complex is stable in high chloride although the compound $ReCl_5$ is said to decompose in water into ReO_4^- and $ReCl_6^{--}$. The trioxide is soluble in hydroxide, but the solution is unstable with respect to decomposition into ReO_4 and ReO_2. However, the barium rhenate, $BaReO_4$, has been described. The dioxide is amphoteric but somewhat inert to both acids and bases. The hydrous sesquioxide is precipitated by hydrolysis of the trichloride. The sulfide, ReS_2, is formed when Re_2S_7 is heated. The highest fluoride which has been reported is ReF_6. The compounds K_2ReF_6 $\cdot ReOF_4$, and ReO_2F_2 have been prepared.

17. Analytical.—Potassium permanganate is the most widely used oxidizing agent in volumetric analysis. Its importance depends upon its ability to oxidize quantitatively a very large number of substances. These include the direct oxidation to a higher oxidation state of ions or compounds of Fe^{++}, Mn^{++}, Cu^+, Sn^{++}, As^{+++}, Sb^{+++}, Ti^{+++}, Mo^{+3}, W^{+5}, U^{+4}, and V^{+4}; the oxidation of the inorganic acids HNO_2, H_2SO_3, H_2S, H_2O_2, and $HCNS$; the oxidation of organic acids or their salts, such as oxalic and formic acids. In addition to these determinations by direct oxidation, many methods of indirect determinations have been worked out, such as the precipitation of Ca, Sr, Ba, Cu, Pb, Zn, Hg (ous), Ce, and La as oxalates, and the subsequent oxidation of the oxalic acid; the determination of phosphate by the precipitation of $(NH_3)_3PO_4 \cdot 12MoO_3$, and the subsequent reduction of the MoO_3 to Mo^{+++} and reoxidation; the determination of potassium by precipitation with cobalt nitrite and the oxidation of the nitrite; and the standardization of $Na_2S_2O_3$ solution by the addition of a known weight of $KMnO_4$ to excess I^-, followed by the titration of the I_2 liberated by the thiosulfate. Powerful oxidizing agents, e.g. PbO_2 may be determined by the addition of a known excess of a reducing agent, e.g. Fe^{++} and its titration by permanganate.

In acid solution, permanganate is reduced to manganous ion: $MnO_4^- + 8H^+ + 5e^- = Mn^{++} + 4H_2O$. Since 5 equivalents of electricity are involved, a one normal (one equivalent of oxidizing power) solution of permanganate is defined as $1/5$ molal, when it is to be employed in the above reaction. Commercial potassium permanganate is not of sufficient purity to permit standardization by directly weighing out the salt; hence the solution is generally standardized in terms of one of the following primary standards: sodium oxalate, oxalic acid, pure iron, or ferrous ammonium sulfate, $(NH_4)_2SO_4 \cdot FeSO_4 \cdot 6H_2O$.

One of the advantages of permanganate is that the distinct color change of the reaction serves as an endpoint indicator. However, care must be taken in titrating a reducing agent with permanganate not to approach the endpoint too rapidly, as excess of the reagent may react with manganous ion to form compounds of Mn^{+3} or Mn^{+4}, which might not be completely reduced.

In alkaline or neutral solutions, permanganate is reduced to the dioxide: $MnO_4^- + 2H_2O + 3e^- = MnO_2 + 4OH^-$; hence a normal solution of permanganate for use under these conditions is defined as $1/3$ molal. One of the important applications of this reaction is in the titration of manganous salts in neutral solution: $3Mn^{++} + 2MnO_4^- + 2H_2O = 5MnO_2 + 4H^+$.

In the gravimetric determination of manganese, it may

be precipitated as the ammonium manganese phosphate, and ignited to the pyrophosphate. Manganous compounds may also be precipitated as the dioxide by strong oxidizing agents, bromine water frequently being employed. Upon ignition, the dioxide yields Mn_3O_4. Gravimetric determination may also be carried out with the manganous carbonate and sulfide.

In the systematic scheme of qualitative analysis, manganese is associated with the group thrown down by ammonium sulfide (Append. VI). A very delicate confirmatory test is the formation of a purple permanganate color when a very small concentration of manganous is boiled with lead dioxide and concentrated nitric acid.

Rhenium is precipitated as the sulfide in acid solution and like stannic sulfide is soluble in excess of sulfide. The element may be determined by precipitation of the slightly soluble $AgReO_4$ or $TlReO_4$, and also by precipitation with 8-hydroxyquinoline.

Technetium may be separated from rhenium by the electrolytic reduction of the pertechnetate in alkaline solution to the dioxide, as under these conditions rhenium does not precipitate.

Chapter XIX

IRON, COBALT, AND NICKEL

1. The first "transition series," in which the electrons in the third quantum state (Append. XVIII) are being increased from 8 to 18, is complete with copper; and the three preceding elements, iron, cobalt, and nickel, constitute a triad possessing many common properties, as might be expected from the fact that the differences in behavior are due merely to the number of d electrons.

The free elements are metals of similar appearance, melting point, density, and other physical properties. They show marked resemblance to all the members of the transition series, although a gradual change in properties may be noted between titanium and nickel (Table I).

The three metals are readily oxidized to the $+2$ state, but the removal of an additional electron to form the $+3$ ion becomes increasingly difficult with increasing atomic number: thus, ferric ion is a good oxidizing agent; cobaltic ion a very powerful oxidizing agent; and nickelic ion is not known. The $+2$ ions are similar in properties to the corresponding ions of other elements of the series, especially the adjacent elements, as has been pointed out under chromium and manganese.

Powerful oxidizing agents acting in alkaline solution form salts in which the elements are in the $+4$ state, or, in the case of iron, the $+6$ state. These are the highest states shown by the group and in this respect they are intermediate to chromium and manganese, on the one hand, in which

TABLE I

FIRST TRANSITION SERIES

	Ti	V	Cr	Mn	Fe	Co	Ni	Cu	Zn
Melting point.	1812	1730	1550	1244	1539	1493	1452	1083	419
Density	4.5	5.9	7.1	7.2	7.9	8.9	8.9	8.9	7.1
Oxidation states	(2),3,4	3,4,5	2,3,6	2,4,6,7	2,3,(6)	2, 3	2, 4	1, 2	2
Oxides..	—	—	—	—	—	—	Ni_2O?	Cu_2O	—
	TiO	VO	CrO	MnO	FeO	CoO	NiO	CuO	ZnO
	Ti_2O_3	V_2O_3	Cr_2O_3	Mn_2O_3*	Fe_2O_3	Co_2O_3	Ni_2O_3*	Cu_2O_3	—
	—	—	—	Mn_3O_4	Fe_3O_4	Co_3O_4	Ni_3O_4	—	—
	TiO_2	VO_2	CrO_2*	MnO_2	FeO_2†	CoO_2	NiO_2	—	—
	—	V_2O_5	—	—	—	—	—	—	—
	—	—	CrO_3	MnO_3	FeO_3†	—	—	—	—
	—	—	—	Mn_2O_7	—	—	—	—	—
Ionization potential ..	6.81	6.71	6.74	7.41	7.83	7.81	7.61	7.68	9.36

* This oxide may be a mixture of higher and lower oxides.
† Oxide known only in compounds.

all of the "transition" electrons may be removed, e.g. in chromate and permanganate, and to copper and zinc, on the other hand, in which one and none, respectively, of the electrons of the 18 group may be readily removed. These relations are further summarized in Table I.

Another important characteristic of iron, cobalt, and nickel is the tendency to form complex ions. This property has been discussed in Chapter **VII** as related to the very high fields of force existing about the "18 electron kernel" type of ion, and since these transition elements are approaching to this structure, it is not surprising that they also possess this property to a high degree.

A number of relations between iron, cobalt, and nickel, and the corresponding members of the second and third transition series, are discussed in connection with these elements, Chapter **XX,** but in general the "horizontal" periodic relations are more marked than the "vertical," e.g., iron resembles cobalt more than it does ruthenium.

IRON

2. Occurrence.—The average percentage of iron in the igneous rocks is given as 5.01. The percentage is doubtless higher in the low lying basaltic rocks, and the central core of the earth (diameter about 2,500 miles) is largely iron. The metallic meteors are generally over 90 per cent iron. Among the elements of the earth's crust (outer ten miles) iron ranks only fourth in abundance.

The free metal is rarely found on the earth's surface, and then the specimen is generally of meteoric origin. Igneous rocks contain ferrous silicates isomorphous with magnesium silicates as $[Mg, Fe]SiO_4$ (cf. **XIV**—Table VI); ferric alumino-silicates as orthoclase, $K[Al, Fe]Si_3O_8$; and numerous sulfides, the more important being pyrrhotite, $FeS(S)_x$, and pyrites, FeS_2.

The weathering of the igneous rocks has resulted in the formation of deposits of oxides and carbonates which are the commercial source of the metal. The principal ores are: hematite, Fe_2O_3; brown ore, $Fe_2O_3nH_2O$, including limonite, $2Fe_2O_3 \cdot 3H_2O$; magnetite, Fe_3O_4; and siderite, spathic iron or "kidney ore," $FeCO_3$.

In addition to the above, hundreds of minerals are known containing iron in combination with practically all of the acid oxides, and with the sulfides and compounds of other positive elements. Iron is also an essential constituent of the haemoglobin of the blood.

3. Pure Iron.—Iron is tetramorphous; the transition temperatures between the forms are given in Table II. **A-iron,** called **ferrite,** is a soft, tough, grey-white metal. The crystal lattice is the body-centered cubic type; the metal is highly paramagnetic. The transition from α- to β-**iron** does not involve a change in the lattice structure, and appears to be largely electronic in nature, as the unusually high magnetic permeability of α-iron disappears in β-iron. The total energy absorbed in the transition is small, and the change appears to start many degrees below the recorded transition point.

TABLE II

ATOMIC AND PHYSICAL PROPERTIES OF IRON

Atomic weight..........	55.84	Density, 20° C.........	7.86
Atomic number.........	26	Electrical resistivity,	
Stable Isotopes.........	54, 56,	ohm-cm.............	10.0×10^{-6}
	57, 58	Size of the Fe^{++} ion,	
Electrons in various		cm. $\times 10^8$..........	0.75
quantum levels, 1st....	2	Ionization potential of	
2d....	8	gas atom, volts.......	7.83
3d....	8 + 6	Tensile strength in lbs.	
4th....	2	per sq. in.:	
Boiling point, ° C........	2800	Iron, cast.........	13,000–33,000
Melting point, ° C.......	1539	Iron, drawn.......	50,000–100,000
Transition temperatures:		Steel.............	40,000–300,000
α to β	760		
β to γ	907		
γ to δ	1400		

Γ-iron is but slightly magnetic in comparison to the α-form. Its lattice structure is face-centered cubic. Γ-iron forms solid solutions with iron carbide, and these may be obtained at room temperature in a metastable state by rapid quenching. The importance of this fact is discussed under Steel. Little is known regarding the properties of δ-iron.

Pure iron is of only slight commercial importance. It may be prepared by heating the oxide in a current of hydrogen, and by the electrolysis of ferrous sulfate solution. In both of these preparations, the iron contains absorbed hydrogen which may be removed by heating in a vacuum. The hydrogen appears to dissolve to form a true solution; the same is true of nitrogen and other gases at higher temperatures.

4. Metallurgy of Pig Iron.—The basic principle involved in the smelting of iron is the reduction of the iron oxides by

carbon monoxide. At a comparatively low temperature, ferric oxide is converted completely to the magnetic oxide: $3Fe_2O_3 + CO = 2Fe_3O_4 + CO_2$. At higher temperatures this oxide is reduced to ferrous oxide, and then to the metal, but these reactions involve measurable equilibria and are reversible, depending upon the relative pressures of carbon monoxide and dioxide.

TABLE III

REACTIONS OF CARBON MONOXIDE AND OXIDES OF IRON

Values for the ratio CO_2/CO at various temperatures

REACTION	TEMPERATURE, ° C.			
	700	800	900	1,000
$Fe_3O_4 + CO = 3FeO + CO_2$	0.68	0.55	0.47	0.40
$FeO + CO = Fe + CO_2$	1.68	2.40	3.24	4.17

The modern blast furnace operates so as to carry out these reactions in a continuous manner. The general outline of this furnace is indicated in Fig. 1. The dimensions are approximately 22 by 90 ft., and the construction is sheet steel lined with difficultly fusible siliceous fire brick. Only ores with low sulfur and phosphorus content are employed, and these may be subjected to a preliminary roasting in order to remove as much sulfur as possible. The ore contains siliceous material, and as all the charge is to be drawn from the furnace in the liquid state, sufficient limestone is added to form an easily fusible calcium silicate slag. Coke is now universally employed as fuel, and is introduced together with the ore and limestone at the top of the furnace.

Dry air, preheated to 425 to 650°, is blown in through a number of water jacketed nozzles or tuyeres near the bottom. The air oxidizes the coke in the lower part of the furnace to carbon monoxide (cf. **XIII—6**). The intense heat of this reaction liquefies the iron which has been reduced in the central part of the furnace by the hot carbon monoxide. From time to time, the molten metal is drawn off, and either run into molds, or else conveyed directly to Bessemer converters, or open hearth furnaces, and made into steel. The crude iron is called cast iron, or **"pig iron,"** from the shape of the casts made in the old-fashioned furnaces. The impurities present depend considerably upon the composition of the ore, the nature of the slag, and the temperature at which the furnace has been maintained. The following percentages are representative: C, 2–4.5; Si, 0.7–3; S, 0.1–0.3; P, 0.–3.0; Mn, 0.2–1. In general, a high temperature of reduction increases the percentage of carbon and silicon, but diminishes that of the sulfur through the reaction: $FeS + CaO + CO = Fe + CaS + CO_2$. Practically all of the phosphorus in the charge collects in the iron as Fe_3P.

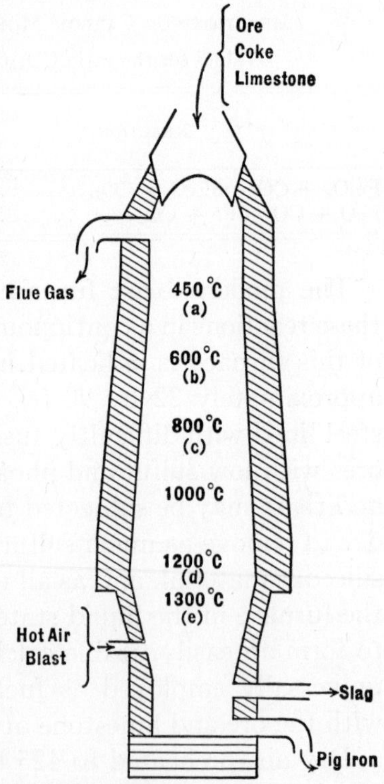

The production of pig iron in the United States reached a peak of 57,000,000 tons in 1944. The melting point of pig iron is about 1150°. The metal is brittle and suitable only for castings not subject to shock. When cooled rapidly, the carbon remains in combination and the product is called **white cast iron;** but when cooled slowly, much of the carbon separates as graphite and the product, known as **grey cast iron,** is softer and tougher.

FIG. 1. Blast furnace (diagrammatic).

Blast furnace slag has the approximate percentage composition: SiO_2, 20–70; CaO and MgO, 25–50; Al_2O_3, 5–20;

CaS, 1–4; FeO, 1. In some cases, the composition is such that the slag may be ground and made into cement. Large quantities are also used in paving, in combination with tar.

The **flue gas** contains considerable heat value through its high carbon monoxide content. Part of the gas is burned in the so-called hot-blast stoves, which are used to preheat the air blast, and the rest is employed to develop power about the plant. The gas is generally cleaned from dust before using for power, and the solid obtained contains appreciable quantities of potassium salts, and constitutes a potential source of this alkali.

5. Wrought Iron.—Wrought iron is manufactured from pig iron by oxidizing out the impurities through melting in a reverberatory furnace with iron oxide and a basic flux. As the iron becomes pure, its melting point rises, and the metal collects in lumps which are removed from the furnace. Wrought iron is soft and malleable. It possesses a fibrous structure due to the inclusion of slag, since the temperature of the process is not high enough to melt the pure iron and obtain a good separation from the slag. Wrought iron, while formerly of great importance, is now largely replaced by mild steel.

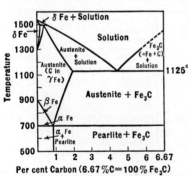

FIG. 2. The iron-carbon diagram.

6. Steel.—Iron which contains from 0.05 to 2.0 per cent carbon and which is capable of being hardened when quenched is called steel. The properties of steel are greatly influenced by small amounts of carbon, as may be best explained by reference to the iron-carbon diagram, Fig. 2.

If a molten solution of less than 4.2 per cent of carbon in iron is cooled, the solid which first separates is a solid solution of carbon or iron carbide in γ-iron, called **austenite**

(The diagram also shows a solution in δ-iron above 1300° but this is somewhat uncertain.) At higher concentrations of carbon, the solid phase which separates is **cementite,** Fe_3C. This is metastable in respect to the decomposition into carbon and iron, but the reaction is not rapid. The eutectic of the austenite-cementite phases lies at about 1150°.

Austenite, containing more than 0.9 per cent carbon, upon cooling yields cementite; if it contains less carbon, it yields α- or β-iron as shown in the diagram. The eutectic temperature is 690°, and the eutectic mixture of α-iron and cementite is known as **pearlite.** However, if austenite is cooled sufficiently rapidly, these transformations do not occur, and the solid solution may thus be obtained at room temperatures as a tough metal of low magnetic susceptibility.

TABLE IV

COMPOSITION AND PHYSICAL PROPERTIES OF SIMPLE CARBON STEELS

NAME	PER CENT CARBON	TENSILE STRENGTH LBS. PER SQ. IN.	ELASTIC LIMIT LBS. PER SQ. IN.
Very mild................	0.05–0.15	45,000– 54,000	27,000–34,000
Mild....................	0.15–0.25	54,000– 68,000	34,000–40,000
Low carbon.............	0.25–0.40	68,000– 78,000	40,000–45,000
Medium carbon..........	0.40–0.60	78,000– 90,000	45,000–55,000
Higher carbon...........	0.60–0.70	90,000–100,000	54,000–64,000
Spring.................	0.70–0.80	100,000–105,000	64,000–72,000
Pearlitic...............	0.85	110,000	78,000
Hypereutectoid..........	0.85–1.5	110,000–180,000	

Various methods of **heat treating** steel are in use. Thus if supercooled high carbon austenite is heated above 750° C. rapid equilibrium is established and some cementite separates. If the steel is held at this temperature for some time and cooled slowly the process is called **annealing;** if cooled rapidly, **quenching. Tempered steel** is held for some time at a temperature below the point at which rapid equilibrium is established.

The properties of the heat treated steel are thus greatly affected by the temperature and length of time of the treatment, as this determines the size of the interlacing crystals. The terms **martensite** and **sorbite** are applied to intermediate stages of the transformation of austenite into pearlite.

7. Many important special steels are made by the addition of elements other than carbon. The presence of other elements greatly modifies the temperature of the iron-carbon phase diagram. Silicon is not only highly soluble in γ-iron, but also catalyzes the decomposition of cementite to carbon, thus rendering the steel soft. Nickel forms a complete series of solid solutions with γ-iron, and since the stable form of nickel is the face-centered cubic-lattice like γ-iron, its presence tends to prevent the transformation of the latter into α-iron. The special high speed tool-steels (Par. **19**) which retain their temper at high temperatures also owe their properties, at least in part, to interference with the change of γ- into α-iron. Phosphorus in steel was formerly considered most undesirable but a number of high phosphorus steels are now important.

The use of **alloy cast iron** has greatly increased in recent years, the principal alloying metals being chromium, nickel, copper, and molybdenum. The following are typical compositions: automobile blocks, C, 3.3, Si, 2.2, Mn, 0.75, Cr, 0.35, Ni, 0.70, Fe, balance; brake drums, C, 3.2, Si, 2.0, Mn, 0.6, Cu, 1.0, Mo, 0.5, Fe, balance.

8. Manufacture of Steel.—The American production of steel is about 50 million tons annually. Various manufacturing processes are employed, depending upon the impurities present and the type of steel desired. By far the largest percentage (91.5) of the steel manufactured in the United States is made by the open-hearth process. Of the remaining, 6.8 per cent is Bessemer and 1.7 per cent electric furnace.

(a) *Open-hearth Steel.* The tremendous expansion of the steel industry in the past 50 years was rendered possible through the development of the basic open-hearth process, whereby high-grade steel may be made from pig iron relatively high in phosphorus and sulfur.

The process consists of heating a charge of pig iron and scrap steel with sufficient iron oxide to oxidize the sulfur, phosphorus, and most of the carbon, in a furnace lined with calcined magnesite or dolomite. The carbon monoxide formed escapes as a gas, while the oxides of sulfur and phosphorus combine with the basic oxides to form a slag. The metal is contained in a shallow hearth (about 40 by 12 feet and 2 feet deep), and the heat is supplied by a gas flame directly over the surface. As mentioned above, the basic oxides also serve as a lining for the hearth. When the desired carbon content is reached, generally after about 8 hours, the heating is stopped and the melted steel is run into large ladles. Some iron low in sulfur and phosphorus is made into steel by the acid open-hearth process, which is essentially the same as the above, except that the hearth lining is silica.

(b) *Bessemer Steel*. In the Bessemer process, a blast of air is blown through molten pig iron until the impurities are oxidized. The acid process, in which the furnace is lined with silica, is applicable only to iron low in sulfur and phosphorus as these elements are not readily oxidized under these conditions. A basic lining is employed in certain European districts, which permits the removal of the phosphorus in the basic slag; however, the iron must be low in sulfur.

The Bessemer converter is a large egg-shaped vessel mounted on trunnions so as to turn about its shorter axis. The molten metal is poured in through the necklike opening in the top, while the converter is in a horizontal position. The air-blast, which enters through perforations in the bottom, is then turned on, and the converter raised to an upright position. The heats of combustion of the carbon and silicon keep the metal molten in spite of the higher melting point of the pure iron. The "blow" is finished in about ten minutes, and the converter is turned on its side so that a calculated quantity of carbon, manganese, or other metals may be added.

(c) *Crucible and Electrothermal Steel.* The finest grades of tool-steel have long been made by heating wrought iron with pure carbon in small crucibles, and the product is known as crucible steel. Much of the high-grade steel is made in small electrically heated furnaces. The method is similar to the open-hearth process, except that the mode of heating permits more careful control. Most of the electric furnace product is alloy steel.

(d) *Case-hardened Steel.* In the manufacture of armor plate, and many auto and other machine parts, it is often desirable to harden the surface and at the same time keep the toughness of the body of the metal. This is accomplished by heating the article, packed in carbon or in cyanide, until the desired amount of carbon is absorbed into the surface. Another form of surface hardening called **nitriding** consists in heating an alloy steel (usually containing Al, Cr, or Mo) in an atmosphere of ammonia. Nitrides of the alloying metals are thus formed on the surface.

9. Reactions of Iron.—Iron is a good reducing agent at ordinary temperature, and a very powerful reducing agent at high temperature, combining readily with all of the negative elements (Table V).

Iron and oxygen do not react in the cold, but when heated they form ferroferric oxide, Fe_3O_4; and at higher temperatures ferric oxide, Fe_2O_3.

The equilibria between iron, iron oxides, and steam are of considerable importance; and the ratios of H_2O/H_2 for the systems, $Fe : FeO$ and $FeO : Fe_3O_4$, and given in Table V. The solid phases in these systems appear to be solid solutions.

At lower temperatures the reaction is entirely $3Fe + 4H_2O = Fe_3O_4 + 4H_2$, as ferrous oxide is unstable in

TABLE V

CONSTANTS FOR THE IRON AND STEAM EQUILIBRIA

		700°	800°	900°	1000° C.
$FeO + H_2 = Fe + H_2O$	H_2O/H_2	0.584	0.706	0.822	0.937
$Fe_3O_4 + H_2 = 3FeO + H_2O$	H_2O/H_2	1.45	2.98	5.50	9.12

respect to iron and Fe_3O_4 below 570°; and at 400°, the ratio, H_2O/H_2, in this equilibrium is about 0.2.

The equilibria between iron, iron oxides, and the oxides of carbon have been discussed in connection with the blast furnace, Par. 4.

Iron dissolves in dilute acids with the evolution of hydrogen and the formation of ferrous salts. Strong oxidizing agents yield ferric compounds, but very powerful oxidizing agents, such as concentrated nitric acid or dichromate, render the metal passive; and in this condition it is not dissolved by hydrogen ion nor will it reduce cupric solutions. Passivity is destroyed by scratching the surface, by the action of reducing agents, or by placing the metal in a powerful magnetic field. The phenomenon appears to be due to the formation of a surface film of oxide.

The **rusting** of iron involves two steps: (1) the oxidation to ferrous ion by acid, usually carbonic, i.e. $Fe + 2H_2CO_3 = Fe^{++} + 2HCO_3^- + H_2$ and (2) the formation of ferric oxide (iron rust) by the atmospheric oxygen: $4Fe^{++} + 8HCO_3^- + O_2 + 6H_2O = 2Fe_2O_3 \cdot H_2O + 8H_2CO_3$.

The first step does not take place readily with pure iron, due to the over-voltage effect of hydrogen on the metal. Rusting is, therefore, favored by the presence of impurities which present surfaces for the escape of the gas. Pure water is about equal to ferrous ion as an oxidizing agent (Append. II), so there is not much driving power to the solution of the metal in pure water; the reaction is, of course, favored by increasing the concentration of hydrogen ion.

TABLE VI

REACTIONS OF IRON

$3Fe + 2O_2 = Fe_3O_4$	Readily at 500°, Fe_2O_3 at higher temp.
$Fe + S = FeS$	Heated
$2Fe + 3X_2 = 2FeX_3$	Halogens except I_2 which gives FeI_2
$2Fe + 2H^+ = Fe^{++} + H_2$	Reaction potential + 0.44 volt
$3Fe + C = Fe_3C$	Above 1,200°
$Fe + Si = FeSi$	Also Fe_2Si
$3Fe + P = Fe_3P$	
$3Fe + 4H_2O_{(steam)} = Fe_3O_4 + 4H_2$	See Table V
$Fe + 5CO = Fe(CO)_5$	See Par. 15
$Fe + CO_2 = FeO + CO$	See Table III
$4Fe + 2NH_3 = 2Fe_2N + 3H_2$	Fe does not react directly with N_2

COMPOUNDS OF IRON

10. Oxidation States.—Iron forms two important series of salts: ferrous, with an oxidation state of + 2, and ferric, with an oxidation state of + 3. In addition, salts are known of ferrate ion, FeO_4^{--}, in which iron has the + 6 oxidation state and there is some evidence for perferrite, FeO_3^{--}.

Oxidation-reduction potentials relating to the oxidation states are given below:

VOLTS

$Fe = Fe^{++} + 2e^-$	+ 0.44
$Fe + 2OH^- = Fe(OH)_2 + 2e^-$	+ 0.88
$Fe^{++} = Fe^{+++} + e^-$	− 0.77
$Fe(OH)_2 + OH^- = Fe(OH)_3 + e^-$	+ 0.56
$Fe(CN)_6^{----} = Fe(CN)_6^{---} + e^-$	(− 0.49)
$Fe^{+++} + 4H_2O = FeO_4^{--} + 8H^+ + 3e^-$	< − 1.9
$Fe(OH)_3 + 5OH^- = FeO_4^{--} + 4H_2O + 3e^-$	< − 0.9

It follows from these values that the reaction, $Fe + 2Fe^{+++} = 3Fe^{++}$, is practically quantitative. Also ferrous iron is readily oxidized to ferric in alkaline solution, but much less readily in acid; in fact, acid ferrous solutions are oxidized to ferric only very slowly by the air, as the reaction potential is above that of oxygen to hydrogen peroxide (Append. II), which is the first step of the oxygen reaction. The ferrates are such powerful oxidizing agents that they are difficult to prepare, and very unstable.

11. Ferrous Compounds.—Ferrous compounds resemble manganous in their solubilities. The **hydroxide,** $Fe(OH)_2$, is precipitated from ferrous solutions by alkalies, but it is only moderately insoluble in water and its solubility is greatly increased in ammonium salts. The pure hydroxide is white, but in the air it quickly turns green, and then reddish-brown through oxidation to ferric hydroxide. The **oxide**, FeO, may be prepared by heating the oxalate, but the product contains some iron and ferric oxide. It burns when heated in air. Ferrous ion has a pale green color.

Ferrous sulfide forms through the direct union of the elements. It forms as a black precipitate when soluble sulfides are added to neutral or basic ferrous solutions, but is readily soluble in acids. The naturally occurring sulfide generally contains an excess of sulfur in solid solution (cf. composition Cu_2S, **VII—8**). Ferrous sulfide combines with sulfur to form the **disulfide**, FeS_2, known as **iron pyrites** or "fools' gold." It occurs in nature as brass-colored cubic crystals. It is not dissolved by dilute acids, but is slowly decomposed by concentrated hydrochloric acid, $FeS_2 + 2HCl = FeCl_2 + H_2S + S$, and rapidly by nitric acid with the oxidation of the sulfur. An orthorhombic modification called **marcasite** also occurs. Pyrite is an important source of sulfur for the manufacture of sulfuric acid.

Ferrous sulfate, $FeSO_4$, is the most important ferrous salt. It is prepared commercially by the oxidation of moist pyrites: $2FeS_2 + 7O_2 + 2H_2O = 2FeSO_4 + 2H_2SO_4$. The hydrate, $FeSO_4 \cdot 7H_2O$, which crystallizes upon evaporation of the water solution, is known as green vitriol or copperas. It is used as a disinfectant, in the manufacture of dyes, and in the preparation of ink.

The common black or blue **inks** contain the ferrous salt of gallotannic acid. This is not colored, but upon exposure to the air the black ferric salt is precipitated. A black or blue dye gives the initial color of the ink.

Ferrous ammonium sulfate, $(NH_4)_2Fe(SO_4)_2 \cdot 6H_2O$, may be crystallized from equimolar solutions of the two sulfates. This salt is very stable toward oxidation by the air, and is employed as a primary standard in quantitative analysis (cf. **XVIII—12**).

Ferrous carbonate, $FeCO_3$, is readily precipitated from ferrous solutions by soluble carbonates. It occurs in nature as the mineral, siderite.

Ferrous halides are readily soluble in water. They may be prepared by various methods, e.g. by dissolving the metal in the halogen acid, or by the action of the halogen upon excess of the metal.

Ferrous oxalate, FeC_2O_4, forms as a yellow precipitate upon the addition of oxalate to a ferrous solution. With excess reagent, it dissolves with the formation of a yellowish red solution containing the complex ion, $Fe(C_2O_4)_2^{--}$.

Aqueous solutions of ferrous ion absorb nitric oxide with the formation of the **ferronitroso complex ion,** $FeNO^{++}$. This is the basis of the "ring test" for nitrates (cf. **XI—39**).

The complex **ferrous cyanides** are discussed in Paragraph **13**.

12. Ferric Compounds.—Ferric oxide, Fe_2O_3, and its hydrate, $Fe_2O_3 \cdot H_2O$, are the most important ores of iron. In the various complex minerals containing this oxide, it generally behaves as an acid oxide, its salts being known as **ferrites.** One of the most common of these compounds is **ferrous ferrite** or **magnetite,** Fe_3O_4, i.e. $Fe(FeO_2)_2$. As its common name indicates, it is highly magnetic, and large specimens are known as "lode stones." Ferrites may be prepared by fusing ferric oxide with basic oxides, e.g. $NaFeO_2$, $Ca(FeO_2)_2$, and **ferrous acid,** $HFeO_2(Fe_2O_3 \cdot H_2O)$, is obtained by the action of water upon sodium ferrite. The oxide exists in many modifications. α-Fe_2O_3, hematite, varies in color from yellow to dark red depending upon the state of subdivision. The ferromagnetic, or γ-Fe_2O_3 also is yellow to red.

Around 3000° ferric oxide loses oxygen to form magnetite, but at lower temperatures, about 1300°, the reaction is slowly reversed: $4Fe_3O_4 + O_2 = 6Fe_2O_3$.

Finely divided ferric oxide under the names **"rouge"** and **"Venetian red,"** is used as an abrasive and as a pigment.

Four forms of precipitated ferric oxide, so-called **ferric hydroxide,** are known. The addition of alkali to ferric solutions precipitates the brown gel which is hydrous α-Fe_2O_3. The slow hydrolysis of most ferric salts yields α-$Fe_2O_3 \cdot H_2O$ which dehydrates to α-Fe_2O_3. The hydrolysis of ferric chloride forms β-$Fe_2O_3 \cdot H_2O$. This also gives α-Fe_2O_3 upon dehydration. The oxidation of ferrous compounds and solutions with certain oxidizing agents forms γ-$Fe_2O_3 \cdot H_2O$ which gives γ-Fe_2O_3 on dehydration. Ferric oxide sols are remarkably stable. They are ordinarily positively charged and may be coagulated by negative ions, but if the negative ion is strongly adsorbed, a reversal of the sign of the charge may occur with the formation of a negative sol.

Ferric oxide is a weak base, and in water solution shows but slightly the acid properties exhibited by the oxide in its mineral compounds, in that it is not soluble in excess of dilute alkali, and only slightly in concentrated alkali.

Due to the weak basic properties of ferric hydroxide, ferric salts are highly hydrolyzed, and their characteristic yellow brown color in solution appears to be due to the colloidal hydroxide or to basic ions. When this is repressed by acid, the yellow color becomes lighter.

Ferric halides, except the iodide, may be prepared by the action of the halogen upon the metal, or by dissolving the hydroxide in acid. Iodide ion is oxidized by ferric ion: $2Fe^{+++} + 2I^- = 2Fe^{++} + I_2$, but the reaction is not complete unless the equilibrium is displaced by the removal of the I_2. The halides are very soluble, forming many hydrates. With excess of halide ion, they form **complex halides;** and many of the complex salts are known, e.g. K_3FeF_6 and $(NH_4)_3FeCl_6$.

Magnetic data indicate that these complex ions are ionic in character and not covalent as, for example, are the complex cyanides. The fluoride is quite stable and in solution does not oxidize iodide.

Hydrogen sulfide in acid solution reduces ferric salts to ferrous with the precipitation of sulfur, but if ammonium sulfide is used, **ferric sulfide**, Fe_2S_3, is precipitated. The pure compound is unstable, but ferric sulfide complexes with other metallic sulfides occur in nature.

Ferric sulfate, $Fe_2(SO_4)_3$, and **ferric nitrate**, $Fe(NO_3)_3$, are both soluble, but tend to form basic salts by hydrolysis. The former, like most sulfates of $+3$ ions, forms **alums,** e.g. $KFe(SO_4)_2 \cdot 12H_2O$.

Ferric phosphate, $FePO_4$, is a common constituent of phosphate rock. It is very slightly soluble, and may be precipitated from an acetic acid solution of ferric ion. It is, however, soluble in strong acids.

Ferric ion, like the ferrous, also forms a **complex oxalate ion,** $Fe(C_2O_4)_3^{---}$, which accounts for the use of oxalic acid in removing ink and iron rust spots from fabrics. The soluble red **thiocyanate** $Fe(SCN)_3$ forms the complex ion, $Fe(SCN)_6^{-3}$, with excess of thiocyanate.

13. Complex Iron Cyanides.—Both ferrous and ferric ion form complex ions with excess cyanide, the former yielding **ferrocyanide,** $Fe(CN)_6^{-4}$, and the latter **ferricyanide,** $Fe(CN)_6^{-3}$. These complex ions are so stable that their solutions show virtually none of the properties of the iron or cyanide ions. The structure of these ions is octohedral, which is the general structure of covalent complexes which involve two d, one s, and three p orbitals of the central atom.

Sodium and potassium ferrocyanide, $Na_4Fe(CN)_6 \cdot 10H_2O$, and $K_4Fe(CN)_6 \cdot 3H_2O$, are usually prepared as by-products from the distillation of coal. A considerable portion of the nitrogen in coal is liberated as hydrogen cyanide, HCN. This is absorbed in iron oxide purifiers as iron cyanide, which is then treated with lime to form calcium ferrocyanide; this, in turn, is converted into the alkali ferrocyanide. Formerly, the ferrocyanides were prepared by fusing nitrogenous material with potash and iron turnings. The potassium compound is commonly called **"yellow prussiate of potash."** The hydrates decompose at about 100°, yielding colorless powders which ignite when heated in air. With concentrated sulfuric acid the cyanide ion is slowly hydrolyzed, forming ammonium ion and carbon monoxide: $K_4Fe(CN)_6 + 6H_2SO_4 + 6H_2O = 2K_2SO_4 + FeSO_4 + 3(NH_4)_2SO_4 + 6CO$. When heated with metallic sodium, the iron is reduced and a mixture of metallic iron and alkali cyanide formed. With hydrochloric acid, the weak **hydroferrocyanic acid,** $H_4Fe(CN)_6$, is formed. This acid may be extracted from concentrated water solution by ether, from which it crystallizes as a colorless compound, stable in dry air, but readily oxidized in moist air.

The ferrocyanide-ferricyanide couple possesses moderately strong oxidizing power. The value of the potential given in Par. **10** is for equal concentration of the two ions and is not corrected for the activities, the E° value is around − 0.36. Ferrocyanides are readily converted into ferricyanides by the action of chlorine in solution. The commercial preparation of **potassium ferricyanide** or **"red prussiate of potash,"** $K_3Fe(CN)_6$, depends upon this oxidation. The ferricyanide ion is not as stable as the ferrous complex, and decomposes slowly in the sunlight.

Alkali ferrocyanides form with ferric ion, first a soluble blue compound, $KFe_2(CN)_6$, called potassium berlinate or soluble Prussian blue, and then a very slightly soluble precipitate of **Prussian blue,** $Fe_7C_{18}N_{18} \cdot 10H_2O$, (*vide infra*), which is an important blue pigment. With ferrous ion, potassium ferrocyanide forms a white precipitate of potassium ferrous-ferrocyanide, $K_2Fe[Fe(CN)_6]$. A number of the ferrocyanides are important in analytical chemistry, especially the compounds with zinc and uranium, $Zn_3K_2[Fe(CN)_6]_2$ and $K_2UO_2[Fe(CN)_6]$.

Ferricyanide yields with ferric ion a deep brown solution, probably of undissociated ferric ferricyanide. With ferrous ion a precipitate, Turnbull's blue, is formed. From X-ray analysis the structure of solid ferric ferricyanide has been determined as a cubic sodium chloride lattice. Each ferri-cyanide ion is thus surrounded by six ferric ions and the cyanide ion serves as a bond between the iron ions, FeCNFe. The structure of potassium berlinate is similar except that alternate small cubes contain a K^+ in the center. The rela-tion of the iron and cyanide is also the same in the potas-sium ferrous-ferrocyanide, $K_2FeFe(CN)_6$, but in this case each small cube is occupied by a K^+. Prussian blue appears to be ferric berlinate $Fe[FeFe(CN)_6]_3$ and the Turnbull's blue ferrous berlinate, $Fe[FeFe(CN)_6]_2$. The linkage be-tween the berlinate ions in the solid is probably of the same type as that found for $FeFe(CN)_6$. A number of copper ferrocyanides are known which are probably derivatives of similar supercomplexes, e.g., $Cu[CuFe(CN)_6]$, and $K_2[CuFe(CN)_6]$. Zinc, however, appears to be unable to co-ordinate with six cyanides and the supercomplex structure is more complicated, e.g. $[Zn_3[Fe(CN)_6]_2]^{-2}$.

Blue print paper is made by treating paper with a solution of ammonium ferricyanide and ferric citrate in the dark. When exposed to light, reduction of the iron by the citrate takes place with the formation of Prussian blue. The print is fixed by washing out the unchanged mixture with water.

One of the cyanide groups, in either the ferro- or ferri-cyanide, may be replaced by other groups; e.g. NO, CO, SO_3^{--}, NO_2^-, H_2O, NH_3, AsO_2^-, forming **complex pentacy-anides**. **Sodium ferri-nitrosopentacyanide**, $Na_2FeNO(CN)_5 \cdot 2H_2O$, gives an intense blue color with sulfide in alkaline solutions, thus constituting a delicate test for the latter substance.

14. Perferrites and Ferrates.—**Barium** and **strontium perferrites,** $BaFeO_3$, and $SrFeO_3$, have been prepared by heating mixtures of the hydroxide with ferric hydroxide in a current of oxygen. The compounds are decomposed by water, and there is but slight evidence for the formation of the dioxide of iron. The ferryl ion, FeO^{++}, may possibly exist at low concentrations under some conditions.

Powerful oxidizing agents in fused alkali or in very concentrated alkaline solution oxidize ferric hydroxide to **ferrate**. **Barium ferrate,** $BaFeO_4$, analogous to the sulfate, is but slightly soluble and is the most stable of the ferrates. It is not decomposed by water or cold dilute sulfuric acid; but with cold hydrochloric acid, chlorine and oxygen are evolved, though the solution first assumes the red color characteristic of FeO_4^{--}.

15. Iron Carbonyls.—Finely divided iron reacts slowly with carbon monoxide to form the **pentacarbonyl,** $Fe(CO)_5$, which may be distilled off by heating to 120°. This substance freezes at $-21°$, boils at 102°, and decomposes when heated above 200°. In the sunlight it decomposes: $2Fe(CO)_5 = Fe_2(CO)_9 + CO$. This latter compound decomposes upon heating to form $Fe_3(CO)_{12}$. The pentacarbonyl dissolves in alkalies: $Fe(CO)_5 + 4OH^- = Fe(CO)_4^{---} + CO_3^{--} + 2H_2O$. Upon acidifying in the cold the **carbonyl hydride,** $Fe(CO)_4H_2$, is liberated. This carbonyl hydride has acid properties and forms many salts. When oxidized with hydrogen peroxide it forms $Fe_3(CO)_{12}$, and when warmed it decomposes: $2Fe(CO)_4H_2 = Fe(CO)_5 + Fe(CO)_3$ (polymerized) $+ 2H_2$. The mercuric salt is prepared by oxidizing the pentacarbonyl with mercuric chloride: $Fe(CO)_5 + H_2O + HgCl_2 = Fe(CO)_4Hg + 2HCl + CO_2$. The structure of

$$Fe_2(CO)_9 \text{ appears to be } (CO)_3Fe\overset{\overset{\displaystyle OC}{\diagup}\diagdown}{\underset{\underset{\displaystyle CO}{\diagdown}\diagup}{-}}CO\overset{}{-}Fe(CO)_3. \text{ It may}$$

be noted that in all of these compounds the iron atom has the same number of electrons (if the two shared with each CO is included) as has the next inert gas krypton. The same is true of the nitrosyl carbonyl $Fe(CO)_2(NO)_2$ if one assumes that the odd electron on the nitric oxide has transferred to the iron.

16. Analytical.—The formation of Prussian blue, through the reaction of ferrocyanide with ferric ion, and ferricyanide with ferrous ion, serve to identify iron in both of the common valence states. Ferric iron may be distinguished also by the deep red color of **ferrisulfocyanide,** $Fe(SCN)_3$, and a bright red compound with pyrocatechol.

In the scheme for the systematic separation of the elements, iron salts are precipitated by ammonium sulfide and hydroxide as ferrous sulfide. The general method of separation from the other members of this analytical group is indicated in Appendix VI. In case phosphate is present, the analytical procedure requires some modification, because ammonium hydroxide will precipitate ferric phosphate from ferric solutions.

The so-called **basic acetate separation,** which is often used in the iron group, is carried out by the addition of ammonium acetate to a slightly acid solution. Upon heating, hydrolysis occurs; and the precipitate may contain Fe, Ga, Cr, V, W, Al, In, Zr, Ti, as hydroxides, basic acetates, phosphates, or vanadates, and the rare earths (if phosphate is present). The method serves to separate these elements from Mn, Zn, Co, Ni, U, alkaline earths, and rare earths (if phosphate is not present), although traces of Zn, Co, Ni, Be, and U may be present in the precipitate.

In gravimetric analysis, iron is usually precipitated as ferric hydroxide by ammonium hydroxide and weighed as ferric oxide. The reagent, **"cupferron,"** $C_6H_5N\cdot NO\cdot ONH_4$, is sometimes used to precipitate iron as the ferric salt. This method has the advantage of precipitating iron (and also Cu, Ti, and Zr) from highly acid solutions, and thus effecting a separation from Al, Cr, Mn, Ni, and Co. When treated with ammonium hydroxide, the precipitate is changed to ferric hydroxide.

Iron is determined in volumetric analysis usually by one of the two reactions: $5Fe^{++} + MnO_4^- + 8H^+ = Mn^{++} + 5Fe^{+++} + 4H_2O$, and $6Fe^{++} + Cr_2O_7^{--} + 14H^+$

$= 6Fe^{+++} + 2Cr^{+++} + 7H_2O$. In the dichromate method the end-point is determined by removing a drop of the solution and testing with ferricyanide, or by the addition of an oxidation indicator, e.g., diphenylamine which gives a blue color upon oxidation. In the permanganate method the color of the reagent serves as an end-point indicator. The dichromate method is readily applicable in the presence of chloride, but permanganate tends to evolve chlorine under these conditions, unless an excess of manganous ion is added (cf. **XVIII—12**).

In the preparation of the ferrous solution before titration, ferric iron may be reduced in various ways, but the most generally employed methods are: (1) reduction by passing the solution through a tube containing zinc amalgam (Jones reductor), (2) reduction with stannous chloride followed by removal of excess stannous ion by mercuric chloride.

Ferric salts in solution may also be titrated directly with titanous chloride, using thiocyanate as an indicator: $Fe^{+++} + Ti^{+++} = Fe^{++} + Ti^{++++}$.

COBALT AND NICKEL

17. Occurrence.—The iron meteors contain about six per cent of nickel, and it seems probable that this percentage also exists in the central core of the earth. However, in the igneous rocks on the earth's crust, the estimated percentage of nickel is 0.020 and cobalt 1×10^{-5}.

The commonest cobalt minerals are: smaltite, $CoAs_2$; cobaltite, $CoAsS$; erythrite, $Co_3(AsO_4) \cdot 8H_2O$; and linnaeite, Co_3S_4. These ores are generally associated with iron, and often nickel, copper, and silver. The principal source of cobalt is the rich silver-cobalt-nickel veins in Ontario, Canada.

The two most important nickel ores are: pentalandite, $NiS \cdot 2FeS$, and garnierite, $[Ni, Mg]SiO_3 \cdot nH_2O$. Extensive deposits of the former mixed with iron and copper sulfide are found in Ontario, Canada, and of the latter in New Caledonia. Nickel also occurs in other complex sulfides, silicates, arsenides, arsenates, tellurides, oxides, and sulfates. Copper ores usually contain small amounts of nickel, which are removed in the electrolytic refining process.

18. Metallurgy.—The cobalt-silver arsenide ore of Ontario is smelted with a suitable flux in a small blast furnace, yielding crude silver bullion, and a speiss of the arsenides of cobalt, nickel, iron, copper, and some silver. This speiss is subjected to successive roasting processes; with silica to remove iron; with sodium nitrate and carbonate to form sodium arsenate; and with salt to form chlorides of cobalt, nickel, copper, and silver. The soluble chloride is extracted with water; the copper precipitated as the metal by reduction, and the cobalt and nickel precipitated as hydroxides.

The separation of cobalt and nickel is effected by the Mond process (see below), or by the formation of potassium cobaltinitrite (Par. **24**), or chloropentammine cobaltichloride (Par. **24**). The metal is made by reducing the oxide with carbon.

The metallurgy of nickel ores is somewhat similar. The product of the blast furnace smelting is a matte of iron, copper, and nickel sulfides. This matte is freed from much of the iron by oxidizing in a Bessemer converter with a silicate slag.

In the Orford process, the Bessemer matte is fused with carbon and sodium sulfate, which effects a separation of rather pure nickel sulfide in the bottom layer. This sulfide is roasted to the oxide, and reduced by carbon to the metal.

In the Mond process, the matte is roasted to the oxide, reduced to the metal by water gas at 300°, and the nickel removed by volatilization as the carbonyl, $Ni(CO)_4$, in a stream of carbon monoxide at a temperature of 50° to 100°. The carbonyl is then decomposed into the metal and carbon monoxide by heating.

Electrolytic refinement of nickel is also employed. The

impure metal is made the anode in a cell using nickel sulfate electrolyte. The pure metal is precipitated on an aluminum cathode. The platinum metals precipitate in the anode mud and the base metals remain in the electrolyte.

19. The Metals.—The important atomic and physical constants of the metals are given in Table VII. Unlike iron, cobalt and nickel do not have at low temperatures a body centered cubic type of crystal lattice, but are face centered. They do, however, process magnetic transitions similar to iron; and the non-magnetic forms are isomorphous with the face centered, or γ-iron. The metals are silver-grey in color, malleable, and ductile.

TABLE VII

ATOMIC AND PHYSICAL PROPERTIES OF COBALT AND NICKEL

	Co	Ni
Atomic weight	58.94	58.69
Atomic number	27	28
Stable Isotopes	57	58, 60, 61, 62, 64
Density	8.9	8.9
Melting point, ° C.	1493	1452
Boiling point, ° C.	3520	2800
Radius of M^{++} in solids, cm. $\times 10^8$	0.72	0.69
Electrical resistivity, ohm-cm	9.7×10^{-6}	6.9×10^{-6}
Tensile strength, lb. per sq. in	35000 (cast)	150000 (drawn)
Transition temperature, magnetic to non-magnetic form, ° C.	1150	360

Cobalt is rapidly developing very extensive industrial applications. Its most important use is as a constituent of the group of alloys known as **stellite,** which contain cobalt and one or more of the metals chromium, tungsten, molybdenum, iron, and nickel. Representative composition of two such alloys are: (1) Co 60, Cr 15, W 20, Mo 5, and (2) Co 30, Fe 52, W 14, Cr 4. These alloys are used as cutting tools in high-speed lathes, as they do not lose their edge with heating; and also as surgical instruments, since they may be sterilized in a flame without injury to the edge or

polish. Cobalt alloys for permanent magnets have extensive use in electrical fields. Typical alloys are: alnico II,
Co 12.5, Al 10, Ni 17, Fe 60.5; vicalloy, Co 52, V 9.5,
Fe 38.5; hyperco, Co 35, Cr 1, Fe 64. Alnico can lift 60
times its own weight. Cobalt-thorium catalysts are
employed in the Fischer-Tropsch production of gasoline.

The electrolytic nickel plating industry is one of the
largest consumers of nickel. The plated coat is hard, suscep-
tible of high polishing, and is resistant to tarnishing. The
electrolyte generally employed is nickel ammonium sulfate.

Finely divided or "active" nickel, prepared by reducing
the oxide below 300°, is employed as a catalyst in a number
of hydrogenation reactions; the most important commercially being the hardening of fats and oils by their combination with hydrogen, and the conversion of carbon monoxide
and steam into carbon dioxide and hydrogen.

TABLE VIII

NICKEL ALLOYS

NAME	PERCENTAGE COMPOSITION	PROPERTIES AND USES
Low nickel steel....	Ni 0.5–2.0, C 0.15, Fe about 96 (often 0.5–1.5 Cu)	Automobiles, railway cars, armor plate
Invar.............	Ni 35, Mn 0.5, C 0.5, Fe 64	Low coef. of expansion
Platenite..........	Ni 46, C 0.15, Fe 54	Glass to metal seals
Monel............	Ni 60, Cu 36, Fe 3.5, Al 0.5	Low heat conductivity, casts, non-corroding
Nickel coins.......	Ni 25, Cu 75	Coins
Constantan........	Ni 40, Cu 60	Thermoelements
Manganin.........	Ni 4, Mn 12, Cu 84	Electrical resistance wire
German silver.....	Ni 20, Cu 55, Zn 25	Jewelry
Nichrome.........	Ni 60, Cr 15, Fe 25	Electrical resistance
Triple Alloy Steel ..	Ni 14, Cr 18, Mo 4, Fe 64	Corrosion resistant
Illium.............	Ni 62, Cu 7, Cr 22, Mo 8, Fe 1	Acid resisting

Nickel forms an unusually large number of alloys of
technical importance (Table VIII). Approximately half of
the 160 million pounds of the metal consumed annually

in the United States went into nickel steel and 40 per cent into nonferrous alloys.

20. Reactions of the Metals.—The difficulty of oxidation increases gradually in going from iron to cobalt and nickel (see Par. **21** and Par. **27** for potential values), but in general the reactions of the three metals are similar. Like iron, they are rendered passive by very powerful oxidizing agents. The principal reactions are summarized in Table IX.

TABLE IX
REACTIONS OF COBALT AND NICKEL

$3Co + 2O_2 = Co_3O_4$	
$2Ni + O_2 = 2NiO$	
$M + 2H^+ = M^{++} + H_2$	Slow at 25°. Cf. Pars. **21** and **27**
$M + H_2O = MO + H_2$	Slow at red heat
$3M + 2NO_3^- + 8H^+ = 3M^{++}$	
$\quad + 2NO + 4H_2O$	Passive with concentrated acid
$M + X_2 = MX_2$	With halogens. Co also forms CoF_3
$4M + 2NH_3 = M_4N_2 + 3H_2$	400 to 600°
$3M + C = M_3C$	Carbides stable only at temperatures of the molten metals
$M + 4CO = M(CO)_4$	Below 100° but with Co only under pressure
$2M + Si = M_2Si$	Co also forms $CoSi$, $CoSi_2$, and $CoSi_3$, and Ni forms $NiSi$ and Ni_3Si_2
$M + S = MS$	

COMPOUNDS OF COBALT

21. Oxidation States.—Cobalt, like iron, forms cobaltous, Co^{++}, and cobaltic, Co^{+++}, ions and compounds, and a few cobaltites, derivatives of the dioxide, CoO_2, which, unlike the corresponding iron oxide, has been prepared. The cobaltic ion is a very powerful oxidizing agent, and for this reason its compounds are not very stable, except those complexes which give a very small concentration of the metal ion. Potential values are summarized below:

	VOLTS $_{25°}$
$Co = Co^{++} + 2e^-$	$+0.277$
$Co^{++} = Co^{+++} + e^-$	-1.84
$Co + 2OH^- = Co(OH)_2 + 2e^-$	$+0.42$
$Co(OH)_2 + OH^- = Co(OH)_3 + e^-$	-0.2
$Co(OH)_3 + OH^- = CoO_2 + 2H_2O + e^-$ .... $ca.$	-1.2
$Co(CN)_6^{-4} = Co(CN)_6^{-3} + e^-$	$+0.8$

22. Cobaltous Compounds.—**Cobaltous oxide,** CoO, may be prepared by the reduction of the higher oxides with hydrogen. When heated in air, it forms the cobaltous cobaltic oxide, Co_3O_4. The rose-colored hydroxide $Co(OH)_2$ is precipitated when alkali hydroxides are added to cobaltous solutions but darkens in the air through oxidation to cobaltic hydroxide. With concentrated ammonia the hydroxide dissolves to form $Co(NH_3)_6^{++}$, with excess of Co^{++} a green or blue modification of $Co(OH)_2$ is precipitated by hydroxide.

Cobaltous halides are readily formed by dissolving the hydroxide in the halogen acid. They are soluble and form a number of hydrates. The **chloride** is sometimes used as a "sympathetic ink," by writing with a solution of the pale pink hexahydrate; the characters are invisible but appear upon warming the paper, due to the formation of the blue anhydrous salt. The color of the ion $Co(H_2O)_6^{++}$ is pink and that of the complex chloride $CoCl_4^{--}$, blue. It has been suggested that upon dehydration, the hexahydrate, $Co(H_2O)_6Cl_2$ forms the complex salt $Co(CoCl_4)$.

The **sulfate** and **nitrate** are soluble and highly hydrated, and the latter readily decomposes to the sesquioxide upon heating.

Cobaltous sulfide is precipitated by sulfide ion in alkaline solution. Like nickel sulfide, it is unusual in that it is not precipitated from acid solutions, but is not soluble, or only very slowly so, in dilute hydrochloric acid.

Sodium bicarbonate precipitates **cobaltous carbonate,** $CoCO_3 \cdot 6H_2O$, at room temperature, and the anhydrous compound at higher temperatures. Basic carbonates are formed by the alkali carbonates.

Cobaltous cyanide, $Co(CN)_2 \cdot 3H_2O$, is but slightly soluble in water, but dissolves in excess of cyanide ion to form a complex **cobaltocyanide** ion, $Co(CN)_6^{-4}$, which, however, is readily oxidized to the cobaltic complex.

Cobaltous oxide forms important pigments upon fusion

with certain negative oxides. **Smalt,** a deep blue pigment, is really a cobalt glass. **Cobalt blue** is largely cobalt aluminate with more or less zincate. **Cobalt green** is cobalt zincate, and **turquoise green** the same with some chromite.

23. Cobaltic Compounds.—Due to the powerful oxidizing nature of cobaltic ion (Par. **21**), its simple salts are difficult to prepare. The **fluoride,** CoF_3, forms when the metal is heated with fluorine, and the **sulfate,** $Co_2(SO_4)_3 \cdot 18H_2O$, may be prepared by the electrolysis of cobaltous sulfate, followed by fractional crystallization. The sulfate forms **alums.** These, as well as the simple sulfate, are blue in color. Solutions of the fluoride and sulfate readily hydrolyze to the hydroxide, $Co(OH)_3$ (probably hydrous cobaltic oxide), which, when ignited in air, forms Co_3O_4.

24. Complex Cobaltic Compounds.—The cobaltic ion forms a remarkable number of complex ions in which it possesses a coordination number of six. These complex ions are more stable than the corresponding cobaltous ions. The reason is indicated by the following scheme which shows the number of electrons in the various orbitals:

	3d	4s	4p	5s
Co^{++}	(· ·) (· ·) (·) (·) (·)	( )	( ) ( ) ( )	( )
$Co(CN)_6^{-4}$	(· ·) (· ·) (· ·)	(· ·) (· ·) (· ·) (· ·) (· ·) (· ·)		(·)

OCTAHEDRAL BOND ORBITALS

Thus $Co(CN)_6^{-4}$ has one electron in a higher s orbital, and this electron is readily lost to form $Co(CN)_6^{-3}$.

The formulae of the more important complexes with ammonia, halides, nitrite, and cyanide are given in Table X; and a few of the more familiar compounds are discussed below:

Chloropentammine cobaltichloride, $Co(NH_3)_5ClCl_2$, forms when an ammonical solution of cobaltous chloride is oxidized by air or hydrogen peroxide. As it is but slightly soluble in concentrated hydrochloric acid, the dark reddish-violet compound is precipitated from the solution by the addition of this acid. The formation of this compound may be used to separate cobalt from nickel. The great stability of the complex is indicated by the fact that the ammonia is not removed by acid. Only two thirds of the chloride is precipitated by silver nitrate, but upon standing in contact with silver oxide it is converted into the hydroxide, $[Co(NH_3)_5H_2O](OH)_3$; and when this is dissolved in hydrochloric acid, the **aquapentammine cobaltichloride,** $[Co(NH_3)_5H_2O]Cl_3$, is formed. This compound is not readily soluble in cold water. When the chloropentammine is heated under slight pressure with concentrated ammonia, the **hexammine cobaltichloride,** $[Co(NH_3)_6]Cl_3$, separates as orange-colored crystals.

Potassium cobaltinitrite, or potassium hexanitrocobaltate, $K_3Co(NO_2)_6$, is prepared by treating a cobaltous salt with potassium nitrite and acetic acid: $Co^{++} + 3K^+ + 5NO_2^- + 2HNO_2 = K_3Co(NO_2)_6 + NO + H_2O$. The potassium salt is but slightly soluble, and is sometimes employed as a pigment, cobalt yellow. The more soluble sodium salt is employed as a reagent in testing for potassium (cf. **IV—25**). The complex nitrite ion is decomposed by alkalies, forming the hydroxides, and by strong acids with the liberation of oxides of nitrogen.

A number of **dinitrotetrammine cobaltic salts** have been

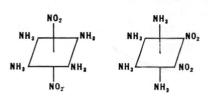

prepared. These compounds exhibit isomerism, due to the two possible arrangements of the coordination groups.

Cobaltous ion in the presence of cyanide is readily oxidized, even by hydrogen ion to form the **cobalticyanide,** $Co(CN)_6^{---}$. This ion is very stable, and like the corresponding ferricyanide, forms precipitates with ions of many of the heavier metals.

TABLE X

COBALTIC COORDINATION COMPOUNDS

+ 3 Cation	Undissociated compounds
$[Co(NH_3)_6]X_3$	$[Co(NH_3)_3(NO_2)_3]$
$[Co(NH_3)_5H_2O]X_3$	− 1 Anion
$[Co(NH_3)_4(H_2O)_2]X_3$	$K[Co(NH_3)_2(NO_2)_4]$
+ 2 Cation	− 2 Anion
$[Co(NH_3)_5Cl]X_2$	$K_2[Co(NH_3)(NO_2)_5]$
$[Co(NH_3)_5NO_2]X_2$	− 3 Anion
$[Co(NH_3)_4H_2O, Cl]X_2$	$K_3[Co(NO_2)_6]$
+ 1 Cation	$K_3[Co(CN)_6]$
$[Co(NH_3)_4Cl_2]X$	
$[Co(NH_3)_4Br_2]X$	
$[Co(NH_3)_4(NO_2)_2]X$	
$[Co(NH_3)_4CO_3]X$	

25. Nomenclature of Complex Compounds.—The following system of nomenclature has been proposed by Werner and is in general use:

(*a*) If the complex is a negative ion, the name of the positive ion is first.

(*b*) In giving the structure of the coordination complex, the following order is followed:

(1) Acid radical: Cl^-, chloro; CO_3^{--}, carbonato; CNS^-, thiocyanato; NO_2^-, nitro, etc.

(2) The water or oxygen groups: H_2O, aqua; O^{--}, oxo; O_2^{--}, peroxo; OH^-, hydroxo.

(3) The ammonia groups. Mono, di, tri, etc.—ammine, also called ammino.

(4) Name of positive element. If complex is a positive ion, the following endings are used: charge + 1, a; charge + 2, o; charge + 3, i; charge + 4, e. If complex is a negative ion, the termination, ate, is added.

(*c*) If the complex is a positive ion, the acid radicals not in the coordination group complete the name. Examples:

$[Co(NH_3)_5Cl]Cl_2$—Chloropentammine cobaltichloride

$K_3[Co(NH_3)_2(NO_2)_4]$—Potassium tetranitrodiammine cobaltate.

26. Cobalt Dioxide and Cobaltites.—Powerful oxidizing agents in alkaline solution, e.g. hypochlorite and hypoiodite, form the dioxide, CoO_2. The sesquioxide, which is prepared by igniting cobaltous nitrate, is generally considered to be the cobaltous cobaltite, $Co(CoO_3)$, as is also the tricobalt tetroxide, Co_3O_4, i.e., $2CoO \cdot CoO_2$. Other cobaltites have been prepared by fusing cobaltous oxide with basic oxides in air, e.g., $MgCoO_3$.

NICKEL COMPOUNDS

27. Oxidation States.—The principal oxidation state of nickel is $+ 2$. No $+ 3$ salts are known, and the $+ 3$ hydroxide which is frequently mentioned in the literature appears to be the dioxide. The dioxide is slightly acidic, and a few salts of it have been prepared. There is some evidence for the formation of a $+ 1$ oxide. Both the 0 and $+ 1$ complex cyanides are brown, $K_4Ni(CN)_4$ and $K_3Ni(CN)_4$. A few nickelates, i.e. K_2NiO_4, have been prepared. Potential values are summarized below:

	VOLTS 25°
$Ni = Ni^{++} + 2e^-$	$+ 0.25$
$Ni^{++} + 2H_2O = NiO_2 + 4H^+ + 2e^-$	$- 1.75$
$Ni + 2OH^- = Ni(OH)_2 + 2e^-$	$+ 0.66$
$Ni + 6NH_3(aq) = Ni(NH_3)_6^{++} + 2e^-$	0.48
$Ni(OH)_2 + 2OH^- = NiO_2 + 2H_2O + 2e^-$	$- 0.49$
$Ni^{++} + 4H_2O = NiO_4^{--} + 8H^+ + 4e^-$	$- 1.8$

28. Nickelous Compounds.—Nickelous compounds are generally green or blue in color, and show many resemblances to cupric compounds. The **hydroxide,** $Ni(OH)_2$, forms as a light green precipitate upon the addition of alkalies to a nickel solution. It is soluble in ammonium hydroxide, due to the formation of the complex nickel ammonia ion $Ni(NH_3)_6^{++}$ which, like the corresponding cupric ion, has a deep blue color. The **oxide,** NiO, results from the direct union of the elements, or from the ignition of the hydroxide or the dioxide. The oxide and hydroxide are readily soluble in acids.

The **halides** are readily soluble, highly hydrated in water, and ammonated in liquid ammonia solutions. The **bromide,** $NiBr_2 \cdot 6NH_3$, is precipitated by the addition of concentrated ammonia to a hot solution of nickel bromide. This property is sometimes utilized in the separation of nickel from cobalt. The **cyanide,** $Ni(CN)_2$, is but slightly soluble in water, but dissolves in excess of cyanide, forming the **complex cyanide ion,** $Ni(CN)_4^{--}$. It differs from the ferrous and cobaltous complex cyanides in that it cannot be oxidized to a nickelic compound, but it may be reduced to the 0 and $+1$ complex, $Ni(CN)_4^{-4}$ and $Ni(CN)_4^{-3}$. The diamagnetic tetra-coordinated complexes of Ni^{++} ($d^1s^1p^2$ orbitals) are planar and not tetrahedral. The complex cyanide is an example.

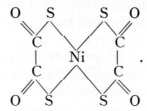

The carbonyl, $Ni(CO)_4$ is tetrahedral and the same is true of the paramagnetic complex ions of Ni^{++}, e.g., $Ni(H_2O)_4^{++}$ and $Ni(N_2H_4)_2^{++}$ (s^1p^3 orbitals).

Below 31°, the **sulfate** crystallyzes as the heptahydrate, $NiSO_4 \cdot 7H_2O$. At higher temperature, two forms of hexahydrated salts are formed, one blue and the other green. **Nickel ammonium sulfate,** $(NH_4)_2Ni(SO_4)_2 \cdot 6H_2O$, is used in nickel electroplating. The **nitrate,** $Ni(NO_3)_2 \cdot 6H_2O$, is extremely soluble in water. Alkali carbonates precipitate nickel from solution as a basic carbonate, but the normal **carbonate,** $NiCO_3 \cdot 6H_2O$, may be precipitated from a solution containing an excess of carbonic acid.

Nickel sulfide, NiS, like cobalt sulfide, is not precipitated from acid solutions by hydrogen sulfide, but is precipitated from ammonia solutions, and the sulfide so formed does not dissolve in dilute hydrochloric acid. The sulfide appears to exist in three modifications. The most soluble modification, which is first formed from alkaline solutions, quickly changes to a form which is less soluble, and also less rapidly soluble, in acid.

29. Nickel Dioxide and Nickelites.—Moderately strong oxidizing agents (Par. **27**) in alkaline solution convert nickelous oxide into a hydrous oxide which may be a solid solution of NiO and NiO_2. With long oxidation the composition appears to approach that of NiO_2. This oxide is an extremely powerful oxidizing agent in acid solution, and readily evolves oxygen under these conditions. **Barium nickelite,** $BaNi_2O_5$, has been prepared by fusing the oxide with barium carbonate. Alkali peroxides form with nickelous salts an oxide of the same general formula as the dioxide, but its reactions indicate that it is the nickelous peroxide of + 2 nickel.

Hydrous nickel dioxide is the oxidizing constituent of the **Edison storage battery.** The cell reaction upon discharge may be represented by the equation: $Fe + NiO_2 + 2H_2O = Fe(OH)_2 + Ni(OH)_2$. The electrodes are iron and nickel dioxide, and the electrolyte, potassium hydroxide. The potential of the cell is about 1.35 volts at 20°, and depends but slightly upon the concentration of hydroxide, since this substance enters into the cell reaction only so far as it affects the activity of the water. A similar battery employing cadmium instead of iron is in use in Europe. This cell has a potential of 1.2 volts.

30. Analytical.—In the systematic scheme for separation of the positive ions (Append. VI), cobalt and nickel are precipitated as sulfides by ammonium sulfide. In the separation from other members of this analytical group, advantage is taken of the slow solubility of the sulfides in cold dilute hydrochloric acid and the non-amphoteric character of the hydroxides. A number of procedures are employed in separating cobalt and nickel; the simplest probably being the precipitation of nickel by dimethylglyoxime, HON

: $C(CH_3)C(CH_3)$: NOH, as $Ni(C_4H_7O_2N_2)_2$ from solutions containing acetate and acetic acid. Other methods of separation depend upon the slight solubility of nickel chloride in an ether-hydrogen chloride solution and upon the conversion of cobalt into its + 3 compounds, e.g. the precipitation of cobalt as potassium cobaltinitrite; the precipitation of the sesquioxide, Co_2O_3, by bromine in neutral solution; and the formation of chloropentammine cobaltichloride.

In gravimetric analysis nickel may be weighed as the nickel dimethylglyoxime, after drying at 120°; as the oxide, NiO; or as the metal after electrolytic precipitation. The electrolytic precipitation is made from an ammoniacal solution, and nickel and cobalt are deposited together.

Cobalt is often precipitated as potassium cobaltinitrite, and as the salt of nitroso-beta-naphtol, $Co(C_{10}H_6ONO)_3$. In both procedures, it is weighed as the oxide, Co_3O_4.

31. A comparison of the potential diagrams of iron, cobalt, and nickel with those of the platinum metals is given in Chapter **XX—36.**

Chapter XX

PLATINUM AND PALLADIUM METALS

1. The triads: ruthenium, rhodium, palladium; and osmium, iridium, platinum, bear the same relation to the second and third transition series that iron, cobalt, and nickel do to the first (cf. **XIX**).

The six elements of these two series are so similar in properties that the separation of the naturally occurring alloys into the pure metals is not simple, and the commercial term "platinum" generally refers to the whole group.

These elements differ from iron, cobalt, and nickel in their greater nobility, and in their even greater tendencies to form complex ions, or coordination compounds.

Although the similarities in the properties are very pronounced, there are, however, distinct changes in both the horizontal and vertical periodic relations, as is indicated in the following table of their oxidation states. (Cf Par. **36**.)

TABLE I

OXIDATION STATES

Fe	2, 3, (4), 6	Co	2, 3, 4	Ni	(1), 2. (3), 4
Ru	2, 3, 4, 6, 7, 8	Rh	(1), (2), 3, 4, (6)	Pd	(1), 2, — 4, (6)
Os	(2), 3, 4, 6, (7), 8	Ir	(1), (2), 3, 4, 6	Pt	(1), 2, (3), 4, (6)

( ) Very unstable.

Among the more important of these relations which may be pointed out are: the similarity of the + 6 compounds of iron, ruthenium, and osmium to those of chromium, molybdenum, and tungsten; the similarity of nickel, palladium,

433

and platinum to copper, silver, and gold; the formation of volatile tetroxides by ruthenium and osmium; the remarkable absorption of hydrogen by nickel, palladium, and platinum, and the increasing tendency to form complex ammonia ions shown by the elements on the right.

2. Occurrence.—The important platinum ores are placer deposits in which the metal occurs as small grains or nuggets, the most extensive deposits being those in Russia, Colombia, and Transvaal. The nickel ores of Ontario contain small amounts of platinum as the mineral sperrylite, $PtAs_2$.

Crude native platinum generally contains all of the platinum metals. The following percentage compositions show the usual range: Pt, 60–80; Fe, 5–10; Pd, 1–2; Rh, 0.5–2; Ru, 0.5–2; Os, 1–10; Ir, 1–10. In addition, metal known as osmiridium is found, which contains largely osmium and iridium with small amounts of the other metals. The percentages of the elements in igneous rocks are extremely low, the approximate values being: Pt, 10^{-9}; Ir, 10^{-10}; Os, 10^{-10}, Rh, 10^{-11}, and Ru, 10^{-11}.

3. Metallurgy.—Platinum is extracted from sand and gravel by washing and gravity concentration processes similar to those used with gold (cf. **VII**). For the separation of the crude metal into its constituents, it is usually first digested with aqua regia. This dissolves the greater part of the metal, but leaves a residue of any osmiridium, which is fused with zinc in order to render it soluble in acid. The separation of the various metals from the solution then becomes a matter of qualitative analysis (Par. **35**).

4. Properties and Uses of the Metals.—The most important atomic and physical constants are summarized in Table II.

Ruthenium and osmium are grey like iron, while the other metals are more like silver. Rhodium is one of the whitest of all the metals. Osmium has the greatest density of any metal, is brittle, and hard enough to scratch glass.

Rhodium and iridium are a little softer, and palladium and platinum very malleable. When the metals are formed by the decomposition of their compounds at comparatively low temperatures, they are left in a finely divided or "spongy" condition. Hydrosols, or colloidal solutions, are readily prepared by striking an arc between electrodes of the metals under water.

TABLE II

ATOMIC AND PHYSICAL PROPERTIES

	Ru	Rh	Pd	Os	Ir	Pt
Atomic weight...........	101.7	102.91	106.7	190.8	193.1	195.23
Atomic number.........	44	45	46	76	77	78
Isotopes...............	96, 98, 99, 100, 101, 102, 104	101, 103	102, 104, 105, 106, 108, 110	186, 187, 188, 189, 190, 192	191, 193	192, 194, 195, 196, 198
Electrons in various quantum levels, 1st....	2	2	2	2	2	2
2d....	8	8	8	8	8	8
3d....	18	18	18	18	18	18
4th....	8 + 7	8 + 8	8 + 10	32	32	32
5th....	1	1		8 + 6	8 + 9	8 + 9
6th....				2		1
Density...............	12.2	12.5	12.0	22.48	22.4	21.45
Melting point, ° C.......	2500	1960	1555	2700	2443	1770
Boiling point, ° C........	4111	3960	3560	4400	4350	4010
Electrical resistivity, 20° C., ohm-cm. × 10⁶.....	10	5.1	10.8	9	6	10.5
Ionization potentials.....	—	7.7	8.3	ca. 8.7	9.0	8.88

Spongy palladium and platinum, like nickel, show a remarkable catalytic effect upon many gas reactions. The use of platinum as a catalyst in the manufacture of sulfuric acid, ammonia, and nitric acid, has been mentioned. Platinum causes the instant explosion of a mixture of oxygen and hydrogen, or the ignition of alcohol vapor in air. An electrode coated with finely divided platinum, called platinum black, has a very low overvoltage for hydrogen and other gases, and is often employed in the construction of electrical cells where a reversible gas electrode is desired. The platinum black surface may be prepared by the electrolytic precipitation of the metal from a chloroplatinate solution. Spongy platinum and palladium absorb large volumes of many gases, the absorption of hydrogen by the latter being especially remarkable (Par. **27**).

The consumption of the platinum metals in the more important industries is given in Table III. Commercial platinum is usually alloyed with the harder metals, especially iridium and rhodium, to make it more durable. The average price per ounce in 1946 for the pure metals was ruthenium, \$35; rhodium, \$125; osmium, \$50; palladium, \$24; iridium, \$125; and platinum, \$35. However, the fluctuations in the prices are quite large.

TABLE III

CONSUMPTION OF PLATINUM METALS IN U. S., 1948

Values in Troy Oz.

	Pt	Pd	OTHERS
Jewelry................	143,000	60,000	17,000
Dental................	22,000	41,000	900
Electrical..............	35,000	91,000	3,500
Chemical..............	31,000	15,000	4,000

5. Platinum, due to its high melting point, incorrodibility, and malleability, is almost indispensable in the manufacture of chemical utensils for high temperature ignitions. Such ware, however, must be handled with some care since it is attacked by a number of reagents, e.g. aqua regia, chlorine solution, ferric chloride, and fused alkalies. It alloys with many metals, especially lead, tin, bismuth, and mercury; and unites with carbon, phosphorus, sulfur, and silicon, becoming brittle. However, alkali carbonates may be ignited in platinum crucibles without damage. Alloys of palladium and gold such as **"palau,"** are employed to some extent as substitutes for platinum in chemical ware.

When pure platinum or platinum-iridium alloys are subjected to high temperature for a long period, appreciable loss of weight occurs, doubtless due to the formation of oxide. Platinum-rhodium alloys, however, are much less subject to such "volatilization." Platinum-iridium alloys are employed in the electrical industry in contact points.

6. Reactions of the Metals.—The more important reactions are summarized in Table IV. Reference should be made to the paragraphs dealing with the states of each element for approximate potential values. All of the metals exhibit "passivity" with strong oxidizing agents, so that they are not dissolved by as many reagents as the potential values would indicate. (See also Par. **5** for additional reactions of platinum.)

TABLE IV

REACTIONS OF PLATINUM METALS

	Ru	Rh	Pd	Os	Ir	Pt
Spongy metal heated in oxygen	RuO_2 at 700–1200	Rh_2O_3 slowly below 1150°	PdO slowly at 700°	OsO_4 at 200°	IrO_2 slowly at 1050°	PtO slowly at 450°
Spongy metal heated in chlorine	K_2RuCl_6 when KCl is present	$RhCl_3$	$PdCl_2$	$OsCl_4$ at 700°	K_2IrCl_5 when KCl is present	$PtCl_2$ at 360°
Hot HNO_3	Insol.	Insol.	Slowly sol. $Pd(NO_3)_2$	Insol.	Insol.	Insol.
Aqua regia	H_2RuCl_5	Very slowly soluble H_3RhCl_6	H_2PdCl_6	OsO_4	Very slowly soluble H_2IrCl_6	$H_2PtCl \cdot$
Fused with KOH + KNO_3	K_2RuO_4	RhO_2	PdO	K_2OsO_4	Ir_2O_3	K_2PtO_3 $\cdot nH_2O$
Fused with $KHSO_4$	Insol.	$KRh(SO_4)_2$	$PdSO_4$	Insol.	$Ir_2(SO_4)_3$	Basic sulfate slowly at 250°

RUTHENIUM COMPOUNDS

7. Oxidation States.—Ruthenium assumes an unusually large number of different oxidation states, 2, 3, 4, 6, 7, and

8. Compounds of the higher states in acid solutions are powerful oxidizing agents, and are reduced to salts of + 3 ruthenium. The metal is oxidized in alkaline solution to ruthenite, RuO_3^{--}, ruthenate, RuO_4^{--}, perruthenate, RuO_4^{-}, or the tetroxide RuO_4 with the potential increasing for each step.

The following are approximate potentials for the more important couples:

	VOLTS 25°
$Ru = Ru^{++} + 2e^-$	$- 0.45$
$Ru^{++} + 5Cl^- = RuCl_5^{--} + e^-$	$- 0.3$
$RuCl_5^{--} + H_2O = RuCl_5OH^{--} + H^+ + e^-$	$- 1.3$
$RuCl_5OH^{--} + 3H_2O = RuO_4 + 5Cl^- + 7H^+ + 4e^-$	$- 1.5$
$Ru + 6OH^- = RuO_3^{--} + 3H_2O + 4e^-$	0.3
$RuO_3^{--} + 2OH^- = RuO_4 + H_2O + 2e^-$	$- 0.6$

8. The + 2 State.—The fact that the oxide, RuO, does not appear to exist indicates that in alkaline solution this state is unstable, probably decomposing to give the metal and ruthenate (+ 6).

In acid solution, **halides** of Ru^{++} may be prepared by the reduction of the + 3 compounds by zinc, hydrogen sulfide, or by cathodic reduction. The solution has an azure blue color; solid **cesium ruthenium chloride,** $Cs_3RuCl_5\cdot2H_2O$, has been obtained from it, but the salt is rapidly oxidized in air.

Potassium ruthenocyanide, $K_4Ru(CN)_6\cdot3H_2O$, is comparatively stable, and forms when ruthenium compounds of higher states are fused with potassium cyanide. It resembles ferrocyanide in the solubilities of its salts, and is oxidized by chlorine, probably to the + 3 cyanide.

9. The + 3 State.—The **chloride,** $RuCl_3$, is formed when the finely divided metal is oxidized by chlorine; the complex chloride, K_2RuCl_5, is readily prepared by the reduction of the + 4 complex, by alcohol, or other mild reducing agents.

The chloride in solution forms a bright red **ammonia**

complex, and with alkalies precipitates the hydrous oxide, Ru_2O_3, which is not soluble in excess of reagent.

The chloride forms a complex with nitric oxide, $RuCl_3\cdot NO\cdot H_2O$, and a large number of **alkali complex chlorides** have been prepared, e.g. $K_2RuCl_5H_2O$, $K_2RuNOCl_5$, and also the **nitrite,** $K_2Ru(NO_2)_5$.

The **bromide,** $RuBr_3$, is similar to the chloride in its reactions. The **iodide,** RuI_3, is but slightly soluble, and does not appear to form complex alkali iodides.

10. The + 4 State.—The dioxide, RuO_2, is obtained by heating the finely divided metal in air. It unites with metal oxides to form **ruthenites,** e.g. $BaRuO_3$. The **sulfate,** $Ru(SO_4)_2$, may be prepared by oxidizing the **sulfide,** RuS_2, with nitric acid or by heating the tetroxide with sulfuric acid. The free tetrachloride has not been prepared; but the potassium **ruthenichlorides,** K_2RuCl_6 and K_2RuCl_5OH, form when potassium ruthenate is dissolved in cold dilute hydrochloric acid.

11. The + 6 and + 7 States.—**Potassium ruthenate,** $K_2RuO_4\cdot H_2O$, forms when the metal is fused with potassium hydroxide and nitrate. It is soluble in water, forming a deep orange red solution. With cold dilute hydrochloric acid, the complex ruthenichloride is formed, but the **ruthenyl chloride,** RuO_2Cl_2, probably forms as an intermediate step. When acted on by chlorine at 60°, the solution becomes dark green through the formation of perruthenate, RuO_4^-. The alkali salts of the latter have been obtained as black crystals possessing a green metallic luster.

12. Ruthenium Tetroxide.—The tetroxide forms in small quantities by the action of oxygen upon finely divided metal, but is best prepared by the oxidation of an alkaline solution of ruthenate, or by the action of hot nitric acid and perchloric acids on compounds of the lower oxidation states. The oxide melts at room temperature to an orange liquid, decomposes around 106°, and unlike osmium tetroxide, it is not poisonous. It is somewhat soluble in water, but the oxide seems to possess neither acidic nor basic properties to any marked degree. In acid solution, it is a powerful oxidizing agent.

OSMIUM COMPOUNDS

13. Oxidation States.—Osmium resembles ruthenium in forming compounds of the positive oxidation states, 2, 3, 4, 6, and 8. In hydrochloric acid osmium may be present as $OsCl_6^{-3}$, $OsCl_6^{--}$, or H_2OsO_5. The oxidation-reduction potentials are extremely complicated, since almost every negative ion gives a different complex ion with the lower states.

VOLTS $_{25^u}$

$$Os + 6Cl^- = OsCl_6^{-3} + 3e^- \dots\dots\dots\dots\dots\dots\dots\dots\dots\dots -0.6$$
$$OsCl_6^{-3} = OsCl_6^{--} + e^- \dots\dots\dots\dots\dots\dots\dots\dots\dots\dots\dots -0.85$$
$$OsCl_6^{--} + 4H_2O_4 = OsO_4 + 6Cl^- + 8H^+ + 4e^- \dots\dots\dots\dots -1.0$$
$$Os + 4OH^- = OsO_2 + 2H_2O + 4e^- \dots\dots\dots\dots\dots\dots\dots -0.15$$
$$OsO_2 + 4OH^- = OsO_4^{--} + 2H_2O + 2e^- \dots\dots\dots\dots\dots\dots -0.1$$
$$Os + 9OH^- = HOsO_5^- + 4H_2O + 8e^- \dots\dots\dots\dots\dots\dots -0.02$$

14. The + 2 State.—The **chloride**, $OsCl_2$, has been prepared by heating the trichloride at 500°, but neither it nor complex chlorides appear to have been prepared in solution. The slightly soluble iodide OsI_2 is precipitated when iodide is added to $OsCl_6^{-3}$. It is claimed that the reduction of the tetroxide with sulfur dioxide yields the **sulfite**, $OsSO_3$; and this, when heated, gives the **oxide**, OsO.

The **complex cyanides**, e.g. $K_4Os(CN)_6$, are probably the most stable compounds of this state.

15. The + 3 State.—The chloride, $OsCl_3 \cdot 3H_2O$, has been prepared by reducing osmic acid with alcohol in the presence of chloride. When treated with sodium carbonate, the **sesquioxide**, Os_2O_3, is formed.

The following are some of the more important complex salts of this state: K_3OsCl_6 (potassium chlorosmite), $K_2OsNOCl_5$, $K_2Os(NO_2)_5$, $KOs(NO)O_2$. The latter compound, called **potassium osmiamate,** is obtained by the action of ammonia on a cold alkaline solution of the tetroxide. It dissolves in hydrochloric acid to form the complex chloride.

16. The + 4 state.—Chlorine reacts with the metal at about 700° to form the **tetrachloride,** $OsCl_4$. It slowly hydrolyzes in water to the hydrous **dioxide,** OsO_2.

Among the complex salts of this state are K_2OsCl_6 (potassium chlorosmate), K_2OsBr_6, K_2OsI_6, and Na_6OsCl_2-$(SO_3)_4$.

17. The + 6 State.—The trioxide is not known, but the metal fused with potassium hydroxide and nitrate gives **potassium osmate,** K_2OsO_4, and this salt is also prepared by reducing an alkaline solution of this tetroxide with alcohol. It is unstable in acid solution. Barium osmate, $BaOsO_4$, is but slightly soluble. Some hexafluoride forms when fluorine is passed over the metal at 250°. It is decomposed by water.

Many complex **osmyl** ions have been prepared, e.g. $OsO_2Cl_4^{--}$, $OsO_2(C_2O_4)_2^{--}$, $OsO_2(NO_2)_4^{--}$, $OsO_3(NO_2)_2^{--}$, $OsO_3Cl_2^{--}$. None of the ions appear to be stable in acid solution.

18. Osmium Tetroxide.—The volatile **tetroxide,** OsO_4, is formed by direct combustion of the metal in air, or by its oxidation with hot concentrated nitric or sulfuric acids. The vapor has an odor resembling chlorine and is extremely poisonous. The oxide is soluble in water, but the solution is only very slightly acid (K_1 for H_2OsO_5 is 8×10^{-13}). Alkalies form weakly bound compounds, e.g. $OsO_4 \cdot 2KOH$, which are readily soluble, and their solution is highly alkaline. As indicated in Par. **13,** the oxide is a powerful oxidizing agent.

The **octafluoride,** OsF_8, and probably the **chloride,** $OsCl_8$, form in small amounts when the metal is heated in the halogen. These compounds are highly volatile and hydrolyze to the tetroxide in water.

RHODIUM COMPOUNDS

19. Oxidation States.—Rhodium forms compounds having as positive oxidation states 1, 2, 3, 4, and 6. Of these the $+ 3$ and $+ 4$ are the more important. Unstable Rh_2O and $RhCl$ have been prepared. The ion, Rh^{++}, is probably stable but in the presence of chloride is readily oxidized to $RhCl_6^{-3}$. Rhodic ion, Rh^{+++}, resembles cobaltic ion in the nature of its coordination compounds, and the dioxide is somewhat similar to cobalt dioxide.

$$\text{VOLTS } 25°$$

$$Rh = Rh^{++} + 2e^- \dots\dots\dots\dots\dots\dots\dots\dots\dots\dots ca. - 0.6$$
$$Rh^{++} = Rh^{+++} + e^- \dots\dots\dots\dots\dots\dots\dots\dots\dots ca. - 0.7$$
$$Rh^{+++} + 2H_2O = RhO_2 + 4H^+ + e^- \dots\dots\dots\dots ca. - 1.4$$
$$RhCl_6^{-3} + 2H_2O = RhO_2 + 4H^+ + 6Cl^- + e^- \dots\dots < - 1.4$$

20. The $+ 3$ State.—The **oxide**, Rh_2O_3, results when the metal is heated in air below 1150°. Above that temperature, the oxide decomposes into the metal and oxygen. The hydrous oxide is precipitated from rhodium solutions by alkalies, and is somewhat soluble in excess of concentrated alkali, doubtless with the formation of **rhodites.**

The **trichloride,** $RhCl_3$, may be prepared by heating the metal in chlorine, and the salt so obtained is not soluble in water or acids. However, hydrated chloride formed by dissolving the sesquioxide in hydrochloric acid, is highly deliquescent. The **bromide,** $RhBr_3$, and **iodide,** RhI_3, have also been prepared. The latter is not readily soluble in hot water. The sulfate, $Rh_2(SO_4)_3$, forms alums. The **sulfide,** Rh_2S_3, is precipitated from acid solutions by hydrogen sulfide; but if excess of hydrogen sulfide is employed, the compound $Rh_2S_3 \cdot 3H_2S$ appears to form, and normal sulfide precipitates but slowly.

The following coordination compounds are analogous to the corresponding cobalt compounds: $K_3[RhCl_6]$, $Na_2[RhCl_5H_2O]$, $[Rh(NH_3)_6]Cl_3$, $[Rh(NH_3)_5Cl]Cl_2$, $K_3[Rh(CN)_6]$, and $K_3[Rh(NO_2)_6]$.

21. Rhodium Dioxide.—Powerful oxidizing agents in alkaline solution, e.g. ClO^-, convert the sesquioxide into the **dioxide,** RhO_2. The dioxide is not soluble in water or alkalies, but dissolves in hydrochloric acid with the evolution of chlorine. Continued action of sodium hypochlorite on the dioxide gives a blue solution which is thought to contain **sodium rhodate,** Na_2RhO_4.

Iridium Compounds

22. Oxidation States.—The important oxidation states of iridium, like those of rhodium, are $+ 3$ and $+ 4$. Powerful oxidizing agents in alkaline solutions form iridates $(+ 6)$, but these are not stable in acid.

The solid chlorides, $IrCl$ and $IrCl_2$, are stable but decompose in the presence of water to the metal and the $+ 3$ chloride.

VOLTS $_{25°}$

$$Ir = Ir^{+++} + 3e^- \dots\dots\dots\dots ca. - 1.0$$
$$Ir^{+++} + 2H_2O = IrO_2 + 4H^+ + e^- \dots\dots ca. - 0.7$$
$$Ir + 6Cl^- = IrCl_4^{-3} + 3e^- \dots\dots - 0.72$$
$$IrCl_6^{-3} = IrCl_6^{-2} + e^- \dots\dots - 1.02$$
$$IrO_2 + 4OH^- = IrO_4^{--} + 2H_2O + 2e^- \dots > - 0.4$$

23. The $+ 3$ State.—The **trichloride,** $IrCl_3$, forms when the finely divided metal is heated in chlorine. This product is not soluble in water, but the hydrated salt formed by dissolving the sesquioxide in hydrochloric acid is readily soluble. The chloride forms complex salts with the alkali chlorides, e.g. K_3IrCl_6; similar compounds are formed by the **bromide** and **iodide.** These compounds are most readily prepared by reduction of the $+ 4$ complex salts in acid solution. With alkalies, the **sesquioxide,** Ir_2O_3, is precipitated, and is soluble in excess of the reagent. With hydrogen sulfide in acid solution, the **sulfide,** Ir_2S_3, forms. Iridium **sulfate,** $Ir_2(SO_4)_3$, forms alums. Other important complex salts are the cyanide, e.g. $Na_3Ir(CN)_6$, and **nitrites,** e.g. $K_3Ir(NO_2)_6$.

24. The + 4 State.—The **dioxide,** IrO_2, is obtained when the finely divided metal is heated to 1100° in air. A hydrated form results from the oxidation of the sesquioxide in air, from the addition of alkalies to the chloroiridates, and upon solution in water of alkali iridates. It is soluble in hydrochloric acid and in sulfuric acid, yielding the **chloride** and **sulfate** in solution. The solid chloride is a dark brown substance very soluble in water and forms stable **complex chlorides,** e.g. K_2IrCl_6. Hundreds of complex ammines and halogen compounds are known.

25. The + 6 state.—Potassium **iridate,** K_2IrO_4, appears to be formed when the metal is fused with potassium hydroxide and nitrate, but oxygen is evolved when the salt is dissolved in water and the dioxide precipitated.

PALLADIUM COMPOUNDS

26. Oxidation States.—The principal states of palladium, like platinum, are + 2 and + 4. There is some evidence for the formation of the monochloride upon heating the dichloride, but in general the + 2 compounds decompose directly into the metal at high temperatures. The trioxide PdO_3 has been reported.

$$\text{VOLTS } 25°$$

$$Pd = Pd^{++} + 2e^-\dots\dots\dots\dots\dots\dots\dots\dots\dots\dots -0.83$$
$$PdCl_4^{--} + 2Cl^- = PdCl_6^{--} + 2e^-\dots\dots\dots\dots\dots\dots -0.29$$
$$Pd + 4Cl^- = PdCl_4^{--} + 2e^-\dots\dots\dots\dots\dots\dots\dots -0.64$$
$$Pd + 2OH^- = Pd(OH)_2 + 2e^-\dots\dots\dots\dots\dots\dots\dots -0.1$$

27. Palladium and Hydrogen.—Palladium absorbs hydrogen to a remarkable extent, 600 to 900 times its own volume at 25°, depending somewhat upon the physical condition of the metal. The pressure-concentration curves for the system indicate the formation of a solid solution of the metal and the hydride of empirical formula, Pd_2H; the absorption is accompanied by a considerable increase in the volume of the metal. The gas is almost completely evolved, *in vacuo* at 100°. The hydrogenated metal is a good reducing agent, e.g. reduces mercuric chloride and ferric salts, and also induces the oxidation by oxygen of many carbon compounds, possibly through the formation of hydrogen peroxide: $Pd_4H_2 + O_2 = 4Pd + H_2O_2$; and $H_2O_2 + CO = H_2O + CO_2$.

28. The + 2 State.—The **halides** are formed by heating the metal in the halogen. The chloride, $PdCl_2 \cdot 2H_2O$, is soluble in water, and with alkalies gives a precipitate of the hydrous oxide, PdO. This is soluble in concentrated ammonia, forming a **complex ammonia** ion, and upon dilution and acidifying slightly with hydrochloric acid, a precipitate of the diammoniate, $PdCl_2 \cdot 2NH_3$, is obtained. The **iodide,** PdI_2, and **cyanide,** $Pd(CN)_2$, are but slightly soluble in water, but dissolve in excess of the precipitating ions. The **sulfide, PdS,** is precipitated from acid solutions by hydrogen sulfide. It is not soluble in ammonium sulfide. The **sulfate** and **nitrate** are readily soluble.

The following types of complex salts have been prepared: $K_2[PdCl_4]$, $Ag_2[PdCl_2 \cdot (OH)_2]$, $K_2[Pd(CN)_4]$, $Na_2[Pd(NO_2)_4]$ $K_2[PdBr_2(NO_2)_2]$, $[PdCl_2 \cdot 2CO]$.

These tetra-coordinated complex ions are planar and not tetrahedral. The planar character of Pd^{++} is also illustrated by the crystal structure of the chloride $PdCl_2$ in which infinite polymerization occurs to give strings of planar groups.

29. The + 4 State.—The hydrous dioxide, $PdO_2 \cdot nH_2O$ is obtained by anodic oxidation of an acid solution of palladous nitrate. A precipitate of the **sesquioxide,** Pd_2O_3, probably $PdO \cdot PdO_2$, first forms but is decomposed by the acid leaving the dioxide. The dioxide decomposes around 200° to the monoxide.

The tetrachloride and bromide have not been prepared in

the pure state, but alkali complexes of the type M_2PdCl_6 are known. The **potassium chloropalladate,** K_2PdCl_6, is prepared by the oxidation of the chloropalladite by chlorine, or by dissolving the dioxide in potassium chloride and hydrochloric acid. It is only slightly soluble in cold water and the same is true of the ammonium salt.

PLATINUM COMPOUNDS

30. Oxidation States.—Platinum forms two important series of compounds corresponding to the oxidation states $+2$ and $+4$, and, in addition, a few comparatively unstable compounds of the $+1$, $+3$, and $+6$ states. It exhibits strong tendencies to form coordination complexes; and the simple salts are, in general, either insoluble or slightly ionized in solution. For this reason, the oxidation-reduction potentials for the various oxidation changes depend very much upon the negative ion present.

VOLTS $_{25°}$

$$Pt + 2H^+ + 4Cl^- = PtCl_4^{--} + 2e \dots -0.73$$
$$PtCl_4^{--} + 2Cl^- = PtCl_6^{--} + 2e^- \dots ca. -0.72$$
$$Pt = Pt^{++} + 2e^- \dots ca. -1.2$$
$$Pt + 4Br^- = PtBr_4^{--} + 2e^- \dots -0.68$$
$$Pt + 2OH^- = Pt(OH)_2^{--} + 2e^- \dots -0.16$$
$$Pt(OH)_2 + 4OH^- = Pt(OH)_6^{--} + 2e^- \dots ca. -0.2$$
$$Pt(OH)_6^{--} + 2OH^- = PtO_4^{--} + 4H_2O + 2e^- \dots -0.4$$

31. The $+2$ State.—**Platinous chloride,** $PtCl_2$, is generally prepared by heating the tetrachloride or chloroplatinic acid. It also forms when spongy platinum is heated in chlorine at $200°$. It is not soluble in water, but dissolves in excess of hydrochloric acid to form a solution of **chloroplatinous acid,** H_2PtCl_4. This acid is most conveniently prepared, however, by the reduction of chloroplatinic acid by sulfur dioxide. The alkali and ammonium salts, e.g. potassium chloroplatinite, K_2PtCl_4. are soluble; but the silver and lead salts are not.

The chloride forms many addition compounds, for example, $PtCl_2CO$ and $PtCl_2 \cdot PCl_3$. The **fluoride is soluble,** but the **bromide** and **iodide** are not. The latter decompose readily: $2PtI_2 = Pt + PtI_4$.

Platinous hydroxide, $Pt(OH)_2$, is prepared by boiling chloroplatinites with equivalent quantities of alkali. With excess of alkali, it decomposes, forming the metal and platinates. It is soluble in the halogen acids, but not in oxy-acids.

The black **sulfide,** PtS, precipitates when hydrogen sulfide is passed into a solution of chloroplatinite. It appears to be even less soluble than HgS.

The more important coördination compounds of $+2$ platinum are given below. The **nitroplatinate,** $Pt(NO_2)_4^{--}$, is especially stable, as the platinum is not precipitated by alkalies or hydrogen sulfide, and strong acids form the nitro-acid, $H_2Pt(NO_2)_4$. Like Ni^{++} and Pd^{++}, these compounds have planar coördination instead of tetrahedral.

Platino-coördination Compounds.

$M_2[PtCl_4]$	$M_2[Pt(CN)_4]$	$[PtCl_2(NH_3)_2]$
$M_2[PtBr_4]$	$M_2[Pt(CNS)_4]$	$[Pt(NH_3)_4]Cl_2$
$M_2[Pt(NO_2)_4]$	$M[PtCl_3 \cdot NH_3]$	$M[Pt(CNS)_3CO]$

32. The + 3 State.—The trichloride may be formed at high temperatures. When warmed with hydrochloric acid the following decomposition occurs: $2\ PtCl_3 + 4Cl^- = PtCl_4^{--} + PtCl_6^{--}$. There is some evidence for the sesquioxide Pt_2O_3. The complex cyanide ion $Pt(CN)_4^-$ is stable.

33. The + 4 State.—When platinum is dissolved in aqua regia, **chloroplatinic acid** is formed in solution; and upon removal of nitric acid by excess of hydrochloric acid, the hexahydrate, $H_2PtCl_6 \cdot 6H_2O$, may be obtained by crystallization. The aqua regia solution also contains the **nitrosyl chloroplatinic chloride,** $PtCl_4(NO)_2Cl_2$. By igniting the chloro-acid in an atmosphere of chlorine, the tetrachloride $PtCl_4$, is obtained. This salt is soluble in water. and when heated to 370° decomposes: $PtCl_4 = PtCl_2 + Cl_2$. The **trichloride** probably forms as an intermediate step.

The chloroplatinates are the most important compounds of the metal. The silver and cesium salts are insoluble, and the rubidium, potassium, and ammonium only slightly soluble; hence these compounds are precipitated when the chloro-acid is treated with a solution of the corresponding positive ion.

Platinum tetrabromide and **iodide** are analogous to the chloride.

When the tetrachloride is heated with an excess of sodium hydroxide, **sodium platinate,** $Na_2Pt(OH)_6$, is formed in solution; upon neutralizing this solution with acetic acid the hydrated dioxide, $PtO_2 \cdot 4H_2O$ or $H_2Pt(OH)_6$, is precipitated. The oxide is soluble in the halogen acids, and in sulfuric acid gives a solution of the sulfate, $Pt(SO_4)_2$.

Platinic sulfide, PtS_2, is precipitated from acid solutions of the chloroplatinate by hydrogen sulfide. It is insoluble in nitric acid, but soluble in ammonium polysulfide.

Hundreds of complex **platiniammino-salts** are known in which platinum generally has the coordination number six. Examples of these complex types are: $[Pt(NH_3)_6]X_4$, $[Pt(NH_3)_4X_2]X_2$, and $[Pt(NH_3)X_5]R$.

Nitroplatinites are oxidized by halogens with the formation of **tetranitro dihalidoplatinates,** e.g. $K_2Pt(NO_2)_4Cl_2$. Complex **platinithiocyanides,** e.g. $K_2Pt(CNS)_6$, have been prepared; but the platinocyanides are oxidized to the $+ 3$ and not the $+ 4$ state, e.g. $AgPt(CN)_4$.

34. Perplatinate.—In alkaline solution, the platinates are coverted by anodic oxidation into perplatinate, e.g. K_2PtO_4. These compounds are decomposed by sulfuric acid, leaving an insoluble **trioxide,** PtO_3, which readily evolves oxygen upon heating.

35. Analytical.—The general principles of the scheme for the separation of the platinum metals, given by Gilchrist and Wichers, are as follows:

Osmium is removed as the tetroxide by distilling with nitric acid. The gas is absorbed in a solution of sulfur dioxide and hydrochloric acid. Ruthenium is next removed as the tetroxide by distillation after the addition of sulfuric acid and sodium bromate. The same absorbing agent is employed.

Rhodium, iridium, and palladium are precipitated and separated from platinum as the hydrous dioxides. The precipitation is made with sodium bicarbonate at about pH 6 from a chloride solution in the presence of sodium bromate. Platinum is precipitated from the filtrate after the addition of hydrochloric acid by saturating with hydrogen sulfide.

The dioxides of rhodium, iridium, and palladium are dissolved in hydrochloric acid and the palladium precipitated with dimethylglyoxime. The latter reagent is destroyed in the filtrate by evaporation with sulfuric acid and the rhodium precipitated as the metal by titanous chloride. The titanium which has been added may be removed with cupferron ($C_6H_5N \cdot NO \cdot ONH_4$) and the iridium precipitated as the hydrous dioxide. After the isolation of the various elements, they are generally converted to the metal and weighed as such.

It is frequently necessary to separate gold from the platinum metal. This is readily accomplished by the precipitation of the metal from a $1.2N$ HCl solution by reduction with hydroquinone. The platinum metals remain in solution.

36. Potential Diagrams.—In order to compare stability relationships in the various oxidation states of the three triods, the following potential diagrams are given for acid solution. It will be noted that for any family (i.e. same number of electrons), the elements become more noble or more electronegative with increasing atomic weight, but the higher oxidation states become relatively more stable. This is particularly true of iron, ruthenium and osmium.

0	+2	+3	+4	+6	+7	+8

$$Fe \underset{0.44}{\quad\quad} Fe^{++} \underset{-0.77}{\quad\quad} Fe^{+++} \underset{<-1.9}{\quad\quad\quad\quad\quad} HFeO_4^-$$

$$Ru \underset{-0.45}{\quad\quad} Ru^{++} \underset{-0.3}{\quad\quad} RuCl_5^{-2} \underset{-1.3}{\quad\quad} RuCl_5OH^- \underset{-1.7}{\quad\quad} HRuO_4^- \underset{-1.6}{\quad\quad} RuO_4^- \underset{-1.0}{\quad\quad} RuO_4$$

$$Os \underset{-0.7}{\quad\quad} Os^{++} \underset{-0.3}{\quad\quad} OsCl_6^{-3} \underset{-0.85}{\quad\quad\quad\quad} OsCl_6^{-2} \underset{-1.0}{\quad\quad\quad\quad} OsO_4$$
$$\underset{-0.6}{\rule{3cm}{0.4pt}}$$

$$Co \underset{0.277}{\quad\quad} Co^{++} \underset{-1.82}{\quad\quad} Co^{+++} \underset{<-1.8}{\quad\quad\quad} CoO_2$$

$$Rh \underset{(-0.6)}{\quad\quad} Rh^{++} \underset{(-0.9)}{\quad\quad} Rh^{+++} \underset{(-1.4)}{\quad\quad} RhO_2 \underset{(-1.4)}{\quad\quad} HRhO_4^-$$
$$\underset{(-0.7)}{\rule{3cm}{0.4pt}}$$

$$Ir \underset{<-1.0}{\quad\quad} Ir^{++} \underset{>-1.0}{\quad\quad} Ir^{+++} \underset{(-1.2)}{\quad\quad} IrO_2 \underset{<-1.4}{\quad\quad} HIrO_4^-$$
$$\underset{-1.0}{\rule{3cm}{0.4pt}}$$

$$Ni \underset{0.25}{\quad\quad} Ni^{++} \underset{-1.75}{\quad\quad\quad\quad} NiO_2 \underset{<-1.8}{\quad\quad} HNiO_4^-$$

$$Pd \underset{-0.98}{\quad\quad} Pd^{++} \underset{<-1.6}{\quad\quad} Pd^{+4}$$
$$\underset{-0.64}{\quad\quad} PdCl_4^{--} \underset{-1.29}{\quad\quad} PdCl_6^{--}$$

$$Pt \underset{(-1.2)}{\quad\quad} Pt^{++} \underset{(-1.1)}{\quad\quad\quad\quad} PtO_2$$
$$\underset{-0.73}{\quad\quad} PtCl_4^{--} \underset{-0.72}{\quad\quad\quad\quad} PtCl_6^{--}$$

Chapter XXI

SCANDIUM, YTTRIUM, AND THE RARE EARTH ELEMENTS

1. Following barium, atomic number 56, there occurs a group of 15 remarkably similar elements known as the Rare Earths, which form $+3$ ions resembling those of scandium and yttrium, the two preceding elements of Main Group III. The existence of this group was long a puzzling problem, as the older forms of the periodic table predicted but one element at this point. The explanation is now given in terms of the electronic structure of the atoms. The distribution of electrons in the various quantum levels in lanthanum, 57, and lutecium, 71, appears to be as follows:

Quantum level.......	1s	2s	2p	3s	3p	3d	4s	4p	4d	4f	5s	5p	5d	6s
Number of electrons La ..	2	2	6	2	6	10	2	6	10		2	6	1	2
Lu ..	2	2	6	2	6	10	2	6	10	14	2	6	1	2

Up to lanthanum, no electrons have gone into the $4f$ level, as the $5s$, $5p$, and $6s$ quantum levels represent lower energies since, in terms of the Bohr picture, electrons in these highly elliptical orbits are on the average closer to the nucleus. When these levels are occupied, the $4f$ levels then become the next most stable positions, and as 14 electrons are required to fill it, we find this group of 15 elements with the same number of outer or valence electrons, and differing only in the number of electrons in a level comparatively deep within the kernel. The elements give up their $5d$ and $6s$ electrons fairly easily, and thus all form ions like La^{+++}.

The history of the rare earths dates from the discovery (about 1800) of two earth-like oxides which were given the names yttria and ceria. Further study of these oxides has resulted in the discovery of all the rare earth elements, except element 61 (cf. Par. 11).

Although crude ceria and yttria generally contain at least traces of almost all of the other rare earths, the former consists largely of the oxides of the elements of atomic numbers 57 to 62; and the latter of oxides of yttrium and the elements 63 to 71; these groups are generally designated as the **Cerium Subgroup** and the **Yttrium Subgroup**.

2. The rare earth elements are so similar that it is extremely difficult, in general, to separate two succeeding elements. There is, however, a gradual change in the properties in going from lanthanum to lutecium; for example, there is a slight decrease in the atomic volume and a corresponding slight decrease in the basic nature of the sesquioxide. Yttrium, being smaller than lanthanum, resembles the heavier members more than it does the lighter ones. Scandium is less basic than yttrium, and resembles aluminum more than the other elements do.

3. Since La^{+++}, with no f electrons, is especially stable, cerium tends to assume the same electron structure which it can do by forming a $+ 4$ ion. Likewise, ytterbium tends to form the Lu^{+++} structure (completed f shell) and in addition to Yb^{+++} forms Yb^{++}. Gadolinium has one f electron in each of the seven f orbitals and Gd^{+++} is more stable than the $+ 3$ ions of neighboring elements. Hence there is considerable tendency for europium to form Eu^{++} and terbium to form Tb^{+4}. It is interesting to note that the densities of europium and ytterbium (Table I) are out of line with the other rare earth metals and resemble more nearly those of the alkaline earth elements.

4. Compounds of most of the rare earths are highly magnetic (Table I). In completed electron shells, the orientation of the electron orbits appears to be such as to give zero resultant electrical moments, but this is not the case in uncompleted groups. Thus lanthanum ion, La^{+++}, and lutecium ion, Lu^{+++}, are not magnetic; but the transitional elements between are highly so.

TABLE I

PROPERTIES OF SCANDIUM, YTTRIUM, AND THE RARE EARTH
ELEMENTS

ATOMIC NUMBER	NAME	SYMBOL	ATOMIC WEIGHT	DENSITY	MELTING POINT	COLOR OF SALTS	MAGNETIC MOMENT (IN WEISS UNITS OF M^{+++})
21	Scandium	Sc	45.10	(2.5)	1397	Colorless	—
39	Yttrium.......	Y	88.92	5.57	1475	"	—
57	Lanthanum....	La	138.92	6.16	887	"	0
58	Cerium	Ce	140.13	6.80	785	-ic orange -ous colorless	11.4
59	Praseodymium	Pr	140.92	6.8	932	Green	17.8
60	Neodymium...	Nd	144.27	7.0	840	Red	18.0
61	Promethium...	Pm	—	—	—	—	—
62	Samarium.....	Sm	150.43	7.7	1350	Pink	8.0
63	Europium.....	Eu	152.0	5.24		Rose	17.9
64	Gadolinium....	Gd	156.9	7.95	ca. 1100	Colorless	40.0
65	Terbium.......	Tb	159.2	8.33		"	47.1
66	Dysprosium ...	Dy	162.46	8.56		Yellow	52.2
67	Holmium......	Ho	163.5	—		"	52.0
68	Erbium.......	Er	167.2	9.16		Red	47.0
69	Thulium	Tm	169.4	9.34		Green	35.6
70	Ytterbium.....	Yb	173.04	7.01		Colorless	21.9
71	Lutetium......	Lu	175.0	9.74	ca. 1800	"	0

5. Somewhat similar considerations apply to the colors of the rare earth compounds. Ions such as Na^+, Cl^-, La^{+++}, and Lu^{+++}, which contain completed electron groups are colorless; while ions of such as Cr^{+++}, Co^{++}, and most of the rare earths, which belong to transition groups, are generally colored. Characteristic absorption lines of the various elements in solutions of their compounds offer an easy method for their detection. The atomic emission spectra are readily excited in the electric arc.

6. Occurrence.—It is estimated that all the rare earths together constitute only 1.5×10^{-4} per cent of the igneous rocks. The order of decreasing abundance of the members of the group is given as: Ce, Nd, La, Y, Sm, Gd, Pr, Er, Yb, Lu, Dy, Ho, Tm, Tb, Eu, and Pm. It may be observed from this order that the elements of odd atomic numbers are, in general, much less abundant than the even-numbered elements; and that the Yttrium Subgroup is less abundant than the Cerium Subgroup. The approximate percentage of scandium in the igneous rocks is 10^{-7}.

The most important source of the Cerium Subgroup is the mineral **monazite,** which is essentially RPO_4 (where R stands for any rare earth element). A typical composition in per cent is: La_2O_3, 15.6; CeO_2, 28.8; Pr_6O_{11}, 3.6; Nd_2O_3, 11.4; Sm_2O_3, 1.2; terbium earth oxides, 0.8; yttrium earth oxides, 0.32; ThO_2, 6.5; U_3O_8, 0.2; P_2O_5, 28.0; Al_2O_3-SiO_2, 2.5. Brazil and Travancore in India are the principal producers of the mineral, which is generally found in alluvial deposits or sands, where it has concentrated due to the high specific gravity of the particles. A phosphate, **xenotime,** which contains largely yttrium earths, also occurs.

Gadolinite is an yttrium silicate of the approximate formula, $Be_2FeY_2Si_2O_{10}$, and cerite is the cerium group silicate, $H_3[Ca, Fe]Ce_3Si_3O_{10}$. **Yttrocerite** is a rare earth with calcium fluoride, approximately $RF_2 \cdot CaF_2$, which contains about equal quantities of the two subgroups. Columbates and tantalates, such as **fergusonite,** $(R)_2O_3[Cb, Ta]_2O_5$, are found, often associated with thoria, zirconia, and uranates. Mineral carbonates also occur.

PREPARATION AND PROPERTIES OF THE METALS

7. Due to the highly electropositive nature of the rare earths, the metals are difficult to prepare. The most satisfactory method is the electrolytic reduction of the oxide in the molten cloride. Reduction with sodium or magnesium generally gives an alloy.

An alloy of the metals of the cerium group is obtained from the rare earth residues of monazite sand, and is called **Misch metal,** or commercially "cerium." Its approximate composition in per cent is: Ce, 50; La, 25; Nd, 15; other rare earths, 10. It is highly pyrophoric, i.e. gives sparks if scratched, especially if alloyed with iron, and is used extensively for cigar lighters, gas lighters, etc. During the World War, it was used in tracer bullets and luminescent shells.

The metals of the cerium group, except promethium, have been prepared in fairly pure form; but those of the yttrium group have not, as the higher melting points of these metals and the greater volatility of their chlorides render the electrolytic process difficult of operation. The melting points and densities are given in Table I. The lower melting metals are about as soft as tin, but the higher melting ones resemble iron. The cerium metals tarnish readily in moist air and ignite when heated. Cerium has a kindling temperature of 165°, neodymium 270°, and lanthanum 445°. The most important reactions are summarized in Table II.

TABLE II
REACTIONS OF RARE EARTH METALS

$4M + 3O_2 = 2M_2O_3$	
$2M + 6H_2O = 2M(OH)_3 + 3H_2$	Slow in cold
$2M + 3X_2 = 2MX_3$	X denotes halogen
$2M + N_2 = 2MN$	Forms with oxide when M burns in air
$M + 2C = MC_2$	At high temperature
$2M + 3S = M_2S_3$	
$2M + 3H_2 = 2MH_3$	Reaction at comparatively low temperature
$M = M_{(aq)}^{+++} + 3e^-$	La + 2.37

COMPOUNDS

8. (*a*) **The + 3 State.**—Important solubility relations of the cerium and yttrium groups are summarized in Table III.

Lanthanum hydroxide is distinctly basic, and the hydroxides of the yttrium group, while less basic, do not dissolve in excess hydroxide. The sulfides, cyanides, simple sulfates, and halides, except fluorides, are all soluble.

Scandium forms a weaker base than any of the yttrium group, but resembles the cerium family in the slight solubility of the double potassium sulfate. Like aluminum, it forms a complex fluoride ion, ScF_4^-.

TABLE III

PROPERTIES OF RARE EARTH COMPOUNDS

	CERIUM GROUP ELEMENTS 57 TO 62	YTTRIUM GROUP YTTRIUM AND ELEMENTS 63 TO 71
Hydroxides............	Somewhat soluble in water	Slightly soluble in water
Carbonates............	Not soluble in water nor $(NH_4)_2CO_3$ solution	Not soluble in water; soluble in $(NH_4)_2CO_3$ solution
Oxalates..............	Not soluble in water nor $(NH_4)_2C_2O_4$ solution	Not soluble in water; soluble in $(NH_4)_2C_2O_4$ solution
Fluorides.............	Not soluble	Not soluble
Potassium sulfates $K_3R(SO_4)_3$..........	Not soluble in K_2SO_4 solution	Soluble in K_2SO; solution
Nitrates..............	Soluble in water; less soluble in HNO_3	Soluble in water; less soluble in HNO_3, especially $Gd(NO_3)_3$
Basic nitrates.........	Somewhat soluble	Slightly soluble
Double nitrates, e.g., $Mg_3R(NO_3)_{12}\cdot24H_2O$...	Easily crystallized	Not readily crystallized
Phosphates RPO_4.......	Not soluble	Not soluble
Formates.............	Slightly soluble	Moderately soluble

9. (*b*) **The + 4 State.**—Cerium forms a well defined series of + 4 compounds. In this state cerium is very similar to thorium, and the element is often considered as a member of the fourth periodic group.

Cerium dioxide is formed upon igniting cerous oxide. The hydrous oxide may be formed by the oxidation of cerous hydroxide in alkaline solution, or by the action of alkalies upon ceric salts. It is soluble in nitric, sulfuric, and cold hydrochloric acids, giving the corresponding salts in solution. The chloride solution readily evolves chlorine upon heating. The **fluoride,** $CeF_4 \cdot H_2O$, is insoluble in water. It forms complex salts with the alkali fluorides. The **iodate,** $Ce(IO_3)_4$, is slightly soluble, resembling the thorium compound. Ceric ion is a powerful oxidizing agent. An accurate $E°$ value cannot be given as the activities are not known. In $1M$ H_2SO_4 and equal concentration of Ce^{+++} and Ce^{+4} the potential is -1.44 and in nitric and perchloric acids, around -1.6. Ceric sulfate is a valuable volumetric reagent. In most respects it is very similar to permanganate but is not as highly colored so that the end-point must be determined by using either a spot plate reagent or an oxidizable dye.

Praseodymium, neodymium, and terbium all form dioxides (or solid solutions of RO_2 in R_2O_3) but they are even more powerful oxidizing agents than CeO_2 and difficult to prepare pure.

10. The $+2$ State.—Compounds of Eu^{++}, Yb^{++}, and Sm^{++} are known, the potential of the couple, $Eu^{++} = Eu^{+++} + e^-$ is 0.43 and the values for the corresponding couples for ytterbium and samarium appear to be about 0.6 and 0.8 respectively. Thus Eu^{++} is the only one of the ions which does not rapidly liberate hydrogen from water. It is readily prepared by the reduction of Eu^{+++} with zinc. The $+2$ ions resemble Ba^{++} in the solubilities of their salts.

11. Radioactivity.—The samarium isotope Sm^{152} is a naturally occurring α-emitter (half-life 10^{12} years) and Nd^{150} and Lu^{176} are naturally occurring β-emitters with half-lives of 5×10^{10} years and 2.4×10^{10} years respectively. The radioactivity of samarium and neodymium are of interest with respect to the stability of element 61. The claims for the existence of this element (formerly called illinium) in nature have not been substantiated. The first positive identification of an isotope of element 61 was made

TABLE IV

ANALYSIS OF RARE EARTH GROUP

(From Noyes and Bray, *Qualitative Analysis for the Rare Elements*)

Precipitate of fluorides of Sc, ‡In, Th, RE. Extract with acid NH₄F

Residue: RE, In, Th as fluorides Fume with H_2SO_4, add water and NH_4OH, filter out the precipitate, dissolve in $HC_2H_3O_2$, pass in H_2S

- **Precipitate, yellow:** In_2S_3

- **Filtrate: RE, Th, as acetates.** Evaporate, add HNO_3, $KClO_3$, and KIO_3

  - **Precipitate:** $Th(IO_3)_4$, $Ce(IO_3)_4$ Add H_2O_2, HNO_3, and KIO_3

    - **Residue** $Th(IO_3)_4$. Evaporate with HCl, add H_2O_2
      - **Precipitate, white:** $ThO_2 \cdot H_2O_2$
    - **Solution:** $Ce(IO_3)_3$ Add NH_4OH
      - **Precipitate, orange:** $CeO_2H_2O_2$

  - **Filtrate: other RE** Add NH_4OH, filter, dissolve the precipitate in HCl, add K_2CO_3

    - **Precipitate: La, Pr, *Nd, *Sm, *Eu, and Y subgroup,** all as $KRE(CO_3)_2$

      Fuse with $NaNO_3$, extract with water, then with $HC_2H_3O_2$ and $NaC_2H_3O_2$.

      - **Residue, brown:** PrO_2 †La_2O_3 ‡Nd_2O_3
      - **Water extract:** *La †Nd †Sm Add NH_4OH, precipitate with K_2CO_3
        - **Precipitate:** $KLa(CO_3)_2$
        - **Filtrate:** Nd, Sm
      - **Acetate extract:** *Nd *Sm †La ‡Pr Yttrium subgroup

    - **Filtrate: Yttrium subgroup: and †Nd, †Sm, †Eu** as $KRE(CO_3)_2$ Add HCl, then NH_4OH, filter. Dissolve the precipitate in HCl, evaporate, add $HCHO_2$ and NH_4CHO_2.
      - **Precipitate:** Nd, Sm, Eu, ‡Y subgroup
      - **Filtrate:** Yttrium subgroup

Solution: NH_4ScF_4 Fume with H_2SO_4

- **Precipitate:** $Sc_2(SO_4)_3$ Add water and NH_4OH, filter
- **Precipitate:** $Sc(OH)_3$ Dissolve in HCl, evaporate, add one drop of *27 N*-HF
- **Precipitate:** ScF_3 Add acid NH_4F
- **Solution:** NH_4ScF_4

458

* A large part, but not all. † A small fraction. ‡ All of the element when associated with certain other elements.

from the fission products of uranium. The isotope 61^{147} with a half-life of 3.7 years is produced with a fission yield of 2.6 per cent. The operation of a uranium pile at a power of 10^5 kw. will produce about 1.5 grams of the isotope per day. The name promethium from the Greek god "Prometheus," the giver of fire, has now been given to element 61.

12. Separation and Analyses.—A fairly satisfactory method of separating scandium, thorium, and most of the members of the cerium subgroup is outlined in Table IV.

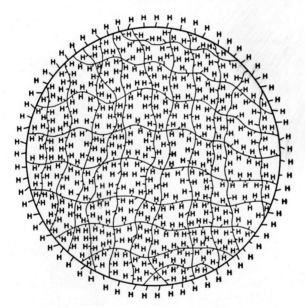

FIG. 1. Schematic representation of cation exchange resin. Picture courtesy Dow Chemical Company.

The complete separation of the neighboring elements of the yttrium rare earth group was formerly accomplished only by repeated fractional crystallization or precipitation. Thus, in the original separation of ytterbium and lutecium, 15,000 crystallizations were made. The separation of neighboring members of the rare earths is now readily effected by mean of the ion-exchange resins (cf. Fig. 1). The process consists essentially of absorbing the mixed rare earths on the top of a long column packed with Amberlite resin. The column is then eluted by pouring through one per cent citric acid solution (in the pH range 5.0–5.5). Under these conditions both the front and rear

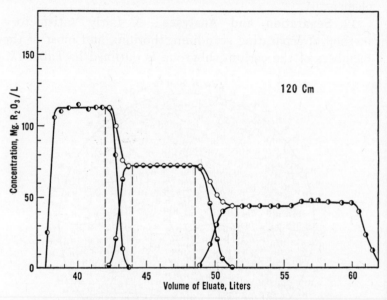

FIG. 2.   Elution curves for sample containing equal weights of Sm_2O_3 ◐; Nd_2O_3 ◖; Pr_6O_{11} ◑.   Picture courtesy Dr. F. H. Spedding.

edges of the elution bond (amount of rare earth eluted per liter plotted against liters of the eluant passed through the column) are steep and the front edge of the one rare earth bond is riding on the rear edge of the proceeding bond as indicated in Fig. 2. The ion-exchange resins have been equally successful in separations of the actinide elements.

The yttrium group is commonly divided into three subgroups, and the members of each subgroup are usually separated as indicated below:

Yttrium *Group*	Terbium Subgroup	{ Eu Gd Tb	Separated by fractional crystallization of double sulfates and ethyl sulfates.
	Erbium Subgroup	{ Dy Ho Er Tm	Separated by fractional crystallization of ethyl sulfates and bromates.
	Ytterbium Subgroup	{ Y Yb Lu	Separated by fractional crystallization of nitrates in nitric acid, bromates, or double ammonium oxalates.

Chapter XXII

THE ACTINIDE ELEMENTS

1. The chemical properties of thorium and protactinium resemble those of hafnium and tantalum respectively, but the properties of uranium and tungsten are markedly different. Thus tungsten is seminoble metal and uranium is highly electropositive. The $+6$ state of tungsten is quite inert and $+6$ uranium is a fair oxidizing agent and the oxide is readily soluble in acids and bases. The lower oxidation states of tungsten are stable only in the form of complex ions which tend to complete the $5d$, $6s$, $6p$ shells such as $W(CN)_8^{-4}$. The $+3$ and $+4$ states of uranium exist in aqueous solution as the simple ions; they do not form highly stable complex ions with cyanide and in general their chemical properties are similar to those of the rare earth elements. With the discovery of the transuranium elements—neptunium, plutonium, americium, curium, berkelium and californium—it became obvious that these elements contained electrons in the $5f$ shell. The point at which the energy of the $5f$ shell drops below that of the $6d$ is somewhat uncertain and may depend upon the physical state of the element and its chemical environment. An interpretation of the spectroscopic data for the gaseous atoms leads to the following electron assignments for the valence electrons, but the distribution in the various shells

89-Ac	90-Th	91-Pa	92-U	93-Np	94-Pu	95-Am	96-Cm	97-Bk
$6d7s^2$	$6d^27s^2$ or $5f6d7s^2$	$5f^26d7s^2$ or $5f6d^27s^2$	$5f^36d7s^2$	$5f^57s^2$ or $5f^46d7s^2$	$5f^67s^2$ or $5f^56d7s^2$	$5f^77s^2$	$5f^76d7s^2$	$5f^86d7s^2$

is doubtless different for the elements as metals. The overall evidence justifies the assumption that the $5f$ series starts with thorium and these elements may be called the "actinides" in the same sense that the rare earths are called "lanthanides."

2. The binding energies of the $5f$ electrons are less than those for the corresponding $4f$ electrons and, as a consequence, the number of electrons which may be removed by oxidation is greater. Thus uranium, neptunium and plutonium all have well defined $+6$ oxidation states. However, as the number of $5f$ electrons increases the stability of the higher oxidation states decreases and the stability of the $+3$ state increases, that is, the elements become increasingly "rare earth" in character. This is evident in the potential values given in Table I.

TABLE I

OXIDATION POTENTIALS IN AQUEOUS SOLUTION VALUES IN
VOLTS FOR EQUAL ION CONCENTRATION

	$X^{+3}-X^{+4}$	$XO_2^+-XO_2^{++}$
Uranium.	$+0.63$	-0.60
Neptunium.	-0.14	-0.94
Plutonium.	-0.95	-1.11
Americium.	ca -2.6	—

A comparison of the various oxidation states for the actinide and lanthanide elements is given in Table II, the values in brackets are for states which exist only as solids, i.e., they are unstable in water solutions.

TABLE II

OXIDATION STATES OF LANTHANIDE AND ACTINIDE ELEMENTS

Atomic No.	57	58	59	60	61	62	63	64	65	66
Element	La	Ce	Pr	Nd	Pm	Sm	Eu	Gd	Tb	Dy
Oxidation						2	2			
States	3	3	3	3	3	3	3	3	3	3
		4	4	(4)					4	
			(5)							

TABLE II (*Cont'd*)

Atomic No.	89	90	91	92	93	94	95	96	97	98
Element	Ac	Th	Pa	U	Np	Pu	Am	Cm	Bk	Cf
Oxidation		(2)		(2)		(2)	(2)			
States	3	(3)	(3)	3	3	3	3	3	3	3
		4	(4)	4	4	4	(4)		4	
			5	5	5	5	(5)			
				6	6	6				

3. Like the rare earths, the elements of this actinide series are colored in those oxidation states in which one or more f electrons are present. In general the absorption bands are sharp as a consequence of the shielding of the f electrons by the other electron shells. The absorption spectra in aqueous solution may be employed for the quantitative and semi-quantitative determination of the elements. As the number of electrons in the f shell increases, there is a contraction of the ionic radii as noted for the rare earth elements. As shown in Table III the ionic radii are only slightly larger than the values for the corresponding rare earth. Because of the similarity of the ionic radii, neighboring elements have compounds with iso-

TABLE III

IONIC RADII OF ACTINIDE AND LANTHANIDE ELEMENTS

NUMBER OF 4f OR 5f ELECTRONS	ACTINIDE SERIES				LANTHANIDES	
	+ 3 STATES		+ 4 STATES			
0	Ac^{+3}	1.11Å	Th^{+4}	0.95Å	La^{+3}	1.04Å
1	(Th^{+3})	(1.08)	Pa^{+4}	0.91	Ce^{+3}	1.02
2	Pa^{+3}	(1.06)	U^{+4}	0.89	Pr^{+3}	1.00
3	U^{+3}	1.04	Np^{+4}	0.88	Nd^{+3}	0.99
4	Np^{+3}	1.02	Pu^{+4}	0.86	Pm^{+3}	(0.98)
5	Pu^{+3}	1.01	Am^{+4}	0.85	Sm^{+3}	0.97
6	Am^{+3}	1.00			Eu^{+3}	0.97

morphous structures and identical crystal types. Examples are: ThF_4, UF_4, NpF_4, PuF_4 and UCl_3, $NpCl_3$, $PuCl_3$, $AmCl_3$.

4. Theoretically, similar lanthanide and actinide ions might be expected to have the same magnetic moments

(cf. **XXI**—4). A comparison is given in Fig. 1. The lower values for the actinide elements appear to be due to the

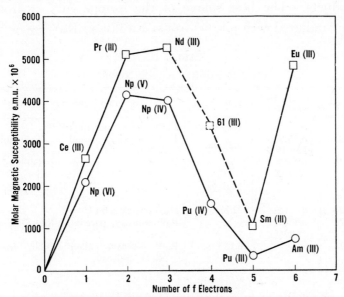

FIG. 1. Plot of molar magnetic susceptibilities of some aqueous actinide and lanthanide ions.

breakdown of the spin vectororbital vector (Russell-Saunders) coupling which occurs in all of the heavier elements.

ACTINIUM

5. Occurrence.—The most stable actinium isotope is the Ac^{227}, half-life 21.7 years. Although it has long been recognized that this isotope always occurs in uranium ores, the origin of the actinium series in U^{235} has only recently been established. The chain is $U^{235} \xrightarrow{\alpha} Th^{231} \xrightarrow{\beta} Pa^{231} \xrightarrow{\alpha} Ac^{227}$.

6. Actinium is separated from uranium ores along with the rare earths, and its isolation from these elements is difficult, especially since its beta radiation is difficult to detect, and its presence cannot easily be determined until sufficient time has elapsed to build up its decomposition products. The best source of the isotope Ac^{227} is from Ra^{226} radiated with pile neutrons: $Ra^{226}(n,\gamma)\ Ra^{227} \xrightarrow{\beta^-} Ac^{227}$.

TABLE IV

ACTINIUM ISOTOPES ATOMIC NUMBER 89

MASS	TYPE OF RADIATION	HALF-LIFE	PRODUCED BY
222	α	very short	Pa^{226} α-decay; parent of Fr^{218}
223	α 99.9% K 0.19%	2.2 min.	Pa^{227} α-decay, parent of Fr^{219} and AcX^{223}
224	α 10% K 90%	2.9 hr.	Pa^{228} α-decay, parent of Fr^{220} and ThX^{224}
225	α	10 days	Ra^{225} β-decay, Th^{225} K-decay, Pa^{229} α-decay, parent of Fr^{221}
226	β^-	22 hrs.	High energy α on U
227	α 1% β^- 99%	21.7 yrs.	Pa^{231} α-decay, parent of $RdAc^{227}$ and AcK^{223}
228	β^-	6.13 hrs.	Ra^{227} β-decay, called $MsTh_2$, from $MsTh_2$ β-decay.

The short life of mesothorium II Ac^{228} leads to its presence only in extremely small quantities in thorium.

7. Chemistry.—Like the rare earths, the potassium complex sulfate, the fluoride, and oxalate are slightly soluble, though the latter dissolves readily in dilute acids. It is not precipitated by hydrogen sulfide. The hydroxide is more basic than lanthanum, is only partially precipitated by ammonium hydroxide, and dissolves readily in ammonium salts.

THORIUM

8. Occurrence.—The most important isotope is Th^{232} (cf. Table V). It is estimated that the igneous rocks contain 12×10^{-6} grams of thorium per gram of rock. **Monazite,** the rare earth phosphate mineral, generally contains 2 to 10 per cent thoria, ThO_2. The deposits of beach sand in Travancore are the principal source of the element. Brazil

ranks second in the production of monazite and there is a
small domestic production from the sands and gravels of
North Carolina, South Carolina and Florida. Other ores
are **thorianite**, a mixed oxide of ThO_2 and U_3O_8, and
thorite, $ThSiO_4$.
Thorium is readily extracted from its ores by digestion
with hydrochloric or sulfuric acids. Ammonia and the
alkalies precipitate the hydroxide, which is not soluble in
excess of the reagent. Thorium and cerium are separated
from the rare earths through the very slight solubilities of
the iodates, $Th(IO_3)_4$ and $Ce(IO_3)_4$, even in rather concentrated acid. Thorium may be separated from cerium by
reduction of the latter to the $+ 3$ state.

TABLE V

THORIUM ISOTOPES. ATOMIC NUMBER 90

MASS	RADIATION	HALF-LIFE	PRODUCED BY
224	α	short	U^{228} α-decay, parent of Ra^{220}
225	α (90%) K (10%)	7.8 min.	U^{229} α-decay, parent of Ra^{221} and Ac^{225}
226	α	30.9 min.	U^{230} α-decay, parent of Ra^{222}
227 (RdAc)	α	18.6 days	Ac^{227} β-decay, parent AcX^{223}
228 (RdTh)	α	1.90 yrs.	$MsTh_2^{228}$ β-decay, parent ThX^{224} U^{232} α-decay, Pa^{228} K-decay
229	α	7000 yrs.	U^{233} α-decay, parent Ra^{225}
230 (Io)	α	8×10^4 yrs.	U_{II}^{234} α-decay, parent of Ra^{226} Pa^{230} K-decay
231 (UY)	$\beta^- e^-$	25.6 hrs.	AcU^{235} α-decay, parent of Pa^{231}. Th-n-2n.
232	α	1.39×10^{10} yrs.	Parent of $MsTh_1^{228}$
233	β^-	23.5 min.	Th-n-γ. Th-d-p.
234 (UX₁)	β^-	24.1 days	U_I^{238} α-decay, parent of UX_2^{234}

9. Thorium Metal.—Because of the highly electropositive character of the element, the metal is extremely difficult to prepare.

$$Th = Th^{+4} + 4e^- \qquad E° = ca\ 2.06$$

However, the reduction may be carried out by heating the
dioxide with calcium in a bomb. The melting point is

1845° C. the boiling point is around 4200° C. and the density 11.2. It may also be prepared by the electrolysis of the fused complex fluorides, K_2ThF_6. The electrical resistivity is given as 10×10^{-6} ohm-cm. The metal is soft and malleable. There are no important uses at present, but the possibility exists of using thorium as an atomic fuel for the production of U^{233} (cf. **XXIII—15**).

10. Chemistry.—Thorium **dioxide,** or **thoria,** appears to possess no acid properties, even when fused with alkali, and in this respect differs from zirconium and hafnium. The unhydrated oxide dissolves but slowly in acids, but the hydrated form, $ThO_2 \cdot 2H_2O$, or thorium **hydroxide,** $Th(OH)_4$, is readily soluble in acids. The hydroxide is formed as a gelatinous precipitate upon the addition of alkali hydroxides or ammonia to thorium salts in solution. Lower oxides have not been prepared, but a hydrated **peroxide** is formed by the action of hydrogen peroxide upon solutions of thorium salts; the formula appears to be $Th_2O_7 \cdot 4H_2O$.

Mixtures of thorium and cerium dioxides, heated to high temperature, exhibit a brilliant white luminescence, the maximum emissibility being obtained with about one per cent of cerium dioxide. Advantage is taken of this fact in the **Welsbach gas mantles,** which are manufactured by saturating fabric with the nitrates of these metals. When ignited, the oxide residue retains the shape of the original fabric. A few per cent of beryllium and magnesium nitrates are usually added to give the ash greater strength. The dioxide is employed in the manufacture of laboratory crucibles to stand temperatures as high as 2300° C.

The **tetrahalides** are prepared by methods characteristic of the group. The **fluoride,** ThF_4, and its hydrate, $ThF_4 \cdot 4H_2O$, are very slightly soluble, as is also the **potassium fluorothorate,** $K_2ThF_6 \cdot 4H_2O$. Various hydrates of the **tetrachloride** may be crystallized from aqueous solution, provided that sufficient acid is present to prevent the precipitation of **basic chlorides.** Halides of lower oxidation states have not been prepared. The **sulfide** may be made by the action of sulfur or hydrogen sulfide upon the heated metal. It is not stable in water solutions. The $+2$ and $+3$ sulfides, ThS and Th_2S_3, may be prepared by reducing ThS_2 with the metal. The former is a silvery semi-metallic substance which has been employed as a ceramic for use with highly electropositive metals. The anhydrous **sulfate** is very hygroscopic and forms hydrates containing 9, 8, 6, 4, and 2 moles of water. The nitrate, $Th(NO_3)_4 \cdot 12H_2O$, may be crystallized from concentrated acid solutions, and the phosphate, $Th_3(PO_4)_4 \cdot 4H_2O$, is formed as a gelatinous precipitate by adding sodium phosphate to a solution of a thorium salt. Both the nitrate and phosphate form many double salts, e.g., $KTh(NO_3)_5 \cdot 9H_2O$ and $NaTh_2(PO_4)_3$. Normal thorium carbonate has not been prepared, but a number of **basic carbonates** and **complex carbonates** are known, e.g., $ThOCO_3 \cdot 2H_2O$ and $(NH_4)_2Th(CO_3)_3 6H_2O$. The basic carbonates are soluble in excess ammonium carbonate, probably with the formation of complex carbonate. The **iodate**, $Th(IO_3)_4$, is but slightly soluble and resembles the corresponding ceric compound.

In gravimetric analysis, thorium is usually precipitated as the hydroxide and weighed as the dioxide. The element may be determined volumetrically by precipitation of the normal molybdate, followed by solution of compound in acid, the reduction of this molybdate in a Jones Reductor and the titration of the molybdenum from the $+3$ to the $+6$ state.

PROTACTINIUM

11. Occurrence.—As indicated in Table VI, the most stable isotope is Pa^{231}, which is a product of the chain, $U^{235} \xrightarrow{\alpha} Th^{231}(UY) \xrightarrow{\beta^-} Pa^{231}$. Since its half-life is 3.4×10^4 years, the steady state amount of the isotope is small (about 7×10^{-8} gram per gram of U).

TABLE VI

PROTACTINIUM ISOTOPES. ATOMIC NUMBER 91

MASS	RADIATION	HALF-LIFE	PRODUCED BY
226	α	1.7 min.	Th-d-8n, parent of Ac^{222}
227	α (80%) K (20%)	38 min.	Np^{231} α-decay, parent of Ac^{223} and $RdAc^{227}$
228	α (2%) K (98%)	22 hrs.	Th-d-6n, parent of Ac^{224} and $RdTh^{228}$
229	α (1%) K (99%)	1.5 days	Th^{230}-d-3n, parent Ac^{225}
230	β^-	17.7 days	Th^{230}-d-2n, parent U^{230}
231	α	3.4×10^4 yrs.	UY^{231} β-decay, parent Ac^{227}
232	β^-	1.3 days	Th^{232}-d-2n
233	$\beta^- e^-$	27.4 days	Th^{233} β-decay, parent U^{233}
234 (UZ^{234})	β^-	6.7 hrs.	UX_2^{234m} Isomeric transition parent of U_2^{234}
234 (UX_2^{234m})	β^- (99.85%) IT (0.15%)	1.14 min.	UX_1^{234} β-decay, parent of UZ^{234} and U_2^{234}

12. Chemistry.—Protactinium resembles tantalum in the generally inert character of the + 5 oxidation state. The pentoxide, Pa_2O_5, is somewhat more basic than the corresponding tantalum oxide and the freshly precipitated oxide dissolves in sulfuric acid, probably with the formation of PaO_2^+. The element may be precipitated from the acid solution as a slightly soluble peroxyacid and as the phosphate. The pentachloride may be prepared by the reaction, $Pa_2O_5 + 5COCl_2 = 2PaCl_5 + 5CO_2$. The optimum temperature for the reaction is around 500° C. A few milligrams of the metal have been prepared by the decomposition of the chloride on a heated tungsten filament. The metal is not readily oxidized by air. The oxide dissolves readily in HF and the fluoride resembles TaF_5. Salt, such as K_2PaF_7, may be crystallized from a solution in excess of KF.

The very unstable uranium X_2, Pa^{234m}, also called brevium, may be separated from its parent element, uranium X_1, by taking advantage of the difference in properties of thorium and tantalum. Thus, the mixture treated with hydrogen fluoride forms the slightly soluble

UX_1F_4, while the uranium X_2 goes into solution, doubtless as the complex fluoride. Uranium Z is formed from UX_2 by an isomeric transition.

URANIUM

13. Occurrence.—The average abundance of uranium in the igneous rocks is given as 4×10^{-6} gram of U per gram of rock, and in the earth's crust, as 0.0004 per cent. It is estimated that the earth's crust to a depth of 20 kilometers contains approximately 1.3×10^{14} tons of uranium. The principal ore is **pitchblende** or **uranite**, U_3O_8, which is frequently associated with the rare earth oxides. Other ores are **carnotite**, $K_2O \cdot 2UO_3 \cdot V_2O_5 \cdot nH_2O$, calcium carnotite, $CaO \cdot 2UO_3 \cdot V_2O_5 \cdot nH_2O$, and autunite $Ca(UO_2)_2(PO_4)_2 \cdot 8H_2O$. Extensive deposits of uranite occur at Great Bear Lake, Canada, and in the Belgian Congo. Fairly extensive deposits of low grade carnotite are found in Colorado, Utah and Arizona. Most oil shales and calcium phosphate rocks run a few thousandth of a per cent of uranium. In view of the very great tonnage of such deposits, they constitute a

TABLE VII

URANIUM ISOTOPES. ATOMIC NUMBER 92

MASS	RADIATION	HALF-LIFE	PRODUCED BY
228	α (80%) K (20%)	9.3 min.	Pu^{232} α-decay, parent of Th^{234}
229	α (20%) K (80%)	58 min.	Th^{232}-α-7n, parent of Th^{225}
230	α	20.8 days	Pa^{230} β-decay, parent of Th^{226}
231	K	4.2 days	Pa-d-2n
232	α	70 yrs.	Pu^{236} α-decay, parent of $RdTh^{228}$
233	α	1.62×10^5 yrs.	Pa^{233} β-decay, parent of Th^{229}
234 (U_{II})	α	2.35×10^5 yrs.	UZ^{234} β-decay, parent of Th^{230}. Natural U 0.0051%
235 (AcU)	α	8.91×10^8 yrs.	Natural U 0.71%, parent of Th^{231}
237	$\beta^- e^-$	6.8 days	Pu^{241} α-decay, parent of Np^{237}
238	α	4.51×10^9 yrs.	Natural U 99.28%, parent of Th^{234}
239	$\beta^- e^-$	23.5 min.	U-n-γ, parent of Np^{239}

high potential source of the element. Uranium is frequently associated with gold and silver ores and the residues from smelters are another extensive source of low grade uranium ores.

As may be noted in Table VII the long lived isotopes of uranium have the mass numbers 238, 235, and 234.

14. Metallurgy.—Pitchblende, U_3O_8, may be roasted in with alkali carbonate in air or with nitrate to convert the oxide to uranate. The ore may then be treated with sulfuric or nitric acid to leach out the uranium as the uranyl salt. Purification of impure uranyl nitrate is accomplished by extraction of the salt from a nitric acid solution into ether. The metal is prepared by the electrolysis of fused potassium uranium fluoride or by the reduction of the dioxide, chloride or fluoride, by calcium or magnesium in a bomb. With most reducing agents it is necessary to preheat the bomb to obtain the metal as a massive product. The *melting point* of the metal is 1130° C., the *boiling point* is 3500° C., and the *density*, 19.05 (α form). The metal is slightly more electropositive than aluminum. The more important reactions of the metal are summarized in Table VIII.

TABLE VIII
REACTIONS OF URANIUM

$U + 3/2H_2 = UH_3$	Rapid at 250° C.
$U + C = UC$	Rapid at 800–1200° C., also forms UC_2
$U + 2Si = USi_2$	Also forms U_5Si, USi, U_2Si_3, and USi_3
$U + 2B = UB_2$	Also forms UB_4
$U + 1/2N_2 = UN$	Rapid at 1300° C., also forms U_2N_3 **and** UN_2
$3U + 4P = U_3P_4$	
$U + O_2 = UO_2$	Rapid at 700–1000° C.
$U + S = US_2$	Also forms U_2S_3
$U + 2F_2 = UF_4$	Also forms UF_5 and UF_6
$U + 2Cl_2 = UCl_4$	Also forms UCl_5 and UCl_6
$U + 2Br_2 = UBr_4$	
$U + 3/2I_2 = UI_3$	Also forms UI_4
$U + 2H_2O = UO_2 + 2H_2$	Slowly with boiling water
$U + 4HCl = UCl_4 + 2H_2$	Rapid with conc. acid
$U + 2H_2SO_4 = U(SO_4)_2 + 2H_2$	Very slow with conc. acid
$U + UO_2 = 2UO$	At 2400° C.

The only important use of the metal is in the nuclear reactors. The 235 isotope which is present in ordinary uranium to the extent of 0.71 per cent is the only naturally occurring isotope fissionable (cf. **XXIII**) with slow neutrons.

15. Oxidation States.—Compounds of $+ 2$, $+ 3$, $+ 4$, $+ 5$ and $+ 6$ oxidation states are known. The $+ 2$ state is highly unstable and few compounds such as US and UO are known. Compounds of the $+ 3$ state, as, for example, UF_3 and UI_3, are stable as solids but U^{+3} reduces water with the evolution of H_2. The ions U^{+4} and UO_2^{++} are stable in aqueous solution but the ion of the $+ 5$ state, UO_2^+, disproportionates into U^{+4} and UO_2^{++}. The following potential diagram summarizes the energy relationship in $1M$ acid solution:

$$
\begin{array}{ccccc}
& 1.85 & 0.61 & -0.62 & -0.05 \\
U & \!\!\!\!\!\!\!\!-\!\!-\!\!-\!\!-\!\!- U^{+3} & \!\!\!\!-\!\!-\!\!-\!\!-\!\!- U^{+4} & \!\!\!\!-\!\!-\!\!-\!\!-\!\!- UO_2^+ & \!\!\!\!-\!\!-\!\!-\!\!-\!\!- UO_2^{++} \\
& & | & & | \\
& & & -0.334 &
\end{array}
$$

16. The $+ 3$ Compounds.—U^{+3} resembles the rare earth ions except for its strong reducing action. The halides UF_3, UCl_3, UBr_3 and UI_3 have been prepared.

17. The $+ 4$ Compounds.—The **hydrated oxide,** $UO_2 \cdot 2H_2O$, precipitates when an alkali is added to a uranous solution. The anhydrous oxide may be formed by heating the hydrate, or by reduction of the uranous uranic oxide, U_3O_8, with hydrogen. This oxide is soluble in strong acids forming green solutions of uranous ion. UO_2 forms series of solid solutions with both UO and UO_3. The **tetrafluoride,** UF_4, may be precipitated from uranous solution by fluoride ion. The other tetrahalides are soluble, however, and the anhydrous chloride may be prepared along with some of the pentachloride by the action of chlorine upon the metal, or CCl_4 upon U_3O_8. The **sulfide,** US_2, forms when the elements are heated together around 500° C. It is also formed by passing H_2S over UCl_4. The **oxysulfide,** UOS, may be prepared by the reaction $UO_2 + H_2S = UOS + H_2O$.

18. The + 6 Compounds.—When uranium ores are extracted with a sulfuric nitric acid mixture, the oxide, U_3O_8, is dissolved to form a yellow solution containing **uranyl ion, UO_2^{++}.** The **trioxide, UO_3,** is difficult to prepare from this solution, as alkalies precipitate alkali uranate. It may, however, be prepared by the decomposition of uranyl nitrate. Upon heating, it forms U_3O_8, and possibly at higher temperatures, U_2O_5. The uranyl ion forms slightly soluble compounds with phosphates, $UO_2HPO_4 \cdot 4H_2O$, $UO_2NH_4PO_4$; arsenates, $(UO_2)_3(AsO_4)_2$; sulfites, $UO_2SO_3 \cdot 4H_2O$; complex alkali fluorides, $K_3UO_2F_2$; and sulfide, UO_2S. The sulfide is soluble in acid and in ammonium carbonate solution. Uranyl halides, acetate, sulfate, and nitrate are soluble.

Uranyl salts show remarkable fluorescence, and are also subject to photochemical reduction by many organic compounds; for example, uranyl sulfate in sulfuric acid solution is reduced by alcohol in the sunlight to uranous sulfate.

The more common **uranates** are di-uranates, e.g., $K_2U_2O_7$. They are not soluble in water, and precipitate when KOH is added to a UO_2^{++}. The sodium salt, known as uranium yellow, is used in the manufacture of fluorescent uranium glass, and also as a porcelain pigment. The uranates are somewhat soluble in excess carbonate with the formation of **carbonate complex** ions such as $UO_2(CO_3)_2^{--}$.

Hydrogen peroxide forms, with uranyl nitrate solution, a precipitate of the **peroxide, $UO_6 \cdot 2H_2O$;** and alkali peroxides form peroxy-uranates, e.g., $Na_2UO_2 \cdot 4H_2O$.

The **hexafluoride, UF_6,** may be prepared by the action of fluorine upon the tetrafluoride. The **pentafluoride** is formed as an intermediate in the reaction, and the pressure of the volatile UF_6 in equilibrium with the UF_4 and UF_5 is 66mm at 215° C. The hexafluoride is used in the gas-diffusion process for the separation of U^{235} from U^{238}. The fluorides U_2F_9 and U_4F_{17} are also known. The former is remarkable in that the crystal structure data show all of the uranium atoms to be equivalent. The **hexachloride** has been prepared but the bromide and iodide appear to be unstable.

19. Analytical.—The uranyl ion gives a deep red precipitate with **ferrocyanide**, $K_2UO_2Fe(CN)_6$. It may also be precipitated as $NH_4UO_2PO_4$. The green fluorescence of UO_2^{++} in ultraviolet light may be employed for the quantitative estimations of small concentration of the ion. The orange-red color of uranyl ion with sodium cresotate may also be used for colorimetric determinations.

NEPTUNIUM

20. Isotopes.—Neptunium (isotope 239) was the first transuranium element to be discovered (1940). This isotope is the decay product of U^{239} formed by neutron capture in U^{238}. It is highly important as the intermediate step in the production of Pu^{239} from U^{238} as carried out in the Hanford Plant, but because of its short life, it is not suitable for extensive studies on the chemistry of the element. However, Np^{237} has a half-life of 2.2×10^6 years and this isotope is available in weighable amounts through its production in the uranium-plutonium chain-reacting units, by the reaction of fast neutrons on U^{238} to form U^{237} (n, 2n reaction). U^{237} thus forms Np^{237} by β^- decay.

TABLE IX

NEPTUNIUM ISOTOPES. ATOMIC NUMBER 93

MASS	RADIATION	HALF-LIFE	PRODUCED BY
231	α	53 min.	U^{238}-d-9n, parent of Pu^{237}
234	K	4.4 days	U^{233}-d-n
235	K (99%) α (1%)	435 days	U^{235}-d-2n
236	β^-	22 hrs.	U^{235}-d-n, parent of Pu^{236}
237	α	2.2×10^6 yrs.	U^{237} β-decay, parent of Pa^{233}
238	β^-	2.1 days	Am^{242} α-decay, parent of Pu^{238}
239	$\beta^- e^-$	2.33 days	U^{239} β-decay, parent of Pu^{239}

21. Chemistry.—The oxidation states $+3$, $+4$, $+5$ and $+6$ are stable in aqueous solutions. The following

potential diagram summarizes the energy relations in
$1M$ HCl. The values are the formal potentials for molal
concentrations of the oxidized and reduced forms of the ions.

$$
\begin{array}{c}
\overbrace{}^{-\,0.44} \\
\text{Np}\xrightarrow{\;1.86\;}\text{Np}^{+3}\xrightarrow{\;-\,0.14\;}\text{Np}^{+4}\xrightarrow{\;-\,0.74\;}\text{NpO}_2{}^{+}\xrightarrow{\;-\,1.14\;}\text{NpO}_2{}^{++} \\
\underbrace{}_{-\,0.94} \\
\underbrace{}_{-\,0.67}
\end{array}
$$

As indicated in this diagram, the metal is highly electropositive and is readily oxidized to the $+ 3$ state. The
Np^{+3}—Np^{+4} couple is reversible and Np^{+3} is rapidly
oxidized to Np^{+4} by oxygen of the air. The $+ 4$ state is
stable and not readily oxidized by air. It is slowly oxidized
to $NpO_2{}^+$ by nitric acid. The Np^{+4}—$NpO_2{}^+$ couple is not
readily reversible since it involves breaking the Np-O bonds
but the $NpO_2{}^+$—$NpO_2{}^{++}$ couple which involves only the
transfer of a single electron is reversible. The oxidation of
neptunol, $NpO_2{}^+$, to neptunyl, $NpO_2{}^{++}$ requires a strong
oxidizing agent. The neptunyl ion in acid is easily reduced
to the $+ 5$ state. In spite of the unfavorable potential the
reduction by HCl on platinum proceeds slowly at room
temperature with the evolution of volatile Cl_2. This
reaction is rapid in hot solutions.

The $+ 3$ ion has a pale purple color and in the solubility
of its salts closely resembles La^{+++}. The chemistry of
Np^{+4} is similar to Th^{+4} in most of the solubility relationships.
The readily precipitated $Np(OH)_4$ has an olive green color.
NpF_4 is slightly soluble and K_2NpF_6 may be precipitated
from a solution of KF and HF. All of the simple salts of
$NpO_2{}^+$ appear to be soluble. The solubilities of the
neptunyl salts are similar to those of uranyl salts.

PLUTONIUM

22. Isotopes.—McMillan and Abelson in 1940 identified
Np^{239} as the product of β decay of U^{239} which had been
produced from U^{238} by a neutron capture. They estab-

lished the 2–3 day half-life by β^- decay but were unable to isolate the expected α-activity of the product isotope 94^{239}. McMillan then bombarded uranium with deuterons hoping to produce another isotope of element 94 with a shorter half-life, and found definite evidence of alpha-activity. This investigation was continued by Wahl working with Seaborg and Kennedy, and the alpha-emitting isotope of element 94, produced by deuteron bombardment, was isolated and its chemistry studied. The new element was named plutonium after Pluto, the second planet beyond Uranus. The first isotope isolated proved to be Pu^{238} and from the knowledge gained by a study of its chemistry, the isotope Pu^{239} was isolated early in 1941. The tremendous importance of this isotope lies in its property of fission with slow neutrons and its ease of production in the carbon-uranium chain reacting pile (cf. **XXIII—16**). Pu^{239}, the longest lived plutonium isotope, has a half-life of only 24,000 years. It does not occur in nature except as a trace (about one part in 10^{14}) in pitchblende where it is continuously formed as the result of the absorption of neutrons (mostly from the spontaneous fission of U^{235}) by uranium 238.

TABLE X

PLUTONIUM ISOTOPES. ATOMIC NUMBER 94

MASS	RADIATION	HALF-LIFE	PRODUCED BY
232	α	22 min.	U^{235}-α-7n, parent of U^{228}
234	α, K	8 hrs.	U^{238}-α-3n
236	α	2.7 yrs.	Np^{236} β-decay, Cm^{240} α-decay, parent of U^{232}
237	K	40	U^{235}-α-2n
238	α	92 yrs.	Np^{238} β-decay, Cm^{242} α-decay
239	αe^-	2.411 × 10^4 yrs.	Np^{239} β-decay
240	α	ca 6000 yrs.	U^{238}-α-2n
241	β^-, α (0.002%)	ca 10 yrs.	U^{238}-α-n, parent of Am^{241} and U^{237}

23. Chemistry.—Plutonium forms compounds in the oxidation states + 3, + 4, + 5, and + 6. A semi-metallic

+ 2 oxide, PuO, is known but this oxidation state is highly unstable. The following potential diagram summarizes the oxidation-reduction potentials for the various couples. The values are for one molal solution of the ions in $1M$ $HClO_4$.

$$\text{Pu}\underset{2.06}{\underline{\hspace{2cm}}}\text{Pu}^{+3}\underset{-0.98}{\underline{\hspace{2cm}}}\text{Pu}^{+4}\underset{-1.12}{\underline{\hspace{2cm}}}\text{PuO}_2^{+}\underset{-0.93}{\underline{\hspace{2cm}}}\text{PuO}_2^{++}$$
$$\underset{-1.02}{\underline{\hspace{5cm}}}$$

From these potentials, it is evident that plutonium resembles uranium in the highly electropositive character of the metal. With respect to the positive oxidation states, it is most remarkable that the energies of the three couples are so nearly the same. As a consequence, it is possible to have solutions which contain appreciable concentration of all four oxidation states in equilibrium. In fact, it is impossible to prepare solutions of Pu^{+4} and PuO_2^{+} which do not contain some of the disproportionation products. The + 5 state is somewhat unstable with respect to the following reaction, which is favored by a high concentration of H^+: $2PuO_2^{+} + 4H^+ = Pu^{+4} + PuO_2^{++} + 2H_2O$ (1). The mechanism of the reaction appears to be the slow reaction: $PuO_2^{+} + Pu^{+3} + 4H^+ = 2Pu^{+4} + 2H_2O$ (2) coupled with the rapid equilibrium: $PuO_2^{+} + Pu^{+4} = PuO_2^{++} + Pu^{+++}$ $K = 8.5$ (3). The disproportionation of Pu^{+4} is the reverse of reaction (2), and the equilibrium constant

$$\frac{(Pu^{+4})^2}{(Pu^{+3})(PuO_2^{+})}$$

for the reaction in $0.5M$ hydrochloric acid is 170 at 25° C.

The direct reduction of + 6 plutonium to the + 5 state by reducing agents such as hydrogen peroxide, hydroxylamine, nitrous acid, silver and sulfur dioxides is fast while the reduction of the + 5 to the + 4 state is slow. In fact, the second step is generally slower than the disproportionation reaction (1). Likewise the oxidation of Pu^{+4} by many

oxidizing agents appears to proceed through the disproportionation reaction.

24. The + 3 State.—The hydroxide, fluoride, oxalate,
phosphate and carbonate are slightly soluble. However,
the hydroxide is distinctly basic and the ion is not highly
hydroxized. Pu^{+3} in aqueous solutions has a purple violet
color.

25. The + 4 State.—Pu^{+4} has a green color and resembles Th^{+4} with respect to the solubilities of its salts, the
more important slightly soluble compounds being: the
fluoride, PuF_4, the potassium **complex fluoride**, K_2PuF_6,
the **iodate**, $Pu(IO_3)_4$, the **phosphate**, $Pu_3(PO_4)_2$ and the
basic carbonate. Hydrogen peroxide reduces Pu^{+4} to
Pu^{+3} and simultaneously oxidizes Pu^{+3} in the reverse
reaction. In sulfuric acid the steady state favors Pu^{+4}
and the + 4 ion is complexed by hydrogen peroxide with
the formation first of a brown complex containing two
plutonium atoms and one peroxide and, at higher peroxide
concentrations, a red complex with two plutonium atoms
and two peroxides, possibly HO-Pu-O-OPu-OOH. At still
higher concentration of hydrogen peroxide, a slightly
soluble plutonium **peroxide** is formed, whose composition
depends upon the negative ion present. The + 4
hydroxide is not soluble in excess of OH^-. The
tetrachloride is unstable with respect to the reaction
$2PuCl_4 = 2PuCl_3 + Cl_2$.

26. The + 5 State.—As discussed in Par. 24, PuO_2^+ is
unstable at high concentration of H^+. The simple salts
of the ion are all soluble.

27. The + 6 State.—PuO_2^{++} in acid solution is a much
stronger oxidizing agent than UO_2^{++}. In most other
respects the chemistry of the two ions is similar. The
addition of soluble hydroxides precipitates slightly soluble
plutonates. The solubility of barium plutonate is much
less than that of sodium plutonate. The latter salt is
fairly soluble in sodium carbonate solutions. The more

important slightly soluble salts of plutonyl ion are the **phosphate, arsenate** and double sodium **acetate** $NaPuO_2(CH_3CO_2)_3$.

AMERICIUM

28. Isotopes.—The bombardment of U^{238} by high energy α particles (accelerated in a cyclotron) produces Pu^{241} by the capture of the α particle and the emission of a neutron. The Pu^{241} gives Am^{241} by β decay. $U^{238}(\alpha, n)Pu^{241}$. $Pu^{241} \xrightarrow{\beta^-} Am^{241}$. The Am^{241} has a half-life of about 500 years and is the most stable of the six isotopes which are now known.

TABLE XI

AMERICIUM ISOTOPES. ATOMIC NUMBER 95

MASS	RADIATION	HALF-LIFE	PRODUCED BY
238	K (?)	1.5 hrs.	Pu^{239}-d-3n
239	K (99.9%), e^-, α 0.1%	12 hrs.	Pu^{239}-d-2n, Pu^{239}-p-n
240	K, e^-	53 hrs.	Pu^{239}-d-n
241	α	490 yrs.	Pu^{241} β-decay
242^m	β^-	16 hrs.	Am^{241}-n-γ, parent of Cm^{242}
242	α 0.2%, β	ca 400 yrs.	Am^{241}-n-γ, parent of Cm^{242} and Np^{238}

29. Chemistry.—The $+3$ oxidation state is highly stable in aqueous solution and is extremely difficult to oxidize or reduce. The color of the Am^{+3} is pink. There is some evidence for the existence of the $+2$ state, as tracer amounts of americium have been reduced by sodium amalgam and precipitated with $BaSO_4$ as a carrier. In this respect americium appears to resemble europium, its homologue in the rare earth group. The hydroxide $Am(OH)_3$ has been oxidized by hypochlorite in 40 per cent K_2CO_3 solution. The product (yellow in color) is soluble in the carbonate and is probably in the $+5$ state. The slightly soluble $+4$ hydroxide is doubtless formed as an intermediate in this oxidation. Very powerful oxidizing agents appear to form AmO_2^{++} in acid solution. Both the

+ 4 and + 6 states are unstable in acid solution with respect to the evolution of oxygen. The potentials of the IV—V and the V—VI couples are probably about − 1.3 and − 1.6 respectively in acid solution. All of the + 3 halides are known and when the fluoride AmF_3 is treated with F_2, there is no oxidation. The chemistry of Am^{+++} resembles Eu^{+++} with respect to the solubilities of its salts in water.

CURIUM

30. Isotopes.—The curium isotopes are summarized in Table XII. Cm^{242} has a half-life of only about five months. It is made by α bombardment of Pu^{239}, (α, n) reaction, and by the action of neutrons on americium. Am^{241} absorbs a neutron to form the short-lived (18 hours) Am^{242} which

TABLE XII

CURIUM ISOTOPES. ATOMIC NUMBER 96

MASS	RADIATION	HALF-LIFE	PRODUCED BY
238	α	*ca* 2.5 hrs.	Pu^{239}-α-5n
240	α	26.8 days	Pu^{239}-α-3n. Parent of Pu^{236}
241	K	55 days	Pu^{239}-α-2n
242	α	150 days	Pu^{239}-α-n. Am^{242} and Am^{242m}
			β-decay. Parent of Pu^{238}
244	α	2 yrs.	Am^{244}-α-p

gives Cm^{242} by β decay. In the short nuclear notation: $Am^{241}(n, \gamma)Am^{242} \cdot Am^{242} \xrightarrow{\beta^-} Cm^{242}$. Weighable amounts of curium have been prepared by the second method. The longest lived isotope, Cm^{241}, has not been prepared except in tracer amounts.

31. Chemistry.—Experiments with tracer amounts and also with milligram quantities of curium, all seem to indicate that only + 3 oxidation state is stable in aqueous solutions. Cm^{+3} appear to resemble the + 3 ions of the rare earths with respect to the solubilities of its salts. One milligram of curium gives eight thousand billion (8×10^{12}) α particles per minute. Because of the enormous energy liberated by this α radiation, studies on the chemistry of curium, except in tracer amounts, must be made by remote-control methods. In a water solution the α particles produce a tremendous number of electrons and positive ions, and in the recombination process, considerable energy is liberated in the visible region of the spectrum. This phenomenon is shown in Fig. 2.

FIG. 2. Photograph of a curium solution in glass tube, taken by its own light. Picture courtesy Dr. G. T. Seaborg.

BERKELIUM

32. An isotope of element number 97, berkelium, has been made by bombarding Am^{241} with alpha-particles. The reaction $(\alpha, 2n)$ forms Bk^{243}. The new element is an alpha-emitter with a half-life of 5 hours. The chemistry, as determined only with tracer amounts, appears to resemble that of curium but differs in that it is possible to oxidize berkelium to the $+ 4$ state in aqueous solutions (Bk^{+3}–Bk^{+4} $ca -1.4$ volts). This increased stability of the $+ 4$ state is in line with the similar situation which exists with respect to gadolinium and terbium and seems to indicate that curium has the $5f^7$ electron structure.·

CALIFORNIUM

33. The isotope, mass number 244 and atomic number 98, has been made by bombarding Cm^{242} with high energy alpha-particles.

$$Cm^{242} + \alpha = Cf^{244} + 2n$$

This isotope is an α-emitter ($E = 7.1$ Mev) and has a half-life of 44 minutes. The separation of the newly formed element from the highly active target material is

extremely difficult, but was accomplished by placing the
sample, as hydroxide, on an ion-exchange column and
eluting with ammonium citrate solution. The elution
process gave a clean-cut separation. Because of the short
half-life and small quantities prepared, a detailed study of
the chemistry of the element is not easy, but the elution
curves indicate that in the + 3 state it resembles
dysprosium.

Chapter XXIII

NUCLEAR REACTIONS

1. The Atomic Nucleus.—The ordinary chemistry of the elements is concerned almost entirely with those atomic properties which depend upon the valence electrons, and the only significance of the atomic nucleus is its positive charge which determines the number of orbital electrons or the atomic number. In this chapter a brief discussion will be given of the properties of the nucleus and their relation to transmutation reactions.

The radius of the nucleus increases from about 2×10^{-13} cm. for helium to about 8×10^{-13} cm. for uranium. The relation of volume to mass is that which would be expected for the close packing of some fundamental mass particle. Moreover, it was early observed that the atomic weights of the lighter elements, Table I, with oxygen taken as 16, were very close to whole numbers which suggested that the nucleus was an aggregate of particles. The assumption was first made that the nucleus was a condensed system of **protons** (hydrogen nuclei) and electrons. However, the discovery of the **neutron** (Par. **17**) with approximately the mass of the protons and zero charge, has led to the more reasonable assumption that the nucleus consists of a close packing of protons and neutrons. Thus the $_8O^{16}$ nucleus may be thought of as eight protons and eight neutrons: the mass number is thus 16 and the total positive charge or atomic number is 8. The decrease in mass ($8 \times 0.0089 + 8 \times 0.0081 = 0.1360$) represents the binding energy of the nuclear particles. Since 1 gram equals 9×10^{20} ergs or 9.311×10^8 electron volts, this binding energy in $_8O^{16}$ is 128 million electron volts. The reason that so many isotopes have atomic weights which are close to whole numbers arises through the fact that the mass contraction in the formation of the oxygen nucleus is an excellent mean value for a large number of elements.

TABLE I

ATOMIC MASSES OF THE LIGHTER ELEMENTS

(These values are for $O^{16} = 16$ instead of the chemial atomic weights which take the mixed oxygen isotopes $= 16$. The latter are obtained by dividing by 1,00023.)

NUCLEUS	ATOMIC MASS	NUCLEUS	ATOMIC MASS
$_0n^1$	1.0089	$_6C^{12}$	12.0036
		$_6C^{13}$	13.0073
$_1H^1$	1.0081		
$_1H^2$	2.0147	$_7N^{14}$	14.0073
$_1H^3$	3.0171	$_7N^{15}$	15.0048
$_2He^3$	3.0171	$_8O^{16}$	16.000
$_2He^4$	4.0039	$_8O^{17}$	17.0046
		$_8O^{18}$	18.0056
$_3Li^6$	6.0167		
$_3Li^7$	7.0180	$_9F^{19}$	19.0045
$_4Be^8$	8.0078	$_{10}Ne^{20}$	19.9986
$_4Be^9$	9.0149		
$_4Be^{10}$	10.0164	$_{13}Al^{27}$	26.9909
$_5B^{10}$	10.0161	$_{14}Si^{28}$	27.9860
$_5B^{11}$	11.0128	$_{14}Si^{29}$	28.9864

2. Radioactivity.—For a given atomic number there is a limited range of the neutron to proton ratio for which the nuclei are stable. This range is greater for the elements of even atomic number than for those of odd and as a result the even atomic numbers have a larger number of isotopes. If the ratio is outside the stable range, nuclear reactions or radioactivity result. Thus if there is too large an excess of neutrons, electron emission or **beta-radiation** occurs. It is not necessary to think of the electron as existing in the nucleus but rather that it is created by the conversion of a neutron into a proton, i.e., neutron equals proton plus electron. The loss of a beta-particle increases the atomic number by one and thus displaces the product to a periodic group one higher than the parent element. The free neutron is a beta-emitter and its half-life is the order of 20 minutes.

$$_0n^1 = \text{proton} + \text{electron} = {}_1H^1$$

If there is too large an excess of protons, a number of reactions may occur. With the heavier elements, an **alpha-particle** is emitted. This particle is the helium $(_2He^4)$ nucleus. Since it has a charge of $+2$ the resulting atom occupies a position in the periodic system two groups

TABLE II

FUNDAMENTAL PARTICLES

	MASS, ATOMIC WEIGHT UNITS $O^{16} = 16$	CHARGE
Neutron	1.0089	0
Proton	1.0076	$(4.80 \times 10^{-16}\text{ esu}) + 1$
Electron	0.00055	-1
Positron	0.00055	$+1$
π meson	0.151	$0 + 1$ and -1
μ meson	0.116	$+1$ and -1
Neutrino	Very small	0

lower than the parent. The alpha-particle is remarkably stable and in general the more abundant isotopes have mass numbers which are multiples of four, so it appears that the group of two protons and two neutrons must have some significance in the nuclear structure. Alpha-radioactivity often occurs with enormous energy, thus the α-particle from thorium C' has an energy of 10.5 million e.v.

Another process which decreases the positive charge on the nucleus is the emission of a **positron**. This process is not known in the naturally occurring radioactive elements but frequently is observed in isotopes produced by bombardment (cf. Par. **18**). The positron appears to be identical with the electron except for the opposite sign of the charge. The failure to observe the particle until recently was due to its short life in the presence of electrons; one positron and one electron react to form two photons or high energy (0.51 Mev) light rays with their mutual annihilation. This process is reversible and the creation of a

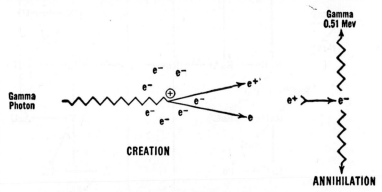

FIG. 1. Creation and annihilation of electron pairs.

positron-electron pair from a high energy photon may occur when a photon with energy in excess of one Mev enters the high positive field near an atomic nucleus. The probability of pair formation increases with the energy of the photon and the charge on the nucleus.

A third method, K-capture, by which the positive charge on a nucleus may be reduced is the reverse of β-radiation, that is, the capture of one of the inner orbital (K) electrons. This process is difficult to observe, but may be detected by means of the X-rays emitted when another electron drops into the vacant K-orbital. It is known to happen in a number of the artificially produced radioactive isotopes and may be taking place in some of the so-called stable isotopes.

The emission of particles from the nucleus is frequently accompanied by very high energy light rays, **gamma-rays,** which have higher frequencies than the hardest X-rays.

TABLE III

TRANSFORMATION SERIES

Group......	3'	4'	5'	6'	7'	0	1	2	3	4	5	6
Atomic No..	81	82	83	84	85	86	87	88	89	90	91	92

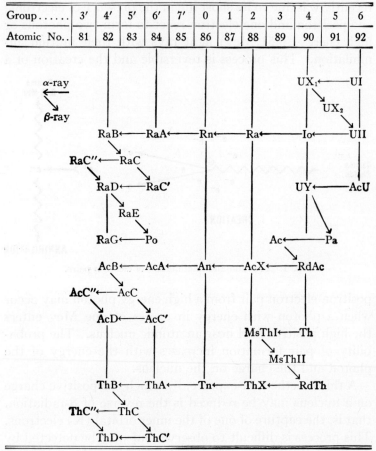

The spectra of α-rays often show several discrete energy groups corresponding to different quantum levels of the product nucleus. In this case the excess of energy in the excited product nucleus is emitted in the form of γ-radiation. The β-ray spectrum shows a continuous distribution of energy among the emitted electrons, terminating in a more or less sharp upper limit. Since the energies of the electrons from the nuclei are different but the energies of the initial and final nuclei are presumably the same, the question of the conservation of energy in the process is difficult to answer. The assumption is made that the energy must be taken away by some new kind of particle still escaping observation. This assumed particle is called the **neutrino**.

3. The Transformation Series.—Uranium and thorium are unstable with respect to lead, and their disintegration occurs in a series of α- and β-emissions, the so-called **uranium series** (starting with U^{238}) and the **thorium series** (starting with Th^{232}). The corresponding end products are RaG (Pb^{206}) and ThD (Pb^{208}). A third series also occurs in nature, the **actinium series.** However, this series does not originate with actinium but with AcU (U^{235}). The end product is Pb^{207}. Some of the radioactive elements undergo both α- and β-disintegrations, thus causing forking in the series. Table III gives the generic relations in the three series. The mass number of the isotopes of the three series may be represented as follows; thorium series, $4n$; uranium series, $4n + 2$; actinium series, $4n + 3$. The $4n + 1$ series does not occur in nature but is now known from artificially prepared isotopes. Pu^{241} may be considered as the starting point but the series is referred to as the neptunium series since Np^{237} is fairly long lived (3×10^6 years).

$$_{94}Pu^{241} \xrightarrow{\beta^-} {}_{95}Am^{241} \xrightarrow{\alpha} {}_{93}Np^{237} \xrightarrow{\alpha} {}_{91}Pa^{233} \xrightarrow{\beta^-} {}_{92}U^{233} \xrightarrow{\alpha}$$

$$_{90}Th^{229} \xrightarrow{\alpha} {}_{88}Ra^{225} \xrightarrow{\beta^-} {}_{89}Ac^{225} \xrightarrow{\alpha} {}_{87}Fr^{221} \xrightarrow{\alpha} {}_{85}At^{217} \xrightarrow{\alpha}$$

$$_{84}Po^{213}$$

$$_{83}Bi^{213} \underset{\alpha}{\overset{\beta^-}{\diagup}} \qquad \underset{\alpha}{\diagdown} {}_{82}Pb^{209} \xrightarrow{\beta^-} {}_{83}Bi^{209}$$

$$_{81}Tl^{209} \overset{\beta^-}{\diagup}$$

The three natural series may also be extended by the new transuranium isotopes.

4n series $\quad {}_{96}Cm^{240} \xrightarrow{\alpha} {}_{94}Pu^{236} \xrightarrow{\alpha} {}_{92}U^{232} \xrightarrow{\alpha} {}_{90}Th^{228}$

4n + 2 series $\; {}_{96}Cm^{242} \xrightarrow{\alpha} {}_{94}Pu^{238} \xrightarrow{\alpha} {}_{92}U^{234}$

4n + 3 series $\qquad\qquad {}_{94}Pu^{239} \xrightarrow{\alpha} {}_{92}U^{235}$

The preparation of many new isotopes of all of the heavy elements has led to parallel series which differ by four mass numbers from the isotopes given above.

4. Other Natural Radioactivities.—Radioactivity in naturally occuring isotopes of the elements lighter than lead are rare but a few cases are known. These are summarized in Table IV. The activity of K^{40} is important since it is the principal source of A^{40} in the atmosphere. This activity also contributes an appreciable amount of heat to the igneous rocks.

TABLE IV

NATURAL RADIOACTIVE ISOTOPES OF THE HIGHER ELEMENTS

ISOTOPE	TYPE OF RADIATION	HALF-LIFE (YRS.)	ENERGY IN MEV	
			PARTICLES	γ-RAY
K^{40}	β^- 90% K 10%	1.5×10^{10}	1.9	1.5
Rb^{87}	β^-	6×10^{10}	0.13	0.03
Sm^{152}	α	1×10^{12}	2.14	..
Nd^{150}	β^-	$ca\ 5 \times 10^{10}$	..	..
Lu^{176}	β^- 33% K 67%	2.4×10^{10}	0.21	0.26
Re^{187}	β^-	4×10^{12}	0.043	..

5. Radioactive Constants.—The rate of decomposition is usually expressed by the fraction, λ, of a given quantity, Q, decomposed in a unit time, $\lambda = (1/Q)(dQ/dt)$. The average life, θ, is $1/\lambda$, and the half period, T, i.e., the time required for the transformation of one half of a given quantity, is 0.69θ. If one element is decomposing to form a second element, which in turn decomposes into a third element, the number of atoms of the first and second elements, N_1 and N_2, when a steady state is reached, is: $N_1\lambda_1 = N_2\lambda_2$. The velocity of the emitted rays is generally expressed relative to that of light, and their penetrating power in cm. of air, aluminum, or lead.   An empirical relation of Geiger and

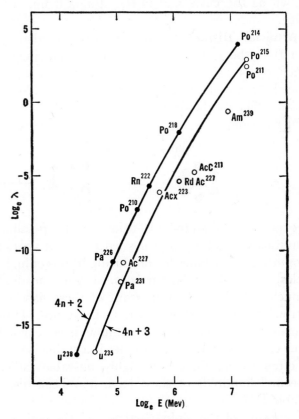

FIG. 2. The Geiger-Nuttall relationship. Logarithm of average life against logarithm of energy of alpha particles.

Nuttall, Fig. 2, states that the logarithm of the average life is inversely proportional to the logarithm of the range of the alpha-particle in air for a given transformation series.

The value of λ for Ra^{226} is 13.8 $\times$ 10^{-12} sec.$^{-1}$, and one

gram of the element contains 2.6×10^{21} atoms. Hence the number of disintegrations per second per gram is $(13,5 \times 10^{-12})(2.6 \times 10^{21})$ or 3.7×10^{10}. This numerical quantity is known as the **curie** and is the standard unit of radio-activity.

6. Artificial Disintegration.—In 1919 Rutherford observed that the fast RaC α-particles in passing through nitrogen gas occasionally (20 times per million α-particles) produced a new long range particle which was identified as a proton. The mechanism of the process proved to be the nuclear reaction,

$$_2He^4 + _7n^{14} = _8O^{17} + _1H^1$$

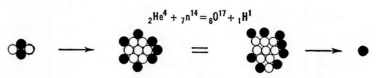

This experiment directed attention to the possibility of transmutation reactions and has led in recent years to the development of machines for producing beams of high speed particles, especially alpha-particles, protons and deuterons ($_1H^2$ nuclei). The most important of these has been the cyclotron invented by Professor E. O. Lawrence. Hundreds of transmutation reactions have now been carried out. In some cases, as above, the product is a stable isotope, but more often the product is a highly unstable radioactive isotope and hundreds of these have now been discovered (cf. Table IV).

The capture of the alpha-particle and the emission of a proton, illustrated above for nitrogen and referred to as

$$_2He^4 + _4Be^9 = _6C^{12} + _0n^1$$

(α, p) reaction, occurs with many of the lighter elements: B^{10}, F^{19}, Ne^{23}, Mg^{24}, Mg^{25}, Mg^{26}, Al^{27}, Si^{28}, P^{31}, and S^{32}.

However, in some cases (e.g., Li^6, Li^7, Be^9, Be^{10}, N^{14}, F^{19}, Na^{23}, Mg^{24}, Al^{27}, and P^{31}) the capture results in the emission of the neutron, (α, n) reaction. This new particle had escaped detection because it produces no ionization along its path. Chadwick first deduced its presence from its ability to eject protons from material containing hydrogen. The neutron reacts with most nuclei and these reactions are considered below, Par **10**.

In addition to the (α, p) and (α, n) reactions discussed above, more complicated reactions occur with high energy alpha-particles. Thus 400 Mev alpha-particles on lead produces among other products Po^{203} with the emission of 7 neutrons (α, 7n) reaction and the same beam on U^{238} gives many activities such as Ra^{223} with the emission of particles having 19 units of mass and 6 units of charge. These high energy reactions are called **spallation** (from the word "spall" meaning "to splinter or crumble").

7. Proton and Deuteron Transmutation.—The proton and deuteron can penetrate the *potential barrier of the positive nucleus much easier than the alpha-particle because of their smaller charge. The following are the more important types of transmutation produced by bombardment with moderately high energy protons:

$$_7N^{14} + {}_1H^1 = {}_6C^{11} + {}_2He^4 \qquad \text{(p, } \alpha\text{)}$$
$$_3Li^7 + {}_1H^1 = 2{}_2He^4 \qquad \text{(p, } \alpha\text{)}$$
$$_5B^{11} + {}_1H^1 = 3{}_2He^4 \qquad \text{(p, } 2\alpha\text{)}$$
$$_4Be^9 + {}_1H^1 = {}_4Be^8 + {}_1D^2 \qquad \text{(p, d)}$$
$$_6C^{12} + {}_1H^1 = {}_7N^{13} + hv \qquad \text{(p, } v\text{)}$$
$$_{20}Ca^{44} + {}_1H^1 = {}_{21}Sc^{44} + {}_0n^1 \qquad \text{(p, n)}$$

The first of these reactions is also shown by Li^6, N^{14}, F^{19}, Na^{23}, and K^{39}. The second reaction is of interest in that the process produced 17 Mev γ-rays.

Bombardment with deuterons leads to the following types of nuclear reactions:

$$_1D^2 + {}_1D^2 = {}_2He^3 + {}_0n^1 \qquad (d, n)$$
$$_1D^2 + {}_1D^2 = {}_1T^3 + {}_1H^1 \qquad (d, p)$$
$$_3Li^7 + {}_1D^2 = 2{}_2He^4 + {}_0n^1 \qquad (d, \alpha n)$$
$$_5B^{10} + {}_1D^2 = {}_6C^{11} + {}_0n^1 \qquad (d, n)$$
$$_{11}Na^{23} + {}_1D^2 = {}_{10}Ne^{21} + {}_2He^4 \qquad (d, \alpha)$$

The first reaction is important as a source of neutrons. The fourth reaction is essentially the same, i.e., a proton is added to the B^{10} nucleus and a neutron liberated and similar reactions are found with Be^9, C^{12}, N^{14}, Na^{23}, Al^{27}, and many other nuclei. Reaction two results in the addition of a neutron to the nucleus and occurs also with Be^9, B^{10}, C^{12}, N^{14}, O^{16}, Na^{23}, Al^{27}, and heavier elements. The formation of helium shown in the last equation is also given by Al^{27}, N^{14}, and many heavier elements. Frequently, a single nucleus bombarded with deuterons will undergo all of the common nuclear reactions, as illustrated in the following example:

$$_{29}Cu^{63} + {}_1D^2 = \begin{cases} {}_{30}Zn^{64} + {}_0n^1 & (d, n) \\ {}_{30}Zn^{63} + 2{}_0n^1 & (d, 2n) \\ {}_{29}Cu^{64} + {}_1H^1 & (d, p) \\ {}_{29}Cu^{62} + {}_1T^3 & (d, t) \\ {}_{28}Ni^{61} + {}_2He^4 & (d, \alpha) \end{cases}$$

Very high energy deuterons, such as the 195 Mev beam from the Berkeley accelerator, produces spallation similar to that discussed under α-reactions. When this beam strikes a target, a reaction known as stripping also occurs by which the proton is stripped from the deuteron and the neutron proceeds in a well defined beam with a peak energy of 90 Mev.

8. Tritium Reactions.—When deuterium is bombarded with tritium, the following reaction occurs:

$$_1H^2 + {}_1H^3 = {}_2He^4 + {}_1n^0.$$

The energy liberated by the reaction is 17.6 Mev. The reaction has a strong resonance effect at about 180 Kev and at this energy of tritium particles the efficiency is greatly enhanced. A number of reactions are known in which the action of tritium is the addition of two neutrons to the bombarded nucleus, e.g.,

$$_{45}Rh^{103} + {}_1H^3 = {}_{95}Rh^{105} + {}_1H^1 \qquad (t, p).$$

9. Photon Induced Reactions.—100 Mev-photons produced by the betatron are capable of inducing numerous nuclear reactions such as (γ, n), (γ, α), (γ, p), (γ, np) and $(\gamma, \alpha n)$. Photons with energies below 10 Mev are not generally effective but the (γ, n) reaction occurs in the case of H^2 and Be^9 with the 2.6 Mev γ-ray from ThC″.

10. Neutron Reactions.—Fast neutrons, such as the stripping beam described above, or neutrons produced by the action of α-particles on beryllium, can readily penetrate into the nucleus, and are very effective in producing disintegrations by collision. The following equations illustrate the two most important nuclear reactions produced:

$$_{13}Al^{27} + {}_0n^1 = {}_{11}Na^{24} + {}_2He^4 \qquad (n, \alpha)$$
$$_{13}Al^{27} + {}_0n^1 = {}_{12}Mg^{27} + {}_1H^1 \qquad (n, p)$$

The first reaction with the neutron capture and the helium emission is given by a large number of elements, some of the more important being Li^6, B^{10}, C^{12}, N^{14}, O^{16}, F^{19}, Ne^{20}, P^{31}, Cl^{35}, Sc^{45}, Mn^{55}, and Co^{59}, and the second type of reaction by Mg^{24}, Si^{28}, P^{31}, S^{32}, Ca^{42}, Cr^{52}, Fe^{56}, and many of the heavier elements. There are also a few examples of neutron capture and deuteron emission (n, d) reaction, and also cases where a fast neutron appears to knock out another neutron $(n, 2n)$ reaction.

Since the neutron has approximately the same mass as the proton, elastic collisions with hydrogen atoms are very effective in reducing the speed of fast neutrons. About twenty collisions suffice to slow down (or cool off) the fast neutrons to the thermal energies of the hydrogen atom. Thus a few centimeters of water or paraffin at room temperature placed in the path of fast neutrons will slow them down from several million volts to an average energy of 0.03 volt. These slow neutrons are readily captured by a large number of nuclei forming isotopes with a mass one unit greater. As an example, thermal neutrons are captured by hydrogen, forming deuterium. The mean life of a neutron in paraffin is only 1.7×10^{-4} seconds. From the data in Table I it is evident that the capture by H^1 results in a decrease in mass and this energy is emitted in the form of γ-radiation, (n, γ) reaction. Among the more common cases of neutron capture are those by C^{12}, Na^{23}, Mg^{26}, Al^{27}, Si^{30}, Cl^{25}, K^{41}, V^{51}, Mn^{55}, Cu^{63}, Ga^{69}, As^{75}, Br^{81}, Cd^{113}, In^{113}, Sb^{123}, I^{127}, Ba^{138}, Hf^{180}, Au^{197}, Th^{232}, and U^{238}.

The most important neutron reaction is that which induces nuclear fission and this is discussed in the following paragraph.

11. Nuclear Fission.—The heavy nuclei, in addition to their instability with respect to α-emission, are also unstable with respect to splitting into two fragments. This process is called nuclear fission. The process results in a decrease in total mass of about 0.2 atomic weight units which is roughly equivalent to 200 Mev.

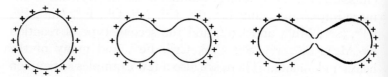

FIG. 3. Schematic representation of nuclear fission.

The Bohr and Wheeler theory of fission pictures the nucleus as a drop whose surface has a high positive charge. A deformation of the drop results in strong repulsion of the two halves because of the charge.

The excitation or deformation energy required to cause fission is 5.9 Mev for U^{238} and 5.3 Mev for U^{235}. For the somewhat lighter elements the excitation energies are larger. Whenever energies in excess of that required for excitation are added, the probability of fission becomes great. Fission may be produced by bombardment with high energy particles but the collision cross sections are very small and the chance of a single particle producing fission is correspondingly small. However, in the case of U^{235} the binding energy liberated on the capture of a neutron is 6.8 Mev which is more than sufficient for fission, and since the capture cross section for slow neutrons is very large, the probability that a single slow neutron in a mass of U^{238} will cause fission becomes great. The tremendous importance of U^{235} lies in the fact that it is the only naturally occurring isotope which does undergo fission with slow neutron capture. The reason that U^{235} fissions with slow neutrons, while U^{238} does not, is the greater neutron binding energy in the product U^{236} over that of U^{239}. This is in agreement with the general rule that binding energies are greater in nuclei with an even number of both protons and neutrons than they are in nuclei with an even number of protons and an odd number of neutrons.

Of the total 200 Mev fission energy, about 175 Mev is spent as kinetic energy of the fission fragments and the balance in the delayed emission of β-particles and γ-rays of the fission products.

12. The Fission Products.—The fission process produces fragments ranging in mass numbers from 72 to 158, with peaks in abundance at 95 and 139, cf. Fig. 4. The newly formed atoms have neutron to proton ratio in excess of the number permitted for stability. This excess of neutrons is reduced in a few cases by neutron emission but generally by a series of β-disintegrations by which the neutrons are converted to protons. There are 64 known series or β-chains involving a total of 170 different radioactive nuclides. The following is a typical example:

$$Xe^{140} \ (16s) \longrightarrow Cs^{140} \ (short) \longrightarrow Ba^{140} \ (12.8d) \longrightarrow$$
$$La^{140} \ (40h) \longrightarrow Ce^{140} \ (stable)$$

Most of the fission products have short half-lives and the total activity falls off rapidly as indicated in Table V.

As the chain decays proceed, the abundance of the various nuclides will increase or decrease because of the differ-

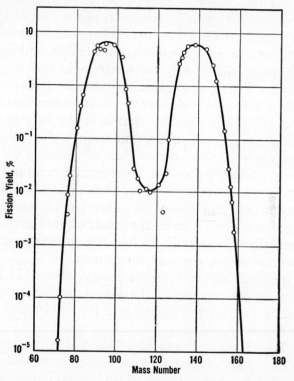

FIG. 4. Fission products of U^{235}.

ences in half-lives, and the principal species contributing to the activity at various times are also given in Table V.

Prewar determinations gave 2.3 as the number of neutrons produced per fission of U^{235}. Over 99 per cent of the neutrons are emitted in the fission process (within 10^{-12} seconds). The "delayed" neutrons are emitted by various fission products, and half-lives (in seconds) of 0.05, 1.5,

TABLE V

GROSS FISSION PRODUCT ACTIVITY

(Values in disintegrations per minute per 10,000 fissions of U^{235} by slow neutron capture for various times after fission)

TIME	NUMBER OF DISINTEGRATIONS	PRINCIPAL NUCLIDES CONTRIBUTING TO THE ACTIVITY
0	(43,800)	....
10 sec.	8500	I^{137}, I^{138}, Kr^{91}, Xe^{140}, Br^{88}, Rb^{90}
1 min.	2790	Cs^{140}, Xe^{139}, Rb^{90}, Kr^{90}, Te^{135}, I^{136}
1 hr.	62	Cs^{138}, Y^{95}, Ba^{139}, Te^{134}, Pr^{146}, La^{142}
1 day	1.74	Xe^{135}, Cb^{97}, Zr^{97}, Y^{93}, I^{133}, Ce^{143}
100 days	0.01	Cb^{95}, Zr^{95}, Y^{91}, Sr^{89}, Ce^{141}, Ru^{103}
1 yr.	0.0014	Ce^{144}, Pr^{144}, Zr^{95}, Pm^{147}, Y^{91}, Sr^{89}
10 yrs.	9.5×10^{-5}	Sr^{90}, Y^{90}, Cs^{137}, Ba^{137}, Pm^{147}, Sm^{151}
100 yrs.	1×10^{-5}	Cs^{137}, Ba^{137}, Sr^{90}, Y^{90}, Sm^{101}, Kr^{85}

4.5, 22 and 55.6 have been established. The last two appear to come from Xe^{137} and Kr^{87} respectively.

13. Nuclear Chain Reactions.—Since a single fission, caused by a neutron, produces more than one neutron, it is possible to set up a chain reaction. To accomplish this in a given mass, at least one of the neutrons emitted per fission must be captured and produce another fission. If the mass is small, the mean free path of the neutrons is large in comparison to the diameter of the mass and the per cent of captures is small. As the total mass is increased the chance of capture increases and finally a mass is reached in which the rate of production and capture is unity. This is the **critical mass** required for the chain reaction. The problem in the construction of the **atomic bomb** was how to bring together two non-critical masses of pure fissionable material in the shortest possible time, so that the resulting mass would produce an uncontrolled chain reaction.

14. The Separation of U^{235}.—The percentage of U^{235} in natural uranium is only 0.71 and the separation of the pure isotope was a major item in the atomic energy program. Two huge plants were constructed in Oak Ridge, Tennessee; one employed the principle of the mass-spectrograph and the other the differential rate of gas diffusion. The first quantities of enriched U^{235} were obtained by the electromagnetic process, but the gas diffusion methods proved to be the most efficient. The gas, UF_6, was allowed to diffuse through several thousand membranes with microscopic holes and separation was attained by the higher velocities of the molecules with the lighter uranium atoms.

15. The Production of Pu^{239}.—Two other nuclei, in addition to U^{235}, are known which undergo fission with slow neutrons. These are U^{233} and Pu^{239}. Neither occur in nature but both are capable of large scale production, the reactions being the following:

$$Th^{232} + n = Th^{233} \xrightarrow{\beta} Pa^{233} \xrightarrow{\beta} U^{233}$$
$$U^{238} + n = U^{239} \xrightarrow{\beta} Np^{239} \xrightarrow{\beta} Pu^{239}$$

The development of the U^{233} process has not been undertaken but the production of plutonium in the reactors at Hanford, Washington, in 1944 was one of the major ac-

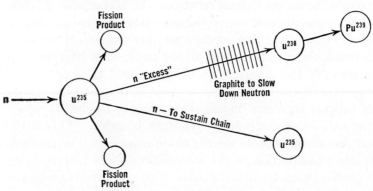

FIG. 5. Diagrammatic representation of Hanford reactor.

complishments of the atomic energy program of World War II. These reactors employ the fission of U^{235} in natural uranium. Since U^{235} concentration is low, the critical mass is many tons. Plutonium is made by the action of the "excess" neutrons on U^{238}. In order to increase the chance of capture of the neutrons by the U^{238}, they are slowed down by passage through graphite block (the moderator). The construction is essentially a giant cube of graphite blocks with horizontal aluminum tubes running through the cube. The tubes contain the uranium in small cylinders

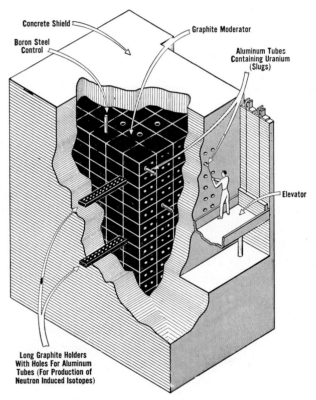

Concrete Shield

Graphite Moderator

Boron Steel Control

Aluminum Tubes Containing Uranium (Slugs)

Elevator

Long Graphite Holders With Holes For Aluminum Tubes (For Production of Neutron Induced Isotopes)

FIG. 6. Slow neutron reactor with graphite moderator.

(slugs) and also serve to carry the water required to cool the slugs. The power level is controlled by vertical rods containing boron which has a very high cross section for neutron capture. When the rods are completely in, the number of neutrons captured by the rods is sufficient to break the chain reaction. After the pile has run for some time, the uranium slugs are discharged, and allowed to "cool" in order for the fission product activity to decrease, cf. Table V. The slugs are then dissolved and the plutonium separated from the unused uranium and the fission products by chemical methods.

16. Power Piles.—The Hanford plant may be described as a slow neutron heterogeneous reactor with graphite as a moderator. It is run at such a low temperature that it would be impossible to convert the energy liberated into power, with appreciable efficiency. The amount of plutonium produced is less than the amount of U^{235} consumed, that is, the **breeding factor** is less than one. If a similar plant could be designed using fuel rods enriched with U^{235}, Pu^{239}, or U^{233} instead of natural uranium, in order to reduce the size; and if materials for construction and cooling could be found which would permit operation at 1000° C. and if the breeding ratio could be increased to one; it should be possible to produce power economically. However the engineering problems are extremely difficult. The cost of the fission fuels, i.e., U^{235}, U^{233}, or Pu^{239}, is so great that they cannot be used as a source of cheap power unless the power reactor is also an efficient breeder of additional fuel. If this is attained, the new fuel produced could be fed back into the fuel rods and the only material consumed would be U^{238} (or Th^{232}). To operate a 100,000 kw power plant with 25 per cent conversion of heat to power would require only 300 lbs of U^{238} per year.

Various other types of chain reactors have also been constructed. Thus a reactor employing a fast neutron chain reaction is in operation at Los Alamos, and a slow neutron heavy-water homogeneous reactor at the Argonne Laboratory. The latter reactor employs a solution of uranium in heavy water which acts as the moderator. Modification of these reactors may be developed for small power plants for military uses such as the propulsion of naval ships.

17. Cosmic Rays and Mesons.—The primary cosmic rays appear to be protons with smaller amounts of all the heavier nuclei. Their energies average around 6 billion electron volts (Bev) although some may be considerably greater. There is no nuclear process which could give rise to such fantastic energies and it is presumed that the high velocities are attained by the accelerating action of electric fields which exist somewhere in space. The interaction of the primary cosmic rays with nuclei in the atmosphere give showers of secondary rays consisting of protons, neutrons, electrons, high-energy gamma rays and **mesons.** The latter, also called mesatrons, are the latest addition to the list of fundamental particles. Several types of mesons have been recognized. The **π-mesons** have a mass 276 times that of the electron, and are both positive and negative, and probably neutral. They are found in the upper atmosphere and have also been produced by bombarding the light elements with 380 Mev alpha-particles. They are unstable (half-life *ca* 10^{-8} seconds) with respect to decomposition into positive or negative **μ-mesons** which have a mass 210 times that of the electron. The π-mesons have a half-life of $2.15 = 10^{-6}$ sec. forming a positron or electron and two neutrinos. The negative π-meson may also be captured by a nucleus with the emission of a number of particles. The negative μ-meson also reacts with nuclei, probably converting a proton to a neutron. This reaction has a low probability with the lighter elements. Low energy π^{+}- and μ^{+}-mesons are not captured by nuclei because of the repulsive forces. The μ-mesons form the bulk of the hard component of the cosmic rays and some penetrate hundreds of feet below the earth's surface. There is evidence for the existence of heavier **V-particles** with a mass several thousand times that of the electron. The total number of cosmic rays (secondary-rays) striking the earth's surface is approximately 2 per cm² per minute.

18. Radiation Health Hazards.—High energy radiations are destructive to living tissue. Alpha- and beta-particles penetrate only a few mm of tissue before all of their energy is dissipated, largely by the liberation of free electrons. The effects of such radiations from an external source are therefore localized on the skin, which, however, may be serious. Taken internally, an alpha- or beta-emitter may become fixed, as for example, radium becomes fixed in the bones by replacing calcium. Bone necrosis and cancer may result if the amount of radium retained is in excess of 0.1 microgram.

X-rays and gamma-rays, since they are very penetrating, produce ion pairs along their entire path through the body. Radiation is measured in terms of its ionizing power and the units, one roentgen, (symbol, r), will produce 1.6×10^{12} ion pairs per gram of air. The absorption within a few days of 500–1000 r of radiation by the whole body is fatal. In the atomic energy program the permissible whole-body radiation exposure is set at 0.1 r per day. However, in a general x-ray, a person may receive 40 r without serious effects. The dosage received per day from cosmic rays is approximately 10^{-3} r.

19. Solar Energy.—The age of the sun appears to be around 3 billion years and to account for the enormous amount of energy radiated in that time it seems necessary to assume that it is supplied by nuclear reactions which use up hydrogen. The temperature of the interior of the sun is estimated at about 19 million degrees and at that temperature the kinetic energies of the atoms are sufficiently large so that lighter nuclei are able to penetrate the repulsive barriers on collision. Some energy is probably contributed by the reaction

$$H^1 + H^1 = H^2 + e^+ + \text{neutrino}$$
$$e^+ + e^- = \text{radiation}$$

which has a total energy of 1.5 Mev. However the rate of

this reaction is low and the following chain reactions have been postulated as the probable source of most of the energy.

$$C^{12} + H^1 = N^{13} + \text{radiation}$$
$$N^{13} \qquad = C^{13} + e^+ + \text{neutrino}$$
$$C^{13} + H^+ = N^{14} + \text{radiation}$$
$$N^{14} + H^+ = O^{15} + \text{radiation}$$
$$O^{15} \qquad = N^{15} + e^+ + \text{neutrino}$$
$$N^{15} + H^1 = C^{12} + He^4$$

Net reaction $4H^1 = He^4$ energy $= 29$ Mev.

The net result is the synthesis of helium from hydrogen, and carbon may be regarded as the catalyst for the reaction. The sun is approximately 30 per cent hydrogen and in order to produce the total energy radiated it is necessary to assume the 10–15 per cent of the original hydrogen has now been consumed.

TABLE VI

Summary of Isotopes

Prepared from table by G. T. Seaborg and I. Perlman.

Symbols: Naturally occurring isotopes indicated by N followed by abundance in per cent; radioactive isotopes indicated by the type of radiaction, followed by value for half-life; β^-, emission of negative electron; β^+, emission of positive electron; α, emission of α-particles; K, capture of k-electron; I.T., isomeric transition; n, emission of neutron.

1 H — **1**, N 99.9844; **2**, N 0.0156; **3**, β^- 12.1 yr.

2 He — **3**, N 1.3 × 10⁻⁴; **4**, N 99.9999; **6**, β^- 0.89 sec.

3 Li — **6**, N 7.39; **7**, N 92.61; **8**, β^-, 2 α 0.88 sec.

4 Be — **7**, K 52 da.; **8**, 2 α 10⁻¹⁵ sec.; **9**, N 100; **10**, β^- 2.5 × 10⁶ yr.

5 B — **10**, N 18.83; **11**, N 81.17; **12**, β^- 0.027 sec.

6 C — **10**, β^+ 20 sec.; **11**, β^+ 20.5 min.; **12**, N 98.9; **13**, N 1.1; **14**, β^- 5100 yr.

7 N — **13**, β^+ 9.93 min.; **14**, N 99.62; **15**, N 0.38; **16**, β^- 7.35 sec.; **17**, β^- n 4.14 sec.

8 O — **14**, β^+ 76.5 sec.; **15**, β^+ 126 sec.; **16**, N 99.757; **17**, N 0.039; **18**, N 0.204; **19**, β^- 29.4 sec.

9 F — **17**, β^+ 70 sec.; **18**, β^+ 112 min.; **19**, N 100; **20**, β^- 12 sec.

10 Ne — **19**, β^+ 20.3 sec.; **20**, N, 90.51; **21**, N 0.28; **22**, N 9.21; **23**, β^- 40 sec.

11 Na — **21**, β^+ (?) 23 sec.; **22**, β^+ 2.6 yr.; **23**, N 100; **24**, β^- 14.8 hr.; **25**, β^- 58.2 sec.

12 Mg — **23**, β^+ 11.6 sec.; **24**, N 78.6; **25**, N 10.11; **26**, N 11.29; **27**, β^- 10.2 min.

13 Al — **25**, ? 8 sec.; **26**, β^+ 6 sec.; **27**, N 100; **28**, β^- 2.3 min.; **29**, β^- 6.7 min.

14 Si — **27**, β^+ 4.9 sec.; **28**, N 92.28; **29**, N 4.67; **30**, N 3.05; **31**, β^- 170 min.

15 P — **29**, β^+ 4.6 sec.; **30**, β^+ 2.5 min.; **31**, N 100; **32**, β^- 14.3 da.; **34**, β^- 12.4 sec.

16 S — **31**, β^+ 2.6 sec.; **32**, N 95.06; **33**, N 0.74; **34**, N 4.18; **35**, β^- 87.1 da.; **36**, N 0.016; **37**, β^- 5.0 min.

17 Cl — **33**, β^+ 2.4 sec.; **34**, β^+ 33 min.; **35**, N 75.4; **36**, β^+, K, β^- 2 × 10⁶ yr.; **37**, N 24.6; **38**, β^- 38.5 min.; **39**, β^- 1 hr.

18 A — **35**, β^+ 1.9 sec.; **36**, N 0.31; **37**, K 34.1 da.; **38**, N 0.06; **39**, β^- 4 min.; **40**, N 99.63; **41**, β^- 110 min.

19 K — **37** ? β^+ 1.3 sec.; **38**, β^+ 7.7 min.; **39**, N 93.3; **40**, N 0.011 β^- 90% K 10% 1.8 × 10⁹ yr.; **41**, N 6.7; **42**, β^- 12.4 hr.; **43**, β^- 22.4 hr.; **44**, β^- 18 min.

20 Ca — **39**, β^+ 4.5 min.; **40**, N 96.96; **42**, N 0.64; **43**, N 0.15; **44**, N 2.06; **45**, β^- 152 da.; **46**, N 0.0033; **47**, β^- 5.8 da.; **48**, N 0.19; **49**, β^- 2.5 hr.; **49**, β^- 30 min.

21 Sc — **41**, β^+ 0.87 sec.; **42**, β^+ 3.92 hr.; **44ᵐ**, I.T. 2.44 da.; **44**, β^+ K 3.92 hr.; **45**, N 100; **46ᵐ**, I.T. 20 sec.; **46**, β^- K 85 da.; **47**, β^- 3.4 da.; **48**, β^- 44 hr.; **49**, β^- 57 min.

22 Ti — **43**, ? 0.58 sec.; **45**, β^+ 3.08 hr.; **46**, N 7.95; **47**, N 7.75; **48**, N 73.45; **49**, N 5.51; **50**, N 5.34; **51ᵐ**, β^- 6 min.; **51**, β^- 72 da.

23 V — **47**, β^+ 33 min.; **48**, β^+ K 16 da.; **49**, K 600 da.; **51**, N 100; **52**, β^- 3.8 min.

24 Cr — **49**, β^+ 41.9 min.; **50**, N 4.49; **51**, K 26.5 da.; **52**, N 83.78; **53**, N 9.43; **54**, N 2.30; **55**, ? 1.3 hr.

TABLE VI (*Cont'd*)

SUMMARY OF ISOTOPES

25 Mn — **51,** β^+ 46 min.; **52**^{m}, β^+, I.T. 21 min.; **52,** β^+ K 5.8 da.; **54,** K 310 da. **55,** N 100; **56,** β^- 2.59 hr.

26 Fe — **52,** β^+ 7.8 hr.; **53,** β^+ 8.9 min.; **54,** N 5.81; **55,** K β^+ 4 yr.; **56,** N 91.64; **57,** N 2.21; **58,** N 0.34; **59,** β^- 46.3.

27 Co — **55,** β^+ 18.2 hr.; **56,** β^+ K 72 da.; **57,** K β^+ 270 da.; **58,** β^+ 15% K 85% 72 da.; **59,** N 100; **60,** β^- 5.3 yr.; **60**^{m}, I.T. β^- 10% 10.7 min.; **61,** β^- 1.75 hr.; **62,** β^- 13.8 min.

28 Ni — **57,** β^+ 36 hr.; **58,** N 67.76; **59,** K 5 × 10^4 yr.; **60,** N 26.16; **61,** N 1.25; **62,** N 3.66; **63,** β^- 300 yr.; **64,** N 1.16; **65,** β^- 2.6 hr.; **66,** β^- 56 hr.

29 Cu — **58,** β^+ 7.9 min.; **59,** β^+ 81 sec.; **60,** β^+ 24.6 min.; **61,** β^+ K 3.4 hr.; **62,** β^+ 10.5 min.; **63,** N 69.09; **64,** K β^- β^+ 12.8 hr.; **65,** N 30.91; **66,** β^- 5 min.; **67,** β^- 56 hr.

30 Zn — **62,** K (?) 9.5 hr.; **63,** β^+ 93% K 7% 38 min.; **64,** N 48.89; **65,** β^+ 1.3% K 98.7% 250 da.; **66,** N 27.81; **67,** N 4.07; **68,** N 18.61; **69**^{m}, I.T. 13.8 hr.; **69,** β^- 57 min.; **70,** N 0.62; **71,** β^- 2.2 min.; **72,** β^- 49 hr.

31 Ga — **64,** β^+ 48 min.; **65,** K 15 min.; **66,** β^+ 9.4 hr.; **67,** K 78.3 hr.; **68,** β^+ 68 min.; **69,** N 60.2; **70,** β^- 20.3 min.; **71,** N 39.8; **72,** β^- 14.3 hr.; **73,** β^- 5 hr.

32 Ge — **66,** ? 140 min.; **67,** β^+ 23 min.; **68,** K 250 da.; **70,** N 20.55; **71,** K 11 da.; **71,** β^+ 39.7 hr.; **72**^{m}, I.T. 5 × 10^{-7} sec.; **72,** N 27.37; **73,** N 7.61; **74,** N 36.74; **75,** β^- 89 min.; **76,** N 7.67; **77,** β^- 12 hr.; **77**^{m}, β^- 59 sec.; **78,** β^- 2.1 hr.

33 As — **71,** β^+ 52 min.; **71,** K 60 hr.; **72,** β^+ 26 hr.; **73,** K 90 da.; **74,** β^- β^+ 17.5 da.; **75,** N 100; **76,** β^- 26.8 hr.; **77,** β^- 40 hr.; **78,** β^- 80 min.

34 Se — **71,** β^+ 44 min.; **72,** K 9.5 da.; **73,** β^+ 6.7 hr.; **74,** N 0.87; **75,** K e^- 127 da.; **76,** N 9.02; **77,** N 7.58; **77**^{m}, I.T. 17.5 sec.; **78,** N 23.52; **80,** N 49.82; **81,** I.T. 59 min.; **81,** β^- 17 min.; **82,** N 9.19; **83**^{m}, β^- 67 sec.; **83,** β^- 25 min.; **84,** β^- 2.5 min.

35 Br — **75,** β^+ K 1.7 hr.; **76,** β^+ 15.7 hr.; **77,** K 95% β^+ 5% 57.2 hr.; **78,** β^+ 6.4 min.; **79,** N 50.5; **80**^{m}, I.T. 4.4 hr.; **80,** β^- β^+ (3%) 18 min.; **81,** N 49.5; **82,** β^- 34 hr.; **83,** β^- 2.4 hr.; **84,** β^- 30 min.; **85,** β^- 3 min.; **87,** β^- n 55.6 sec.; **87,** β^- n 4.51 sec.; **88,** β^- 16 sec.

36 Kr — **77,** K 70% β^+ 30% 1.1 hr.; **78,** N 0.342; **79,** β^+ 2% K 98% 34 hr.; **80,** N 2.223; **81,** I.T. ? 55 sec.; **82,** N 11.50; **83,** N 11.48; **83**^{m}, I.T. 113 min.; **84,** N 57.02; **85,** β^- 4.5 hr.; **85,** β^- 9.4 yr.; **86,** N 17.43; **87,** β^- 74 min.; **88,** β^- 3 hr.; **89,** β^- 2.6 min.; **90,** β^- 33 sec.; **91,** β^- 9.3 sec.; **92,** β^- 2.3 sec.; **93,** β^- 2.2 sec.; **94,** β^- 1.4 sec.; **97,** β^- short.

37 Rb — **81,** β^+ 5 hr.; **82,** β^+ 6.3 hr.; **84,** β^+ 40 da.; **85,** N 72.8; **86,** β^- 19.5 da.; **87,** N 27.2 β^- 6.3 × 10^{10} yr.; **88,** β^- 17.5 min.; **89,** β^- 15 min.; **90,** β^- short; **91,** β^- short; **93,** β^- short; **94,** β^- short; **97,** β^- short.

38 Sr — **84,** N 0.56; **85**^{m}, I.T. 70 min.; **85,** K 65 da.; **86,** N 9.86; **87**^{m}, I.T. 2.7 hr.; **87,** N 7.02; **88,** N 82.56; **89,** β^- 53 da.; **90,** β^- 25 yr.; **91,** β^- 9.7 hr.; **92,** β^- 2.7 hr.; **93,** β^- 7 min.; **94,** β^- 2 min.; **97,** β^- short.

39 Y — **87**^{m}, I.T. 14 hr.; **87,** K 80 hr.; **88,** β^+ 2 hr.; **88,** K 105 da.; **89,** N 100; **90,** β 62 hr.; **91**^{m}, I.T. 51 min.; **91,** β^- 57 da.; **92,** β^- 3.5 hr.; **93,** β^- 10 hr.; **94,** β^- 20 min.; **97,** β^- short.

TABLE VI (*Cont'd*)

SUMMARY OF ISOTOPES

40 Zr — **89**, I.T. or K 4.5 min.; **89**, β^+ 80.1 hr.; **90**, N 51.46; **91**, N 11.23; **92**, N 17.11; **94**, N 17.40; **95**, β^- 65 da.; **96**, N 2.80; **97**, β^- 17.0 hr.

41 Nb — **90**, β^+ 15.6 hr.; **91ᵐ**, I.T. 62 da.; **92**, β^- 10.1 da.; **92**, β^- 21.6 hr.; **93**, N 100; **93ᵐ**, I.T. 42 da.; **94ᵐ**, I.T. β^- 6.6 min.; **94**, ? longer than 10⁴ yr.; **95ᵐ**, I.T. 90 hr.; **95**, β^- 35 da.; **96**, β^- 2.8 da.; **97**, β^- 68 min.; **98**, β^- 30 min.

42 Mo — **92**, N 15.86; **93**, β^+ 6.7 hr.; **94**, N 9.12; **95**, N 15.7; **96**, N 16.5; **97**, N 9.45; **98**, N 23.75; **99**, β^- 67 hr.; **100**, N 9.62; **101**, β^- 14.6 min.; **102**, β^- 12 min.; **105**, β^- short.

43 Tc — **92**, β^+ 4.5 min.; **93**, β^+ 2.7 hr.; **94ᵐ**, I.T. 53 min.; **94**, β^+, K 65%, < 53 min.; **95**, K 56 da.; **95**, K 20 hr.; **96**, K 4.3 da.; **97ᵐ**, I.T. 90 da.; **97**, ? > 100 yr.; **98**, β^- 2.7 da.; **99ᵐ**, I.T. 6 hr.; **99**, β^- 9.4 × 10⁵ yr.; **100**, β^- 80 sec.; **101**, β^- 14 sec.; **102**, β^- < 1 min.; **105**, β^- short.

44 Ru — **95**, β^+ K 1.65 hr.; **96**, N 5.68; **97**, K 2.8 da.; **98**, N 2.22; **99**, N 12.81; **100**, N 12.70; **101**, N 16.98; **102**, N 31.34; **103**, β^- 42 da.; **104**, N 18.27; **105**, β^- 4.5 hr.; **106**, β^- 1 yr.; **107**, β^- 4 min.

45 Rh — **100**, K β^+, 19.4 hr.; **101**, K 4.3 da.; **102**, β^+ β^- 210 da.; **103**, N 100.00; **103ᵐ**, I.T. 57 min.; **104ᵐ**, I.T. 4.2 min.; **104**, β^- 44 sec.; **105**, β^- 36.5 hr.; **106**, β^- 30 sec.; **107**, β^- 24 min.

46 Pd — **100**, K 4 da.; **101**, K, β^+ 10%, 9 hr.; **102**, N 0.8; **103**, K 17 da.; **104**, N 9.3; **105**, N 22.6; **106**, N 27.2; **108**, N 26.8; **109**, β^- 13 hr.; **110**, N 13.5; **111**, β^- 26 min.; **112**, β^- 21 hr.

47 Ag — **104**, β^+ 73 min.; **105**, K 45 da.; **106**, β^+ 24.5 min.; **106**, K 8.2 da.; **107**, N 51.35; **107ᵐ**, I.T. 44 sec.; **108**, β^- 2.3 sec.; **109ᵐ**, I.T. 40.4 sec.; **109**, N 48.65; **110**, β^- 24.2 sec.; **110**, K 225 da.; **111**, β^- 7.5 da.; **112**, β^- 3.2 hr.; **113**, β^- 5.3 hr.

48 Cd — **105**, β^+ 33 min.; **106**, N 1.21; **107**, K 6.7 hr.; **108**, N 0.88; **109**, K 330 da.; **110**, N 12.39; **111ᵐ**, I.T. 48.7 min.; **111**, N 12.75; **112**, N 24.07; **113**, N 12.26; **113ᵐ**, I.T. 2.3 min.; **114**, N 28.86; **115**, β^- 2.33 da.; **115ᵐ**, β^- 43 da.; **116**, N 7.58; **117**, β^- 170 min.

49 In — **109**, K β^+ 6.5 hr.; **110**, β^+ 65 min.; **111**, K 2.7 da.; **111ᵐ**, I.T. 20 min.; **112**, β^+ 9 min.; **113ᵐ**, I.T. 105 min.; **113**, N 4.23; **114ᵐ**, I.T. 48 da.; **114**, β^- 72 sec.; **115ᵐ**, I.T. 4.5 hr.; **115**, N 95.77; **116**, β^- 13 sec.; **116**, β^- 54.3 min.; **117**, β^- 117 min.

50 Sn — **112**, N 0.90; **113**, K 105 da.; **114**, N 0.61; **115**, N 0.35; **116**, N 14.07; **117**, N 7.54; **118**, N 23.98; **119**, 8.62; **119ᵐ**, I.T. 13 da.; **120**, N 33.03; **121**, β^- 28 hr.; **121**, β^- 36 min.; **121**, ? β^- 130 da.; **121**, β^- 28 hr.; **122**, N 4.78; **123**, β^- 10 da.; **124**, N 6.11; **125**, β^- 10 min.; **126**, β^- 70 min.

51 Sb — **117**, K 2.8 hr.; **118**, K 5.1 hr.; **118**, β^+ 3.3 min.; **119**, K 39 hr.; **120**, β^+ 17 min.; **120**, K 6 da.; **121**, N 57.25; **122ᵐ**, I.T. 3.5 min.; **122**, β^- 2.8 da.; **123**, N 42.75; **124**, β^- 60 da.; **124ᵐ**, I.T. β^- 21 min.; **124ᵐ**, β^- I.T. 1.3 min.; **125**, β^- 2.7 yr.; **126**, β^- 60 min.; **127**, β^- 93 hr.; **129**, β^- 4.2 hr.; **132**, β^- 5 min.; **133**, β^- < 10 min.; **134**, β^- < 10 min.

52 Te — **117**, ?, β^+ 2.5 hr.; **118**, K 6 da.; **119**, K 4.5 da.; **120**, N 0.091; **121ᵐ**, I.T. 143 da.; **121**, K 17 da.; **122**, N 2.49; **123**, N 0.89; **124**, N 4.63; **125**, N 7.01; **125ᵐ**, I.T. 60 da.; **126**, N 18.72; **127ᵐ**, I.T. 90 da.;

TABLE VI (*Cont'd*)

SUMMARY OF ISOTOPES

127, β^- 9.3 hr.; **128**, N 31.72; **129**^{m}, I.T. 32 da.; **129**, β^- 72 min.; **130**, N 34.46; **131**^{m}, I.T. 30 hr.; **131**, β^- 25 min.; **132**, β^- 77 hr.; **133**, β^- 60 min.; **134**, β^- 43 min.; **135**, β^- < 2 min.

53 I — **124**, β^+ 4.0 da.; **125**, K 56 da.; **126**, β^- 13 da.; **127**, N 100; **128**, β^- 25.0 min.; **129**, β^- long; **130**, β^- 12.6 hr.; **131**, β^- 8.0 da.; **132**, β^- 2.4 hr.; **133**, β^- 22 hr.; **134**, β^- 54 min.; **135**, β^- 6.7 hr.; **136**, β^- 1.8 min.; **137**, β^- n 22 sec.; **138**, β^- 5.9 sec.; **139**, β^- 2.6 sec.

54 Xe — **124**, N 0.094; **126**, N 0.088; **127**, I.T. 75 sec.; **127**, I.T. 34 da.; **128**, N 1.90; **129**, N 26.23; **130**, N 4.07; **131**, N 21.17; **132**, N 26.96; **133**, β^- 5.3 da.; **134**, N 10.54; **135**, β^- 9.2 hr.; **135**^{m}, I.T. 15.6 min.; **136**, N 8.95; **137**, β^- 3.8 min.; **138**, β^- 17 min.; **139**, β^- 41 sec.; **140**, β^- 16 sec.; **141**, β^- 1.7 sec.; **143**, β^- 1.3 sec.; **144**, β^- short; **145**, β^- 0.8 sec.

55 Cs — **130**, ? 30 min.; **131**, K 10.2 da.; **132**, K 7.1 da.; **133**, N 100; **134**^{m}, β^- 3.15 hr.; **134**, β^- 2.3 yr.; **136**, β^- 13.7 da.; **137**, β^- 37 yr.; **138**, β^- 33 min.; **139**, β^- 9.7 min.; **140**, β^- 65 sec.; **141**, β^- short; **142**, β^- short; **143**, β^- short; **144**, β^- short; **145**, β^- short.

56 Ba — **130**, N 0.101; **131**, K 12.0 da.; **132**, N 0.097; **133**^{m}, I.T. 38.8 hr.; **133**, K > 20 yr.; **134**, N 2.42; **135**^{m}, I.T. 28.7 hr.; **135**, N 6.59; **136**, N 7.81; **137**^{m}, I.T. 2.63 min.; **137**, N 11.32; **138**, N 71.66; **139**, β^- 84 min.; **140**, β^- 308 hr.; **141**, β^- 18 min.; **142**, β^- 6 min.; **143**, β^- < 1 min.; **144**, β^- short; **145**, β^- short.

57 La — **135**, K 19.5 hr.; **136**, β^+ 2.1 hr.; **137**, ? > 400 yr.; **138**, N 0.089; **139**, N 99.91; **140**, β^- 40.4 hr.; **141**, β^- 3.7 hr.; **142**, β^- 74 min.; **143**, β^- 20 min.; **144**, β^- short; **145**, β^- short.

58 Ce — **135**, β^+ 16 hr.; **136**, N 0.193; **137**, K 36 hr.; **138**, N 0.25; **139**, K 140 da.; **140**, N 88.48; **141**, β^- 28 da.; **142**, N 11.07; **143**, β^- 33 hr.; **144**, β^- 275 da.; **145**, β^- 1.8 hr.; **146**, β^- 14.6 min.

59 Pr — **140**, β^+ 3.5 min.; **141**, N 100; **142**, β^- 19.3 hr.; **143**, β^- 13.8 da.; **144**, β^- 17.5 min.; **145**, β^- 4.5 hr.; **146**, β^- 24.6 min.

60 Nd — **141**, β^+ 3%, K 97% 2.42 hr.; **142**, N 27.13; **143**, N 12.20; **144**, N 23.87; **145**, N 8.30; **146**, N 17.18; **147**, β^- 11.0 da.; **148**, N 5.72; **149**, β^- 1.7 hr.; **150**, N 5.60; **150**, β^- 5 × 10^{10} yr.; **151**, β^- 21 min.

61 Pm — **142**, K 200 da.; **147**, β^- 3.7 yr.; **148**, β^- 5.3 da.; **149**, β^- 47 hr.; **151**, β^- 12 min.

62 Sm — **144**, N 3.16; **147**, N 15.07; **148**, N 11.27; **149**, N 13.84; **150**, N 7.47; **151**, β^- 20 yr.; **152**, N 26.63, α, 1 × 10^{12} yr.; **153**, β^- 47 hr.; **154**, N 22.53; **155**, β^- 25 min.; **156**, β^- 10 hr.

63 Eu — **150**, β^+ 27 hr.; **151**, N 47.77; **152**, β^- 9.2 hr.; **152**, β^- long; **153**, N 52.23; **154**, β^- > 20 yr.; **155**, β^- 2 yr.; **156**, β^- 15.4 da.; **157**, β^- 15.4 hr.

64 Gd — **152**, N 0.20; **153**, K 155 da.; **154**, N 2.15; **155**, N 14.78; **156**, N 20.59; **157**, N 15.71; **158**, N 24.78; **160**, N 21.79; **161**, β^- 18 hr.; **161**, β^- 4.5 min.

65 Tb — **152**, K 4.5 hr.; **153**, K 5.1 da.; **154**, β^+ K 17.2 hr.; **155**, K 1 yr.; **159**, N 100; **160**, β^- 3.9 hr.; **160**, β^- 73.5 da.; **161**, β^- 420 da.; **161**, β^- 5.5 da.

TABLE VI (Cont'd)
SUMMARY OF ISOTOPES

66 Dy — **156**, N 0.052; **157** (?), β^+ 2.2 min.; **158**, N 0.09; **160**, N 2.294; **161**, N 18.88; **162**, N 25.53; **163**, N 24.97; **164**, N 28.18; **165**^{m}, I.T. 1.25 min.; **165**, β^- 145 min.

67 Ho — **160**, K 20 min.; **161** or **162**, K 60 da.; **162** or **161**, K β^+ 4.5 hr.; **163**, K 7 da.; **164**, β^- 35 min.; **165**, N 100; **166**, β^- 27.0 hr.

68 Er — **162**, N 0.10; **164**, N 1.5; **165**, β^+ 1.1 min.; **166**, N 32.9; **167**, N 24.4; **168**, N 26.9; **169**, β^- 9.4 da.; **170**, N 14.2; **171**, β^- 7.5 hr.; **171**, β^- 20 hr.

69 Tm — **166**, β^+, K 7.7 hr.; **167**, K 9 da.; **167** (?), K 100 da.; **169**^{m}, I.T. 10^{-6} sec.; **169**, N 100; **170**, β^- 127 da.; **170**^{m}, I.T. 2.5×10^{-6} sec.; **171**, β^- 500 da.

70 Yt — **168**, N 0.06; **169**, K 33 da.; **170**, N 4.21; **171**, N 14.26; **172**, N 21.49; **173**, N 17.02; **174**, N 29.58; **175**, β^- 99 hr.; **176**, N 13.38; **177**, β^- 2.4 hr.

71 Lu — **170**, K β^+ 2.15 da.; **171**, K 9 da.; **172** (?), (?) > 100 da.; **175**, N 97.5; **176**, N 2.5 β^- 7.3 $\times 10^{10}$ yr.; **176**^{m}, β^- 3.67 hr.; **177**, β^- 6.8 da.

72 Hf — **174**, N 0.18; **175**, K 70 da.; **176**, N 5.30; **177**, N 18.47; **178**, N 27.10; **179**, N 13.84; **180**, N 35.11; **181**, β^- 46 da.

73 Ta — **176**, K 8.0 hr.; **177**, K 2.66 da.; **178** (?), K β^- 16 da.; **180**, K 8.2 hr.; **181**^{m}, I.T. 2×10^{-5} sec.; **181**, N 100; **182**, β^- 117 da.; **182**^{m}, I.T. 0.40 sec.; **182**, β^- 16.2 min.

74 W — **179** or **178**, K 135 min.; **180**, N 0.122; **181**, K 140 da.; **182**, N 25.77; **183**, N 14.24; **184**, N 30.68; **185**, β^- 73.2 da.; **186** N 29.17; **187**, β^- 24.1 hr.

75 Re — **182**, K 64 hr.; **183** or **184**, K 13 hr.; **184** or **183**, K 80 da.; **184**, β^- K 50 da.; **185**, N 37.07; **186**, β^- 92.8 hr.; **187**, N 62.93 β^- 4 $\times 10^{12}$ yr.; **188**, β^- 18.9 hr.

76 Os — **184**, N 0.018; **185**, K 97 da.; **186**, N 1.59; **187**, N 1.64; **188**, N 13.3; **189**, N 16.1; **190**, N 26.4; **191**, β^- 15.0 da.; **192**, N 41.0; **193**, β^- 32 hr.

77 Ir — **190**, K 10.7 da.; **191**, N 38.5; **192**^{m}, I.T. 1.5 min.; **192**, β^- 70 da.; **193**, N 61.5; **194**, β^- 19.0 hr.

78 Pt — **191**, K 3 da.; **192**, N 0.78; **193**, K 4.33 da.; **194**, N 32.8; **195**, N 33.7; **196**, N 25.4; **196**^{m}, I.T. 80 min.; **197**, β^- 18 hr.; **197**, β^- 3.3 da.; **198**, N 7.23; **199**, β^- 31 min.

79 Au — **191**, K or β^+ 1 da.; **192**, K 4.7 hr.; **193**, K 15.8 hr.; **194**, K 39.5 hr.; **195**, K 185 da.; **196**, β^- K 5.5 da.; **197**, N 100; **197**^{m}, I.T. 7.5 sec.; **198**, β^- 2.69 da.; **199**, β^- 3.3 da.; **200** or **202**, β^- 48 min.

80 Hg — **196**, N 0.15; **197**, K 23 hr.; **197**, K 64 hr.; **198**^{m}, I.T. 0.3×10^{-6} sec.; **198**, N 10.1; **199**, N 17.0; **200**, N 23.3; **201**, N 13.2; **202**, N 29.6; **203**, β^- 45.8 da.; **204**, N 6.7; **205**, β^- 5.5 min.

81 Tl — **198**, K 1.8 hr.; **199**, K 7 hr.; **200**, K 27 hr.; **201**, K 75 hr.; **202**, K 11.8 da.; **203**, N 29.1; **204**, β^- 2.7 yr.; **205**, N 70.9; **206**, β^- 4.23 min.; **207**, (AcC'), β^- 4.76 min.; **208**, (ThC') β^- 3.1 min.; **209**, β^- 2.2 min.; **210**, (RaC') β^- 1.32 min.

82 Pb — **199**, K 1 hr.; **200**, K 18 hr.; **201**, K 8 hr.; **203**, I.T. or K 52 hr.; **204**, N 1.5; **204**^{m}, I.T. 68 min.; **206**, N 23.6; **207**, N 22.6; **208**,

TABLE VI (*Cont'd*)

SUMMARY OF ISOTOPES

N 52.3; **209**, β^- 3.32 hr.; **210** (RaD), β^- 22 yr.; **211** (AcB), β^- 36.1 min.; **212** (ThB), β^- 10.6 hr.; **214**, (RaB), β^- 26.8 min.

83 Bi — **197**, α 2 min.; **198**, α 9 min.; **199**, α, K 27 min.; **200**, α, K 62 min.; **204**, K 12 hr.; **206**, K 6.4 da.; **208**, K short; **209**, N 100; **210** (RaE), β^- 5 da.; **211** (AcC), α 99.68% β 0.32% 2.16 min.; **212** (ThC), α 33.7% β^- 66.3% 60.5 min.; **213**, β^- 98% α 2% 47 min.; **214** (RaC), α 0.04% β^- 99.96% 19.7 min.

84 Po — **203**, α 40 min.; **205**, α 4 hr.; **206**, K 90% α 10% 9 da.; **207**, K 5.7 hr.; **208**, α 3 yr.; **210**, α 138 da.; **211** (AcC'), α 5 $\times$ 10^{-3} sec.; **212** (ThC'), α 3 $\times$ 10^{-7} sec.; **213**, α 4 $\times$ 10^{-6} sec.; **214** (RaC'), α 1.5 $\times$ 10^{-4} sec.; **215** (AcA), α, β^- 10^{-4} % 1.8 $\times$ 10^{-3} sec.; **216** (ThA), α, β^- 0.014% 0.158 sec.; **218** (RaA), α 99.96% β^- 0.04% 3.05 min.

85 At — **207**, α 1.7 hr.; **208**, α 4.5 hr.; **210**, K 8.3 hr.; **211**, α 40% K 60% 7.5 hr.; **212**, α 0.25 sec.; **214**, α short; **215**, α 10^{-4} sec.; **216**, α 3 $\times$ 10^{-4} sec.; **217**, α 0.018 sec.; **218**, α short.

86 Rn — **216**, α very short; **217**, α 10^{-3} sec.; **218**, α 0.019 sec.; **219** (An), α 3.92 sec.; **220** (Tn), α 54.5 sec.; **222** (Rn) α 3.825 da.

87 Fr — **218**, α very short; **219**, α 0.02 sec.; **220**, α 27.5 sec.; **221**, α 4.8 min.; **223** (AcK) β^- 21 min.

88 Ra — **220**, α short; **221**, α 31 sec.; **222**, α 38 sec.; **223** (AcX), α 11.2 da.; **224** (ThX), α 3.64 da.; **225**, β^- 14.8 da.; **226**, α 1622 yr.; **227**, β^-; **228** (MSTh₁), β^- 6.7 yr.

Isotopes of elements 89–96 listed in Chapter **XXII**.

Glossary

ABSORPTION COEFFICIENT.—The probability of absorption of an incident beam of radiation as it traverses some material. In the integrated form of the defining equation: ($I = I_0 e^{-ux}$) where I_0 is the intensity of the impinging beam and I, the intensity of the beam after passing through thickness, x, u is the absorption coefficient.

ACID.—A substance which gives hydrogen ion in solution, or which neutralizes bases yielding water. In general, an acid is a molecule with a positive field which is capable of neutralizing a basic molecule having a "free" electron pair.

ACTINIDES.—The elements which contain $5f$ electrons.

ACTIVITY.—Cf. Appendix IV.

ALLOTROPY.—The property shown by certain elements of being capable of existence in more than one form, due to differences in the arrangement of atoms or molecules. (See Monotropic and Enantiotropic.)

ALPHA-PARTICLES.—Doubly charged helium atoms shot off during one type of radioactive change.

AMPERE.—Unit of electric current strength; one coulomb per second; the international ampere is the current which deposits 0.0011180 g. of silver per second.

ÅNGSTROM UNIT.—10^{-10} meters; 10^{-8} cm.

ANGULAR MOMENTUM.—Product of the angular velocity and moment of inertia. The latter is analogous to the mass in simple translation. Unit expressed in g. cm.^{2}/sec.

ANHYDRIDE (of acid or base).—An oxide which when combined with water gives an acid or base.

ANODE.—The electrode at which oxidation occurs.

ATMOSPHERE.—Unit of pressure. Defined as pressure exerted by a column of mercury 76 cm. high; 1.01325×10^6 dynes per cm.^{2}; 14.7 lb. per sq. inch.

ATOM.—The unit particle of an element. A nucleus of definite integral positive charge surrounded by electrons.

513

ATOMIC NUMBER.—The net positive charge on the nucleus of an atom; the ordinal number of an atom in the periodic system.

ATOMIC WEIGHT.—Weight of an atom referred to the oxygen atom as 16,000,—(chemical definition). The physical atomic weights refer to $O^{16} = 16.000$ and may be converted to chemical atomic weights by multiplying by the factor 1.00275.

AVOGADRO'S NUMBER.—The number of molecules in a mole; 6.0228×10^{23}.

AVOGADRO'S RULE.—Equal volumes of all gases, at the same temperature and pressure, contain the same number of molecules (approximately).

BAR.—Unit of pressure; $= 10^6$ dyne cm.^{2}; one atmosphere $= 1.013$ bar.

BASE.—A substance which gives hydroxide ion in solution, or which neutralizes acids, yielding water.

BASE ELEMENT.—An easily oxidized element, as opposed to a noble element.

BEV.—Abbreviation for billion electron volts.

BOILING POINT.—The temperature at which the vapor pressure of a liquid reaches standard atmospheric pressure.

BRITISH THERMAL UNIT (BTU).—Heat required to raise 1 lb. of water 1° F.

CALORIE.—Unit of energy. Small calorie (denoted by cal.) is heat required to raise 1 g. of water 1° C. kcal. = 1000 cal. Value varies with temperature. 1 cal. (15° C.) = 4.183 joules.

CATALYST.—A substance which by its presence alters the rate of a reaction and itself remains unchanged at the end of the reaction.

CATHODE.—The electrode at which reduction occurs.

CATHODE RAYS.—A stream of electrons.

CENTIGRADE (C.).—Temperature scale in which freezing point of water is called 0° and boiling point 100°.

CHEMILUMINESCENCE.—Emission of light during a chemical reaction.

COLLOID.—A phase dispersed to such a degree that the surface forces become an important factor in determining its properties.

COMPONENT.—One of the minimum number of substances required to state the composition of all phases of a system.

CONCENTRATION.—The amount of a substance in weight, moles, or equivalents contained in unit volume.

CONDUCTANCE.—Reciprocal of resistance. $C = \bar{C} A/L$, where A is cross section, L, length, and $\bar{C}$, *specific conductance*.

COORDINATION NUMBER OF AN ATOM.—The number of atoms, molecules, or radicals which are held about a central atom in relatively stable positions.

COULOMB.—The quantity of electricity transferred in one second by a current of one ampere; a coulomb can deposit 0.0011180 g. of silver.

COVALENT BOND.—The term frequently applied to an electron pair bond.

CRITICAL PRESSURE.—The pressure exerted by a system at its critical temperature.

CRITICAL TEMPERATURE.—The highest temperature at which a liquid and its vapor may coexist as distinct phases.

CRITICAL VOLUME.—The volume of unit mass at the critical temperature and pressure.

CURIE.—The amount of radon which can exist in a steady state, "equilibrium," with 1 g. of radium. It is now used as a unit of the rate of disintegration of any radioactive substance and is defined as that quantity of substance which gives the same number of disintegration as 1 g. of radium, 3.7×10^{10} disintegrations per sec.

DECOMPOSITION VOLTAGE.—Cf. Appendix I.

DEGREE OF FREEDOM.—The number of the variables determining the state of a system (usually pressure, temperature, and concentrations of the components) to which arbitrary values can be assigned.

DEGREE OF IONIZATION.—Cf. Appendix III.

DELIQUESCENT.—The term applied to a salt which absorbs moisture from the atmosphere.

DENSITY (volume-density).—The mass per unit volume: g. per cc.

DEUTERON.—The nucleus of the deuterium atom.

DIAMAGNETIC.—An object of diamagnetic material will acquire a magnetic moment opposite to the magnetic field. When a diamagnetic substance is placed in a magnetic field, the lines of force are spread out. (See Paramagnetic.)

DIELECTRIC CONSTANT.—The force between two point charges $(e, \acute{e})$ separated by the distance r in a uniform medium is $f = e\acute{e}/kr^2$ where k is called the dielectric constant.

DIFFUSION LAW.—The rates of diffusion of two gases are inversely proportional to the square roots of the densities of the gases.

DISTRIBUTION LAW.—A substance distributes itself between two immiscible solvents so that the ratio of its concentrations in the two solvents is approximately a constant (and equal to the ratio of the solubilities of the substance in each solvent). Requires modification if more than one molecular species is formed.

DYNE.—Unit of force. The force which will impart to a mass of 1 g. an acceleration of 1 cm. per sec.^{2}; 1 g. = 980 dynes.

EFFLUENT.—Any solution which has passed through a bed of adsorbing material.

ELECTROMOTIVE FORCE.—See Potential.

ELECTRON.—The unit charge or atom of negative electricity; 4.80239 $\times$ 10^{-10} electrostatic units.

ELECTRON AFFINITY.—The energy of attachment of an additional electron to a neutral atom.

ELECTROPOSITIVE ELEMENT.—An element that is readily oxidized, i.e., forms compounds of positive valence number, syn— base element.

ELEMENT.—A substance composed entirely of atoms of the same atomic number.

ELUATE.—A solution of material removed from a solid adsorbent by a solvent (eluent).

ENANTIOTROPIC.—Crystal forms capable of existing in reversible equilibrium with each other.

ENERGY.—Work, or the capacity for doing work.

ENTROPY.—A measure of the irreversibility of a process; multiplied by the absolute temperature it is the energy required to restore a system which has changed from state A to B to its original state. The property is extensive; for all pure crystals it is zero at the absolute zero.

EQUILIBRIUM, CHEMICAL.—A state of affairs in which a chemical reaction and its reverse reaction are taking place at equal velocities, so that the concentrations of reacting substances remain constant.

EQUIVALENT (g. equivalent weight).—(1) Acid or base: the amount (weight) of substance necessary to give one mole of hydrogen or hydroxyl, respectively, in a neutralization reaction; (2) oxidizing or reducing agent; a mole of substance divided by the number of electrons in the half reaction for the reduction of oxidation considered.

EQUILIBRIUM CONSTANT.—The product of the concentrations (or activities) of the substances produced at equilibrium in a chemical reaction divided by the product of concentrations of the reacting substances, each concentration raised to that power which is the coefficient of the substance in the chemical equation.

ERG.—Work done by a force of 1 dyne acting through a distance of one cm.

EUTECTIC.—The term applied to a minimum in the freezing point-composition curve of a system.

FAHRENHEIT.—Temperature scale in which 32° denotes the freezing point and 212° the boiling point of water.

FARAD.—Capacity of a condenser which is charged to a potential of 1 volt by 1 coulomb.

FARADAY.—96,501 international coulombs per gram equivalent; the charge of 1 mole (6.0228×10^{23}) of electrons; the amount of electricity required to precipitate one mole of a singly charged ion.

FISSION PRODUCTS.—The products formed by nuclear fission.

FLUORESCENCE.—The emission of light (other than reflected light) by a substance under illumination.

FLUX.—In metallurgy, a substance which will unite with some of the reaction products to form an easily fusible magma.

FORCE.—That which is capable of imparting acceleration to a mass.

FORMAL CHARGE.—The net charge on an atom in a molecule, calculated by assuming that the electrons in a bonding pair are equally shared by the two atoms.

FORMAL CONCENTRATION.—Concentrations expressed as the number of gram-formula weights per liter.

FORMAL POTENTIAL.—The potential of a reaction in which the concentration of all substances are 1 formal.

FREE ENERGY.—Cf. Appendix III.

GAMMA-RAY.—A very high frequency light wave originating in the nucleus of an atom.

GAS.—A state of matter in which a given mass of a substance has neither definite size nor shape.

GAS CONSTANT.—The constant of the ideal gas equation relating volume, pressure, temperature, and mass (number of moles). $PV = NRT$. $R = 8.3144 \times 10^7$ ergs per degree per mole; 0.082054 liter atmos. per degree per mole; 1.98719 cal. (15°) per degree per mole.

GRAM.—A unit of mass (or weight). The mass (approximately) of 1 cc. of water at 4° C.

GRAM ATOM.—A mass in grams numerically equal to the atomic weight.

GRAM MOLECULE.—See Mole. A mass in grams numerically equal to the molecular weight of the substance in question.

GRAVITATION CONSTANT.—The standard acceleration of gravity, 980.665 cm/sec².

HEAT.—A form of energy.

HUMIDITY.—The amount of water vapor per unit volume of gas. *Relative humidity* is the ratio of the actual partial pressure of water vapor to the equilibrium pressure, water (liquid) to water vapor, at the same temperature.

HYDRATED OXIDE.—An oxide which precipitates as a definite compound with water.

HYDROLYSIS.—A reaction involving the splitting of water into its ions, and the formation of a weak acid or base or both.

HYDROUS OXIDE.—An oxide which precipitates with an indefinite amount of adsorbed water.

ION.—A charged atom or chemical radical.

IONIZATION POTENTIAL.—The potential required to transfer an electron from its normal quantum level to infinity.

ISOBAR.—One of several atoms having the same mass number but differing in atomic number.

ISOMERISM.—Existence of molecules having the same number and kinds of atoms but in different configurations.

ISOMORPHOUS.—Substances which have the same crystalline structures and are mutually soluble in the solid state.

ISOTOPES.—The term applied to atomic species having the same atomic number but different nuclear structure, as indicated by different atomic weight or different type of radioactivity.

JOULE.—Unit of energy = 10^7 ergs; work done per second in forcing 1 ampere through a resistance of 1 ohm.

JOULE-THOMSON EFFECT.—The temperature change in a gas when it expands without doing external work.

KELVIN.—Name applied to absolute-centigrade or thermodynamic temperature scale.

KERNEL.—The atomic nucleus plus all of the electrons except those in the valence shell.

KILO.—Prefix denoting 1000.

LANTHANIDES.—The elements from atomic number 57 to 71, formed by the entrance of the $4f$ electrons.

LATENT HEAT.—The heat absorbed or evolved in an isothermal reversible process such as melting or vaporization.

LATTICE ENERGY.—The energy required to separate the ions of a crystal to an infinite distance from each other.

LITER.—A unit of volume, 1000 cc.

LOSCHMIDT'S NUMBER.—Equivalent to Avogadro's number.

MASS.—Quantity of matter. Determined as the resistance offered by an object to a change of its motion, i.e., inertia.

MASS LAW.—See Equilibrium Constant.

MEGA.—Prefix meaning 1,000,000.

MELTING POINT.—The temperature at which a solid is in equilibrium with its liquid form (varies with pressure).

MESON (also called mesatron).—One of the fundamental particles, cf. Chapter XXIII.

METAL.—A substance possessing so-called metallic properties, i.e., electric conductivity, heat conductivity, high reflectivity, luster, etc., properties due to the high degree of freedom possessed by electrons of the substance.

MEV.—The abbreviation for million electron volts.

MHO.—One reciprocal ohm.

MICRO.—Prefix denoting 10^{-6}.

MICRON.—(μ) Unit of length $= 10^{-6}$ meters $= 10^{-3}$ mm.

MILLI.—Prefix denoting 10^{-3}.

MOLAL.—Concentration expressed in moles of solute per 1000 g., of solvent.

MOLAR.—Concentration expressed in moles of solute per 1000 cc. of solution.

MOLE.—The weight of a substance in grams, numerically equal to its molecular weight; a "gram-molecule."

MOLECULAR VOLUME.—Volume occupied by one mole. 22.41151 at 0° C. and 1 atm.

MOLECULAR WEIGHT.—The sum of the atomic weights of all the atoms of the molecule.

MOLECULE.—The smallest physical unit of a substance.

MOMENT OF FORCE.—The moment about a point $=$ force $\times$ perpendicular distance from point to line of force.

MOMENT OF INERTIA.—The sum of the products of each element of mass times the square of its distance from its axis of rotation.

MOMENTUM.—The product of mass times velocity.

MONOTROPIC.—Crystal forms one of which is always metastable with respect to the other.

NEUTRINO.—The particle whose existence is postulated to account for the apparent non-conservation of energy in β-radiation.

NEUTRON.—The elementary particles of atomic weight 1.009 and zero change.

NORMAL SOLUTION.—One having a concentration of 1 equivalent per liter.

NUCLEON.—The name given to particles of mass number one, i.e., protons and neutrons.

NUCLEUS.—The positively charged center of the atom. The atom minus the orbital electrons.

NUCLIDE.—A species of atom having a given number of protons and neutrons in its nucleus.

OCTET.—The term applied to a group of eight electrons in the outer atomic shell.

OHM.—Unit of electrical resistance. The resistance of a uniform column of mercury at 0° C. which has a mass of 14.4521 g. and a length of 106.300 cm.

OHM-CENTIMETER.—Unit of volume resistivity. A resistance of one ohm across a centimeter cube.

OVERVOLTAGE.—Cf. Appendix I.

OXIDATION.—An increase in the oxidation state number of an element; the loss of electrons by an atom or group of atoms.

OXIDATION STATE OR NUMBER.—The charge on a simple ion or for a complex ion or molecule: the charge which is assumed on an atom to account for the number of electrons involved in the oxidation (or reduction) of the atom to the free element.

PARAMAGNETIC.—An object of paramagnetic material will acquire a magnetic moment parallel to the magnetic field, and the lines of magnetic force will converge toward it.

PASSIVE.—The term applied to the condition produced by treating certain metals with powerful oxidizing agents whereby the metal is rendered in effect more electronegative, e.g., iron treated with fuming nitric acid is rendered passive, and in this condition is not oxidized by silver nitrate solution as is non-passive iron.

PHASE.—All of the homogeneous regions of a system which are of the same kind.

PHASE RULE.—In a system at equilibrium, the number of phases plus the number of degrees of freedom equals the number of components plus two.

PHOSPHORESCENCE.—Remission of light after previous illumination.

PHOTOELECTRIC EFFECT.—The emission of electrons under the action of light.

PHOTON.—A "particle" of radiant energy. ($E = h\nu$.)

PLANCK'S CONSTANT.—The constant relating the energy and frequency of radiation. $E = h\nu$, $h = 6.554 \times 10^{-27}$ erg. sec.

POLARIZATION (electrical).—Refers to a distribution of electrical charges that gives rise to an external electric field.

POLARIZATION (light).—Light is said to be polarized which exhibits different properties in different directions at right angles to the line of propagation.

POLYMORPHISM.—The ability to exist in two or more crystalline forms.

POSITRON.—The positive counterpart of the negative electron.

POTENTIAL (electric, gravitational, etc., at a point in a field).— The work required to move a unit quantity (electron, gram, etc.) from the standard position, or position of reference, to the point in question.

POWER.—The timerate of doing work, e.g., ergs per second.

PRESSURE.—Normal force per unit area.

PROTON.—The unit charge or atom of positive electricity; the nucleus of the hydrogen isotope of mass number one.

QUANTUM NUMBER.—One of the integers defining the energy of an atom.

RADIOACTIVITY.—Changes involving the partial disintegration of the atomic nucleus. Cf. Chapter XXII.

REDUCTION.—The opposite of oxidation; decrease in positive oxidation number; gain in number of electrons by an atom or group of atoms.

REFRACTIVE INDEX.—The ratio of the sine of the angle of incidence of a beam of light from a vacuum upon a substance to the sine of the angle of refraction. $n = \sin i / \sin r$. It is also the ratio of velocity of light in vacuum to that in the medium.

REPLACEMENT SERIES.—The arrangement of the metals in order of the values of their oxidation potentials.

RESISTANCE (electrical) R.—Defined as the quotient of the potential E, between two surfaces, divided by the resulting current I, flowing from one to the other, as defined by Ohm's law, $R = E/I$.

ROENTGEN.—The quantity of radiation which produces 2.083×10^9 ion pairs per cc. of air.

RYDBERG'S CONSTANT.—A fundamental constant appearing in

the expression relating the terms of the hydrogen spectrum.

SOLUBILITY.—The amount of solute (expressed in grams, moles, etc.) present in a given amount (grams, moles, volume, etc.) of solvent or of solution at saturation.

SOLUBILITY PRODUCT.—The equilibrium constant for the solution of a solid strong electrolyte, e.g., for Cu_2S, $K = (Cu^+)^2 \times (S^{--})$.

SOLUTE.—That constituent of a solution which is considered to be dissolved in the other, the solvent. The solvent is usually present in larger amount than the solute.

SOLUTION.—A homogeneous mixture, the proportion of whose constituents may be varied within certain limits. Solutions may be either liquid, solid, or gaseous.

SOLVENT.—That constituent of a solution which is present in larger amount; or, the constituent which is liquid in the pure state, in the case of solutions of solids or gases in liquids.

SPALLATION.—An induced nuclear reaction in which an atom ejects a large number of particles.

SPECIFIC GRAVITY.—The ratio of the mass of a certain volume of a substance to the mass of the same volume of a reference substance, generally water, for solids and liquids, and air for gases. The reference substance is at a specified temperature.

SPECIFIC HEAT.—The heat required to raise a unit mass (1 g.) of a substance 1 degree.

SPECIFIC VOLUME.—The volume of 1 gram of a substance.

SPECTRUM.—Light resolved into its component frequencies, as by a prism or diffraction grating.

STANDARD CONDITIONS (of a gas).—0° C. and one atmosphere, or 760 mm. pressure.

STANDARD POTENTIAL.—Cf. Appendix I.

STEPHAN'S CONSTANT.—The constant relating total black body radiation and the absolute temperature. $J = \sigma T^4$. $\sigma = 5.672 \times 10^{-5}$ erg per cm.^{2} per sec. per deg.^{4}

STOICHIOMETRIC.—Pertaining to weight relations in chemical reactions.

SURFACE TENSION.—The contractive force of a surface measured along unit length of its edge, usually expressed in dynes per cm.; this is numerically equal to the work done in extending the surface 1 cm.^{2}, in ergs per cm.^{2}

SYSTEM.—An isolated group of substances.

TEMPERATURE.—The condition which determines whether heat

will flow to or from one body to another. See also Kelvin, Centigrade.

THERMOELECTRIC FORCE.—The potential between the junctions of two metal wires which arises when the two junctions are at different temperatures.

TRIPLE POINT (in one component system).—Temperature and pressure at which three phases are in equilibrium, usually refers to liquid-solid-gas systems.

VALENCE.—The number of electron pair bonds which an atom shares with other atoms. In inorganic chemistry the term is often used to mean oxidation state (cf. above).

VAN DER WAALS' EQUATION.—An equation relating the volume, pressure, and temperature of an imperfect gas in terms of two empirical constants. $(P + a/v^2)(v - b) = RT$.

VISCOSITY.—The internal friction of a fluid; the reciprocal of fluidity.

VOLT.—The potential difference required to produce a current of one ampere through a resistance of one ohm.

WATT.—Unit of power, work performed at the rate of one joule per second.

WAVE LENGTH (of light).—Distance between consecutive corresponding points in the light wave. Expressed in units of length, Ångstrom, microns, etc. Sodium yellow line = 5890 Å = 589 × 10^{-6} mm. = 0.589 μ.

X-RAYS.—High frequency light waves originating from the electrons of the kernel.

Appendix I

SUMMARY OF FUNDAMENTAL CONCEPTS RELATING TO ELECTROLYTIC OXIDATION AND REDUCTION

(1) An electric current is carried through a solution of an electrolyte by the motion of its ions; the positive ions moving toward the cathode and the negative ions toward the anode. The current carried by each species of ion is proportional to its concentration and velocity.

(2) Electricity is transferred from the electrolyte to the electrodes through the mechanism of electrode reactions, also called "half reactions," which always involve the liberation of electrons at the anode and the using up of electrons at the cathode. The substances entering into either electrode reaction may be positive ions, negative ions, or neutral molecules.

(3) The sum of the two electrode reactions is the cell reaction. If this reaction takes place spontaneously, we have a **battery** or **electric cell** capable of doing external work. If this reaction is not spontaneous, an external electromotive force must be used to force electricity through the cell and the process is called **electrolysis.**

(4) **Faraday Laws.**—The extent of the electrode reactions is proportional to the total current that passes, and the passage of one Faraday (96,500 coulombs) of electricity causes the electrode reaction to proceed to such an extent that one equivalent of each substance involved in the cell reaction is used up or produced.

(5) At the cathode that reduction process occurs which has the highest oxidation potential; and at the anode that oxidation process occurs which has the highest reduction potential, with the exception that the speed of a given electrode reaction may be so slow that a reaction requiring a larger amount of free energy may

take place first. Use may be made of a table of oxidation-reduction potentials, Appendix II, in order to predict the reaction that should theoretically take place at each electrode.

The potential of the cell reaction is the difference in potential of the two half reactions, e.g.,

$$Zn = Zn^{++} + 2e^- \qquad 0.7620 \text{ volt}$$
$$2Ag = 2Ag^+ + 2e^- \qquad -0.7995 \text{ volt}$$

$$Zn + 2Ag^+ = Zn^{++} + 2Ag \qquad 1.5615 \text{ volts}$$

(6) The standard potential values are based upon measurements with very small currents. In general, if a solution is being electrolyzed with appreciable current, the potential required is greater than the reversible electrode potentials, due to irreversible changes taking place.

$$E_{electrolysis} = E_{0(reversible)} + E_{irreversible}$$

The irreversible potential required is known as **overvoltage** and may be traced to three general causes:

First. The potential necessary to overcome the resistance of the solution.

Second. If a large current is flowing, the resistance of the electrolyte may increase very markedly, due to the rapidity with which the ions are being used up in the immediate vicinity of the

TABLE I

OVERVOLTAGES, IN VOLTS, OF HYDROGEN, OXYGEN, AND CHLORINE AT 25° C.

CURRENT DENSITIES IN AMPERES PER CM.²

NATURE OF ELECTRODE	H_2 IN 1 M H_2SO_4 Current Density 0.001 / 0.01 / 0.1 / 1.0				H_2 IN 1 M NaOH Current Density 0.01	O_2 IN 1 M NaOH Current Density 0.01 / 0.1 / 1.0			O_2 IN 1 M H_2SO_4 Current Density 0.1	Cl_2 IN NaCl Current Density 0.01 / 0.1	
Pt (smooth)		0.07	0.28	0.68	0.54	0.85	1.28	1.49	0.4	0.03	0.05
Pt (black)	0.003	0.03	0.04	0.05		0.52	0.64	0.77		0.02	0.03
Au	0.12	0.39	0.59	0.80		0.96	1.24	1.63			
Cu	0.35	0.58	0.80	1.25	0.91	0.58	0.66	0.79			
Ag	0.30	0.76	0.87	1.08	0.61	0.73	0.98	1.13			
Al	0.50	0.83	1.00	1.29							
Sn	0.40	1.08	1.22	1.23	0.94						
Zn		0.75	1.06	1.23	1.05						
Pb		1.09	1.18	1.26							
Fe	0.22	0.56	0.81	1.29	0.54	0.55					
Hg	0.6	1.04	1.06	1.12							
C (graphite)	0.31	0.78	0.98	1.22		0.90	1.09	1.24			0.25

electrodes.   This effect is sometimes known as **concentration polarization.**

Third. Many of the electrode reactions are slow, and in order to get them to go with the speed required by large currents, additional potential or driving force must be used.   This is especially true of gas reactions.   These overvoltages depend not only upon the current density but also upon the nature of the electrode, as is indicated by the experimental results given in Table I. Overvoltage decreases with increasing temperature.

TABLE II

OVERVOLTAGES OF METAL IONS, VOLTS

ELECTRODE	CURRENT DENSITY, I/cm.²		
	0.0001	0.002	0.1
Fe in Fe^{++}	0.129	0.141	0.3
Cu in Cu^{++}	0.011	0.013	0.02
Ag in Ag^{+}			0.00
Zn in Zn^{++}			0.02
Ni in Ni^{++}			0.8

Appendix II

STANDARD OXIDATION–REDUCTION POTENTIALS

Values, in Volts, Referred to the Hydrogen-Hydrogen Ion Couple as Zero, Are for Unit Activities and Temperature of 25° C.

(Cf. notes at end of table)

Acid Solutions

Couple	E°	Couple		E°
$Li = Li^+ + e^-$	3.045	$Mn = Mn^{++} + 2e^-$		1.18
$K = K^+ + e^-$	2.925	$V = V^{++} + 2e^-$	*ca.*	1.18
$Rb = Rb^+ + e^-$	2.925	$Ti + H_2O = TiO^{++}$		
$Cs = Cs^+ + e^-$	2.923	$\quad + 2H^+ + 4e^-$		0.89
$Ba = Ba^{++} + 2e^-$	2.90	$B + 3H_2O = H_3BO_3$		
$Sr = Sr^{++} + 2e^-$	2.89	$\quad + 3H^+ + 3e^-$		0.87
$Ca = Ca^{++} + 2e^-$	2.87	$Si + 2H_2O = SiO_2$		
$Na = Na^+ + e^-$	2.714	$\quad + 4H^+ + 4e^-$		0.86
$La = La^{+++} + 3e^-$	2.52	$2Ta + 5H_2O = Ta_2O_5^-$		
$Nd = Nd^{+++} + 3e^-$	2.44	$\quad + 10H^+ + 10e^-$		0.81
$Gd = Gd^{+++} + 3e^-$	2.40	$Zn = Zn^{++} + 2e^-$		0.763
$Mg = Mg^{++} + 2e^-$	2.37	$Cr = Cr^{+++} + 3e^-$		0.74
$Y = Y^{+++} + 3e^-$	2.37	$H_2Te = Te + 2H^+$		
$Lu = Lu^{+++} + 3e^-$	2.25	$\quad + 2e^-$		0.72
$H^- = \frac{1}{2}H_2 + e^-$	2.25	$2Nb + 5H_2O = Nb_2O_5$		
$H(g) = H^+ + e^-$	2.10	$\quad + 10H^+ + 10e^-$		0.65
$Sc = Sc^{+++} + 3e^-$	2.08	$AsH_3 = As + 3H^+ + 3e^-$		0.60
$Th = Th^{+4} + 4e^-$	1.90	$Ga = Ga^{+++} + 3e^-$		0.53
$Be = Be^{++} + 2e^-$	1.85	$SbH_3(g) = Sb + 3H^+$		
$U = U^{+++} + 3e^-$	1.80	$\quad + 3e^-$		0.51
$Hf = Hf^{+4} + 4e^-$	1.70	$P + 2H_2O = H_3PO_2$		
$Al = Al^{+++} + 3e^-$	1.66	$\quad + H^+ + e^-$		0.51
$Ti = Ti^{++} + 2e^-$	1.63	$H_2PO_2 + H_2O = H_3PO_3$		
$Zr = Zr^{+4} + 4e^-$	1.53	$\quad + 2H^+ + 2e^-$		0.50
$Si + 6F^- = SiF_6^{--}$		$Fe = Fe^{++} + 2e^-$		0.440
$\quad + 4e^-$	1.2	$Cr^{++} = Cr^{+++} + e^-$		0.41
$Ti + 6F^- \rightleftharpoons TiF_6^{--}$		$Cd = Cd^{++} + 2e^-$		0.403
$\quad + 4e^-$	1.18	$H_2Se = Se + 2H^+ + 2e^-$		0.40

Acid Solutions (Cont'd)

COUPLE	$E°$	COUPLE	$E°$
$Ti^{++} = Ti^{+++} + e^-$	ca. 0.37	$Re + 4H_2O = ReO_4^-$ $+ 8H^+ + 7e^-$	− 0.363
$In = In^{+++} + 3e^-$	0.342		
$Tl = Tl^+ + e^-$	0.3363	$Rh + 6Cl^- = RhCl_6^{---}$	
$Co = Co^{++} + 2e^-$	0.277	$+ 3e^-$	− 0.44
$H_3PO_3 = H_3PO_4 + 2H^+$ $+ 2e^-$	0.276	$S + 3H_2O = H_2SO_3$ $+ 4H^+ + 4e^-$	− 0.45
$V^{++} = V^{+++} + e^-$	0.255	$ReO_2 + 2H_2O = ReO_4^-$	
$V + 4H_2O = V(OH)_4^+$ $+ 4H^+ + 5e^-$	0.253	$+ 4H^+ + 3e^-$	− 0.51
		$Cu = Cu^+ + e^-$	− 0.521
$Ni = Ni^{++} + 2e^-$	0.250	$Te + 2H_2O = TeO_2(s)$	
$Mo = Mo^{+++} + 3e^-$	ca. 0.2	$+ 4H^+ + 4e^-$	− 0.529
$Ag + I^- = AgI + e^-$	0.151	$2I^- = I_2 + 2e^-$	− 0.5355
$Sn = Sn^{++} + 2e^-$	0.136	$3I^- = I_3^- + 2e^-$	− 0.536
$Pb = Pb^{++} + 2e^-$	0.126	$Te + 2H_2O = TeOOH^+$	
$Ge + 2H_2O = GeO_2$ $+ 4H^+ + 4e^-$	0.1	$+ 3H^+ + 4e^-$	− 0.559
$W + 3H_2O = WO_3(c)$ $+ 6H^+ + 6e^-$	0.09	$HAsO_2 + 2H_2O$ $= H_3AsO_4 + 2H^+$ $+ 2e^-$	− 0.559
$H_2 = 2H^+ + 2e^-$	0.00	$MnO_4^{--} = MnO_4^- + e^-$	− 0.564
$PH_3(g) = P + 3H^+$ $+ 3e^-$	− 0.06	$Pt + 4Br^- = PtBr_4^{--}$ $+ 2e^-$	− 0.58
$Ti^{+++} + H_2O = TiO^{++}$ $+ 2H^+ + 2e^-$	− 0.1	$2SbO^+ + 3H_2O = Sb_2O_5$ $+ 6H^+ + 4e^-$	− 0.581
$SiH_4 = Si + 4H^+ + 4e^-$	− 0.102	$Pd + 4Br^- = PdBr_4^{--}$ $+ 2e^-$	− 0.6
$CH_4 = C + 4H^+ + 4e^-$	− 0.13	$Ru + 5Cl^- = RuCl_5^{--}$	
$H_2S = S + 2H^+ + 2e^-$	− 0.141	$+ 3e^-$	− 0.60
$Sn^{++} = Sn^{+4} + 2e^-$	− 0.15	$U^{+4} + 2H_2O = UO_2^{++}$	
$2Sb + 3H_2O = Sb_2O_3$ $+ 6H^+ + 6e^-$	− 0.152	$+ 4H^+ + 2e^-$	− 0.62
$Cu^+ = Cu^{++} + e^-$	− 0.153	$Pd + 4Cl^- = PdCl_4^{--}$ $+ 2e^-$	− 0.62
$Bi + H_2O + Cl^-$ $= BiOCl + 2H^+$ $+ 3e^-$	− 0.16	$Au + 4CNS^-$ $= Au(CNS)_4^- + 3e^-$	− 0.66
$H_2SO_3 + H_2O = SO_4^{--}$ $+ 4H^+ + 2e^-$	− 0.17	$H_2O_2 = O_2 + 2H^+ + 2e^-$	− 0.682
$As + 2H_2O = HAsO_2(aq)$ $+ 3H^+ + 3e^-$	− 0.247	$Pt + 4Cl^- = PtCl_4^{--}$ $+ 2e^-$	− 0.73
$Re + 2H_2O = ReO_2$ $+ 4H^+ + 4e^-$	− 0.252	$Se + 3H_2O = H_2SeO_3$ $+ 4H^+ + 4e^-$	− 0.74
$Bi + H_2O = BiO^+$ $+ 2H^+ + 3e^-$	− 0.32	$2CNS^- = (CNS)_2 + 2e^-$	− 0.77
$U^{+4} + 2H_2O = UO_2^{++}$ $+ 4H^+ + 2e^-$	− 0.334	$Ir + 6Cl^- = IrCl_6^{---}$ $+ 3e^-$	− 0.77
$Cu = Cu^{++} + 2e^-$	− 0.337	$Fe^{++} = Fe^{+++} + e^-$	− 0.771
$Fe(CN)_6^{-4}$ $= Fe(CN)_6^{---} + e^-$	− 0.36	$2Hg = Hg_2^{++} + 2e^-$	− 0.789
		$Ag = Ag^+ + e^-$	− 0.7991
$V^{+++} + H_2O = VO^{++}$ $+ 2H^+ + e^-$	− 0.361	$Rh = Rh^{+++} + 3e^-$	ca. − 0.8
		$Os + 4H_2O = OsO_4(c)$ $+ 8H^+ + 8e^-$	− 0.85
		$Hg_2^{++} = 2Hg^{++} + 2e^-$	− 0.920

Acid Solutions (Concluded)

Couple	E°	Couple	E°
$HNO_2 + H_2O = NO_3^-$ $+ 3H^+ + 2e^-$	$- 0.94$	$N_2H_5^+ + 2H_2O$ $= 2NH_3OH^+ + H^+$ $+ 2e^-$	$- 1.42$
$NO + 2H_2O = NO_3^-$ $+ 4H^+ + 4e^-$	$- 0.96$	$\frac{1}{2}I_2 + H_2O = HIO + H^+$ $+ e^-$	$- 1.45$
$Pu^{+3} = Pu^{+4} + e^-$	$- 0\ 97$	$Pb^{++} + 2H_2O = PbO_2$ $+ 4H^+ + 2e^-$	$- 1.455$
$Pt + 2H_2O = Pt(OH)_2$ $+ 2H^+ + 2e^-$	$- 0.98$	$Au = Au^{+++} + 3e^-$	$- 1.50$
$Pd = Pd^{++} + 2e^-$	$- 0.987$	$H_2O_2 = HO_2 + H^+ + e^-$	$- 1.5$
$IrBr_6^{-4} = IrBr_6^{-3} + e^-$	$- 0.99$	$Mn^{++} = Mn^{+++} + e^-$	$- 1.51$
$NO + H_2O = HNO_2$ $+ H^+ + e^-$	$- 1.00$	$Mn^{++} + 4H_2O = MnO_4^-$ $+ 8H^+ + 5e^-$	$- 1.51$
$Au + 4Cl^- = AuCl_4^-$ $+ 3e^-$	$- 1.00$	$Br_2 + H_2O = HBrO$ $+ H^+ + e^-$	$- 1.59$
$VO^{++} + 3H_2O$ $= V(OH)_4^+ + 2H^+$ $+ e^-$	$- 1.00$	$2BiO^+ = Bi_2O_4 + 2H_2O$ $+ 4H^+ + 2e^-$	$- 1.59$
$IrCl_6^{---} = IrCl_6^{--}$ $+ e^-$	$- 1.017$	$IO_3^- + 3H_2O = H_5IO_6$ $+ H^+ + 2e^-$	$- 1.6$
$TeO_2 + 4H_2O$ $= H_6TeO_6(c) + 2H^+$ $+ 2e^-$	$- 1.02$	$\frac{1}{2}Cl_2 + H_2O = HClO$ $+ H^+ + e^-$	$- 1.63$
$Pu^{+4} + 2H_2O = PuO_2^{++}$ $+ 4H^+ + 2e^-$	$- 1.04$	$HClO + H_2O = HClO_2$ $+ 2H^+ + 2e^-$	$- 1.64$
$2Br^- = Br_2(l) + 2e^-$	$- 1.0652$	$Au = Au^+ + e^-$	$ca. - 1.68$
$H_2SeO_3 + H_2O = SeO_4^{--}$ $+ 4H^+ + 2e^-$	$- 1.15$	$Ni^{++} + 2H_2O = NiO_2$ $+ 4H^+ + 2e^-$	$- 1.68$
$ClO_3^- + H_2O = ClO_4^-$ $+ 2H^+ + 2e^-$	$- 1.19$	$PbSO_4 + 2H_2O = PbO_2$ $+ SO_4^{--} + 4H^+$ $+ 2e^-$	$- 1.685$
$\frac{1}{2}I_2 + 3H_2O = IO_3^-$ $+ 6H^+ + 5e^-$	$- 1.195$	$MnO_2 + 2H_2O = MnO_4^-$ $+ 4H^+ + 3e^-$	$- 1.695$
$HClO_2 + H_2O = ClO_3^-$ $+ 3H^+ + 2e^-$	$- 1.21$	$2H_2O = H_2O_2 + 2H^+$ $+ 2e^-$	$- 1.77$
$2H_2O = O_2 + 4H^+ + 4e^-$	$- 1.229$	$Co^{++} = Co^{+++} + e^-$	$- 1.82$
$Mn^{++} + 2H_2O = MnO_2$ $+ 4H^+ + 2e^-$	$- 1.23$	$Fe^{+++} + 4H_2O = FeO_4^{--}$ $+ 8H^+ + 3e^-$	$- 1.9$
$Tl^+ = Tl^{+++} + 2e^-$	$- 1.25$	$Ag^+ = Ag^{++} + e^-$	$- 1.98$
$2NH_4^+ = N_2H_5 + 3H^+$ $+ 2e^-$	$- 1.275$	$2SO_4^{--} = S_2O_8^{--} + 2e^-$	$- 2.01$
$PdCl_4^{--} + 2Cl^-$ $= PdCl_6^{--} + 2e^-$	$- 1.288$	$O_2 + H_2O = O_3 + 2H^+$ $+ 2e^-$	$- 2.07$
$2Cr^{+++} + 7H_2O$ $= Cr_2O_7^{--} + 14H^+$ $+ 6e^-$	$- 1.33$	$H_2O = O(g) + 2H^+$ $+ 2e^-$	$- 2.42$
$NH_4^+ + H_2O = NH_3OH^+$ $+ 2H^+ + 2e^-$	$- 1.35$	$2F^- = F_2 + 2e^-$	$- 2.65$
$2Cl^- = Cl_2 + 2e^-$	$- 1.3595$	$H_2O = OH + H^+ + e^-$	$- 2.8$
		$2HF(aq) = F_2 + 2H^+$ $+ 2e^-$	$- 3.06$

Basic Solutions

Couple	E°	Couple	E°
$Ca + 2OH^- = Ca(OH)_2 + 2e^-$	3.03	$Te^{--} = Te + 2e^-$	1.14
$Sr + 2OH^- + 8H_2O = Sr(OH)_2 \cdot 8H_2O + 2e^-$	2.99	$HPO_3^{--} + 3OH^- = PO_4^{---} + 2H_2O + 2e^-$	1.12
$Ba + 8H_2O + 2OH^- = Ba(OH) \cdot 8H_2O + 2e^-$	2.97	$Mo + 6OH^- = MoO_4^{--} + 4H_2O + 6e^-$	1.05
$La + 3OH^- = La(OH)_3 + 3e^-$	2.90	$Zn + 4NH_3 = Zn(NH_3)_4^{++} + 2e^-$	1.03
$Lu + 3OH^- = Lu(OH)_3 + 3e^-$	2.72	$In + 3OH^- = In(OH)_3 + 3e^-$	1.0
$Mg + 2OH^- = Mg(OH)_2 + 2e^-$	2.69	$SO_3^{--} + 2OH^- = SO_4^{--} + H_2O + 2e^-$	0.93
$2Be + 6OH^- = Be_2O_3^{--} + 3H_2O + 4e^-$	2.62	$Se^{--} = Se + 2e^-$	0.92
$Th + 4OH^- = Th(OH)_4 + 4e^-$	2.48	$Sn + 3OH^- = HSnO_3^- + H_2O + 2e^-$	0.91
$Al + 4OH^- = H_2AlO_3^- + H_2O + 3e^-$	2.35	$Ge + 5OH^- = HGeO_3^- + 2H_2O + 4e^-$	0.9
$P + 2OH^- = H_2PO_2^- + e^-$	2.05	$HSnO_2^- + H_2O + 3OH^- = Sn(OH)_6^{--} + 2e^-$	0.90
$B + 4OH^- = H_2BO_3^- + 3e^-$	1.79	$Fe + 2OH^- = Fe(OH)_2 + 2e^-$	0.877
$Si + 6OH^- = SiO_3^{--} + 3H_2O + 4e^-$	1.70	$H_2 + 2OH^- = 2H_2O + 2e^-$	0.828
$U(OH)_4 + 2Na^+ + 4OH^- = Na_2UO_4 + 4H_2O + 2e^-$	1.61	$Cd + 2OH^- = Cd(OH)_2 + 2e^-$	0.809
$H_2PO_2^- + 3OH^- = HPO_3^{--} + 2H_2O + 2e^-$	1.57	$Co + 2OH^- = Co(OH)_2 + 2e^-$	0.73
$Mn + 2OH^- = Mn(OH)_2 + 2e^-$	1.55	$Ni + 2OH^- = Ni(OH)_2 + 2e^-$	0.72
$Cr + 3OH^- = Cr(OH)_3 + 3e^-$	1.3	$AsO_2^- + 4OH^- = AsO_4^{---} + 2H_2O + 2e^-$	0.67
$Zn + 2OH^- = Zn(OH)_2 + 2e^-$	1.245	$Sb + 4OH^- = SbO_2^- + 2H_2O + 3e^-$	0.64
$Cd + S^{--} = CdS + 2e^-$	1.24	$As + 4OH^- = AsO_2^- + 2H_2O + 3e^-$	0.68
$Ga + 4OH^- = H_2GaO_3^- + H_2O + 3e^-$	1.22	$ReO_2 + 4OH^- = ReO_4^- + 2H_2O + 3e^-$	0.594
$Zn + 4OH^- = ZnO_2^{--} + 2H_2O + 2e^-$	1.216	$Re + 8OH^- = ReO_4^- + 4H_2O + 7e^-$	0.584
$Cr + 4OH^- = CrO_2^- + H_2O + 3e^-$	1.2	$Re + 4OH^- = ReO_2 + H_2O + 4e^-$	0.576
$6V + 33OH^- = 16H_2O + HV_6O_{17}^{---} + 30e^-$	1.15	$Te + 6OH^- = TeO_3^{--} + 3H_2O + 4e^-$	0.57
		$Fe(OH)_2 + OH^- = Fe(OH)_3 + e^-$	0.56

Basic Solutions (Concluded)

COUPLE	$E°$	COUPLE	$E°$
$O_2^- = O_2 + e^-$	0.56	$I^- + 6OH^- = IO_3^- + 3H_2O + 6e^-$	-0.26
$Pb + 3OH^- = HPbO_2^- + H_2O + 2e^-$	0.54	$ClO_2^- + 2OH^- = ClO_3^- + H_2O + 2e^-$	-0.33
$S^{--} = S + 2e^-$	0.48	$2Ag + 2OH^- = Ag_2O + H_2O + 2e^-$	-0.344
$2Bi + 6OH^- = Bi_2O_3 + 3H_2O + 6e^-$	0.44	$ClO_3^- + 2OH^- = ClO_4^- + H_2O + 2e^-$	-0.36
$2Cu + 2OH^- = Cu_2O + H_2O + 2e^-$	0.358	$TeO_3^{--} + 2OH^- = TeO_4^{--} + H_2O + 2e^-$	-0.4
$Se + 6OH^- = SeO_3^{--} + 3H_2O + 4e^-$	0.366	$OH^- + HO_2^- = O_2^- + H_2O + e^-$	-0.4
$Tl + OH^- = Tl(OH) + e^-$	0.3445	$4OH^- = O_2 + 4H^+ + 4e^-$	-0.401
$OH + 2OH^- = HO_2^- + H_2O + e^-$	0.24	$Ni(OH)_2 + 2OH^- = NiO_2 + 2H_2O + 2e^-$	-0.49
$Cr(OH)_3 + 5OH^- = CrO_4^{--} + 4H_2O + 3e^-$	0.13	$I^- + 2OH^- = IO^- + H_2O + 2e^-$	-0.49
$Cu_2O + 2OH^- + H_2O = 2Cu(OH)_2 + 2e^-$	0.080	$Ag_2O + 2OH^- = 2AgO + H_2O + 2e^-$	-0.57
$HO_2^- + OH^- = O_2 + H_2O + 2e^-$	0.076	$MnO_2 + 4OH^- = MnO_4^{--} + 2H_2O + 2e^-$	-0.60
$TlOH + 2OH^- = Tl(OH)_3$	0.05	$RuO_4^{--} = RuO_4^- + e^-$	-0.60
$Mn(OH)_2 + 2OH^- = MnO_2 + H_2O + 2e^-$	0.05	$S + 6OH^- = SO_3^{--} + 3H_2O + 6e^-$	-0.61
$NO_2^- + 2OH^- = NO_3^- + H_2O + 2e^-$	-0.01	$Br^- + 6OH^- = BrO_3^- + 3H_2O + 6e^-$	-0.61
$Os + 9OH^- = HOsO_5^- + 4H_2O + 8e^-$	-0.02	$ClO^- + 2OH^- = ClO_2^- + H_2O + 2e^-$	-0.66
$2Rh + 6OH^- = Rh_2O_3 + 3H_2O + 6e^-$	-0.04	$IO_3^- + 3OH^- = H_3IO_6^{--} + 2e^-$	-0.7
$SeO_3^{--} + 2OH^- = SeO_4^{--} + H_2O + 2e^-$	-0.05	$2AgO + 2OH^- = Ag_2O_3 + H_2O + 2e^-$	-0.74
$Pd + 2OH^- = Pd(OH)_2 + 2e^-$	-0.07	$Br^- + 2OH^- = BrO^- + H_2O + 2e^-$	-0.76
$Hg + 2OH^- = HgO(r) + H_2O + 2e^-$	-0.098	$3OH^- = HO_2^- + H_2O + 2e^-$	-0.88
$Ir + 6OH^- = Ir_2O_3 + 3H_2O + 6e^-$	-0.1	$Cl^- + 2OH^- = ClO^- + H_2O + 2e^-$	-0.89
$Mn(OH)_2 = Mn(OH)_3 + e^-$	-0.1	$FeO_2^- + 4OH^- = FeO_4^{--} + 2H_2O + 3e^-$	-0.9
$Pt + 2OH^- = Pt(OH)_2 + 2e^-$	-0.15	$ClO_2^- = ClO_2 + e^-$	-1.16
$Co(OH)_2 + OH^- = Co(OH)_3 + e^-$	-0.17	$O_2 + 2OH^- = O_3 + H_2O + 2e^-$	-1.24
$PbO(r) + 2OH^- = PbO_2 + H_2O + 2e^-$	-0.248	$OH^- = OH + e^-$	-2.0

Notes on the Use of the Table of Oxidation-Reduction Potentials

The above table of important oxidation-reduction potentials has been prepared for ready reference. Additional values for couples less frequently employed will be found under the various elements.

The $E°$ values for couples involving $1M$ H^+ have been given in the first part of the table and those for couples involving $1M$ OH^- in the second part. The potential of many couples is independent of pH and although these have been included in the table for acidic reactions, they might have been repeated for the latter table.

The couples are arranged in order of increasing oxidizing power, that is, the oxidized form of any couple has sufficient energy to oxidize the reduced form of any couple of higher positive potential.

The convention regarding the sign of the $E°$ values is that used throughout the text. The couple is written with the electrons on the right side and the sign is positive if the reduced form of the couple (written on left side) is a better reducing agent than H_2.

The values, which are referred to the potential of the hydrogen-hydrogen ion couple as zero, are for 25° C. and all gas pressures, 1 atmosphere, and all activities (Append. IV), 1 molal, unless otherwise stated.

The potential at other concentrations and pressures at 25° C. is given by the expression:

$$E = E° - \frac{0.059}{n} \log Q,$$

where Q is the product of the activities (solutes in moles per liter and gases in atmospheres) of the products divided by the product of the activities of the reacting substances, each activity raised to that power whose exponent is the coefficient of the substance in the half reaction, and n is the number of moles of electrons involved in the half reaction as written. Activities of pure solids and liquids are taken as unity.

Example:

$$2Cl^-(1M) = Cl_2(1 \text{ atm.}) + 2e^-; \quad E^0 = -1.358$$

$$2Cl^-(0.01M) = Cl_2(5 \text{atm.}) + \quad 2e^-; E = E^0 - \frac{0.059}{2} \log \frac{5}{(0.01)^2}$$

$$E = -1.358 - 0.138 = -1.496$$

These potential values merely represent the difference in energies of the products and the reacting substances and as such give no information as to the speed of the reaction; indeed the mechanism of the reaction may be such that it cannot take place in spite of a favorable potential value. Thus, $Fe = Fe^{+++} + 3e^-$; $+ 0.04$ volt, indicates that H^+ would oxidize iron to the ferric state, but the mechanism of the reaction is $Fe = Fe^{++} + 2e^-$, $+ 0.44$ volt, and $Fe^{++} = Fe^{+++} + e^-$, $- 0.77$ volt, and H^+ cannot bring about the second step.

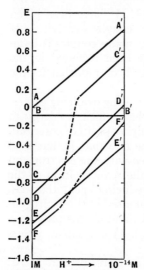

FIG. 1. Change of E with concentration of H^+.

In general it may be stated that many of the reactions given are not capable of experimental attainment under equilibrium conditions for one of two reasons: (1) the reaction is slow, as, for example, the reduction of sulfuric acid to sulfurous acid in dilute solutions, or the evolution of hydrogen on zinc which may require an overvoltage of 1.2 volts; or (2) the final and initial substances cannot exist together because of an intermediate state, as for example, the $Fe - Fe^{+++}$ couple which gives Fe^{++}, or $Cl^- + H_2O = HClO + H^+ + 2e^-$, which would give Cl_2 at $1M$ H^+.

Two half reactions may be added or subtracted to give a third half reaction but the potential of the third reaction is derived by the *addition or subtraction of the free energies* (Append. III) and not by the addition of the potential values. However, if two half reactions are subtracted to give a complete reaction, the potential of the reaction is the *difference in the potentials of the two couples*.

The change in the half reaction-potentials with change in H^+ concentration for a number of couples is shown graphically in Fig. 1. The various couples given in the figure are as follows:

A $\frac{1}{2}H_2 = H^+ + e^-$
A′ $\frac{1}{2}H_2 + OH^- = H_2O + e^-$
B $Br^- + Ag = AgBr + e^-$
C $Fe^{++} = Fe^{+++} + e^-$
C′ $OH^- + Fe(OH)_2 = Fe(OH)_3 + e^-$

D $2H_2O + NO = NO_3^- + 4H^+ + 3e^-$
D' $4OH^- + NO = NO_3^- + 2H_2O + 3e^-$
E $H_2O = \frac{1}{2}O_2 + 2H^+ + 2e^-$
E' $2OH^- = \frac{1}{2}O_2 + H_2O + 2e^-$
F $N_2O + 3H_2O = 2HNO_2 + 4H^+ + 4e^-$
F' $N_2O + 6OH^- = 2NO_2^- + 3H_2O + 4e^-$

Potential diagrams are convenient for summarizing energy relationships between the various oxidation states of an element. Thus in the following illustration,

$$
\begin{array}{ccccc}
 & 0.9 & 1.1 & -0.5 & -0.9 \\
\text{M}\rule{1cm}{0.4pt}\text{M}^+\rule{1.5cm}{0.4pt}\text{M}^{++}\rule{1cm}{0.4pt}\text{M}^{+3}\rule{1cm}{0.4pt}\text{MO}_2, \\
\lfloor \rule{3cm}{0pt} 1.0 \rule{2cm}{0pt} \rfloor
\end{array}
$$

the numerical values are $E°$ potentials for the couples involving the oxidation state to the left (reducing agent) and to the right (oxidizing agent), e.g.,

$$M^{+3} + 2H_2O = MO_2 + 4H^+ + e^- \qquad E° = -0.9 \text{ volts}$$

In the above illustration the $+1$ state is unstable, since the M–M^+ couple is less positive than the M^+–M^{++} couple.

$$2M^+ = M + M^{++} \qquad E° = 0.2 \text{ volts.}$$

The $+2$ and $+3$ states are stable with respect to similar disproportionation reactions. The metal and M^+ should be readily oxidized by H^+,

$$M + 2H^+ = M^{++} + H_2 \qquad E° = 1.0 \text{ volt.}$$

M^{++} should be oxidized by atmospheric oxygen.

$$2M^{++} + O_2 + 2H^+ = 2M^{+3} + H_2O_2 \qquad \begin{aligned} E° &= -0.5 - (-0.68) \\ &= 0.18 \text{ volt} \end{aligned}$$

The $+3$ state should not be oxidized by O_2 since the M^{+3}–MO_2 couple is more negative than the H_2O_2–O_2 couple. However M^{+3}, even in $1M$ H^+, should be oxidized by strong oxidizing agents such as chlorine.

$$2M^{+3} + Cl_2 + 4H_2O = 2MO_2 + 2Cl^- + 8H^+$$

$$E° = -0.9 - (-1.36) = 0.46 \text{ volt.}$$

Appendix III

FREE ENERGY VALUES AND THEIR USE

Summary of concepts relating to free energy data, and their use in predicting the direction and extent to which a given reaction will proceed:

(1) The free energy of a process is the maximum available work which is obtainable in going from the initial to the final state. The free energy change, ΔF, of a chemical reaction is the free energies of formation (from their elements) of the products of the reaction, less the free energy of formation of the reacting substances. *Example:* $CaO + 2HCl = CaCl_2 + H_2O$; $\Delta F = F_{CaCl_2} + F_{H_2O} - F_{CaO} - 2F_{HCl}$.

(2) The free energy values for the substances in Table I refer to energy of formation from the elements at $25°$ in their standard states or states of unit activity, which are pure solid, pure liquid, gas at one atmosphere, and solute at 1 molal activity. The free energy of a reaction, in which all the substances are at unit activity and at temperature T, is designated as $\Delta F°_T$. The free energies of all elements and of H^+ are taken as zero in their standard states.

(3) The relation between the free energy change for substances in their standard states and the equilibrium constant, K, is
$$- RTln_eK = \Delta F°_T, \text{ or } - 1364 \log_{10}K = \Delta F°_{298°K} \text{ (in cal.)}$$
where R is the gas constant and T the absolute temperature. The more general relation is:

$$- RTlnK/Q = \Delta F_T$$

where Q has the same form as the equilibrium constant, but the concentrations refer to the values of the substances in their initial and final states. If these are unity, then Q is unity and the free energy is $\Delta F°$.

Example: We may calculate the equilibrium constant for the reaction: $Cl_{2(aq.)} + H_2O_{(liq.)} = H^+ + Cl^- + HClO_{(sol.)}$, from

536

the value $\Delta F°_{298} = 4600$.   Hence $- \log_{10} K = 4600/1364$; $K = (H^+)(Cl^-)(HClO)/(Cl_2) = 4.3 \times 10^{-4}$.

(4) It follows from this relation that a large negative value for ΔF means a large value for K or that the reaction as written is capable of proceeding to practical completion. It must be emphasized again, however, that free energies give no information as to the speed of the reaction.

(5) The reversible electromotive force, E, is a direct measure of the maximum available work or free energy of a chemical reaction: $n \cdot 23066$. $E = - \Delta F$ where n is the number of Faradays of electricity which flow through the circuit, and ΔF is given in calories.

Example: $Ag^+ + \frac{1}{2}H_2 = H^+ + Ag$; $E° = 0.7995$.

$$\Delta F° = - 0.7995 \times 23066 = - 18440 \text{ cal.}$$

Since the free energies of H_2, H^+, and Ag are zero by definition, $F°_{298}$ of Ag^+ is 18440.

Example: To calculate the solubility product of AgCl at 25° C.

$$\begin{array}{ll} Ag + Cl^- = AgCl + e^- & - 0.2222 \text{ volt} \\ Ag = Ag^+ + e^- & - 0.7995 \quad " \\ \hline Ag^+ + Cl^- = AgCl & 0.5773 \text{ volt} \end{array}$$

Hence $\Delta F° = - 0.5773 \times 23066 = - 1365 \log 1/K$, and $K = 1.8 \times 10^{-10}$.

TABLE OF STANDARD FREE ENERGIES OF FORMATION AT 25° C.

Values for many positive ions which may be calculated directly from the oxidation-reduction potentials have not been included, cf. Ag^+, P.(5) above.

SUBSTANCE	$\Delta F°$	SUBSTANCE	$\Delta F°$
$H_2O(g)$	− 54,635	$HBrO(aq)$	− 19,900
$H_2O(liq)$	− 56,690	$HBrO_3(aq)$	5,000
OH^-	− 37,595	I_3^-	− 12,310
$H_2O_2(aq)$	− 31,470	$HI(g)$	310
$HF(g)$	− 64,700	$HI(aq)$	− 12,350
$HF(aq)$	− 70,000	$HIO_3(aq)$	− 32,250
HF_2^-	− 137,300	ICl_2^-	− 38,350
$HCl(g)$	− 22,769	$H_2S(g)$	− 7,892
$HCl(aq)$	− 31,350	$H_2S(aq)$	− 6,540
$HClO(aq)$	− 19,100	$SO_2(g)$	− 71,790
$HClO_2(aq)$	70	$H_2SO_3(aq)$	− 128,590
$HClO_3(aq)$	− 620	$H_2SO_4(aq)$	− 177,340
$HClO_4(aq)$	− 2,470	$H_2Se(g)$	17,000
$HBr(g)$	− 12,720	$H_2Se(aq)$	18,400
$HBr(aq)$	− 24,574	SeO_3^{--}	− 89,330

TABLE OF STANDARD FREE ENERGIES (*Cont'd*)

SUBSTANCE	ΔF°	SUBSTANCE	ΔF°
SeO_4^{--}	− 105,420	C_6H_6(liq)	41,300
H_2SeO_3(aq)	− 101,800	CCl_4(liq)	− 16,430
H_2Te(g)	33,100	C_2H_2(g)	50,000
H_2Te(aq)	34,100	C_2H_4(g)	16,282
TeO_3^{--}	− 108,000	SiH_4(g)	− 9,400
H_6TeO_6(aq)	− 167,900	SiO_2(quartz)	− 192,400
NH_3(g)	− 3,976	SiO_3^{--}	− 212,000
$NH_4(OH)$(aq)	− 63,050	SiF_6^{--}	− 511,000
NH_2OH(aq)	− 5,600	$SiCl_4$(liq)	− 136,900
NH_3OH^+	− 13,540	GeO_2(c)ppt	− 114,300
$N_2H_5^+$	21,000	H_2GeO_3(aq)	− 169,200
N_2H_4(aq)	30,560	SnO(c)	− 61,500
HN_3(aq)	71,300	SnO_2(c)	− 124,200
NO(g)	20,719	$Sn(OH)_2$(c)	− 117,600
NO_2(g)	12,390	$Sn(OH)_4$(c)	− 227,500
NO_2^-	− 8,250	$Sn(OH)_6^{--}$	− 310,500
NO_3^-	− 26,430	$HSnO_2^-$	− 98,000
N_2O_4(g)	23,491	PbO(c) red	− 45,250
$H_2N_2O_2$(aq)	8,600	$Pb(OH)_2$(c)	− 100,600
PH_3(g)	4,360	PbO_2(c)	− 52,340
H_3PO_2(aq)	− 125,100	Pb_3O_4(c)	− 147,600
H_3PO_3(aq)	− 204,800	$PbCl_2$(c)	− 75,040
H_3PO_4(aq)	− 274,200	$PbBr_2$(c)	− 62,240
AsH_3(g)	42,000	PbI_2(c)	− 41,530
$HAsO_2$(aq)	− 96,250	PbS(c)	− 22,150
As_4O_6(c)	− 275,360	$PbSO_4$(c)	− 193,890
As_2O_5(c)	− 184,600	$PbCO_3$(c)	− 149,700
H_3AsO_4(aq)	− 183,800	$PbCrO_4$(c)	− 203,600
SbH_3(g)	35,300	GaO_3^{--}	− 148,000
SbO^+	− 42,000	$Ga(OH)_3$(c)	− 199,000
Sb_4O_6(c)	− 298,000	Ga_2O_3(c)	− 237,200
Sb_2O_5(c)	− 200,500	In_2O_3(c)	− 200,500
BiO^+	− 34,500	$In(OH)_3$(c)	− 182,000
$Bi(OH)_3$(c)	− 137,000	Tl_2O(c)	− 32,500
$BiOCl$(c)	− 77,000	$Tl(OH)$(c)	− 45,500
$BiCl_4^-$	− 114,200	$Tl(OH)_3$(c)	− 123,000
CH_4(g)	− 12,140	$Tl_2(SO_4)$(c)	− 196,800
CO(g)	− 32,808	$TlCl$(c)	− 21,000
CO_2(g)	− 94,260	$TlBr$(c)	− 39,700
H_2CO_3(aq)	− 149,000	TlI(c)	− 29,700
$HCOOH$(aq)	− 85,100	ZnO(c)	− 76,050
HCO_3^-	− 140,310	$Zn(OH)_2$(c)	− 132,600
CO_3^{--}	− 126,220	ZnS(c) ppt.	− 43,200
$HCHO$(aq)	− 31,000	ZnO_2^{--}	− 93,030
CH_3OH(liq)	− 39,750	$ZnCO_3$(c)	− 174,800
HCN(aq)	26,800	CdO(c)	− 53,790
CN^-	39,600	$Cd(OH)_2$(c)	− 112,460
CNS^-	21,200	CdS(c)	− 33,600

TABLE OF STANDARD FREE ENERGIES (*Cont'd*)

SUBSTANCE	$\Delta F°$	SUBSTANCE	$\Delta F°$
$CdCO_3(c)$	− 160,200	$Pd(OH)_2(c)$	− 72,000
$HgO(c)$ red	− 13,990	$PdCl_4^{--}$	− 96,700
$Hg(OH)_2(aq)$	− 65,700	$PdCl_6^{--}$	− 99,600
$HgCl_4^{--}$	− 102,400	$Pt(OH)_2$	− 68,200
$Hg_2Cl_2(c)$	− 50,350	$PtCl_4^{--}$	− 91,900
$Hg_2Br_2(c)$	− 42,714	$'PtCl_6^{--}$	− 123,100
$Hg_2I_2(c)$	− 26,600	$PtS(c)$	− 21,600
HgI_4^{--}	− 51,150	$PtS_2(c)$	− 25,600
$HgS(c)$ black	− 11,050	$CoO(c)$	− 49,000
$Hg_2S(c)$	− 1,600	$Co(OH)_2(c)$	− 109,000
HgS_2^{--}	11,600	$Co(OH)_3(c)$	− 142,600
$Hg_2SO_4(c)$	− 149,120	$CoS(c)$ ppt.	− 19,800
$Cu_2O(c)$	− 34,980	$CoCO_3(c)$	− 155,570
$CuO(c)$	− 30,400	$RhO(c)$	− 16,000
$Cu(OH)_2(c)$	− 85,300	$Rh_2O(c)$	− 19,100
$CuCl(c)$	− 28,200	$Rh_2O_3(c)$	− 50,000
$CuBr(c)$	− 23,810	$RhCl_6^{---}(c)$	− 158,300
$CuI(c)$	− 16,620	$IrO_2(c)$	− 28,000
$CuSO_4·5H_2O(c)$	− 449,300	$Ir_2O_3(c)$	− 42,000
$Cu_2S(c)$	− 20,600	$IrCl_6^{--}$	− 111,200
$CuS(c)$	− 11,700	$IrCl_6^{---}$	− 134,700
$Cu(NH_3)_4^{++}$	− 28,100	$FeO(c)$	− 58,400
$Ag_2O(c)$	− 2,586	$Fe_2O_3(c)$	− 177,100
$AgO(c)$	2,600	$Fe(OH)_2(c)$	− 115,570
$AgCl(c)$	− 26,224	$Fe(OH)_3(c)$	− 165,000
$AgBr(c)$	− 22,930	$FeS(c)$	− 23,320
$AgI(c)$	− 15,850	$FeCO_3(c)$	− 161,060
$AgCN(c)$	39,200	$RuO_2(c)$	− 40,700
$Ag_2S(c)$ rhom.	− 9,620	$RuO_4(g)$	− 33,000
$Ag_2CrO_4(c)$	− 154,700	$OsO_4(g)$	− 67,900
$AgNO_2(c)$	4,744	$OsO_4(c)$ white	− 70,500
$Ag_2C_2O_4(c)$	− 137,200	$OsO_2(c)$	− 50,000
$AgNO_3(c)$	− 7,690	$OsCl_6^{--}$	− 119,000
$AgCNS(c)$	23,300	$OsS_2(c)$	− 34,400
$Au_2O_3(c)$	39,000	$MnO(c)$	− 86,800
$Au(OH)_3(c)$	− 69,300	$Mn(OH)_2(c)$	− 146,900
$H_2AuO_3^-$	− 45,800	$MnO_2(c)$ pyrolusite	− 111,100
$AuCl(c)$	− 4,200	$MnS(c)$ ppt.	− 52,100
$AuCl_4^-$	− 56,200	$MnCO_3(c)$ ppt.	− 194,300
$AuBr_4^-$	− 38,100	$ReO_2(c)$	− 90,200
$Au(CN)_2^-$	64,400	$HReO_4(aq)$	− 189,400
$Au(CNS)_4^{--}$	128,800	$Cr_2O_3(c)$	− 250,200
$NiO(c)$	− 51,700	$Cr(OH)_2(c)$	− 141,000
$NiO_2(c)$	− 47,500	$Cr(OH)_3(c)$	− 215,300
$NiS(c)\alpha$	− 16,400	$MoO_2(c)$	− 117,300
$NiS(c)\gamma$	− 26,000	$MoO_3(c)$	− 161,950
$Ni(CN)_4^{--}$	117,100	$MoS_3(c)$	− 57,600
$PdO(c)$	− 14,400	$WO_2(c)$	− 124,400

TABLE OF STANDARD FREE ENERGIES (*Cont'd*)

SUBSTANCE	$\Delta F°$	SUBSTANCE	$\Delta F°$
$WO_3(c)$	$-$ 182,470	$AmO_2(c)$	$-$ 231,000
$WS_2(c)$	$-$ 46,200	$Am(OH)_3(c)$	$-$ 300,000
$V_2O_3(c)$	$-$ 271,000	$Be(OH)_2(c)$	$-$ 196,200
V_2O_5	$-$ 344,000	$MgO(c)$	$-$ 136,130
Nb_2O_5	$-$ 432,000	$Mg(OH)_2(c)$	$-$ 199,270
Ta_2O_5	$-$ 470,600	$MgSO_4(c)$	$-$ 280,500
$TiO_2(c)$ rutile	$-$ 203,800	$CaO(c)$	$-$ 144,400
$TiO(OH)_2(c)$	$-$ 253,000	$Ca(OH)_2(c)$	$-$ 214,330
$Ti_2O_3(c)$	$-$ 346,000	$CaCO_3(c)$ calcite	$-$ 269,780
$TiCl_4(liq)$	$-$ 161,200	$CaSO_4·2H_2O(c)$	$-$ 429,190
$ZrO_2(c)$	$-$ 244,400	$SrO(c)$	$-$ 133,800
$Zr(OH)_4(c)$	$-$ 370,000	$Sr(OH)_2(c)$	$-$ 207,800
$HZrO_3^-$	$-$ 287,700	$SrSO_4(c)$	$-$ 318,900
$HfO_2(c)$	$-$ 258,000	$SrCO_3(c)$	$-$ 271,900
$B_2O_3(c)$	$-$ 283,000	$BaO(c)$	$-$ 126,300
$B_2H_6(g)$	19,800	$Ba(OH_2)(c)$	$-$ 204,700
$H_3BO_3(c)$	$-$ 230,200	$BaSO_4(c)$	$-$ 323,400
$H_3BO_3(aq)$	$-$ 230,240	$BaCO_3(c)$	$-$ 272,200
$B_4O_7^{--}$	$-$ 616,000	$Li(OH)(c)$	$-$ 105,900
BF_4^-	$-$ 343,000	$LiCl(c)$	$-$ 91,700
$Al_2O_3(c)$	$-$ 376,770	$Li_2SO_4(c)$	$-$ 316,600
$Al(OH)_3(c)$	$-$ 271,900	$Na(OH)(c)$	$-$ 90,100
AlF_6^{---}	$-$ 539,600	$NaCl(c)$	$-$ 91,785
$Sc(OH)_3(c)$	$-$ 293,500	$Na_2SO_4(c)$	$-$ 302,520
ScF_6^{---}	$-$ 565,000	$Na_2CO_3(c)$	$-$ 250,400
$Y(OH)_3(c)$	$-$ 307,100	$NaHCO_3(c)$	$-$ 203,600
$La(OH)_3(c)$	$-$ 313,200	$KOH(c)$	$-$ 89,500
$Gd(OH)_3(c)$	$-$ 308,000	$KCl(c)$	$-$ 97,592
$ThO_2(c)$	$-$ 278,400	$K_2SO_4(c)$	$-$ 314,620
$Th(OH)_4(c)$	$-$ 379,000	$K_2CO_3(c)$	$-$ 261,200
$UO_2(c)$	$-$ 257,000	$Rb(OH)(c)$	$-$ 87,100
$UO_3(c)$	$-$ 283,000	$RbCl(c)$	$-$ 96,800
$UF_4(c)$	$-$ 421,000	$Rb_2SO_4(c)$	$-$ 312,800
$UF_5(c)$	$-$ 421,000	$Rb_2CO_3(c)$	$-$ 249,300
$U(OH)_4(c)$	$-$ 351,600	$Cs(OH)(c)$	$-$ 84,900
$UCl_6(c)$	$-$ 241,500	$CsCl(c)$	$-$ 96,600
$Pu(OH)_3(c)$	$-$ 280,200	$Cs_2SO_4(c)$	$-$ 310,700
$Pu(OH)_4(c)$	$-$ 340,000	$Cs_2CO_3(c)$	$-$ 243,600

Appendix IV

IONIZATION OF STRONG ELECTROLYTES

The freezing point lowering of a molal solution of a strong electrolyte such as sodium chloride is somewhat less than twice the molal freezing point lowering (cf. Hildebrand, *Prin. of Chem.*, p. 59) and the assumption was formerly made that the sodium chloride was only partially ionized. It is now believed that the sodium chloride is completely ionized in the sense that

TABLE I

Activity Coefficient of Typical Electrolytes at 25° C.

Molality	0.01	0.05	0.10	1.0
KOH	0.90	0.82	0.80	0.76
$AgNO_3$	0.90	0.77	0.72	0.40
KIO_3	0.88	0.76	0.69	
$BaCl_2$	0.72	0.56	0.49	0.39
$CdCl_2$	0.47	0.28	0.21	0.06
K_2SO_4	0.71	0.52	0.43	
H_2SO_4	0.54	0.34	0.26	0.13
$MgSO_4$	0.40	0.22	0.18	0.06
$CuSO_4$	0.41	0.21	0.16	0.05
$La(NO_3)_2$	0.57	0.39	0.33	
NaCl	0.90	0.82	0.78	0.66
$NaNO_3$	0.90	0.82	0.77	0.55
$ZnCl_2$	0.71	0.56	0.50	0.33
NH_4Cl	0.88	0.79	0.74	0.57
$CdSO_4$	0.40	0.21	0.17	0.04
NaI	0.91	0.86	0.83	0.80

the ions are capable of independent motion, and that the apparent non-ionization is due to the forces acting between an ion and its neighbors in general rather than its attachment to any particular ion. Since this force causes a departure of the ions from the behavior of perfect solutions, it is necessary to use a corrected con-

541

centration, called **activity,** a, in all thermodynamic relations, and the ratio of the activity to the concentration (molality) is defined as the **activity coefficient,** $\gamma = a/c$. At infinite dilution the force between the ions is zero, and the activity equals the concentration, i.e., $\gamma = 1$ (Fig. 1). As the concentration increases, the activity

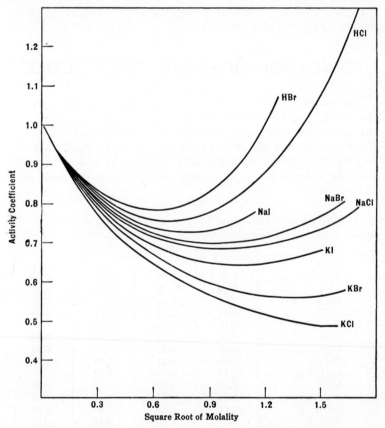

FIG. 1.   Activity coefficient of hydrogen and alkali halides.

coefficient becomes less than unity, due to the attraction of the oppositely charged ions (Debye and Hückel theory), but at high concentrations other factors enter such as the force of repulsion between the large hydrated ions, or the change in hydration of the ions, and the coefficient may become greater than unity.

It is not possible to measure the activity of an ion of one sign independent of the ion of opposite sign, i.e., Na^+ is not independent of Cl^- in NaCl; hence the activity is determined as the mean of both ions, and the activity coefficient expressed as the mean activity divided by the mean molality. The mean activity and molality are defined in such a manner (cf. Lewis and Randall, *Thermodynamics*, p. 328) that the ratio approaches unity at infinite dilution for all types of salts.

Appendix V

CRYSTAL FORMS AND TYPES OF CRYSTAL LATTICE

A crystal is classified according to the **elements of symmetry** which it possesses. Symmetry is determined by the following operations required to bring the crystal into coincidence with its original position.

(a) **Rotation about an Axis.**—If a crystal can be revolved about an axis through its center so that similar faces recur n times in one rotation, it is said to possess n fold symmetry about this axis. Only axes of two-, three-, four-, and six-fold symmetry are known or in fact are possible with a system of particles at finite distances apart.

(b) **Reflection in a Plane.**—A crystal which may be divided by a plane into two parts, mirror images of each other, is said to possess symmetry about this plane.

(c) **Inversion about the Center.**—If every line drawn through the center cuts similar parallel faces on opposite sides of the center, the crystal is said to possess a center of symmetry.

(d) **Simultaneous Rotation and Reflection.**—If a crystal can be revolved about an axis so that n times in one rotation faces recur which are alternate mirror images, the crystal is said to possess an axis of composite symmetry. Only four- and six-fold axes of composite symmetry can occur.

Crystal Classes.—There are 31 possible combinations of these four types of symmetry and these, together with the crystal without any symmetry, constitute the 32 crystal types.

The 32 types are grouped into six **crystal systems** with the following characteristics:

(1) **Isometric or Cubic.**—This system includes all crystals having three interchangeable axes at right angles. All crystals have 4 axes of three-fold symmetry. One of the most important

544

forms is the cube which has 3 axes of four-fold symmetry, 4 axes of three-fold symmetry which also have six-fold composite symmetry, 6 axes of two-fold symmetry, nine planes of symmetry and a center of symmetry. Other forms are the octahedron, dodecahedron, and tetrahedron.

(2) **Tetragonal.**—One four-fold axis (may be four-fold composite axis) and two interchangeable axes at right angles to the principal axis and to each other. The tetragonal prism is a common form.

(3) **Hexagonal.**—One three-fold or six-fold axis of symmetry. Three interchangeable lateral axes of reference are generally employed which are perpendicular to the axes of symmetry and intersect each other at 120°. Hexagonal prisms, hexagonal bipyramids, and rhombohedra are common forms.

FIG. 1. Body-centered cubic. Structure of Cr, Fe (alpha), Li, Na, K, Mo, Ta, V, W.

FIG. 2. Face-centered cubic. Structure of Ag, Al, Au, Ca, Ce, Co (cubic), Cu, Fe (gamma), Ir, Ni, Pb, Pt, Th, A.

FIG. 3. Hexagonal close-packed. Structure of Be, Cd, Ce, Co, Hf, Mg, Os, Ti, Tl, Zn, Zr.

FIG. 4. Diamond type. Structure of C (diamond), Si, Sn (grey).

FIG. 5. Sodium chloride type. Structure of lithium, sodium and potassium halides: CaO, SiO, MgS, VN, NiO, CoO, FeO, AgCl, AgBr, PbS, MgO, CoF.

FIG. 6. Cesium chloride type. Structure of CsCl, CsBr, CsI, TlCl, TlBr, TlI.

FIG. 7. Zinc oxide type. Structure of ZnO, AgI, TaN, AlN, BeO.

FIG. 8. Zinc sulfide (sphalerite) type. Structure of ZnS, HgS, CuCl, CuBr, CuI, AgI.

FIG. 9. Cuprous oxide type. Structure of Cu₂O, Ag₂O.

FIG. 10. Calcium fluoride type. Structure of CaF₂, Li₂S, Li₂O, Cu₂Se, Na₂S, BaF₂,PbF₂,SrF₂,HgF₂, ThO₂, CdF₂, CeO₂, UO₂, PrO₂, SrCl₂. Ratio of radius of M to radius of X > 0.6.

FIG. 11. Rutile type. Structure of TiO₂, PbO₂, MnF₂, TeO₂, FeF₂, ZnF₂, CoF₂, NiF₂, SnO₂, MgF₂, NbO₂, MoO₂, WO₂, IrO₂, VO₂, MnO₂. Ratio of radius of M to radius of X < 0.6.

FIG. 12. Manganous hydroxide type. Structure of Mn(OH)₂, ZrS₂, CdI₂, Mg(OH)₂, Ca-(OH)₂.

FIG. 13. Wurtzite, ZnS, type. Structure of NH₄F, BeO, ZnO, CdS, MgTe, CdSe, AlN.

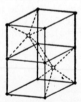

FIG. 14. NiAs type. Structure of FeS, CoS, NiS, FeSe, CoSe, CoTe.

FIG. 15. Perowskit type. Structure of CaTiO₃, KIO₃, CaZrO₃, CaSnO₃, LaAlO₃, KMgF₃.

This system is often divided so as to give a **Rhombohedral class,** crystals of which may be referred to 3 axes, all equal and all inclined unequally.

(4) **Orthorhombic.**—Crystals with three non-interchangeable axes of symmetry at right angles to each other. The rhombic prism and rhombic pyramid are common forms.

(5) **Monoclinic.**—Crystal with a single axis of symmetry but not three-, four-, or six-fold. Two additional axes of reference are chosen at right angles to the axis of symmetry and usually oblique to each other. A rhombic prism having a two-fold axis, a plane, and a center of symmetry is a common form.

(6) **Triclinic.**—Crystal possesses no direction of symmetry. Reference axes are non-interchangeable and in general at oblique angles. Two classes, with and without center of symmetry.

Appendix VI

QUALITATIVE ANALYSIS SCHEME

BASIC CONSTITUENTS

SEPARATION OF THE BASIC CONSTITUENTS INTO GROUPS

(From A. A. Noyes' Qualitative Chemical Analysis)

Solution in dilute nitric acid containing all the common basic constituents. Add NH₄Cl.

Precipitate: Silver-Group (Bi, Pb, Ag, Hg) as chlorides.	Filtrate: Saturate with H₂S gas.				
	Precipitate: Copper-Group and Tin-Group as sulfides. Treat with (NH₄)₂S₄.		**Filtrate:** Add NH₄OH and (NH₄)₂S.		
	Residue: Copper-Group (Hg, Pb, Bi, Cu, Cd), as sulfides.	Solution: Tin-Group (As, Sb, Sn), as ammonium sulfo-salts.	**Precipitate:** Aluminum-Group and Iron-Group, as hydroxides and sulfides. Dissolve in acid, add NaOH and Na₂O₂.		**Filtrate:** Add (NH₄)₂CO₃.
			Filtrate: Aluminum-Group (Al, Cr, Zn), as sodium salts.	Precipitate: Iron-Group (Mn, Fe, Co, Ni), as hydroxides.	Precipitate: Alkaline-Earth Group (Ba, Sr, Ca, Mg), as carbonates.
					Filtrate: Alkali-Group (NH₄, K, Na), as nitrates and chlorides.

ANALYSIS OF THE SILVER GROUP

Precipitate: BiOCl, PbCl₂, AgCl, Hg₂Cl₂. Treat with HCl.

Precipitate BiCl₃.	Residue: PbCl₂, AgCl, Hg₂Cl₂. Treat with hot water.			
Solution BiCl₃. Evaporate, pour into water.	Solution: PbCl₂. Add H₂SO₄.	Residue: AgCl, Hg₂Cl₂. Pour NH₄OH through the filter.		
Precipitate: BiOCl.	Precipitate: PbSO₄.	Black residue: Hg and NH₂HgCl.	Solution: (NH₃)₂AgCl. Add HNO₃.	White precipitate: AgCl.

549

SEPARATION OF THE COPPER AND TIN GROUPS

Hydrogen sulfide precipitate: HgS, PbS, Bi_2S_3, CuS, CdS, As_2S_3, As_2S_5, Sb_2S_3, Sb_2S_5, SnS, SnS_2. Treat with ammonium polysulfide.

Residue: HgS, PbS, Bi_2S_3, CuS, CdS.	Solution: $(NH_4)_3AsS_4$, $(NH_4)_3SbS_4$, $(NH_4)_2SnS_3$. Add HCl.	
	Precipitate: As_2S_5, Sb_2S_5, SnS_2.	Filtrate: NH_4Cl. Reject.

ANALYSIS OF THE COPPER GROUP

Residue from Ammonium Sulfide Treatment: HgS, PbS, Bi_2S_3, CuS, CdS. Boil with HNO_3.

Residue: HgS. Add Br_2 solution.		Solution: Pb, Bi, Cu, Cd as nitrates. Add H_2SO_4, evaporate, add water.			
Residue: Sulfur.	Solution: $HgBr_2$. Add $SnCl_2$.	Precipitate: $PbSO_4$. Dissolve in NH_4Ac. Add K_2CrO_4.	Filtrate: add NH_4OH.		
	White or grey precipitate: Hg_2Cl_2 or Hg.	Yellow precipitate: $PbCrO_4$.	Precipitate: $Bi(OH)_3$. Add Na_2SnO_2.	Filtrate: $Cu(NH_3)_4SO_4$, $Cd(NH_3)_4SO_4$.	
			Black residue: Bi.	To a small part add HAc and $K_4Fe(CN)_6$.	To the remainder add KCN and H_2S.
				Red precipitate: $Cu_2Fe(CN)_6$. White precipitate: $Cd_2Fe(CN)_6$.	Yellow precipitate: CdS. Solution: $K_3Cu(CN)_4$.

550

ANALYSIS OF THE TIN GROUP

Precipitate from Ammonium Sulfide Solution: As_2S_5, Sb_2S_5, SnS_2. Heat with 10 cc. 12 normal HCl.

Solution: $SbCl_3$, $SnCl_4$. Dilute to 50 cc., heat, and pass in H_2S.

Residue: As_2S_5. Dissolve in HCl and $KClO_3$.

Orange precipitate: Sb_2S_3. Dissolve in HCl, add Sn and Pt.

Solution: $SnCl_4$. Cool, dilute, pass in H_2S.

Solution: H_3AsO_4. Add NH_4OH, NH_4Cl, and $MgCl_2$.

Black deposit: Sb. Treat with NaClO.

Yellow precipitate: SnS_2. Evaporate without filtering, add Pb, boil.

White precipitate: $MgNH_4AsO_4$. Dissolve in HCl and add H_2S.

Black deposit: Sb.

Solution: $SnCl_2$. Add $HgCl_2$.

Yellow precipitate: As_2S_5, As_2S_3, and S.

White precipitate: Hg_2Cl_2.

SEPARATION OF THE ALUMINUM AND IRON GROUPS

The Ammonium Hydroxide and Ammonium Sulfide Precipitate: $Al(OH)_3$, $Cr(OH)_3$, FeS, ZnS, MnS, CoS, NiS. Dissolve in HCl and HNO_3, add NaOH.

Precipitate: $Fe(OH)_3$, $Mn(OH)_2$, $Co(OH)_2$, $Ni(OH)_2$.
Solution: $NaAlO_2$, $NaCrO_2$, Na_2ZnO_2.
Add Na_2O_2 and filter.

Precipitate: $Fe(OH)_3$, $MnO(OH)_2$, $Co(OH)_3$, $Ni(OH)_2$.

Filtrate: $NaAlO_2$, Na_2CrO_4, Na_2ZnO_2.

551

Filtrate from the Sodium Hydroxide and Peroxide Treatment: Na_2ZnO_2, $NaAlO_2$, Na_2CrO_4. Acidify with HNO_3 and add NH_4OH.

Precipitate: $Al(OH)_3$. Dissolve in HNO_3. Add $Co(NO_3)_2$, evaporate, ignite. Blue residue: $Co(AlO_2)_2$.	Filtrate: add HAc and $BaCl_2$.	
	Precipitate: $BaCrO_4$. Dissolve in HCl and H_2SO_4, evaporate. Green color: $CrCl_3$.	Filtrate: Zinc salt. Pass in H_2S. White precipitate: ZnS. Dissolve in HNO_3. Add $Co(NO_3)_2$ and Na_2CO_3, ignite. Green residue: $CoZnO_2$.

ANALYSIS OF THE IRON GROUP

Precipitate produced by sodium hydroxide and peroxide:
A. Phosphate absent: $MnO(OH)_2$, $Fe(OH)_3$, $Co(OH)_3$, $Ni(OH)_2$, $Zn (OH)_2$.
B. Phosphate present: Also $BaCO_3$, $SrCO_3$, $CaCO_3$, $MgCO_3$, $FePO_4$, $Ca_3(PO_4)_2$, etc. Dissolve in HNO_3 and H_2O_2, evaporate, heat with HNO_3 and $KClO_3$.

Solution: Test a portion for a phosphate with $(NH_4)_2MoO_4$.
A. Phosphate absent: add NH_4OH.
B. Phosphate present: add NH_4Ac and $FeCl_3$, dilute and boil.

Precipitate: MnO_2. Add HNO_3 and bismuth peroxide. Violet color: $HMnO_4$.	Precipitate: A. $Fe(OH)_3$. B. Basic ferric acetate and $FePO_4$.	Filtrate: add NH_4OH, pass in H_2S. Precipitate: ZnS, CoS, NiS.	Filtrate: A. Ammonium salts. Reject. B. Ba, Ca, Sr, Mg. Treat with Alkali-Earth group.

SEPARATION OF ZINC, NICKEL, AND COBALT

Hydrogen sulfide precipitate: ZnS, NiS, CoS. Treat with dil. HCl.

Solution: $ZnCl_2$, $NiCl_2$, $CoCl_2$, add NaOH and Na_2O_2.	Residue: NiS, CoS. Dissolve in HCl and HNO_3.
Filtrate: Na_2ZnO_2. Add HAc and H_2S.	Precipitate: $Ni(OH)_2$, $Co(OH)_3$, add HCl, evaporate.
White precipitate: ZnS.	Residue: $NiCl_2$, $CoCl_2$, add HCl and ether.
	Yellow residue: $NiCl_2$. Dissolve in water, add tartaric acid, NaOH and H_2S.	Blue solution: $CoCl_2$, evaporate, add HAc and KNO_2.
	Brown coloration: presence of nickel.	Yellow precipitate: $K_3Co(NO_2)_6$.

ANALYSIS OF THE ALKALINE-EARTH GROUP

Ammonium carbonate precipitate: $BaCO_3$, $SrCO_3$, $CaCO_3$, $MgCO_3$, $(NH_4)_2CO_3$. Dissolve in HAc, add NH_4Ac and K_2CrO_4.

Precipitate: $BaCrO_4$. Dissolve in HCl, evaporate		Filtrate: add NH_4OH and alcohol.		
Test in flame.	Add HAc, NH_4Ac, and K_2CrO_4.	Precipitate: $SrCrO_4$. Treat with $(NH_4)_2CO_3$.	Filtrate: Ca and Mg salts. Add $(NH_4)_2C_2O_4$.	
Green color: Ba.	Precipitate: $BaCrO_4$.	Residue: $SrCO_3$. Dissolve in HAc. Add $CaSO_4$.	Precipitate: CaC_2O_4. Dissolve in dilute H_2SO_4, add alcohol.	Filtrate: add NH_4OH and Na_2HPO_4.
		Precipitate: $SrSO_4$.	Precipitate: $CaSO_4$.	Precipitate: $MgNH_4PO_4$.

553

ANALYSIS OF THE ALKALI GROUP

Filtrate from Ammonium Carbonate precipitate: NH_4, Na, K salts. Evaporate and ignite the residue.

Vapor: NH_4 salts.	Residue: KCl, NaCl. Add $HClO_4$, evaporate, add alcohol.	
	Residue: $KClO_4$. Dissolve in hot water, add $Na_3Co(NO_2)_6$.	Solution: $NaClO_4$. Saturate with HCl gas.
	Yellow precipitate: $K_2NaCo(NO_2)_6$.	Precipitate: NaCl. Dissolve in water, add $KSb(OH)_6$.
		Crystalline precipitate: $NaSb(OH)_6$.

ACIDIC CONSTITUENTS

DETECTION OF THE READILY VOLATILE ACIDIC CONSTITUENTS

Heat the substance with dilute H_2SO_4.

Vapors: CO_2, SO_2, H_2S, NO_2, Cl_2, Br_2, I_2, HCN. Expose to the vapors.

$Ba(OH)_2$ solution.	PbAc paper.	Starch and KI paper.	$Fe(OH)_2$ or $Fe(OH)_3$ and NaOH on paper.
White turbidity: $BaCO_3$ or $BaSO_3$. (Shows carbonate, sulfite, or thiosulfate.)	Black color: PbS. (Shows sulfide.)	Blue color: I_2. (Shows nitrite, hypochlorite, chlorate, bromate, or iodide.)	Formation of $Na_4Fe(CN)_6$. Dip in HCl.
			Blue color: $Fe_4(Fe(CN)_6)_3$. (Shows cyanide.)

Detection of the Acidic Constituents Precipitated from Acid Solutions by Barium and Silver Salts

<table>
<tr><td colspan="4">To a HNO_3 solution of the substance add $BaCl_2$.</td><td colspan="3">To a HNO_3 solution of the substance add $Cd(NO_3)_2$.</td></tr>
<tr><td rowspan="3">Precipitate: $BaSO_4$.
(Shows sulfate.)</td><td colspan="3">Filtrate: add Br_2.</td><td rowspan="3">Yellow precipitate: CdS.
(Shows sulfide.)</td><td colspan="2">Filtrate: Add $AgNO_3$.</td></tr>
<tr><td rowspan="2">Precipitate: $BaSO_4$.
(Shows sulfite.)</td><td colspan="2">Filtrate: add NH_4Ac.</td><td rowspan="2">Precipitate: AgCl, AgBr, AgI, $(AgCN)_2$, AgSCN.
(Shows halides, cyanide or thiocyanates.)</td><td>Filtrate: $AgClO_3$, $AgBrO_3$. Add H_2SO_3.</td></tr>
<tr><td>Yellow precipitate: $BaCrO_4$.
(Shows chromate.)</td><td>Filtrate: add $CaCl_2$.
Precipitate: CaF_2.
(Shows fluoride.)</td><td>Precipitate: AgCl, AgBr.
(Shows chlorate or bromate.)</td></tr>
</table>

Detection of Phosphate and the Separate Halides

<table>
<tr><td colspan="5">To portions of the HNO_3 solution of the substance.</td></tr>
<tr><td>Add $(NH_4)_2MoO_4$.</td><td>Add $FeCl_3$.</td><td colspan="3">Add NaAc, HAc, $KMnO_4$, and $CHCl_3$.</td></tr>
<tr><td rowspan="3">Yellow precipitate: $(NH_4)_3PO_4$, $12MoO_3$.
(Shows phosphate.)</td><td rowspan="3">Red color: $Fe(SCN)_3$.
(Shows thiocyanate.)</td><td rowspan="3">Chloroform layer, purple: I_2. (Shows iodide.)</td><td colspan="2">Water layer: add H_2SO_4, more $KMnO_4$ and $CHCl_3$.</td></tr>
<tr><td rowspan="2">Chloroform layer, orange: Br_2.
(Shows bromide.)</td><td>Water layer: Boil out the Br_2, add HNO_3 and $AgNO_3$.</td></tr>
<tr><td>Precipitate: AgCl.
(Shows chloride.)</td></tr>
</table>

Appendix VII

STRUCTURE OF MOLECULES AND IONS

LINEAR — $HgCl_2(g)$, $HgBr_2(g)$, $HgI_2(g)$, CO_2, C_3O_2, SCO, C_4H_2, CH_3CN, CH_3NC, CS_2, C_2N_2, H_2CN_2, N_3^-, NNO, CH_3MgI, FHF^-, $BrIBr^-$, $ClIBr^-$, $AuCl_2^-$, $Ag(CN)_2^-$, BO_2^-, BeO_2^{--}, I_3^- (with 3 electron pairs about center I?).

PLANE TRIANGULAR — BCl_3, $B(CH_3)_3$, NO_3^-, CO_3^{--}, $C(NH_2)_3^+$, SO_3, $CuCl_3^-$, $Ni(CN)_3^-$, H_2CO, $OCCl_2$ (Cl–C–Cl, 117°), $SCCl_2$ (Cl–C–Cl, 116°), CH_3NO_2 (O–N–O, 127°).

PLANAR — C_6H_6, $(HCOOH)_2(g)$, $CH_3NNCH_3(g)$.

BENT OR V-SHAPED — FOF (100°), ClOCl (115°), OClO (125°), ClO_2^- (114°), ONCl (125°), ONBr, ClSCl (103°), $(CH_3)_2O$ (111°), O_3, $(CH_3)_2S$, ONO (110–120°), NO_2^- (132°), OSO (122°), H_2S (92°), H_2O (105°).

PYRAMIDAL — PF_3 (F–P–F, 104°), PCl_3 (Cl–P–Cl, 101°), PBr_3 (Br–P–Br, 100°), PI_3(I–P–I, 98°), AsF_3, $AsCl_3$ (Cl–As–Cl, 103°), $AsBr_3$ (Br–As–Br, 100°), AsI_3 (I–As–I, 100°), $SbCl_3$ (Cl–Sb–Cl, 104°), $SbBr_3$ (Br–Sb–Br, 96°), SbI_3 (I–Sb–I, 98°), $P(CH_3)_3$ (C–P–C, 100°), $PFCl_2$ (Cl–P–Cl, 102°), $N(CH_3)_3$ (C–N–C, 108°), NH_3 (H–N–H, 108°), SO_3^{--} (O–S–O, 111°), ClO_3^- (O–Cl–O, 107°).

SQUARE PLANAR — XY_4 ions and molecules of Pd^{++}, Pt^{++}, Cu^{++}, Ag^{++}, Au^{+++}, Ni^{++} (if diamagnetic), ICl_4^-.

TETRAHEDRAL — P_4, As_4, $Ni(CO)_4$, NH_4^+, BF_4^-, BeF_4^{-2}, $Li(NH_3)_4$, SiO_4^{-4}, AlO_4^{-5}, SO_4^{-2}, PO_4^{-3}, $H_2PO_2^-$, ClO_4^-,

CrO_4^{--}, MnO_4^-, MnO_4^{--}, $SnBr_4$, $Pb(C_2H_5)_4$, $TiCl_4$, $GeCl_4$, $SiCl_4$, $Cu(CN)_4^{---}$, and other Cu^+ complex ions, $Ni(H_2O)_4^{++}$, $Ni(N_2H_4)_2^{++}$ and other paramagnetic complex ions of Ni^{++}, $(CH_3)_3PtCl$, and Pt^{+4} complex ions, $M(CM)_4^{--}$ when M is Zn, Cd, or Hg, SnS_4^{-4}, AsS_4^{-3}, CCl_4 and all carbon compounds with four single bonds, $H_2Fe(CO)_4$.

TRIGONAL
BIPYRAMID
PCl_5, PF_5, PF_3Cl_2, $MoCl_5$, $(CH_3)_3SbX_2$.

SQUARE
PYRAMID
IF_5 (?).

OCTA-
HEDRAL
In general, all XY_6 compounds and complex ions. In UF_6, WF_6, MoF_6 (as gases) the M–F distances of the three axes are different. In MoS_2 (crystal) six sulfur atoms form a triangular prism about a molybdenum atom.

SEVEN-
CORNERED
POLYHEDRON
ZrF_6^{---}, IF_7 (?).

HEXADRAL
(CUBE) OR
SQUARE AR-
CHIMEDEAN
ANTIPRISM
$W(CN)_8^{-4}$, $Mo(CN)_8^{-4}$, and $Ca(C_2H_5OH)_8^{++}$ probably the former. $(ZrF_8)^{-4}$ (?), $(TaF_8)^{-3}$ (?).

Appendix VIII

DENSITY OF WATER

DENSITY OF WATER IN GRAMS PER CUBIC CENTIMETER

t° C.	DENSITY	t° C.	DENSITY	t° C.	DENSITY
0	0.999867	16	0.998969	32	0.995052
1	0026	17	8801	33	0.994728
2	9968	18	8621	34	4397
3	9992	19	8430	35	4058
4	1.000000	20	8229	36	0.993711
5	0.999992	21	8017	37	3356
6	9968	22	0.997795	38	0.992993
7	9929	23	7563	39	2622
8	9876	24	7321	40	0.992244
9	9808	25	7069	50	0.98804
10	9727	26	0.996808	60	0.9832i
11	9632	27	6538	70	0.97778
12	9524	28	0.996258	80	0.97180
13	9404	29	0.995969	90	0.96531
14	0.999271	30	5672	100	0.95835
15	9126	31	5366	150	0.9173
				200	0.8628

APPARENT DENSITY OF WATER,
WHEN WEIGHED IN AIR WITH BRASS WEIGHTS,
IN GRAMS PER CUBIC CENTIMETER

t° C.	DENSITY	t° C.	DENSITY	t° C.	DENSITY
15	0.99805	20	0.99718	25	0.99604
16	.99790	21	.99697	26	.99579
17	.99774	22	.99676	27	.99552
18	.99756	23	.99653	28	.99524
19	.99738	24	.99629	29	.99496
				30	.99466

Appendix IX

DENSITY OF MERCURY

Density of Mercury in Grams per Cubic Centimeter

t° C.	Density	t° C.	Density	t° C.	Density
− 20	13.6450	15	13.5584	45	13.4849
− 10	6202	16	5560	50	4727
− 5	6078	17	5535	55	4605
0	5955	18	5511	60	4484
1	5930	19	5486	65	4362
2	5905	20	5461	70	4241
3	5880	21	5437	75	4120
4	5856	22	5412	80	3999
5	5831	23	5388	85	3878
6	5806	24	5363	90	3757
7	5782	25	5339	95	3637
8	5757	26	5314	100	3516
9	5732	27	5290	110	328
10	5708	28	5265	150	232
11	5683	29	5241	200	113
12	5658	30	5216	300	12.8760
13	5634	35	5094	400	6380
14	5609	40	4971	500	3950

Appendix X

EQUILIBRIUM PRESSURE OF WATER — WATER VAPOR

PRESSURE IN MM. OF MERCURY

(Cf. also Fig. 2, Chap.III)

t° C.	mm.	t° C.	mm.	t° C.	mm.
0	4.5687	39	51.997	78	327.05
1	4.9091	40	54.865	79	340.73
2	5.2719	41	57.870	80	354.87
3	5.6582	42	61.017	81	369.51
4	6.0693	43	64.310	82	384.64
5	6.5067	44	67.757	83	400.29
6	6.9718	45	71.362	84	416.47
7	6.4660	46	75.131	85	433.19
8	7.9909	47	79.071	86	450.47
9	8.5484	48	83.188	87	468.32
10	9.1398	49	87.488	88	486.76
11	9.7671	50	91.978	89	505.81
12	10.432	51	96.664	90	525.47
13	11.137	52	101.55	91	545.77
14	11.884	53	106.65	92	566.71
15	12.674	54	111.97	93	588.33
16	13.510	55	117.52	94	610.64
17	14.395	56	123.29	95	633.66
18	15.330	57	129.31	96	657.40
19	16.319	58	135.58	97	681.88
20	17.363	59	142.10	98	707.13
21	18.466	60	148.88	99	733.16
22	19.630	61	155.95	100	760.00
23	20.858	62	163.29	101	787.59
24	22.152	63	170.92	102	816.01
25	23.517	64	178.86	103	845.28
26	24.956	65	187.10	104	875.41
27	26.471	66	195.67	110	1075.37
28	28.065	67	204.56	120	1491.28
29	29.744	68	213.79	130	2030.28
30	31.510	69	223.37	140	2717.63
31	33.366	70	233.31	150	3581.2
32	35.318	71	243.62	160	4651.6
33	37.369	72	254.30	170	5961.7
34	39.523	73	265.38	180	7546.4
35	41.784	74	276.87	190	9442.7
36	44.158	75	288.76	200	11689.0
37	46.648	76	301.09	209	14042.5
38	49.259	77	313.85		

Appendix XI

SOLUBILITY PRODUCTS AND ACID IONIZATION CONSTANTS

Bromides	K
CuBr	5.3×10^{-9}
PbBr$_2$	6.3×10^{-6}
Hg$_2$Br$_2$	5.2×10^{-23}
AgBr	3.3×10^{-13}
TlBr	3.6×10^{-6}

Fluorides	
BaF$_2$	1.7×10^{-6}
CaF$_2$	3.4×10^{-11}
MgF$_2$	6.4×10^{-9}
PbF$_2$	2.7×10^{-8}
SrF$_2$	3×10^{-9}

Carbonates	
BaCO$_3$	4.9×10^{-9}
CdCO$_3$	2.5×10^{-14}
CaCO$_3$	4.8×10^{-9}
CoCO$_3$	1.0×10^{-12}
CuCO$_3$	1.4×10^{-10}
FeCO$_3$	2.1×10^{-11}
PbCO$_3$	1.5×10^{-13}
MgCO$_3$·3H$_2$O	1×10^{-5}
MnCO$_3$	8.8×10^{-11}
Hg$_2$CO$_3$	9×10^{-17}
NiCO$_3$	1.4×10^{-7}
Ag$_2$CO$_3$	8.2×10^{-12}
SrCO$_3$	9.4×10^{-10}
ZnCO$_3$	6×10^{-11}

Hydroxides	
Al(OH)$_3$	1.9×10^{-33}
Sb$_2$O$_3$(SbO$^+$, OH$^-$)	10^{-17}
AsOOH(AsO$^+$, OH$^-$)	5×10^{-15}
Ba(OH)$_2$·8H$_2$O	5×10^{-3}
Be$_2$O(OH)$_2$(2Be^{++}, 4OH$^-$)	1×10^{-40}
BiOOH(BiO$^+$, OH)	1×10^{-12}
Cd(OH)$_2$	1.2×10^{-14}
Ca(OH)$_2$	7.9×10^{-6}
Cr(OH)$_3$	6.7×10^{-31}
Co(OH)$_2$	2×10^{-16}
Cu$_2$O(Cu$^+$, OH$^-$)	1.2×10^{-15}
Cu(OH)$_2$	5.6×10^{-20}
Ga(OH)$_3$	5×10^{-37}
Au$_2$O$_3$(Au^{+++}, 3OH$^-$)	8.5×10^{-46}
HfO(OH)$_2$(HfO^{++}, 2OH$^-$)	10^{-25}
Fe(OH)$_2$	1.6×10^{-15}
Fe(OH)$_3$	4×10^{-38}
La(OH)$_3$	10^{-20}
Pb(OH)$_2$	2.8×10^{-16}
Mg(OH)$_2$	5.5×10^{-12}
Mn(OH)$_2$	7.1×10^{-15}
Hg$_2$O(Hg$_2^{++}$, 2OH$^-$)	1.6×10^{-23}
HgO(Hg^{++}, 2OH$^-$)	1.7×10^{-26}
Ni(OH)$_2$	1.6×10^{-14}
Pd(OH)$_2$	1×10^{-24}
Pt(OH)$_2$	1×10^{-35}
Ag$_2$O(Ag$^+$, OH$^-$)	2.0×10^{-8}

Chlorides	
CuCl	1.8×10^{-7}
PbCl$_2$	1.7×10^{-5}
Hg$_2$Cl$_2$	1.1×10^{-18}
AgCl	1.7×10^{-10}
TlCl	1.9×10^{-4}
BiOCl(BiO$^+$, Cl$^-$)	7×10^{-9}

Chromates	
BaCrO$_4$	2×10^{-10}
PbCrO$_4$	1.8×10^{-14}
Ag$_2$CrO$_4$	1.1×10^{-12}
SrCrO$_4$	3.6×10^{-5}

Hydroxides (Cont'd)	K	Oxalates (Cont'd)	
$Sr(OH)_2 \cdot 8H_2O$	3.2×10^{-4}	$Hg_2C_2O_4$	1×10^{-13}
$Tl(OH)$	7.2×10^{-1}	$Ag_2C_2O_4$	1.1×10^{-11}
$Tl(OH)_3$	1×10^{-44}	$SrC_2O_4 \cdot H_2O$	5.6×10^{-8}
$Th(OH)_4$	1×10^{-50}		
$Sn(OH)_2$	5×10^{-26}	Sulfates	
$Sn(OH)_4$	1×10^{-56}	$BaSO_4$	9.9×10^{-11}
$TiO(OH)_2(TiO^{++}, 2OH^-)$	1×10^{-30}	$CaSO_4 \cdot 2H_2O$	2.4×10^{-5}
$Ti_2O_3(Ti^{+++}, 3OH^-)$	1×10^{-40}	$PbSO_4$	1.8×10^{-8}
$UO_2(OH)_2(UO_2^{++}, 2OH^-)$	2×10^{-15}	Hg_2SO_4	6.2×10^{-7}
$Zn(OH)_2$	4.5×10^{-17}	Ag_2SO_4	1.2×10^{-5}
$NH_4OH(Aq.\ diss.)$	1.65×10^{-5}	$SrSO_4$	2.8×10^{-7}

Iodates		VALUES FOR IONIZATION OF ONE H^+	
$Ba(IO_3)_2 \cdot 2H_2O$	1.2×10^{-9}		
$Ca(IO_3)_2 \cdot 6H_2O$	1.9×10^{-6}	Acids	
$Cu(IO_3)_2$	1.3×10^{-7}	$H_3AlO_3(s)$	4×10^{-13}
$Pb(IO_3)_2$	3.2×10^{-13}	$HSbO_2$	10^{-11}
$Hg_2(IO_3)_2$	1.3×10^{-18}	H_3AsO_3	6×10^{-10}
$AgIO_3$	3.0×10^{-8}	H_3AsO_4	4.8×10^{-3}
$TlIO_3$	4.5×10^{-6}	$H_2AsO_4^-$	10^{-7}
		$HAsO_4^{--}$	10^{-13}
Iodides		H_3BO_3	5.8×10^{-10}
CuI	1.1×10^{-12}	$H_2B_4O_7$	10^{-4}
PbI_2	8.7×10^{-9}	$HB_4O_7^-$	10^{-9}
Hg_2I_2	4.5×10^{-29}	$HBrO$	2×10^{-9}
AgI	8.5×10^{-17}	H_2CO_3	4.3×10^{-7}
TlI	5.8×10^{-8}	HCO_3^-	4.7×10^{-11}
		HCO_2H	1.8×10^{-4}
Sulfides		$H_2C_2O_4$	5.9×10^{-2}
CdS	1.4×10^{-28}	$HC_2O_4^-$	6.4×10^{-5}
Bi_2S_3	1.6×10^{-72}	HCN	4×10^{-10}
$CoS\alpha$	7×10^{-23}	$HOCN$	1.2×10^{-4}
Cu_2S	2.5×10^{-50}	$HClO$	2.98×10^{-8}
CuS	4×10^{-38}	$HClO_2$	10^{-2}
FeS	1×10^{-19}	$H_2CrO_3(s)$	9×10^{-17}
PbS	1.0×10^{-29}	$HCrO_4^-$	3.2×10^{-7}
MnS	5.6×10^{-16}	HF	6.7×10^{-4}
Hg_2S	1×10^{-45}	$H_3GaO_3(s)$	1×10^{-15}
HgS	3×10^{-53}	H_2GeO_3	2.6×10^{-9}
$NiS\alpha$	3×10^{-21}	H_5IO_6	2.3×10^{-2}
PtS	1×10^{-68}	$H_4IO_6^-$	1×10^{-6}
Ag_2S	1.0×10^{-51}	HIO	1×10^{-11}
Tl_2S	1.2×10^{-24}	$H_2PbO_2(s)$	2.1×10^{-16}
SnS	8×10^{-29}	HNO_2	4.5×10^{-4}
ZnS	4.5×10^{-24}	HN_3	1×10^{-4}
		$H_2N_2O_2$	9×10^{-8}
Oxalates		$HN_2O_2^-$	1×10^{-11}
$CaC_2O_4 \cdot H_2O$	2.3×10^{-9}	H_2OsO_5	8×10^{-13}
$Ce_2(C_2O_4)_3 \cdot 10H_2O$	2.5×10^{-29}	H_2O	1.008×10^{-14}
$BaC_2O_4 \cdot 2H_2O$	1.1×10^{-7}	OH^-	$< 10^{-36}$
MgC_2O_4	8.6×10^{-5}	H_2O_2	2.4×10^{-12}

Acids (*Cont'd*)		*Complex ions*	
H_3PO_4	7.5×10^{-3}	$Ag(NH_3)_2^+$	6×10^{-8}
$H_2PO_4^-$	6.2×10^{-8}	$Cu(NH_3)_2^+$	1.3×10^{-11}
HPO_4^{--}	10^{-12}	$Cu(NH_3)_4^{++}$	4.6×10^{-14}
H_3PO_3	1.6×10^{-2}	$Cd(NH_3)_4^{++}$	2×10^{-7}
$H_2PO_3^-$	7×10^{-7}	$Co(NH_3)_6^{++}$	2×10^{-34}
H_3PO_2	1×10^{-2}	$Ni(NH_3)_4^{++}$	4.8×10^{-8}
H_2Se	1.7×10^{-4}	$Zn(NH_3)_4^{++}$	1×10^{-9}
HSe^-	1×10^{-10}	CuI_2^-	1.4×10^{-9}
$HSeO_4^-$	1×10^{-2}	$CuCl_2^-$	2.9×10^{-6}
H_3SiO_3	1×10^{-10}	$Cd(CN)_4^{--}$	1.4×10^{-17}
H_2S	1.1×10^{-7}	$Zn(CN)_4^{--}$	1.3×10^{-17}
HS^-	1.0×10^{-15}	$Cu(CN)_2^-$	1×10^{-16}
H_2SO_3	1.2×10^{-2}	$Ag(CN)_2^=$	3.8×10^{-19}
HSO_3^-	1×10^{-7}	$Au(CN)_2^-$	5×10^{-39}
HSO_4^-	1.2×10^{-2}	$Fe(CN)_6^{-4}$	10^{-27}
H_2Te	2.3×10^{-3}	$Fe(CN)_6^{-3}$	10^{-44}
HTe^-	1×10^{-5}	$Ag(S_2O_3)_2^{-3}$	4.2×10^{-14}
H_2TeO_3	2×10^{-3}	$AuCl_4^-$	5×10^{-22}
$H_2SnO_2(s)$	6×10^{-18}	$PdCl_4^{--}$	6×10^{-14}
H_2ZrO_3	10^{-18}	$PtCl_4^{--}$	10^{-16}
$N_2H_5^+$	1×10^{-8}	$PtBr_4^{--}$	10^{-18}
N_2H_4	1×10^{-15}	HgS_2^{--}	2×10^{-55}

Appendix XII

BUFFER SOLUTIONS

The following solutions may be employed to maintain desired concentrations of H^+ or OH^-. These concentrations are expressed as $pH = \log_{10} 1/(H^+)$ e.g., $0.01N$ H^+ has a pH of 2.

SORENSEN'S PHOSPHATE SOLUTIONS

KH_2PO_4, 9.078 g. per liter, and $Na_2HPO_4 \cdot 2H_2O$, 11.876 g. per liter

Na₂HPO₄ (cc.)...	0.25	0.5	1.0	2.0	3.0	4.0	5.0	6.0	7.0	8.0	9.0	9.5
KH₂PO₄ (cc.)....	9.75	9.5	9.0	8.0	7.0	6.0	5.0	4.0	3.0	2.0	1.0	0.5
pH.............	5.29	5.59	5.91	6.24	6.47	6.64	6.81	6.98	7.17	7.38	7.73	8.04

ACETIC ACID-ACETATE SOLUTIONS, BY WALPOLE-CLARK

CH₃COOH m per l	0.185	0.176	0.164	0.147	0.126	0.102	0.080	0.059	0.042	0.019
CH₃COONa m per l	0.015	0.024	0.036	0.053	0.074	0.098	0.120	0.1	0.158	0.181
pH.............	3.6	3.8	4.0	4.2	4.4	4.6	4.8	5.0	5.2	5.6

CLARK AND LUBS, BORATE SOLUTIONS

X cc. of 0.2M NaOH added to 50 cc. of a mixture of 0.2M H₃BO₃ + 0.2M KCl and diluted to 200 cc.	cc.	2.61	3.97	5.90	8.50	12.00	16.30	21.30	26.70	32.00	36.85	40.80	43.90
	pH	7.8	8.0	8.2	8.4	8.6	8.8	9.0	9.2	9.4	9.6	9.8	10.0

Appendix XIII

INDICATORS

CLARK AND LUBS' LIST, COVERING RANGE FROM STRONG ACID TO
STRONG BASE

Abbreviations: c, colorless; r, red; y, yellow; b, blue; pu, purple; o, orange;
v, violet.

INDICATOR	USEFUL RANGE $pH = \log_{10} \frac{1}{(H^+)}$
Thymol blue	r 1.2–2.8 y
Bromphenol blue	y 3.0–4.6 b
Bromcresol green	y 3.8–5.4 b
Methyl red	r 4.2–6.3 y
Chlorphenol red	y 5.0–6.6 r
Bromcresol purple	y 5.2–6.8 pu
Bromthymol blue	y 6.0–7.6 b
Phenol red	y 6.8–8.4 r
Cresol red	y 7.2–8.8 r
Metacresol purple	y 7.6–9.2 pu
Thymol blue	y 8.0–9.6 b
O-cresolpnthalein	c 8.2–9.8 r

INDICATORS IN COMMON USE

INDICATOR	pH RANGE
Methyl orange	r 3.1 — 4.4 y
Resorcin blue	r 4.4 — 6.2 b
Litmus	r 4.5 — 8.3 b
Phenolphthalein	c 8.3 — 10.0 r
Cresol red	y 8.0 — 9.6 pu
Methyl violet	y 0.15 — 3.2 v
Trinitrobenzene	c 12.0 — 14.0 o

Appendix XIV

CHANGE OF RESISTANCE OF METALS
WITH TEMPERATURE

R/R₀ is the ratio of the resistance to the value at 0° C. Insert shows supraconductivity of mercury.

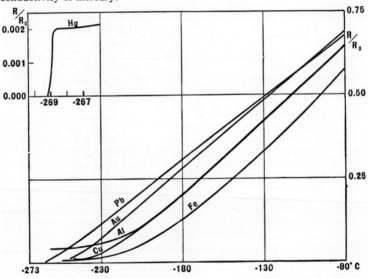

SPECIFIC HEAT OF METALS
AND COMPOUNDS AT LOW TEMPERATURES

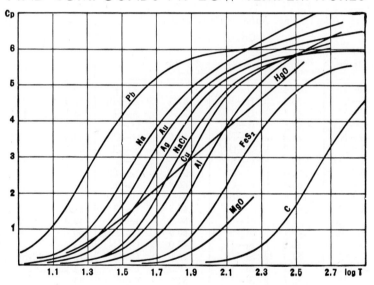

Appendix XVI

COVALENT BOND ENERGIES AND ATOMIC RADII

Values from Pauling. *Nature of Chemical Bond.* Cornell University Press, 1939

COVALENT BOND ENERGIES

BOND	ENERGY KCAL./MOLE	BOND	ENERGY KCAL./MOLE	BOND	ENERGY KCAL./MOLE
H—H	103.4	H—Cl	102.7	As—Cl	60.3
C—C	58.6	H—Br	87.3	As—Br	48.0
Si—Si	42.5	H—I	71.4	As—I	33.1
Ge—Ge	42.5	C—Si	57.6	O—F	58.6
N—N	23.6	C—N	48.6	O—Cl	49.3
P—P	18.9	C—O	70.0	S—Cl	66.1
As—As	15.1	C—S	54.5	S—B	57.2
O—O	34.9	C—F	107.0	Se—Cl	66.8
S—S	63.8	C—Cl	66.5	Cl—F	86.4
Se—Se	57.6	C—Br	54.0	Br—Cl	52.7
F—F	63.5	C—I	45.5	I—Cl	51.0
Cl—Cl	57.8	Si—O	89.3	I—Br	42.9
Br—Br	46.1	Si—S	60.9	C≡C	100
I—I	36.2	Si—F	143.0	C≡C	123
C—H	87.3	Si—Cl	85.8	C=O	142 formaldehyde
Si—H	75.1	Si—Br	69.3	C=O	152 ketones
N—H	83.7	Si—I	51.1	C=N	94
P—H	63.0	Ge—Cl	104.1	C≡N	150 cyanides
As—H	47.3	N—F	68.8	C=S	103
O—H	110.2	N—Cl	38.4	O=O	96 ′Δ O₂
S—H	87.5	P—Cl	62.8	N≡N	170 normal N₂
Se—H	73.0	P—Br	49.2		
H—F	147.5	P—I	35.2		

TETRAHEDRAL COVALENT RADII

ELEMENT	RADIUS IN Å	ELEMENT	RADIUS IN Å
Be	1.06	As	1.18
B	0.88	Se	1.14
C	0.77	Br	1.11
N	0.70	Ag	1.53
O	0.66	Cd	1.48
F	0.64	In	1.44
Mg	1.40	Sn	1.40
Al	1.26	Sb	1.36
Si	1.17	Te	1.32
P	1.10	I	1.28
S	1.04	Au	1.50
Cl	0.99	Hg	1.48
Cu	1.35	Tl	1.47
Zn	1.31	Pt	1.46
Ga	1.26	Bi	1.46
Ge	1.22		

OCTAHEDRAL RADII

ELEMENT	RADIUS IN Å	ELEMENT	RADIUS IN Å
Fe^2	1.23	Ir^3	1.32
Co^2	1.32	Pt^4	1.31
Co^3	1.22	Ti^4	1.36
Ni^2	1.39	Zn^4	1.48
Ru^2	1.33	Sn^4	1.45
Rh^3	1.32	Pb^4	1.50
Pd^4	1.31	Se^4	1.40
As^2	1.33		

Appendix XVII

TABLE OF CONVERSION FACTORS

Values in agreement with International Critical Tables

Length and volume

1 Meter = 39.37 in. = (100/2.54) in.	
1 Yard (U.S.) = 91.44018 cm.	log = 1.9611371
1 Yard (British) = 91.43992 cm.	log = 1.9611350
1 Liter = 1000.027 cm.^{3}	log = 3.0000117
1 Cubic foot (U.S.) = 28317.0 cm.^{3}	log = 4.4520474
1 Gallon (U.S.) = 3785.4 cm.^{3}	log = 3.5781157
1 Gallon (British) = 4546.1 cm.^{3}	log = 3.6576376
1 Quart, dry (U.S.) = 1101–23 cm.^{3}	log = 3.0418770
1 Quart, liquid (U.S.) = 946.358 cm.^{3}	log = 2.9760557
1 Fluid ounce (U.S.) = 29.5737 cm.^{3}	log = 1.4709057

Weight

1 Grain = 64.799 mg.	log = 1.8115677
1 Ounce (avoirdupois) = 28.350 g.	log = 1.4525458
1 Pound (avoirdupois) = 453.59243 g. = 1000/2.2046223	log = 2.6566658
1 Ton, short (2000 pounds) = 907.185 kg.	log = 2.9576958
1 Ton, long (2240 pounds) = 1016.047 kg.	log = 3.0069138

Pressure

1 Pound weight per sq. in. (U.S.) = 68947.3 dynes cm.$^{-2}$	log = 4.8385173
1 Centimeter of water at 4° C. = 980.638 dynes cm.$^{-2}$	log = 2.9915090
1 Inch of water at 4° C. (U.S.) = 2490.827 dynes cm.$^{-2}$	log = 3.3963436
1 Centimeter of mercury at 0° C. = 13332.24 dynes cm.$^{-2}$	log = 4.1249031
1 Inch of mercury at 0° C. (U.S.) = 33863.95 dynes cm.$^{-2}$	log = 4.5297377

Density

1 Gram per milliliter = specific gravity, t°/4° = 0.999973 g. cm.$^{-3}$	log = $\bar{1}$.9999883
1 Pound per cu. in. (U.S.) = 27.67974 g. cm.$^{-3}$	log = 1.4221621
1 Pound per cu. ft. (U.S.) = 0.016018 g. cm.$^{-3}$	log = $\bar{2}$.2046183
1 Pound per gal. (U.S.) = 0.1198257 g. cm.$^{-3}$	log = $\bar{1}$.0785502

Energy

1 Cubic centimeter-atmosphere 0.10133 = 0.101325 joules (absolute)	log = $\bar{1}$.0057167
1 Gram calorie (15°) = 4.185 joules absolute	log = 0.6216955
1 British Thermal Unit (39° F.) = 1060.4 joules (abs.)	log = 3.0254697
1 British Thermal Unit (mean) = 1054.8 joules (abs.)	log = 3.0231701
1 British Thermal Unit (60° F.) = 1054.6 joules (abs.)	log = 3.0230878

Work

    1 Watt (International) = 1.00032 watt (absolute)   log = 0.0001390
    1 Kilogram-meter per sec. = 9.80665 watt (abs.)   log = 0.9915207
    1 Foot-pound per sec. (U.S.) = 1.355821 watt (abs.)   log = 0.1322022
    1 Horsepower (U.S., British) = 746.00 watt (abs.)   log = 2.8727388
    1 Horsepower (Continental Europe) = 736.00 watt (abs.)   log = 2.8660778
    1 Cheval-vapeur (75 kg.–m. per sec.) = 735.499 watt (abs.)   log = 2.8665820

Temperature

    Fahrenheit $x°$ F. = (5/9) $(x - 32)°$ C.
    Reaumur $x°$ R. = (5/4) $x°$ C.

Appendix XVIII

THE ELECTRON STRUCTURE OF THE ELEMENTS

ATOMIC NUMBER	ELEMENT	NUMBER OF ELECTRONS IN EACH QUANTUM GROUP																			
		1_s	2_s	2_p	3_s	3_p	3_d	4_s	4_p	4_d	4_f	5_s	5_p	5_d	5_f	5_g	6_s	6_p	6_d	7_s	7_p
1	H	1																			
2	He	2																			
3	Li	2	1																		
4	Be	2	2																		
5	B	2	2	1																	
6	C	2	2	2																	
7	N	2	2	3																	
8	O	2	2	4																	
9	F	2	2	5																	
10	Ne	2	2	6																	
11	Na	2	2	6	1																
12	Mg	2	2	6	2																
13	Al	2	2	6	2	1															
14	Si	2	2	6	2	2															
15	P	2	2	6	2	3															
16	S	2	2	6	2	4															
17	Cl	2	2	6	2	5															
18	A	2	2	6	2	6															
19	K	2	2	6	2	6		1													
20	Ca	2	2	6	2	6		2													
21	Sc	2	2	6	2	6	1	2													
22	Ti	2	2	6	2	6	2	2													
23	V	2	2	6	2	6	3	2													
24	Cr	2	2	6	2	6	5	1													
25	Mn	2	2	6	2	6	5	2													
26	Fe	2	2	6	2	6	6	2													
27	Co	2	2	6	2	6	7	2													
28	Ni	2	2	6	2	6	8	2													
29	Cu	2	2	6	2	6	10	1													
30	Zn	2	2	6	2	6	10	2													
31	Ga	2	2	6	2	6	10	2	1												
32	Ge	2	2	6	2	6	10	2	2												
33	As	2	2	6	2	6	10	2	3												

Atomic Number	Element	Number of Electrons in Each Quantum Group																			
		1_s	2_s	2_p	3_s	3_p	3_d	4_s	4_p	4_d	4_f	5_s	5_p	5_d	5_f	5_g	6_s	6_p	6_d	7_s	7_p
34	Se	2	2	6	2	6	10	2	4												
35	Br	2	2	6	2	6	10	2	5												
36	Kr	2	2	6	2	6	10	2	6												
37	Rb	2	2	6	2	6	10	2	6			1									
38	Sr	2	2	6	2	6	10	2	6			2									
39	Y	2	2	6	2	6	10	2	6	1		2									
40	Zr	2	2	6	2	6	10	2	6	2		2									
41	Cb	2	2	6	2	6	10	2	6	4		1									
42	Mo	2	2	6	2	6	10	2	6	5		1									
43	Tc	2	2	6	2	6	10	2	6	6		2									
44	Ru	2	2	6	2	6	10	2	6	7		1									
45	Rh	2	2	6	2	6	10	2	6	8		1									
46	Pd	2	2	6	2	6	10	2	6	10											
47	Ag	2	2	6	2	6	10	2	6	10		1									
48	Cd	2	2	6	2	6	10	2	6	10		2									
49	In	2	2	6	2	6	10	2	6	10		2	1								
50	Sn	2	2	6	2	6	10	2	6	10		2	2								
51	Sb	2	2	6	2	6	10	2	6	10		2	3								
52	Te	2	2	6	2	6	10	2	6	10		2	4								
53	I	2	2	6	2	6	10	2	6	10		2	5								
54	Xe	2	2	6	2	6	10	2	6	10		2	6								
55	Cs	2	2	6	2	6	10	2	6	10		2	6				1				
56	Ba	2	2	6	2	6	10	2	6	10		2	6				2				
57	La	2	2	6	2	6	10	2	6	10		2	6	1			2				
58	Ce	2	2	6	2	6	10	2	6	10	1	2	6	1			2				
59	Pr	2	2	6	2	6	10	2	6	10	2	2	6	1			2				
60	Nd	2	2	6	2	6	10	2	6	10	3	2	6	1			2				
61	Pm	2	2	6	2	6	10	2	6	10	4	2	6	1			2				
62	Sm	2	2	6	2	6	10	2	6	10	5	2	6	1			2				
63	Eu	2	2	6	2	6	10	2	6	10	6	2	6	1			2				
64	Gd	2	2	6	2	6	10	2	6	10	7	2	6	1			2				
65	Tb	2	2	6	2	6	10	2	6	10	8	2	6	1			2				
66	Dy	2	2	6	2	6	10	2	6	10	9	2	6	1			2				
67	Ho	2	2	6	2	6	10	2	6	10	10	2	6	1			2				
68	Er	2	2	6	2	6	10	2	6	10	11	2	6	1			2				
69	Tu	2	2	6	2	6	10	2	6	10	12	2	6	1			2				
70	Yb	2	2	6	2	6	10	2	6	10	13	2	6	1			2				
71	Lu	2	2	6	2	6	10	2	6	10	14	2	6	1			2				
72	Hf	2	2	6	2	6	10	2	6	10	14	2	6	2			2				
73	Ta	2	2	6	2	6	10	2	6	10	14	2	6	3			2				
74	W	2	2	6	2	6	10	2	6	10	14	2	6	4			2				
75	Re	2	2	6	2	6	10	2	6	10	14	2	6	5			2				
76	Os	2	2	6	2	6	10	2	6	10	14	2	6	6			2				
77	Ir	2	2	6	2	6	10	2	6	10	14	2	6	9							
78	Pt	2	2	6	2	6	10	2	6	10	14	2	6	9			1				
79	Au	2	2	6	2	6	10	2	6	10	14	2	6	10			1				

Atomic Number	Element	Number of Electrons in Each Quantum Group																			
		1_s	2_s	2_p	3_s	3_p	3_d	4_s	4_p	4_d	4_f	5_s	5_p	5_d	5_f	5_g	6_s	6_p	6_d	7_s	7_p
80	Hg	2	2	6	2	6	10	2	6	10	14	2	6	10			2				
81	Tl	2	2	6	2	6	10	2	6	10	14	2	6	10			2	1			
82	Pb	2	2	6	2	6	10	2	6	10	14	2	6	10			2	2			
83	Bi	2	2	6	2	6	10	2	6	10	14	2	6	10			2	3			
84	Po	2	2	6	2	6	10	2	6	10	14	2	6	10			2	4			
85	At	2	2	6	2	6	10	2	6	10	14	2	6	10			2	5			
86	Rn	2	2	6	2	6	10	2	6	10	14	2	6	10			2	6			
87	Fr	2	2	6	2	6	10	2	6	10	14	2	6	10			2	6		1	
88	Ra	2	2	6	2	6	10	2	6	10	14	2	6	10			2	6		2	
89	Ac	2	2	6	2	6	10	2	6	10	14	2	6	10			2	6	1	2	
90	Th	2	2	6	2	6	10	2	6	10	14	2	6	10	1		2	6	1	2	
91	Pa	2	2	6	2	6	10	2	6	10	14	2	6	10	2		2	6	1	2	
92	U	2	2	6	2	6	10	2	6	10	14	2	6	10	3		2	6	1	2	
93	Np	2	2	6	2	6	10	2	6	10	14	2	6	10	4		2	6	1	2	
94	Pu	2	2	6	2	6	10	2	6	10	14	2	6	10	5		2	6	1	2	
95	Am	2	2	6	2	6	10	2	6	10	14	2	6	10	6		2	6	1	2	
96	Cm	2	2	6	2	6	10	2	6	10	14	2	6	10	7		2	6	1	2	
97	Bk	2	2	6	2	6	10	2	6	10	14	2	6	10	8		2	6	1	2	
98	Cf	2	2	6	2	6	10	2	6	10	14	2	6	10	9		2	6	1	2	

Appendix XIX

ABUNDANCE OF THE ELEMENTS

I. Abundance in the Sun, (Atoms per 10,000 Atoms of Si)

(Values by H. Brown)

Z	Element	Value	Z	Element	Value	Z	Element	Value
1	H	3.5×10^8	29	Cu	4.6	57	La	0.021
2	He	3.5×10^7	30	Zn	1.6	58	Ce	0.023
3	Li	...	31	Ga	0.65	59	Pr	0.0096
4	Be	...	32	Ge	2.5	60	Nd	0.033
5	B	...	33	As	4.8	61	Pm	...
6	C	80,000	34	Se	0.25	62	Sm	0.012
7	N	160,000	35	Br	0.42	63	Eu	0.0028
8	O	220,000	36	Kr	...	64	Gd	0.017
9	F	90	37	Rb	0.071	65	Tb	0.0052
10	Ne	240,000	38	Sr	0.41	66	Dy	0.02
11	Na	462	39	Y	0.10	67	Ho	0.0057
12	Mg	8,870	40	Zr	1.5	68	Er	0.016
13	Al	882	41	Nb	0.009	69	Tm	0.0029
14	Si	10,000	42	Mo	0.19	70	Yb	0.015
15	P	130	43	Tc	...	71	Lu	0.0048
16	S	3,500	44	Ru	0.093	72	Hf	0.007
17	Cl	170	45	Rh	0.035	73	Ta	0.0031
18	A	2,200	46	Pd	0.032	74	W	0.17
19	K	69	47	Ag	0.027	75	Re	0.0041
20	Ca	670	48	Cd	0.026	76	Os	0.035
21	Sc	0.18	49	In	0.01	77	Ir	0.014
22	Ti	26	50	Sn	0.62	78	Pt	0.087
23	V	2.5	51	Sb	0.017	79	Au	0.0082
24	Cr	95	52	Te	...	80	Hg	?
25	Mn	77	53	I	0.018	81	Tl	?
26	Fe	18,300	54	Xe	...	82	Pb	0.27
27	Co	99	55	Cs	0.001	83	Bi	0.0021
28	Ni	1,340	56	Ba	0.039	90	Th	0.012
						92	U	0.0026

II. Abundances of Elements in Meteorites (Per Cent by Weight)

(Values by H. Brown)

Z	Element	Value	Z	Element	Value	Z	Element	Value
1	H	0.063	29	Cu	1.3×10^{-2}	57	La	1.3×10^{-4}
2	He	...	30	Zn	4.8×10^{-2}	58	Ce	1.5×10^{-4}
3	Li	2×10^{-4}	31	Ga	2.0×10^{-3}	59	Pr	6.0×10^{-5}
4	Be	6×10^{-5}	32	Ge	8.2×10^{-3}	60	Nd	2.2×10^{-4}
5	B	2×10^{-4}	33	As	1.6×10^{-2}	61	Pm	...
6	C	7×10^{-2}	34	Se	9×10^{-4}	62	Sm	7.8×10^{-5}
7	N	5×10^{-5}	35	Br	1.5×10^{-4}	63	Eu	2.0×10^{-5}
8	O	24.61	36	Kr	...	64	Gd	1.2×10^{-4}
9	F	2×10^{-3}	37	Rb	2.7×10^{-4}	65	Tb	3.8×10^{-5}
10	Ne	...	38	Sr	1.6×10^{-3}	66	Dy	1.5×10^{-4}
11	Na	0.47	39	Y	4.0×10^{-4}	67	Ho	4.3×10^{-5}
12	Mg	9.5	40	Zr	6.0×10^{-3}	68	Er	1.3×10^{-4}
13	Al	1.0	41	Nb	3.8×10^{-5}	69	Tu	2.2×10^{-5}
14	Si	12.3	42	Mo	8.1×10^{-4}	70	Yb	1.2×10^{-4}
15	P	0.18	43	Tc	...	71	Lu	3.9×10^{-5}
16	S	1.08	44	Ru	4.2×10^{-4}	72	Hf	6×10^{-5}
17	Cl	5×10^{-2}	45	Rh	1.6×10^{-4}	73	Ta	2.5×10^{-5}
18	A	...	46	Pd	1.5×10^{-4}	74	W	1.4×10^{-3}
19	K	0.12	47	Ag	1.3×10^{-4}	75	Re	3.4×10^{-5}
20	Ca	1.2	48	Cd	1.3×10^{-4}	76	Os	3.4×10^{-4}
21	Si	3.5×10^{-4}	49	In	5×10^{-5}	77	Ir	1.2×10^{-4}
22	Ti	6×10^{-2}	50	Sn	3.3×10^{-3}	78	Pt	7.6×10^{-4}
23	V	5.6×10^{-3}	51	Sb	9×10^{-5}	79	Au	7.2×10^{-5}
24	Cr	0.22	52	Te	?	80	Hg	?
25	Mn	0.19	53	I	1.0×10^{-4}	81	Tl	?
26	Fe	45.7	54	Xe	...	82	Pb	2.5×10^{-3}
27	Co	0.26	55	Cs	6×10^{-6}	83	Bi	2.0×10^{-5}
28	Ni	3.51	56	Ba	5.4×10^{-4}	90	Th	1.2×10^{-4}
						92	U	2.8×10^{-4}

Appendix XX

TABLE OF DENSITIES, MELTING POINTS, BOILING POINTS, COLORS, AND SOLUBILITIES OF INORGANIC COMPOUNDS

Values for densities are in grams per cc. Temperatures 15–25° C. Values for solubilities are in grams of anhydrous salt per 100 grams of water solution. Abbreviations for colors: bk, black; bl, blue; br, brown; c, colorless or white if finely divided; d, dark; gr, green; gy, grey; l, light; or, orange; pk, pink; pu, purple; r, red; ro, rose; sil, silver; v, violet; w, white; y, yellow.

Formula	Density	Melting Point °C.	Boiling Point °C.	Color	Solubility in Water
Aluminum					
Al	2.71	658.6	2330	gy-w	sol. H$^+$ and OH$^-$
Al$_2$O$_3$	4.00	2045	2977	c	v. sl. sol.
Al$_2$O$_3$·H$_2$O	3.41	d. 360		c	0.0001(20°)
Al(C$_2$H$_3$O$_2$)$_3$		d.		c	sol. but hydr.
Al(C$_2$H$_3$O$_2$)$_2$OH				c	sl. sol.
Al(BrO$_3$)$_3$·9H$_2$O		62.3		c	sol.
AlBr$_3$	3.01	97.5	265	c	sol.
Al$_4$C$_3$	2.36	high		y	giv. Al(OH)$_3$ + CH$_4$
Al(ClO$_3$)$_3$·6H$_2$O		d.		c	v. sol.
AlCl$_3$	2.44	190 (2½ at.)	180.2	c	6 aq. 41.4(15°)
AlF$_3$	3.07	> 1271	1272	c	sl. sol.
Al(OH)$_3$	2.4	d.		c	v. sl. sol.
AlI$_3$	3.98	191	385.5	br	6 ap. v. sol.
Al(NO$_3$)$_3$·9H$_2$O		73	d. 134	c	4 aq. 38.9(25°)
AlN		2150		gy	not sol.
AlPO$_4$	2.59	high		c	v. sl. sol.
Al$_2$(SO$_4$)$_3$	2.7	d. 770		c	18 aq. 26.6(20°)
AlNH$_4$(SO$_4$)$_2$·12H$_2$O	1.64	93		c	6.2(20°), 26.0(80°)
Al$_2$S$_3$	2.02	1100	sub. 1550	y	hydr.
AlTl(SO$_4$)$_2$·12H$_2$O	2.32	91		c	5.1(15°)
AlK(SO$_4$)$_2$·12H$_2$O	1.76	92		c	4.8(15°), 60.6(100°)
Al$_6$O$_4$·Si$_2$O$_4$	3.15	d. 1810		c	v. sl. sol.
Ammonia					
NH$_3$	0.82(79°)	− 77.7	− 33.4	c	47.5(0°), 6.9(100°)
NH$_4$OH		− 79	d.	c	cf. NH$_3$
(NH$_4$)$_2$O		− 79	d.	c	
NH$_4$C$_2$H$_3$O$_2$(acetate)	1.07	114.0		c	60(40°)
NH$_4$H$_2$AsO$_4$	2.31			c	sol.
NH$_4$AsO$_2$				c	v. sol.
NH$_4$Br	2.33		sub. 542	c	41.1(15°), 56.1(100°)

Formula	Density	Melting Point °C.	Boiling Point °C.	Color	Solubility in Water
$(NH_4)_2CO_3 \cdot H_2O$		d.		c	50(15°)
NH_4HCO_3	1.59			c	21(30°)
NH_4Cl	1.54	d. 350	520 p.	c	22.9(0°), 29.3(30°)
NH_4ClO_4	1.95	d.		c	20.8(20°), 57(100°)
$(NH_4)_2CrO_4$	1.8	d. 180		y	28(30°)
NH_4CNO		d.		c	sol.
NH_4CN		d. 36		c	sol.
$(NH_4)_2Cr_2O_7$	2.15	d.		r-br	32(30°)
NH_4F		d.		c	v. sol.
NH_4I	2.56	d.	sub. 551	c	67(25°)
NH_4IO_3	3.31	d. 150		c	2.5(0°), 12.6(100°)
$NH_4MgAsO_4 \cdot 6H_2O$	1.93	d.		c	0.038(20°)
$NH_4MgPO_4 \cdot 6H_2O$	1.65	d.		c	0.024(15°)
$(NH_4)_6Mo_7O_{24} \cdot H_2O$		d.		c	sol.
NH_4NO_2	α1.66	169.6	d. 210		
	β1.72		d. 210		70(30°)
NH_4NO_2	1.69	d.		c	sol.
$(NH_4)_2C_2O_4 \cdot H_2O$	1.50			c	4.2(20°), 9.3(50°)
NH_4MnO_4	2.21	d. 60		g	8(15°)
$(NH_4)_2S_2O_8$	1.98	d. 120		c	34(0°)
$(NH_4)_2PtCl_6$	3.06	d.		y	0.67(20°), 1.25(100°)
$(NH_4)_2PtCl_4$		d.		y	sol.
$(NH_4)_2PdCl_6$	2.42	d.		r	sl. sol.
$(NH_4)_2HPO_4$	1.62	d.		c	v. sol.
$NH_4H_2PO_4$	1.803			c	18.0(50°)
$(NH_4)_3PO_4 12MoO_3$ $\cdot 3H_2O$		d.		y	0.03(15°)
$(NH_4)_2SO_4$	1.77	d.		c	41.4(0°), 43.8(30°)
$(NH_4)_2S$		d.		y	v. sol. giv. HS⁻
$(NH_4)_2SO_3 \cdot H_2O$		d.		c	v. sol.
$(NH_4)_2Se$			d.	br	sol.
NH_4CNS	1.31(13°)	146	d. 170	c	55(0°), 62(20°)
$(NH_4)_2C_4H_4O_6$	1.60	d.		c	5.9(15°)
Antimony					
Sb	6.68	630	1440	gr	not sol.
$HSb(OH)_6$	6.6	d.		c	sl. sol.
H_3SbO_3		d.		c	v. sl. sol.
Sb_2O_3	5.67	655	1456	c	0.002(15°)
Sb_2O_4	4.07	1060		c	v. sl. sol.
Sb_2O_5	3.78	450	1060	y	v. sl. sol.
$SbBr_3$	4.15	96.6	280	y	sol. hydr.
$SbCl_3$	3.14	73.4	221	c	910 g./100 g. H_2O at 20°
$SbCl_5$	2.34	3.0	92 at 30 mm.	y	hydr.
SbF_3	4.38	292		c	83(25°)
SbF_5	2.99	6	149.5	c	hydr.
SbH_3	1. 2.26	− 88	− 18	c	0.12 (1 atm.p.)
SbI_3 **Trig**	4.85	170.5	401	y	hydr.
SbI_5		79		br	
SbOCl		d. 170		c	v. sl. sol.
$Sb_2(SO_4)_3$	3.63	d.		c	hydr.
Sb_2S_3	4.64	546		bk, r	0.000175
Sb_2S_5	4.12			or	v. sl. sol.
Sb_2Se_3		617		gy	v. sl. sol.
Sb_2Te_3		625		gy	
$(SbO)KC_4H_4O_6$ $\cdot \frac{1}{2}H_2O$	2.61	½ aq. 100		c	7.0(25°)
Argon					
A	1. 1.40	− 189.3	−185.8	c	5, 6 cc.(0°)
Arsenic					
As	5.7	817 (36 atm.)	610	sil	not sol

Formula	Density	Melting Point °C.	Boiling Point °C.	Color	Solubility in Water
H₃AsO₄·½H₂O	2-2.5	36.14	1 aq. 160	c	sol.
H₄As₂O₇		206 d.		c	sol.
As₂O₃	3.7	313	460	c	2.04(25°)
As₂O₅	4.15	315		c	cf. H₃AsO₄
AsBr₃	3.54	31	221	y	sol.
AsCl₃	l. 2.16	− 16.1	130	c	sol.
AsCl₅		− 40		c	hydr.
AsF₃	l. 2.66	− 5.95		c	hydr.
AsF₅		− 80.3	− 52.8	c	hydr.
AsH₃		− 116.3	− 62.5	c	sl. sol.
AsI₃	4.39	146	403	or-r	6(25°)
AsOCl				br	sol.
As₂S₂ α, β	α3.51				
	β3.25	β307	565	r	v. sl. sol.
As₂S₃	3.43	300	700	r & y	0.00005
As₂S₅		sub.		y	v. sl. sol.
Barium					
Ba	3.78	717	1640	y-w	giv. Ba(OH)₂ + H₂
BaO	5.72	1923		c	8 aq. 3.36(20°), 47.6(80°)
BaO₂	4.96	d.		gy	v. sl. sol.
Ba(C₂H₃O₂)₂·H₂O	2.19	d.		c	43.3(26°)
BaHAsO₄·H₂O	3.93	d.		c	sl. sol.
Ba(BrO₃)₂·H₂O	3.99			c	0.3(0°), 5.67(100°)
BaBr₂·2H₂O	3.69	an. 847	1827	c	60(20°)
BaCO₃ α, β	α4.43	β1740(90 atm.)	d.	c	0.002(20°), 0.006(100°)
Ba(ClO₃)₂·H₂O	3.18	d. 120		c	21.5(25°), 33.9(100°)
BaCl₂·2H₂O	3.10	an. 960	1827	c	26.3(20°), 37.0(100°)
BaCrO₄	4.98			y	0.00038(20°)
BaF₂	4.83	1353	2277	c	0.16(18°)
BaH₂	4.21	d. 675		c	giv. Ba(OH)₂ + H₂
Ba(OH)₂·8H₂O	2.13	77.9		c	cf. BaO
Ba(IO₃)₂·H₂O	5.5	aq. 130		c	0.028(20°), 0.20(100°)
BaI₂	5.15	d. 711	1727	c	6 aq. 66.5(20°)
Ba(NO₃)₂	3.24	585	d.	c	1 aq. 38.6(20°)
BaC₂O₄	2.66	d.		c	2 aq. 0.0024(25°)
Ba(ClO₄)₂		505		c	66.5(25°)
Ba(MnO₄)₂	3.77	d.		gr	62.5(11°), 75.4(25°)
BaMoO₄	4.65			c	0.0058(23°)
Ba₃(PO₄)₂	4.11	1727		c	v. sl. sol.
BaH₄(PO₄)₂	2.90			c	sol.
BaHPO₄	4.16			c	0.01(20°)
Ba₂P₂O₇	4.11			c	0.01
BaSO₄	4.50	1350		c	0.00024(20°)
BaSO₃			d.	c	0.02(20°)
BaS	4.25	2200		gy-gr	hydr.
Beryllium					
Be	1.73	1284	2507	gr-w	0.36(0°)
BeO	3.03	2400	3900	c	2 × 10⁻⁵(20°)
Be(OH)₂		d.		w	hot. sol.
BeBr₂		490	474	c	sol.
BeCO₃·4H₂O		d. 100		c	0.36(0°)
BeCl₂	1.90	450	487	c	v. sol.
BeF₂	2.1	697	1327	c	giv. oxy-salt
BeI₂	4.20	480	sub.	c	sol.
Be(NO₃)₂·3H₂O		60		c	sol.
BeC₂O₄·3H₂O				c	40 g./100 g. H₂O at 25°
BeSO₄·4H₂O	1.71	2 aq. 100	d.	c	29.8(25°)
Bismuth					
Bi	9.80	271	1420	gy-w	not sol.
HBiO₃	5.75	d. 120		r	evol. O₂
Bi₂O₃	8.9	817	1900	y	v. sl. sol.

Formula	Density	Melting Point °C.	Boiling Point °C.	Color	Solubility in Water
Bi_2O_5	5.10	d. 150		r	v. sl. sol.
$Bi(OH)_3$	4.36	d. 100		c	0.00014
$BiBr_3$	5.7	218	460.8	y	hydr.
$Bi_2O_2CO_3 \cdot H_2O$	6.86	d.		c	v. sl. sol.
$BiCl_2$				v	d.
$BiCl_3$	4.7	232	441	c	hydr. sol. in HCl
BiF_3	5.32	727		gy	sl. sol.
$BiOCl$	7.72	high		c	v. sl. sol.
$BiOF$	7.5			c	v. sl. sol.
BiI_3	5.7	439	d. 500	gy-bl	hydr.
$Bi(NO_3)_3 \cdot 5H_2O$	2.83	d. 30		c	v. sol. in dil. HNO_3
$BiONO_3 \cdot H_2O$	4.93	d. 260		c	v. sl. sol.
$BiPO_4$	6.32	d.		c	v. sl. sol.
Bi_2S_3	7.39	706		br	0.000018(18°)
$Bi_2(SO_4)_3$	5.1	d. 418		c	hydr. sol. in H_2SO_4
Boron					
B	2.45	2040	2530	br	not sol.
H_3BO_3	1.43	185		c	4.8(20°), 28.7(100°)
B_2O_3	1.85	450	1250	c	cf. H_3BO_3
BBr_3	l. 2.60	− 45	91.0		hydr.
B_6C	2.6	2350		bk	not sol.
BCl_3	l. 1.43	− 107	12.5	c	hydr.
BF_3		− 128	− 101.9	c	1.06 cc/cc H_2O at 0°, 1 atm.
B_2H_6		− 165.5	− 92.4	c	sl. sol.
B_4H_{10}		− 120	16	c	sl. sol.
$B_{10}H_{14}$	0.94	99.5		c	sl. sol.
BI_3	l. 3.35	43	210	c	hydr.
B_2S_3	1.55	310		c	hydr.
BN	2.34		5.3000	w	hydr. slow.
Bromine					
Br_2	3.4	− 7.3	58.78	br	4.0(0°), 3.3(25°)
$HBrO_3$		d. 100		l-y	v. sol.
$BrCl \cdot 10H_2O$		d. 7		y	v. sol. hydr.
BrF_3		5	135	y	hydr.
Cadmium					
Cd	8.6	320.9	767	sil	v. sl. sol.
CdO	8.15		s. 1559	br	cf. $Cd(OH)_2 \cdot$Sol. H^+
$Cd(OH)_2$	4.79	3.300		c	0.00026(25°)
$Cd(C_2H_3O_2)_2 \cdot 3H_2O$	2.01			c	v. sol.
$CdBr_2$	5.19	568	1136	y	4 aq. 48.8(18°)
$CdCO_3$	4.26	d. < 500		c	v. sl. sol.
$CdCl_2 \cdot 2.5H_2O$	3.32	an. 568	980	c	56.3(30°)
CdF_2	6.64	1110	1747	c	4.3(25°)
$CdI_2 \; \alpha$	α5.67	α388	α796	br	α46.0(18°)
$Cd(NO_3)_2 \cdot 4H_2O$	2.45	59.4	132	c	58.4(30°)
CdC_2O_4	3.32	d. 340		c	0.0033(18°)
$Cd_3(PO_4)_2$		1500		c	v. sl. sol.
$CdSiO_3$	4.93	1155		c	v. sl. sol.
$3CdSO_4 \cdot 8H_2O$	3.09			c	43.4(26°), 1aq. 60.8(100°)
$CdSO_4$	4.69	1000		c	
CdS	4.6	1750(100 atm.)		yl	0.00013(18°)
Calcium					
Ca	1.55	851	1482	sil	$Ca(OH)_2 + H_2$
CaO	3.32	2707		c	cf. $Ca(OH)_2$
$Ca(OH)_2$	2.34	d. 580		c	0.165(20°), 0.08(100°)
$Ca(C_2H_3O_2)_2 \cdot H_2O$		d.		gy	25.8(20°), 22.9(100°)
$CaBr_2$	3.35	760	1827	c	6 aq. 58.8(20°)
CaC_2	2.22	2300		gy	giv. $Ca(OH)_2 + C_2H_2$
$CaCO_3$ (Aragonite)	2.93		d.	c	0.00153(25°)
$CaCO_3$ (Calcite)	2.71	1282	d.	c	0.00143(25°)

Formula	Density	Melting Point °C.	Boiling Point °C.	Color	Solubility in Water
$CaCl_2$	2.15	782	2027	c	cf. 6 aq.
$CaCl_2 \cdot 6H_2O$	1.68	29.92		c	42.7(20°), 2 aq. 61.4(100°)
$CaCrO_4$			d.	y	2 aq. 14(20°)
CaF_2	3.18	1418	2407	c	0.0016(18°)
CaH_2	1.7	d. 675		c	giv. $Ca(OH)_2 + H_2$
$Ca(ClO)_2 \cdot 4H_2O$		d.		c	v. sol.
CaI_2	3.96	740	1227	y-w	6 aq. 67(20°)
Ca_3N_2	2.63	900		l-br	hydr. slowly
$Ca(NO_3)_2 \cdot 4H_2O$ α, β	α1.82	α42.7	132	c	54.8(18°)
CaC_2O_4	2.2	d.		c	0.0006(18°), 0.0014(95°)
$Ca(MnO_4)_2 \cdot 4H_2O$	2.4	d.		pu	v. sol.
Ca_3P_2	2.51	> 1600		r	giv. PH_3
$Ca_3(PO_4)_2$	3.14	1670		c	0.0025
$CaHPO_4 \cdot 2H_2O$	2.31	d.		c	0.02(25.4°)
$CaH_4(PO_4)_2 \cdot H_2O$	2.22	d.		c	1.8(30°)
$Ca_2P_2O_7$	3.09	1230		c	sl. sol.
$Ca(H_2PO_2)_2$		d.		c	sol.
$3Ca_3(PO_4)_2 \cdot CaFCl$	3.14	1270		c	v. sl. sol.
$CaSO_4$	2.96	1297		c	cf. 2 aq.
$CaSO_4 \cdot 2H_2O$	2.32	2 aq. 163		c	0.208(25°)
CaS	2.81			c	hydr.
$CaSO_3$				c	0.17(15°)
$CaSeO_4 \cdot 2H_2O$	2.76			c	2 aq. 7.6(20°)
Carbon					
C (diamond)	3.51			c	
C (graphite)	2.25		s. 4347	bl	v. sl. sol.
CO	l. 0.81	− 205	− 191.5	c	0.0044(0°), 0.0018(50°)
CO_2	s. 1.53	− 56.2	s. − 78.5	c	0.335(0°), 0.145(20°),
	l. 1.10				0.06(60°)
C_3O_2	1.11	− 107	6.3	c	giv. malonic acid
CH_4		− 182.5	− 161.5		sl. sol.
CBr_4	l. 3.42	90.1	187	w	v. sl. sol.
CCl_4	l. 1.59	− 24.0	77.1	c	0.08(20°)
CF_4		− 183.7	−182.0	c	sl. sol.
CI_4	4.32	171		r	hydr.
COS	l. 1.24	− 138.8	− 50.24	c	0.122(25°)
CS_2	l. 1.26	− 112.1	46.3	c	0.18(20°)
C_2N_2	0.87	− 27.84	− 21.15	c	sl. sol.: $(C_2N_2)_n$ more sol.
Cerium					
Ce	6.9	785	2527	gy	v. sl. sol.
Ce_2O_3	6.9			c	v. sl. sol.
CeO_2	7.3	1950		l-y	v. sl. sol.
$CeCl_3$	3.92	802	1610	c	sol.
$Ce_2(CO_3)_3 \cdot 5H_2O$				c	v. sl. sol.
CeF_3	5.8	1460	2327	c	v. sl. sol.
$Ce(IO_3)_4$				c	0.015(20°)
$Ce(NO_3)_3 \cdot 6H_2O$		3 aq. 150	d. 200	r	sol.
$Ce(NO_3)_4$				y	sol.
$Ce_2(C_2O_4)_3 \cdot 9H_2O$		8 aq. 110		c	4 × 10^{-5}(25°)
$Ce_2(SO_4)_3$	3.91			c	8 aq. 8.7(20°)
$Ce(SO_4)_2 \cdot 4H_2O$				y	sol.
$CeBr_3 \cdot 3H_2O$		an. 732	1557	c	sol.
$CeI_3 \cdot 9H_2O$		an. 752	1417	c	sol.
$CeF_4 \cdot H_2O$	5.0	an. 977	d	c	sl. sol.
Cesium					
Cs	1.90	28.4	690	sil	$CsOH + H_2$
Cs_2O	4.36			or	giv. $CsOH$
Cs_2O_3	4.25	400		gy	d.
CsO_2	3.77	600		y	giv. $CoOH + HO_2^-$
$CsOH$	3.67	272.5		c	79.4(15°)
$CsBr$	4.44	632	1300	c	55(25°)

Formula	Density	Melting Point °C.	Boiling Point °C.	Color	Solubility in Water
Cs_2CO_3			d. 610	c	v. sol.
CsCl	3.97	642	1300	c	65(20°), 73(100°)
CsF	3.59	682	1251	c	1.5 aq. v. sol.
CsI	4.51	621	1280	c	28(0°), 51.5(35.6°)
$CsNO_3$	3.68	407	d.	c	18.7(20°), 66.3(100°)
Cs_2SO_4	4.24	1010		c	61(20°)
Chlorine					
Cl_2	s. 1.9	− 100.98	− 34.05	l-y	0.63(25°)
$Cl_2·8H_2O$	1.23	d. 9.6		l-y	1.85(20°) Under P.
$HClO_3·7H_2O$	1.28	d.		c	v. sol.
$HClO_4$	l. 1.77	− 112		c	1 aq. 77.7(17°)
Cl_2O	0.00385	− 20	2.0	y-r	2 vol/vol H_2O at 0°
ClO_2	0.00298	− 76	11	r	10.8(18°)
Chromium					
Cr	7.1	1550	2482	sil	not sol.
CrO_3	2.7	d. 190	d.	r	62.8(25°)
Cr_2O_3	5.21	2265		gr	v. sl. sol.
$Cr(OH)_2$				y-br	evol.$_2$ H
$Cr(OH)_3·2H_2O$				gr	v. sl. sol.
$CrCl_2$	2.75	815	1302	bl	v. sol.
$CrCl_3$	2.7	1302	s.	v	70(25°) v. slowly sol.
Cr_3C_2	6.68	1890	3810	gr	not sol.
CrF_3	3.8	1100	1427	gr	v. sol.
$Cr(NO_3)_3·9H_2O$		36.5		pu	v. sol.
$Cr(PO_4)·3H_2O$				bl-gr	sl. sol.
$CrSO_4·7H_2O$				bl	12 g. 7 aq./100 g. H_2O(0°)
$Cr_2(SO_4)_3·18H_2O$	1.7	12 aq. 100		v	120 g. 18 aq./100 g. H_2O- (20°)
Cr_2S_3	3.7			d-br	hydr. slowly
Cobalt					
Co	8.9	1493	3520	gy-w	not sol.
CoO	5.68	1805		br	v. sl. sol.
Co_2O_3	5.18	d. 900		br	v. sl. sol.
Co_3O_4	6.07			bl	v. sl. sol.
$Co(OH)_2$	3.60	d.		r	v. sl. sol.
$Co(OH)_3$				bl	3.2×10^{-4}
$Co(C_2H_3O_2)_2·4H_2O$	1.72			v	sol.
$Co_3(AsO_4)_2·8H_2O$	2.9			r	v. sl. sol.
$CoBr_2·6H_2O$		an. 687		r	67(60°)
$CoCO_3$	4.13	d.		r	v. sl. sol.
$Co_2(CO)_8$	1.73	51	d. 135	or	v. sl. sol.
$CoCl_2·6H_2O$	1.92	an. 727	an. 1050	r	33.3(20°)
$CoCl_2$	2.94	724	1050	r	sol.
CoI_2	5.68	520		v	2 aq. 79(46°)
$Co(NO_3)_2·6H_2O$	1.88	57		r	49.7(18°)
$Co_3(PO_4)_2·8H_2O$				l-r	v. sl. sol.
$CoSO_4·7H_2O$	1.95	an. 989		r	26.6(20°), 45.3(100°)
$Co_2(SO_4)_3$				bl	hydr.
CoS	5.45	1100		br	0.00038
$Co(CN)_2·2H_2O$		d. 280		gy	sl. sol.
$CoF_2·2H_2O$	an. 4.43			r	sol.
CoC_2O_4	2.325			r	0.003
CoSe	7.65			y	v. sl. sol.
CoSi	7.1	1327			not. sol.
$CoCrO_4$		d.		y br	v. sl. sol.
Copper					
Cu	8.92	1083	2582	r	v. sl. sol.
Cu_2O	6.0	1230	1800	r	v. sl. sol.
CuO	6.4	d. 1026 at 153 mm. O_2		bk	v. sl. sol.
$Cu(OH)_2$	3.68	d.		bl	v. sl. sol.

Formula	Density	Melting Point °C.	Boiling Point °C.	Color	Solubility in Water
$Cu(C_2H_3O_2)_2H_2O$	1.88	115	d. 240	gr	18.5(21.5°)
$CuSO_4·4NH_3·H_2O$		d. 150		bl	sol. giv. $Cu(NH_3)_4^{++}$
$Cu_3(AsO_4)_2·4H_2O$				bl-gr	v. sl. sol.
$CuHAsO_3$		d.		gr	v. sol.
$CuBr$	4.72	488	1355	br	sl. sol.
$CuBr_2$		498		bl	sol.
Cu_2CO_3	4.40	d.		y	v. sl. sol.
$2CuCO_3·Cu(OH)_2$	3.88	d. 220		bl	v. sl. sol.
$CuCl$	3.53	430	1490	c	1.5(25°)
$CuCl_2·2H_2O$	2.39	d. 110	d.	gr	43.5(20°)
$CuCl_2$	3.054	498	d.	l-y	
$CuCN$		474		c	v. sl. sol.
$Cu_2Fe(CN)_6·7H_2O$				r-br	v. sl. sol.
CuI	5.62	588	1336	gy-br	0.0004(18°)
$Cu(NO_3)_2·6H_2O$	2.05	d. 26.4	d.	bl	55.6(20°)
$Cu_3(PO_4)_2·3H_2O$				bl	
$CuSO_4$	3.6	d. 620		c	
$CuSO_4·5H_2O$	2.29		1aq.d.230	bl	18.7(25°), 42.4(100°)
Cu_2S, Rhom.	5.6	tr. 103		bk	
Cu_2S, Cub.	5.76	1130		bk	0.00005(18°)
CuS	4.6	d. 220		bk	0.000033(18°)
$CuCNS$	2.85	1084		c	v. sl. sol.
Dysprosium					
Dy	8.56	ca. 1100		gy	sol. H^+
Dy_2O_3	7.81			w	sl. sol.
$DyBr_3$		881	1477	y	sol.
$DyCl_3$		654	1507	y	sol.
DyF_3		1357	2327	y	sl. sol.
Erbium					
Er	9.16	1250		gy	sol. H^+
$ErBr_3$		950	1457	r	sol.
$ErCl_3$	4.4	774	1497	r	sol.
ErF_3		1347	2227	r	sl. sol.
ErI_3		1020	1377	r	sol.
Europium					
Eu	5.24	1150		gy	sol. H^+
$EuBr_3$		702	1497	pk	sol.
$EuCl_2$		727	2027	pk	sol.
$EuCl_3$		623	1547	pk	sol.
EuF_3		1377	2377	pk	sl. sol.
EuI_3		877	1377	pk	sol.
Fluorine					
F_2	l. 1.14	− 217.96	− 187.92	c	d. O_3 + HF
F_2O	l. 1.65	− 223.8	− 144.8	c	v. sl. sol.
Gadolinium					
Gd		ca. 1100			evol. H_2
Gd_2O_3	7.41			c	v. sl. sol.
$GdCl_3$	4.62	609	1527	c	sol.
$Gd_2(SO_4)_3$	4.14			c	8 aq. 2.4(25°)
$Gd_2(C_2O_4)_3·10H_2O$		d. 110		c	0.11(25°)
$GdBr_3·6H_2O$	2.84	an. 765	1487	c	sol.
GdF_3		1377	2377	c	sl. sol.
GdI_3		926	1377	c	sol.
Gallium					
Ga	5.91	29.78	2071	sil	not sol.
$GaCl_2$		170.5	535	c	v. sol.
$GaCl_3$	2.37	77.5	200	c	v. sol.
Ga_2O_3		1740		c	sl. sol.
$GaBr_3$		124.5	278	c	sol.
Ga_2S_3	3.5	1250		c	sl. sol.

Formula	Density	Melting Point °C.	Boiling point °C.	Color	Solubility in Water
Germanium					
Ge	5.36	960	2700	sil	
GeO_2	4.70	1116			0.40(20°)
GeH_4	l. 1.52	− 165.9	− 88.36	c	sl. sol.
Ge_2H_6	l. 1.98	− 109	− 30.8	c	sl. sol.
$GeCl_4$	l. 1.87	− 49.5	83.1	c	hydr.
$GeBr_4$	l. 3.13	26.1	187.1	gy	hydr.
GeI_4	4.32	144	375	y	hydr.
$GeF_4·2H_2O$		15	s − 36.8	c	sol.
GeS	3.54	625		w	sl. sol.
Gold					
Au	19.3	1063	2660	y-w	not sol.
Au_2O_3		d. 160		bl	v. sl. sol.
AuOH		d.		r-br	giv. Au_2O_3 + Au
$Au(OH)_3$		d. 250		y-vr	v. sl. sol.
AuBr		d. 115		y-gy	v. sl. sol.
$AuBr_3$		d. 160		br	sol.
$HAuBr_4·5H_2O$		27		r	sol.
AuCl	7.4	d. 289.5		y	v. sl. sol.
$AuCl_3$	3.9	d. 254	s. 265	y-r	40
Au_2Cl_4	5.1	d. 250		r	d.
AuCN		d.		y	v. sl. sol.
$Au(CN)_3·6H_2O$		d. 50			v. sol.
Au_2S_2		d. 140		bk	v. sl. sol.
Au_2S_3	8.75	d. 197		br	v. sl. sol.
$Au_2O_3·2SO_3·H_2O$					sol.
$HAu(NO_3)_4·3H_2O$	2.84	d. 72		r-y	sol.
Hafnium					
Hf	12.1	2230	5230	r-gy	not sol.
HfO_2	9.68	2780		c	v. sl. sol.
$HfOCl_2·8H_2O$				c	sol.
K_2HfF_6				c	3.0(20°)
$HfBr_4$		420		c	sol.
$HfCl_4$		432		c	sol.
Helium					
He		− 272 110 atm.	− 268.9	c	0.00858 vol/vol H_2O(20°)
Hydrogen					
H_2	l. 0.08	− 259.15	− 252.77	c	1.93×10^{-4}(0°) 1.56×10^{-4}(25°)
HBr	l. 2.16	− 86.86	− 66.7	c	65.9(25°)
HCl	l. 1.194	− 114.2	− 85	c	64.2(20°), 61.6(50°)
HCN	0.699	− 13.1	25.70	c	v. sol.
HF	l. 0.988	− 83.0	19.9	c	52.6−(35°)
HI	l. 2.84	− 50.8	− 35.35	c	20.3−(10°)
HN_3		− 80	37	c	sol.
H_2S	l. 0.96	− 85.5	− 60.3	c	0.38(20°)
H_2Se	l. 2.12	− 65.73	− 41.3	c	2.7 vol/vol H_2O(22.5°)
H_2Te	l. 2.57	− 51	− 2.2	c	sol.
H_2O_2	l. 1.44	− 2.0	158	c	v. sol.
H_2O	1.0(4°)	0	100	c	
Holmium					
Ho	8.76	ca. 1200		gy	sol. H^+
$HoBr_3$		914	1467	y	sol.
$HoCl_3$	4.5	718	1502	y	sol.
HoF_3		1357	2327	y	sl. sol.
HoI_3		1010	1307	y	sol.
Iodine					
I_2	4.93	113.6	183	pu-bk	0.0181(11°), 0.092(55°)
HIO_3	4.63	d. 110		c	cf. I_2O_5

Formula	Density	Melting Point °C.	Boiling Point °C.	Color	Solubility in Water
H_5IO_6				c	v. sol.
IO_2	4.21	d. 130		y	giv. $HIO_3 + I_2$
I_2O_5	4.80	d. 300		c	2 aq. 71.7(16°)
$ICl\alpha$	l. 3.24	33.2	97	r-br	hydr. $HIO + Cl^-$
ICl_3	3.11	33	s. 101 (16 atm.)	y	hydr.
IBr	4.41	42	116	pu-bk	hydr.
IF_5	l. 3.5	− 9	97	c	hydr.
Indium					
In	7.3	156.4	1450	sil	not sol.
In_2O_3	7.18			l-y	v. sl. sol.
$InCl_3$	4.0	586	s.	c	v. sol.
InI_3		210		y	sol.
$In_2(SO_4)_3$	3.44			c	sol.
Iridium					
Ir	22.4	2443	4350	sil	not sol.
IrO_2				gy	v. sl. sol.
$IrCl_2$		d. 775		br	v. sol.
$IrCl$	5.30	d. 763		d-gr	sol. if hydrated
$IrCl_4·2NH_4Cl$	2.86	d.		d-r	0.9(27°)
$IrCl_3·3NH_4Cl$				gr-br	sol.
$Ir_2(SO_4)_3(NH_4)_2SO_4$ ·24H$_2$O		106		y-r	sol.
Iron					
Fe	7.86	1535	2800	gy	not sol.
FeO		1368		c	v. sl. sol.
Fe_2O_3	5.12	d. 1560		r	v. sl. sol.
Fe_3O_4	5.2	1594		bk	v. sl. sol.
$Fe(OH)_2$				gr	0.0096(18°)
$Fe(OH)_3$	3.4–3.9	1 aq. 500		r-br	v. sl. sol.
$FeOH(C_2H_3O_2)_2$				r	v. sl. sol.
$FeSO_4(NH_4)_2SO_4$ ·6H$_2$O	1.86			bl-gr	25.0(25°)
FeAs	7.83	1020		w	v. sl. sol.
$FeBr_3·6H_2O$		27		r	v. sol.
$FeBr_2$	4.64	684	927	r	6 aq. 54.3(25°)
$FeCO_3$	3.8	d.		gr-br	0.0065(20°)
Fe_3C	7.4	1837		gy	not sol.
$Fe(CO)_5$	1.46	− 21	105	gr	v. sl. sol.
$FeCl_2·4H_2O$	1.93		an. 1026	gr-w	41.5(25°)
FeF_2	4.09	1102	1827	gy	sol.
$FeCl_3·6H_2O$		37	280	r-y	47.9(20°)
$FeCl_3$	2.8	304	319	r	
FeF_3	3.18	1027	1327	gy	sol.
$FeCl_2$	2.7	677	1026	gy	sol.
$Fe_4[Fe(CN)_6]_3$		d.		bl	v. sl. sol.
$FeI_2·4H_2O$	2.87	an. 177		gr	v. sol.
$Fe(NO_3)_2·6H_2O$		d. 60		gr-w	45.5(20°)
$Fe(NO_3)_3·6H_2O$	1.68	47.2	d.	gy	v. sol.
Fe_2N	6.35	d.		gy	not sol.
$FeC_2O_4·2H_2O$	2.28	d. 160		y	0.022
$Fe_2(C_2O_4)_3$		d. 100			v. sol.
Fe_3P	6.74	1100		gy	not sol.
$Fe_3(PO_4)_2·8H_2O$	2.58			bl	v. sl. sol.
$FePO_4·2H_2O$	2.87			y	v. sl. sol.
$FeSO_4·7H_2O$	1.89	64	d.	bl-gr	21(20°)
$Fe_2(SO_4)_3·9H_2O$	2.1			y	v. sol.
FeS	4.8	1195		bl	0.0006(18°)
FeS_2	5.0			y	v. sl. sol.
Fe_2S_3	4.3	d.		y-gr	v. sl. sol. giv. FeS + S
$Fe(CNS)_3·3H_2O$				r	v. sol.

Formula	Density	Melting Point °C.	Boiling Point °C.	Color	Solubility in Water
Krypton					
Kr		− 157.2	− 153.2	c	sl. sol.
Lanthanum					
La	6.15	887	2730	gy	La(OH)$_3$ + H$_2$
La$_2$O$_3$	6.51	> 2000	4210	c	giv. sl. OH$^-$
La$_2$(CO$_3$)$_3$·8H$_2$O	2.7			c	v. sl. sol.
LaCl$_3$	3.95	852	1607	c	sol.
La(IO$_3$)$_3$				c	1.7(25°)
La(NO$_3$)$_3$·6H$_2$O		40	d. 126	c	60.2(25°)
La$_2$(SO$_4$)$_3$·9H$_2$O	2.82	d.		c	2.91(0°), 1.86(30°)
LaBr$_3$		783	1577	c	sol.
LaF$_3$		1427	2327	c	sl. sol.
LaI$_3$		761	1437	c	sol.
Lead					
Pb	11.34	327.4	1750	gy	
PbO	9.53	886	1472	y	0.002(20°)
PbO$_2$	9.38	d. 290		br	v. sl. sol.
Pb$_3$O$_4$	9.1	d. 500		r	v. sl. sol.
Pb(OH)$_2$		d. 145		c	0.016(20°)
Pb(C$_2$H$_3$O$_2$)$_2$·2H$_2$O	2.55	d. 75		c	v. sol. hydr.
Pb$_3$(AsO$_4$)$_2$	7.30	1042		c	v. sl. sol.
Pb(C$_2$H$_5$)$_4$	l. 1.66		83 (14 mm.)	c	v. sl. sol.
Pb(BO$_2$)$_2$·H$_2$O	5.60	high temp.		c	v. sl. sol.
PbBr$_2$	6.66	497	914	y	0.455(0°), 4.55(100°)
PbCO$_3$	6.6	d. 315		c	0.00015(20°)
2PbCO$_3$·Pb(OH)$_2$	6.14	d. 400		l-y	v. sl. sol.
PbCl$_2$	5.85	498	954	c	0.637(0°), 3.20(100°)
PbCl$_4$	l. 3.18	− 15	d.	c	hydr. evol. Cl$_2$
PbCrO$_4$	6.3	844		y	7 × 10^{-6}(20°)
PbF$_2$	8.24	824	1290	c	0.068(27°)
PbI$_2$	6.16	412	872	y	0.044(0°), 0.434(100°)
Pb(IO$_3$)$_2$		d. 300		c	0.003(25°)
Pb(NO$_3$)$_2$	4.53	d. 470		c	34.3(20°)
PbC$_2$O$_4$	5.28	d. 300		c	0.00015(18°)
PbCl$_2$·PbO	7.21	d. 524		c	v. sl. sol .
Pb$_3$(PO$_4$)$_2$	ca 7.1	1014		c	0.000014(20°)
Pb(PO$_3$)$_2$		800		c	v. sl. sol.
PbS	7.5	1114	s. ca.1000	bk	2.9 × 10^{-5}(18°)
PbSO$_3$				c	v. sl. sol.
PbSO$_4$	6.2	1087		c	0.0042(20°)
Pb$_2$O(SO$_4$)	6.92	970		c	v. sl. sol.
Pb(CNS)$_2$	3.82	d. 190		y	0.5(20°)
PbSiO$_3$	6.49	766		c	v. sl. sol.
Pb(CH$_3$)$_4$		− 27.5	106.1		hydr. slow
Lithium					
Li	0.53	179	1367	sil	giv. LiOH + H$_2$
Li$_2$O	2.01	> 1700		c	giv. LiOH
LiOH	2.54	462		c	11.3(10°), 14.9(100°)
LiC$_2$H$_3$O$_2$·2H$_2$O		70	d.	c	75(15°)
LiHCO$_3$				c	5.5(13°)
LiBr	3.46	552	1310	c	2 aq. 66.2(34°)
Li$_2$CO$_3$	2.11	618		c	1.51(0°), 0.725(100°)
LiCl	2.07	614	1380	c	1 aq. 45.9(25°)
LiClO$_4$	2.43	236	d. 410	c	37.4 (25°)
LiF	2.30	847	1681	c	0.26(18°)
LiH	0.82	680		c	giv. LiOH + H$_2$
LiI		440	1171		3 aq. 62(20°)
LiNH$_2$	1.18	390		c	hydr.
LiNO$_3$	2.4	250		c	3 aq. 42.9(22°)
Li$_3$PO$_4$	2.54	837		c	0.04

Formula	Density	Melting Point °C.	Boiling Point °C.	Color	Solubility in Water
Li_2S	1.66	847		c	v. sol.
Li_2SO_4	2.22	857		c	1 aq. 25.7(20°)
Li_2SiO_3	2.33	1177		c	sol.
Lutetium					
Lu	9.94	ca. 1800			
$LuCl_3$	3.98	892	1457	c	sol.
$LuBr_3$		1045	1207	c	sol.
Magnesium					
Mg	1.74	650	1126	w	giv. $Mg(OH)_2$ slowly
MgO	3.65	2642		c	giv. $Mh(OH)_2$ slowly
$Mg(OH)_2$	2.36	d.		c	0.0009(18°)
$Mg(C_2H_3O_2)_2 \cdot 4H_2O$	1.45			c	v. sol.
$MgNH_4AsO \cdot 6H_2O$	1.93	d.		c	0.021(20°)
$MgNH_4PO_4 \cdot 6H_2O$	1.72	d.		c	0.02
$MgBr_2$	3.72	711	1227	c	6 aq. 49.1(20°)
$MgCO_3$	3.08	d. 350		c	0.01(18°) hydr.
$3MgCO_3 \cdot Mg(OH)_2$ $\cdot 3H_2O$	2.18			c	v. sl. sol.
$MgCl_2 \cdot 6H_2O$	1.56	an. 712	an. 1418	c	35.3(20°)
MgF_2	3.0	1253	2227	c	0.009(20°)
MgI_2	4.25		927	c	8 aq. 59.7(18°)
$Mg(NO_3)_2 \cdot 6H_2O$	1.46	95	5 aq. 330	c	43.1(18°)
$MgC_2O_4 \cdot 2H_2O$		d.		c	0.07
$MgHPO_4 \cdot 3H_2O$	2.10			c	0.3
$Mg_2P_2O_7$	2.60	1383		c	v. sl. sol.
$MgSO_4$	2.66	1185		c	
$MgSO_4 \cdot 7H_2O$	1.68	d. 70		c	26.8(25°)
MgS	2.8	> 2000		gy	hydr.
Manganese					
Mn	7.2	1244	2087	gy-pk	giv. $Mn(OH)_2 + H_2$
Mn_2O_7	1. 2.4	< − 20	exp.	r	v. sol.
MnO	5.18	1780		gy-gr	v. sl. sol.
Mn_2O_3	4.8	d. 1080		bk	v. sl. sol.
MnO_2	5.02			bk	v. sl. sol.
Mn_3O_4	4.7	1560		bk	v. sl. sol.
$Mn(OH)_2$	3.26	d.		l-pk	0.002
$Mn_2O_3 \cdot H_2O$	3.26	d.		br	v. sl. sol.
$Mn(C_2H_3O_2)_2 \cdot 4H_2O$	1.59			l-r	3
$NH_4MnPO_4 \cdot 7H_2O$				c	0.003
$MnBr_2$	4.38	698	1027	ro-r	4 aq. 58.8(20°)
$MnCO_3$	3.12	d.		ro	0.0065(25°)
$MnCl_2$	2.98	650	1190	pk	
$MnCl_2 \cdot 4H_2O$	2.01	d. 58.01		r-or	43.6(25°)
MnF_2	3.98	856	2027	ro	0.18(25°)
MnF_3	3.54			r	hydr.
MnI_2	5.01	638	827	ro	v. sol.
$Mn(NO_3)_2 \cdot 6H_2O$	1.82	d. 25.8		ro	63(25°)
$MnC_2O_4 \cdot 2\frac{1}{2}H_2O$	2.43	d. 150		pk-ro	0.03(25°)
$Mn_3(PO_4)_2 \cdot 7H_2O$				ro	sl. sol.
$Mn_2P_2O_7$	3.71			ro	sl. sol.
$MnSiO_3$	3.48	1273		r	v. sl. sol.
MnS	3.99	1615		l-ro	0.0007
MnS_2	3.46			r	d.
$MnSO_4$	3.25	700		ro	
$MnSO_4 \cdot 5H_2O$	2.11	d.		ro	39.3(25°)
Mercury					
Hg	14.19	− 38.87	356.57	sil	not sol.
Hg_2O	9.8	d. 100		bk	v. sl. sol.
HgO	11.14	d. 100	d.	y and r	0.00515(25°)
$Hg(C_2H_3O_2)_2$	3.27	d.		c	25 g./100 g. $H_2O(25°)$

Formula	Density	Melting Point °C.	Boiling Point °C.	Color	Solubility in Water
$Hg_3(AsO_4)_2$				y	sl. sol.
Hg_2Br_2	7.31		s. 345	y	$3.9 \times 10^{-6}(25°)$
$HgBr_2$	6.05	241	319	l-y	0.6(25°)
Hg_2CO_3		d. 130		y	v. sl. sol.
Hg_2Cl_2	7.15	302	383.7	c	0.0003(25°)
$HgCl_2$	5.44	277	304	c	6.89(25°), 35.1(100°)
Hg_2CrO_4		d.		r	sl. sol.
$Hg(CN)_2$	4.00	d.		c	8.5(20°)
Hg_2F_2	8.73	570		c	sol.
HgF_2	8.95	645	650	c	sol.
Hg_2I_2	7.70	d. 290	d.	y	$2 \times 10^{-8}(25°)$
HgI_2	6.27	257	354	y	0.004(17.5°)
$Hg_2(NO_3)_2 \cdot 2H_2O$	4.78	70		c	sol.
$Hg(NO_3)_2 \cdot \frac{1}{2}H_2O$	4.3	79		c	sol.
$NHg_2Br \cdot 3NH_4Br$		d. 180		c	v. sl. sol.
$Hg_6(PO_4)_2$				c	v. sl. sol.
$Hg_3(PO_4)_2$				w to y	v. sl. sol.
Hg_2S				bk	v. sl. sol.
HgS	$\alpha8.1$	s. 580		r	
	$\beta7.7$	s. 446		bk	v. sl. sol.
$Hg_2(SO_4)$	7.56	d.	d.	c	0.06(25°)
$HgSO_4$	6.47	850		c	sol.
Molybdenum					
Mo	10.2	2610	4804	gy	not sol.
$MoO_3 \cdot 2H_2O$	3.12			y	0.18(23°), 1.70(70°)
MoO_2	4.52			r	v. sl. sol.
Mo_2O_3				y to bl	v. sl. sol.
MoO_3	4.50	785	1151	y	0.107(18°), 1.705(70°)
$MoCl_2$		d.		y	v. sl. sol.
$MoCl_3$		d.		w	sol.
$MoCl_5$		194	268	bl	v. sol.
MoF_6		17	36	c	hydr.
$MoOF_4$	3.0	98	180	c	sol.
MoS_2	4.8	1185		bl	v. sl. sol.
Mo_2S_3	5.91			gy	v. sl. sol.
MoS_3		d.		r-br	sl. sol.
Neodymium					
Nd	7.0	840		gy	sol. H^+
$NdBr_3$		684	1537	pk	sol.
$NdCl_3$		760	1577	pk	sol.
NdF_3		1410	2327	pk	sl. sol.
NdI_3		771	1367	pk	sol.
Neon					
Ne		− 248.5	− 245.9	c	1.5 cc./100 cc. $H_2O(20°)$
Nickel					
Ni	8.9	1455	2800	sil	not sol.
NiO	7.45			gr	v. sl. sol.
$Ni_2O_4 \cdot 2H_2O$	3.41			gy	v. sl. sol.
$NiO_2 \cdot xH_2O$		d.		bk	v. sl. sol.
$Ni(OH)_2$	4.36			gr	0.0013
$Ni(C_2H_3O_2)_2$	1.80	d.		gr	sol.
$NiCl_2NH_4Cl \cdot 6H_2O$	1.64			gr	v. sol.
$NiSO_4 \cdot (NH_4)_2SO_4$ $\cdot 6H_2O$	1.92			gr	25(3.5°)
$Ni_3(AsO_4)_2$	4.98			y	v. sl. sol.
$NiBr_2$	4.64	963	s.	y	6 aq. 57.3(25°)
$NiCO_3$		d.		l-gr	0.0093(25°)
$2NiCO_3 \cdot 3Ni(OH)_2$ $\cdot 4H_2O$		d.		l-gr	v. sl. sol.
$Ni(CO)_4$	l. 1.31	− 25	42.4	c	0.018(9.8°)
$NiCl_2$	3.54	1001	s. 987	y	53.8(0°), 87.6(100°)

Formula	Density	Melting Point °C.	Boiling Point °C.	Color	Solubility in Water
$Ni(CN)_2 \cdot 4H_2O$		4 aq. 200		gr	sol.
NiI_2		797	s.	bl	6 aq. 59.7(20°)
$Ni(NO_3)_2 \cdot 6H_2O$	2.05	56.7		gr	v. sol.
$Ni_3(PO_4)_2 \cdot 7H_2O$				gr	v. sl. sol.
NiS	4.6	797		bk	0.00036(18°)
$NiSO_4 \cdot 7H_2O$	1.948	99		gr	25.5(15°)
Niobium					
Nb	8.4	2487	5130	gr	not sol.
Nb_2O_3	4.61	1460		c	v. sl. sol.
NbF_5	3.29	75.5	225	c	hydr.
$NbCl_5$	2.75	212	240.5	y	hydr.
Nitrogen					
N_2	l. 0.83	− 210.01	− 195.8	c	0.0019(20°)
HNO_3	l. 1.502	− 41.59	86	c	v. sol.
NO	l. 1.27	− 163.6	151.7	c	0.0056(25°)
$NO_2(N_2O_4)$	l. 1.45	− 11.2	21.15	y-br	giv. $NHO_2 + HNO_3$
N_2O	l. 1.23	− 90.82	− 88.5	c	0.121(20°)
N_2O_3	l. 1.45	− 111	2	bl	giv. HNO_2
N_2O_5		30	32.5	c	giv. HNO_3
$NH_2 \cdot NH_2$	l. 1.01	1.4	113.5	c	v. sol.
$N_2H_4H_2O$	l. 1.03	− 40	118.5	c	v. sol.
$N_2H_4 \cdot 2HNO_3$		104		c	v. sol.
$N_2H_4 \cdot HCl$		92.6		c	sol.
$N_2H_4 \cdot 2HCl$	1.42	198		c	sol.
$N_2H_4HClO_3$		exp. 80		c	sol.
$N_2H_4H_2SO_4$	1.37	254		c	3.0(22°)
NH_2OH	1.35	− 31.1	58	c	sol. H_2O, alcohol
$NH_2OH \cdot HCl$	1.67	157		c	sol.
$(NH_2OH)_2H_2SO_4$		170		c	sol.
N_3H		− 80	36	c	sol.
NH_2NO_2		d. 72		c	hydr.
NOF		− 132.5	− 59.9	c	giv. $HNO_2 + HF$
NCl_3	l. 1.65		71	y	hydr.
$NOCl$	l. 1.41	− 64.5	− 5.8	y-r	sl. sol.
$NOBr$		− 55.5	−2	d-br	hydr.
$NOBr_3$	l. 2.64	− 40	ca. 32	br	hydr.
NH_3I_2	l. 2.46	− 2	d. 15	d-br	v. sl. sol.
NI_3NH_3	3.5	d. > 20		d-br	v. sl. sol.
NF_3		− 208.5	− 129.1		
NO_2F	2.24	− 166.0	− 72.4		
NO_3F		− 181	− 80		
NO_2Cl	l. 1.32	− 145	− 15.3		
N_2S_5	l. 1.90	10		r	d.
N_4S_4	2.22	180	s. 135	y-r	giv. NH_3, SO_2, $H_2S_2O_4$
$N_2O_3 \cdot 2SO_3$	2.14	230	357.3	c	hydr.
NO_2SO_3H		d. 73		c	hydr.
$SO_2(NH_2)_2$		92		c	hydr.
NH_2SO_3H	2.03	d. 205		c	hydr.
$NH(SO_2NH_4)_2$	1.96	357		c	giv. $(NH_4)_2SO_4$
Osmium					
Os	22.48	2700	4400	bl	not sol.
OsO_2	7.9			bl-r	v. sl. sol.
OsO_4	4.91	40.1	130	y	5.8(15°)
$OsCl_2$				gr	sl. sol.
$OsCl_3$				br	sl. sol.
$OsCl_4$				r to y	sl. sol.
OsF_6			203		hydr.
OsF_8		34.5	47.3	c	giv. OsO_4
OsS_2				y	sl. sol.
OsS_4		d.		bl	not sol.

Formula	Density	Melting Point °C.	Boiling Point °C.	Color	Solubility in Water
Oxygen					
O_2	l. 1.13	-218.77	-182.97	l-bl	0.00434(20°), 0.00079 (90°)
O_3		-251.4	-110.51	bl	0.0026(15°)
Palladium					
Pd	12.0	1555	3560	sil	not sol.
PdO		d. 877		bk	v. sl. sol.
PdO_2		d. 200		bk	v. sl. sol.
$Pd(OH)_2$				br	v. sl. sol.
$PdBr_2$				br	v. sl. sol.
$PdCl_2$		678		d-br	sl. sol.
PdI_2		d. 350		bk	v. sl. sol.
$Pd(NO_3)_2$		d.		y	sol.
PdS		970		bk	v. sl. sol.
Pd_2S	7.3	d. 800		gr	
PdS_2		d.		br	v. sl. sol.
$PdSO_4 \cdot 2H_2O$				br	v. sol.
$(NH_4)_2PdCl_4$	2.17			y-gr	sol.
$(NH_4)_2PdCl_6$	2.42			r	sl. sol.
$Pd(CO)_2Cl_2$		1.42		y-r	d.
Phosphorus					
P_4 yellow	1.82	44.2	280	y	0.0003(15°)
P_4 red	2.35	590 (43 atm.)	s. 417	r	v. sl. sol.
P_2O_3	2.13	23.8	175.3	c	giv. H_3PO_3
P_2O_4	2.53	> 100	s. ca. 180	c	giv. H_2PO_3
$P_2O_5\alpha$	2.39	572	591	c	giv. H_3PO_4
H_3PO_3	1.65	70.1	d. 200	y	v. sol.
H_3PO_2	1.49	26.5	d.	c	v. sol.
H_3PO_4	1.83	42.35	d.	c	86(24°)
HPO_3	2.2–2.5	sub. at w. heat		c	sol.
$H_4P_2O_7$		61		c	89(23°)
PBr_3	l. 2.85	-40	172.9		hydr.
PBr_5			s. 83.8	y	hydr.
PCl_3	l. 1.57	-92	76	c	hydr.
PCl_5		160	s. 159	l-y	hydr.
P_2Cl_4		-28	180	c	hydr.
$POCl_3$	l. 1.67	1.1	105.1	c	hydr.
PH_4Cl		28 (46 atm.)		c	sol.
PF_3	3.02	-151.5	-101.2	c	hydr.
PF_5	4.49	-93.8	-84.5	c	hydr.
POF_3	3.63	-39.4	-40	c	hydr.
PH_3	l. 0.75	-133.75	-87.72	c	sl. sol.
P_2H_4	l. 1.01	< -10	57.5 (735 mm.)	c	v. sl. sol.
PI_3		61		r	hydr.
P_2I_4		124.5		r	hydr.
PH_4I			s. 61.8 (708)	c	sol.
P_2S_3		296	490	gy-y	d.
P_2S_5	2.03	276	514	gy-y	d.
P_4S_3	2.03	172.5	407.5	y	not. sol. d. by hot water
$PSBr_3$	2.85	38.0			hydr.
Platinum					
Pt	21.45	1770	4010	sil-gy	not sol.
PtO		555		v-bk	v. sl. sol.
PtO_2		430		bk	v. sl. sol.
$Pt(OH)_2$		d.		bk	v. sl. sol.
$PtBr_2$		d. 300		br	v. sl. sol.
$PtBr_4$		d. 180			0.41(20°)
$PtCl_2$	5.87	d. 581		gr-gy	v. sl. sol.

Formula	Density	Melting Point °C.	Boiling Point °C.	Color	Solubility in Water
$PtCl_4 \cdot 8H_2O$	2.43	d.		r	v. sol.
$H_2PtCl_6 \cdot H_2O$	2.43	d.		r-br	sol.
PtI_2		d. 325		bk	v. sl. sol.
PtI_4		d. 100		br-bk	sol.
PtP_2O_7	4.85	d. > 600		gr-y	v. sl. sol.
PtS	8.90	d.		bk	v. sl. sol.
PtS_2	5.27	d.		y-br	v. sl. sol.
$Pt(SO_4)_2 \cdot 4H_2O$				y	sol.
Plutonium					
Pu	19				
Pu_2O_3	10.6	ca. 2000		sil	sl. sol.
PuO_2	11	2190		y	sl. sol.
$Pu(OH)_3$				bl	sl. sol.
$PuCl_3$	5.6	760		bl	sol.
$PuBr_3$		681		bl-gr	sol.
PuF_4	7.5			br	sl. sol.
$PuO_2(NO_3)_2 \cdot 6H_2O$	2.8			or	sol.
Polonium					
Po	9.4	252	970	gy	
Potassium					
K	0.86	63.5	779	sil	giv. KOH + H_2
K_2O	2.32			gy	giv. KOH
KO_2		> 280		y	giv. KOH + H_2O_2 + O_2
KH	0.80	d.		c	giv. KOH + H_2
KOH	2.04	410	1327	c	2 aq. 53(22°), 1 aq. 66 (110°)
$KC_2H_3O_2$	1.8	292		c	255 g./100 g. H_2O(20°)
$K_2Al_2O_4 \cdot 3H_2O$				c	sol.
$KSbO_3$				c	sl. sol.
$KSbOC_4H_4O_6 \cdot \frac{1}{2}H_2O$	2.61			c	7.85(25°)
K_2AsO_4				c	sol.
KH_2AsO_4	2.87	288		c	15.9(6°)
$KAsO_2$				c	sol.
$KAuCl_4$		357		y	38.2(20°)
$K_2B_4O_7 \cdot 5H_2O$		5 aq. red heat		c	sol. hydr. sl.
$KBrO_3$	3.27	d. 370		c	3.1(0°), 11.7(40°)
KBr	2.75	742	1380	c	39.4(20°), 51.2(100°)
K_2PtBr_6	4.66	d. > 400			2.0(20°)
K_2CO_3	2.29	897		c	2 aq. 53(25°)
$KHCO_3$	2.17	d.		c	18.3(0°), 28.1(30°)
KCl	1.99	770	1407	c	22.0(0°), 25.8(25°)
$KClO$		d.		c	v. sol.
$KClO_3$	2.32	368		c	3.2(0°), 9.2(30°)
$KClO_4$	2.52	d. 400		c	0.7(0°), 15.8(100°)
K_2PtCl_6	3.50	d. 250		y	0.5(0°), 5(100°)
K_2CrO_4	2.73	975		y	38.6(20°)
$K_2Cr_2O_7$	2.69	398		r	4.7(0°), 50.5(100°)
$K_3Co(NO_2)_6 \cdot \frac{3}{2}H_2O$		d. 200		y	0.09(0°)
KCN	1.52	623		c	v. sol.
$KCNO$	2.05			c	sol.
$KAg(CN)_2$				c	12.5
$K_3Fe(CN)_6$	1.89			r	29.0(15.6°)
$K_4Fe(CN)_6 \cdot 3H_2O$	1.85	3 aq. 70		y	19.7(20°), 39(75°)
KF	2.48	857	1500	c	2 aq. 49(21°)
KBF_4	2.50	d. 500		c	sol.
$3KF \cdot AlF_3$		1035		c	sol.
K_2SiF_6	2.66			c	0.12(17.5°), 0.95(100°)
KI	3.12	682	1324	c	59.0(20°)
KI_3	3.50	45	d. 225	br	sol.
KIO_3	3.89	560		c	7.5(20°)
KIO_4	3.62	582		c	0.66(13°)

Formula	Density	Melting Point °C.	Boiling Point °C.	Color	Solubility in Water
K_2MnO_4		d. 190		d-gr	sol.
$KMnO_4$	2.70	d. < 240		pu	7.1(25°), 20(65°)
K_2MoO_4		919		c	v. sol.
KNO_2	1.91	297	d. 350	c	75.8(25°)
KNO_3	2.11	338	d. 400	c	24.9(20°), 71(100°)
KNH_2		338		c	hydr.
$K_2C_2O_4 \cdot H_2O$	2.13			c	27.4(25°)
K_3PO_4		1340		c	sl. sol.
K_2HPO_4		d.		c	v. sol.
KH_2PO_4	2.34	96	d. > 200	c	25 g./100 g. $H_2O(7°)$
$K_4P_2O_7$	2.33	1090		c	sol.
K_2HPO_3		d.		c	v. sol.
K_2SiO_3		976		c	sol.
K_2SeO_4	3.07			c	52.6(18°)
K_2S	1.80	471		br	sol. hydr.
K_2S_5		206		y	v. sol.
$K_2SO_3 \cdot 2H_2O$		d.		c	v. sol.
$KHSO_4$	2.35	210		c	v. sol.
K_2SO_4	2.66	1074		c	10.75(25°), 19.4(100°)
$K_2S_2O_7$	2.28	> 300		c	sol.
$K_2S_2O_8$		d. < 100		c	1.6(0°), 5.0(20°)
$KCNS$	1.89	179		c	v. sol.
$K_2C_4K_2O_6 \cdot \frac{1}{2}H_2O$	1.98			c	59(17°)
$K_2WO_4 \cdot 2H_2O$	3.12	an. 927		c	sol.
$KReO_4$	4.89	350		c	1.2(20°)
Praseodymium					
Pr	6.5	932		gy	evol. H_2
Pr_2O_3	6.87			y-gr	sl. sol.
$PrCl_3$	4.02	776	1597	gr	51(13°)
Pr_2S_3	5.04			br	d.
$Pr_2(SO_4)_3$	3.72			gr	8 aq. 12.4(18°)
$PrBr_3$		693	1547	gy	sol.
PrF_3		1370	2377	gy	sl. sol.
PrI_3		733	1377	gy	sol.
Radium					
Ra	5	960	1140	sil	evol. H_2
$RaBr_2$	5.79	927	1677	y	sol.
$RaCl_2$	4.91	1027	1727	c	sol.
Radon					
Rn		− 71	− 6.2		
Rhenium					
Re		3147		sil	not sol.
Re_2O_7	8.2	296	362.4	y	sol.
ReF_6		18.8	48		hydr.
ReF_4		124.5	797		hydr.
ReO_3		160			sol.
Rhodium					
Rh	12.5	1960	3960	gy-w	not sol.
RhO				gy	v. sl. sol.
Rh_2O_3				gy	v. sl. sol.
RhO_2				br	v. sl. sol.
$Rh(OH)_3$		d.		bk	v. sl. sol.
$RhCl_3$		d. 475		r	sol. if hydrated
$Rh(NO_3)_2 \cdot 2H_2O$				r	sol.
$Rh_2(SO_4)_3 \cdot 12H_2O$				l-y	v. sol.
RhS		d.		bl	v. sl. sol.
Rubidium					
Rb	1.53	39.0	679	sil	giv. RbOH + h.
Rb_2O	3.72	d. 400		c	giv. RbOH
Rb_2O_2	3.65	600		y	giv. RbOH + H_2O_2
RbO_2	3.05	280		y	giv. RbOH + H_2O_2 + O_2

Formula	Density	Melting Point °C.	Boiling Point °C.	Color	Solubility in Water
RbOH	3.20	300		c	36.4(30°)
RbBr	3.35	677	1352	c	51.2(16°)
Rb₂CO₃		837		c	v. sol.
RbCl	2.76	717	1381	c	47.7(20°)
RbF		833	1410	c	sol.
RbI	3.55	638	1304	c	60(17°)
RbNO₃	3.11	305		c	34.8(20°)
Rb₂S	2.91			c	v. sol.
Rb₂SO₄	3.61	1060		c	32.5(20°)
Ruthenium					
Ru	12.2	2506	4111	gy	not sol.
Ru₂O₃				bl-bk	v. sl. sol.
RuO₂	7.2			v	v. sl. sol.
RuO₄	5.77	25.5	100.8 183 mm.	y	sl. sol.
Ru(OH)₃				bk	v. sl. sol.
RuCl₃				br	sol.
RuS₂				bk	v. sl. sol.
RuSi	5.4			w	v. sl. sol.
Samerium					
Sm	6.93	1350		gy	sol. H⁺
Sm₂O₃	7.43			y	sl. sol.
SmBr₃·6H₂O	2.97	an. 644		y	sol.
SmCl₃	4.46	678		gn	sol.
SmF₃		1397	2327	y	sl. sol.
SmI₃		820		y	sol.
Scandium					
Sc	2.5	1397	2730	sil	evol. H₂
Sc₂O₃	3.86			c	v. sl. sol.
ScCl₃		967	967	c	v. sl. sol.
Sc(NO₃)₃		150		c	sol.
Sc₂(SO₄)₃	2.58			c	5 aq. 28.5(25°)
ScF₃		1223	1527	c	sl. sol.
ScI₃		945	909	c	sol.
ScBr₃	3.91	960	929	c	sol.
Selenium					
Se	4.5–4.8	217.4	684.8	gy	not sol.
H₂SeO₃	3.00	d.		c	62.5(20°)
H₂SeO₄	2.95	60		c	v. sol.
SeO₂	3.95	340	s. 322	c	giv. H₂SeO₃
SeF₄		− 13.2	93	c	hydr.
SeF₆		s. − 46.6	− 34.6 p	c	hydr. slow.
SeCl₄		s. 196		c	hydr.
Silicon					
Si	2.4	1410	2477	gy	not sol.
H₂SiO₃	2.2			c	sl. sol.
H₄SiO₄	1.57			c	sl. sol.
SiO₂, quartz	2.65	cristobalite 1728		c	v. sl. sol.
SiO₂, glass	2.20		2230	c	v. sl. sol.
SiBr₄	2.81	5	153	c	hydr.
SiC	3.17	> 2700	s. 2210 diss.		v. sl. sol.
SiCl₄	l. 1.48	− 67.6	57	c	hydr.
SiF₄		− 90.3	s. − 95.5		hydr.
SiH₄	l. 0.68	− 185	− 111.4	c	sl. sol.
Si₂H₆	l. 0.69	− 132.5	− 14.3	c	sl. sol.
Si₃H₈	l. 0.725	− 117	53	c	sl. sol.
Si₄H₁₀	l. 0.79	− 84.3	108.4	c	sl. sol.
SiI₄		120.5	290	c	hydr.
Silver					
Ag	10.5	960.8	2193	sil	not sol.

Formula	Density	Melting Point °C.	Boiling Point °C.	Color	Solubility in Water
Ag_2O	7.14	d. 300		br	0.00215(20°)
Ag_2O_2	7.44	d. > 100		bk	v. sl. sol.
$AgC_2H_3O_2$	3.26	d.		gr	1.021(20°), 2.52(80°)
Ag_3AsO_3		d. 150		y	0.00115(20°)
Ag_3AsO_4	6.66			d-r	0.00085(20°)
$AgBr$	6.47	430	1533	l-y	8.4×10^{-6}
$AgBrO_3$	5.21	d.		c	0.159(20°)
Ag_2CO_3	6.08	d. 218		c	0.002
$AgClO_3$	4.43	230	d. 270	c	sol.
$AgClO_4$	2.81	d. 486		c	84(25°)
$AgCl$	5.56	455	1557	c	0.00015(20°)
Ag_2CrO_4				d-r	0.0025(18°)
$Ag_2Cr_2O_7$		d.		r	0.0083(15°)
$AgCN$	3.95	350		c	0.00002(25°)
$AgCNO$	4.00	d.		c	0.003(18°)
$Ag_3Fe(CN)_6$				or	0.00007(20°)
$Ag_4Fe(CN)_6 \cdot H_2O$				y	v. sl. sol.
$AgNO_2$	4.45	d. 140		c	0.4(25°)
AgF	5.85	435		y	4 aq. 57.5(15°)
AgI	5.67	557	1506	y	$2.5 \times 10^{-7}(25°)$
$AgIO_3$	5.52	> 200		c	0.0038(18°)
AgN_3		exp. 251.5		bk	v. sl. sol.
$AgNO_3$	4.35	209	d. 440	c	68.3(20°)
$Ag_2C_2O_4$	5.03	exp. 140		c	0.004(25°)
$AgMnO_4$		d.		bl-bk	1.5(25°)
Ag_2P_3	4.63	d.		gy	v. sl. sol.
$AgPO_3$	6.37	209			v. sl. sol.
Ag_3PO_4	6.37	849		l-y	0.0006(25°)
$Ag_4P_2O_7$	5.31	585		c	v. sl. sol.
Ag_2S	7.32	842		bk	v. sl. sol.
Ag_2SO_3		d. 100		c	sl. sol.
Ag_2SO_4	5.45	660		c	0.8(25°)
$AgCNS$				c	0.00002(25°)
Sodium					
Na	0.97	97.5	914	sil	giv. NaOH & H_2
Na_2O	2.27			gy	giv. NaOH
Na_2O_2		d. 30		y-w	giv. NaOH & HO_2^-
$NaOH$	2.13	322	1378	c	1 aq. 51.7(25°)
$NaC_2H_3O_2$	1.53	324		c	46 g./100 g. H_2O(20°)
$NaAlO_2$		1650		c	sol.
$NaSb(OH)_6$				c	0.03(12°)
$Na_3AsO_4 \cdot 12H_2O$	1.76	86.3		c	10.4(17°)
$Na_2HAsO_4 \cdot 12H_2O$	1.72	28		c	27(21°)
Na_2HAsO_3	1.87			c	v. sol.
$NaBO_2$		966	> 1400	c	sol.
$Na_2B_4O_7 \cdot 10H_2O$	1.73	75	d. 200	c	1.6(10°), 5 aq. 34(100°)
$NaBr$	3.20	747	1390	c	2 aq. 47.5(20°)
$NaBrO_3$	3.34	381		c	27.7(20°)
Na_2CO_3	2.53	854		c	
$Na_2CO_3 \cdot H_2O$	1.55			c	31(100°)
$Na_2CO_3 \cdot 10H_2O$	1.46			c	23.0(25°)
$NaHCO_3$	2.20			c	8.8(20°)
$NaClO_3$	2.49	255		c	50(20°)
$NaClO_4$		482		c	sol.
$NaCl$	2.16	800	1465	c	26.4(20°), 28.2(100°)
$NaClO \cdot 2.5H_2O$		57.5		c	v. sol.
$Na_2PtCl_4 \cdot 4H_2O$		d. 100		r	sol.
$Na_2PtCl_6 \cdot 6H_2O$	2.50			r	sol.
$Na_2CrO_4 \cdot 10H_2O$	1.48			y	33.4(10°)
$Na_2Cr_2O_7 \cdot 2H_2O$	2.52	320		r	64.3(20°)
$NaCN$		562	1496	c	v. sol.

Formula	Density	Melting Point °C.	Boiling Point °C.	Color	Solubility in Water
NaCu(CN)$_2$	1.01	d. 100		c	sol.
Na$_3$Fe(CN)$_6$H$_2$O				r	sol.
Na$_4$Fe(CN)$_6$·10H$_2$O	1.46			y	20.07(25°)
Na$_2$Fe(CN)$_5$NO·2H$_2$O	1.72			r	v. sol.
Na$_2$CbO$_3$	4.19			l-y	sol.
NaF	2.79	995	1704	c	4.3(18°)
3NaF·AlF$_3$	2.90	1000		c	sol.
Na$_2$SiF$_6$	2.68			c	0.65(17.5°), 2.4(100°)
NaCHO$_2$	1.92	253		c	46.9(21°)
NaH	0.92			c	giv. NaOH + H$_2$
NaI	3.67	662	1300	c	2 aq. 64.8(25°)
NaIO$_3$	4.27	d.		c	2.4(0°), 25.3(100°)
Na$_2$MnO$_4$·10H$_2$O		d.		gr	v. sol.
Na$_2$MoO$_4$		687		c	2 aq. 39.4(20°)
NaNH$_2$		210		c	hydr.
NaNO$_2$	2.17	271	d. 320	c	44.9(15°)
NaNO$_3$	2.26	310		c	46.8(20°)
Na$_2$C$_2$O$_4$				c	3.1(15°), 4.3(50°)
NaH$_2$PO$_2$·H$_2$O				c	sol.
Na$_2$HPO$_3$·5H$_2$O				c	sol.
NaPO$_3$	2.48	988		c	sl. sol.
NaH$_2$PO$_4$·H$_2$O	2.07	d. 190		c	2 aq. 48(25°)
Na$_2$HPO$_4$·12H$_2$O	1.52	34.6		c	11(25°)
Na$_3$PO$_4$·12H$_2$O	1.62	an. 1340		c	v. sol.
Na$_4$P$_2$O$_7$·10H$_2$O	1.82	an. 970		c	3.1(0°), 23.1(80°)
NaKCO$_3$·6H$_2$O	1.63	6 aq. 100		c	v. sol.
Na$_2$SeO$_4$	3.10			c	10 aq. 30.3(20°)
Na$_2$SiO$_3$		1088		c	v. sol.
Na$_2$Si$_4$O$_9$				c	v. sol.
Na$_2$Sn(OH)$_6$				c	37(20°)
Na$_2$S	1.85	978		y	9 aq. 16.2(22°)
Na$_2$S$_5$		251.8		y	v. sol.
Na$_2$SO$_3$	2.63			c	7 aq. 20.1(18°)
Na$_2$S$_2$O$_3$·5H$_2$O	1.68	d. 48.0		c	41.2(20°), 2 aq. 73(100°)
NaHSO$_4$	2.74	> 315		c	v. sol.
Na$_2$SO$_4$	2.69	884		c	29.9(100°)
Na$_2$SO$_4$·10H$_2$O	1.46	d. 32.4		c	16.1(20°)
NaCNS		323		c	v. sol.
Na$_2$C$_4$H$_4$O$_6$·2H$_2$O	1.82			c	v. sol.
Na$_3$VO$_4$		ca. 866		c	sol.
Na$_2$WO$_4$	4.18	702		c	2 aq. 42.2(20°)
NaMnO$_4$·3H$_2$O	2.46	d. 170		pu	v. sol.
NaReO$_4$		300		c	20(20°)
Strontium					
Sr	2.6	771	1384	sil	giv. Sr(OH)$_2$ + H$_2$
SrO	4.7			gy-w	giv. Sr(OH)$_2$
Sr(OH)$_2$	3.62			c	8 aq. 0.4(0°), 21.8(100°)
SrBr$_2$	4.22	653	1877	c	
SrBr$_2$·6H$_2$O	2.36	d. 20		c	50.0(20°)
SrCO$_3$	3.70	1497 (60 atm.)		c	0.001(18°)
SrCl$_2$	3.05	872	2027	c	
SrCl$_2$·6H$_2$O	1.93	d. 61		c	35.0(20°), 45.4(60°)
Sr(ClO$_3$)$_2$	3.15	d. 120		c	63.6(18°)
SrCrO$_4$	3.89			y	0.11(15°)
SrF$_2$	2.44	1400	2427	c	0.0017(18°)
SrI$_2$	4.54	507		c	
SrI$_2$·6H$_2$O	4.41			c	64.2(20°)
Sr(NO$_3$)$_2$	2.99	570		c	
Sr(NO$_2$)$_2$·4H$_2$O	2.2			c	41.5(20°)
SrC$_2$O$_4$·H$_2$O		d.		c	0.006(20°)

Formula	Density	Melting Point °C.	Boiling Point °C.	Color	Solubility in Water
SrHPO₄	3.54			c	v. sl. sol.
SrS	3.70	> 2000		c	sol. hydr.
SrSO₃		d.		c	0.003(17°)
SrSO₄	3.96	d. 1580		c	0.01(20°)
SrSiO₃	3.65	1580		c	v. sl. sol.
Sulfur					
S(M)	1.96	119.0	444.6	y	not sol.
S(R)	2.07	112.8	444.6	y	not sol.
SO₂	l. 1.43	− 75.46	− 10	c	10.0(20°), 4.5(50°)
SO₃, α	l. 1.92	16.83	43.3	c	g. H₂SO₄
H₂SO₄	l. 1.83	10.38		c	v. sol.
H₂SO₄·H₂O	l. 1.84	8.62	290	c	v. sol.
H₂SO₄·2H₂O	l. 1.65	− 38.9	167	c	v. sol.
H₂S₂O₇	l. 1.9	35.0	d.	c	g. H₂SO₄
SOBr₂	l. 2.68	− 52	138	or-r	giv. SO₂ + HBr
SOClBr	l. 2.31		115 d.	y	d.
SCl₄		− 30		y-br	d
S₂Cl₂	l. 1.67	− 80	138	y-r	giv. HCl + S + H₂S₂O₃ slowly
SOCl₂	l. 1.63	− 104.5	75.7	c	giv. SO₂ + HCl
SO₂Cl₂	l. 1.66	− 46	69.1	c	sl. sol. 0°, d. by hot H₂O
SO₃SO₂Cl₂	l. 1.84	− 37.5	153	c	giv. H₂SO₄ + HCl slowly
S₂O₃Cl₄				w	d.
SF₆	l. 1.91	− 50.7 (P)	− 63.5	c	sl. sol. hot d.
SOF₂	l. 2.93	− 110	− 43.85	c	giv. SO₂ + HF
SO₂F₂		− 120(65 mm.)	− 52	c	10 vol./100 vol. H₂O(9°)
SF₄		− 124	− 40	c	hydr. slow
S₂F₁₀		− 92	29.1	c	hydr. slow
Tantalum					
Ta	16.6	2997	6000	gy	not sol.
Ta₂O₅	8.73	1890		c	v. sl. sol.
TaBr₅	4.67	267	345	y	sol. hydr.
TaCl₅	3.68	234	234	y	sol. hydr.
TaF₅	4.74	96.8	229	c	sol. hydr.
TaI₅		367	397	c	hydr.
Tellurium					
Te, α	6.24	450	1087	gy	not sol.
H₂TeO₃	3.05	d. 40		c	sl. sol.
H₆TeO₆	3.05			c	30(18°)
TeO₂	5.89		s. 450	y	giv. H₂TeO₃
TeO₃	5.08	d.		c	giv. H₆TeO₆
TeBr₂		ca. 280	339	gy	hydr.
TeCl₂	7.05	175	324	bk	hydr. to TeO
TeCl₄		224.1	388	w	hydr.
TeF₆		− 37.7	s. − 38.6	c	hydr.
TeI₂				bk	hydr. to TeO
TeI₄	8.40	259		d-br	hydr. slowly
Terbium					
Tb	8.33	ca. 1100		gy	sol. H⁺
TbBr₃		827	1487	c	sol.
TbCl₃	4.35	588	1517	c	sol.
TbF₃		1367	2377	c	sl. sol.
TbI₃		952	1327	c	sol.
Thallium					
Tl	11.85	303.6	1457	bl-w	not sol.
Tl₂O		300	500	y	giv. TlOH
Tl₂O₃	br. 9.65			br	
	bk. 10.19	717		bk	v. sl. sol.
TlOH			139 diss.	y	343 g./liter (18.5°)
Tl(OH)₃		> 340		br	v. sl. sol.
TlBr	7.56	460	815	l-y	0.05(20°)

Formula	Density	Melting Point °C.	Boiling Point °C.	Color	Solubility in Water
$TlBrO_3$				c	0.35(20°)
Tl_2CO_2	7.11	273		c	3.8(15°), 20(100°)
$TlCl$	7.00	427	807	c	0.34(20°), 1.9(90°)
$TlClO_4$	4.89	501		c	17(30°)
TlF		327	655	c	44(15°)
TlI	7.09	440	824	y	0.0064(20°), 0.1(100°)
TlN_3		334		y	v. sl. sol.
$TlNO_3$	5.55	207	433	c	3.8(0°), 23.3(50°)
$(NH_4)_3TlCl_6 \cdot 2H_2O$	2.39			c	sol.
Tl_3PO_4	6.89			c	0.5(15°)
$Tl_4P_2O_7$	6.79	> 120		c	sol.
Tl_2S	8.0	449		bl-bk	0.02(20°)
Tl_2SO_4	6.77	632		c	4.64(20°), 15.6(100°)
Tl_2Se		398		gy	sl. sol.
Thorium					
Th	11.2	1845	4230	gy	evol. H_2
ThO_2	9.69	> 2800		c	v. sl. sol.
$Th(OH)_4$		d.		c	v. sl. sol.
$ThBr_4$	5.67	679	857	c	v. sol.
$ThCl_4$	4.59	765	922	c	v. sol.
$Th_3(PO_3)_4$	4.08			c	sl. sol.
ThS_2	6.8	d.		y	v. sl. sol.
$Th(SO_4)_2 \cdot 9H_2O$	2.77	d. 406		c	1.36(20°)
$ThO_2 \cdot SiO_2$	5.3			c	v. sl. sol.
$K_2ThF_6 \cdot H_2O$				c	$6 \times 10^{-5}(25°)$
Thulium					
Tm	9.35	ca. 1600		gy	sol. H^+
$TmCl_3$		821	1487	c	sol.
TmF_2		1337	2227	c	sl. sol.
Tin					
Sn	w. 7.31	231.9	2337	w	not sol.
	g. 5.75				
$H_2Sn(OH)_6$				c	v. sl. sol.
$H_2SnCl_6 \cdot 6H_2O$	1.93			c	sol.
SnO	6.95			bk	
				d-gr	v. sl. sol.
SnO_2	7.0	1127		gy-w	v. sl. sol.
$Sn(OH_2)$		d. 160		w	$1.6 \times 10^{-1}(25°)$
$SnBr_2$	5.12	232	638	y	sol.
$SnBr_4$	l. 3.34	30.0	205	c	hydr.
$SnCl_2$		246.8	623	c	
$SnCl_2 \cdot 2H_2O$	2.7	d. 37.7	d.	c	70.1(25°)
$SnCl_4$	l. 2.23	− 33.2	113	c	sol. hydr.
SnI_2	5.21	320	718	r	0.77(20°), 3.9(100°)
SnI_4	4.46	144.5	344	r-y	hydr.
SnS	5.08	880	1230	br	v. sl. sol.
SnS_2	4.5			y	v. sl. sol.
$SnSO_4$		d. 360		c	16(20°)
SnH_4		− 150	− 51.8	c	d.
$Sn(SO_4)_2 \cdot 2H_2O$				c	sol. hydr.
Titanium					
Ti	4.5	1812	3130	gy	not sol.
TiC				bl-bk	giv. $Ti(OH)_2$
Ti_2O_3	4.6	2130		vi	v. sl. sol.
TiO_2 (Rutile)	4.26	1835		bl	v. sl. sol.
$TiO_2 \cdot 2H_2O$		d.		w	v. sl. sol.
$TiBr_4$		38.2	230	y	sol. hydr.
$TiCl_2$		677	1477	bk	sol.
$TiCl_3$		d. 440		v	sol.
$TiCl_4$	1.7	− 23	136	l-y	sol. hydr.
TiN	5.18	2930		br-r	not sol.

Formula	Density	Melting Point °C.	Boiling Point °C.	Color	Solubility in Water
TiS_2				gr	hydr. slowly
Tungsten					
W	19.3	3380	5630	gy-bk	not sol.
H_2WO_4	5.5			y	v. sl. sol.
WO_2	12.11			br	v. sl. sol.
WO_3	7.16	1470		y	v. sl. sol.
WC	15.7	2870	6000	gy	not sol.
W_2C	16.06	2877	6000	gr	not sol.
WCl_2				gy	sol. hydr.
WCl_4	4.62	d.		gy	sol. hydr. to WO_2
WCl_5	3.87	244	275.6	bk	sol.
WCl_6	3.52	284	337	d-bl	hydr. to WO_3
WBr_5		276	333	d-br	sol.
WF_6		2.5	17.3	c	hydr.
WI_2	6.9			br	hydr.
WI_4	5.2			bk	sol. hydr. to WO_2
WS_2	7.5	d. 1250		gy	not sol.
Uranium					
U	18.7	1132	3500	w	evol. H_2
UO_2	10.9	2176		bk	v. sl. sol.
UO_3	7.29			y	v. sl. sol.
U_3O_8	7.31			gr	v. sl. sol.
UBr_4	4.84			bk	v. sol.
UC_2	11.3	2260	4100	gy	giv. UO_2 + hyd-carbn.
UCl_4	4.72			gr	sol.
UF_6	4.68	69.2 (2 atm.)	s. 56	y	sol. hydr.
UI_4	5.6	s. 500		bk	sol.
$UO_2(IO_3)_2$	5.2	d. 250		y	0.12(18°)
US_2		> 1100		gy	v. sl. sol.
$U(SO_4)_2 \cdot 4H_2O$		4 aq., 300		gr	9.8(24°)
$UO_2(C_2H_3O_2)_2 \cdot 2H_2O$	2.89	d. 275		y	sol.
$UO_2(NO_3)_2 \cdot 6H_2O$	2.74	60	118	y	57(25°)
$UO_2(HPO_4) \cdot 4H_2O$				y	not sol.
UO_2S		d.		br	sl. sol.
$UO_2SO_4 \cdot 3H_2O$	3.28	d. 100		y	14.8(15.5°)
Vanadium					
V	5.96	1730	3530	l-gy	not sol.
HVO_3				y	sl. sol.
$H_4V_2O_7$				br	sl. sol.
VO	5.76			gr	v. sl. sol.
VO_2	4.40	1542		d-gr	v. sl. sol.
V_2O_3	4.87	1977		bk	v. sl. sol.
V_2O_5	3.56	670		or & y	giv. HVO_3
VC	5.4	2830	5900	gy	not sol.
VCl_2	3.23	727	1377	gr	sol.
VCl_3	3.00	d.	d.	pk	sol.
VCl_4	l. 1.82	− 26	152	r	sol. giv. $VOCl_2$
VF_5	2.18	102	111.2	y	hydr.
VN	5.63	2027		gr-br	not sol.
V_2S_3	4.7			bk	v. sl. sol.
V_2S_5	3.000			bk	v. sl. sol.
$VOCl_3$	1.82	− 79	127	y	hydr.
V_2Si	5.48			w	not sol.
Xenon					
Xe	s. 2.7	− 111.9	− 108.1	c	21.8 cc./100 cc. $H_2O(0°)$
Ytterbium					
Yb	7.01	ca. 1800			evol. H_2
Yb_2O_3	9.17			c	v. sl. sol.
$YbCl_3 \cdot 6H_2O$	2.57			gr	v. sol.
$Yb_2(SO_4)_3$	3.79			c	8 aq. 30.7(0°), 4.5(100°)
$Yb_2(C_2O_4)_3 \cdot 10H_2O$				c	0.000033(25°)

Formula	Density	Melting Point °C.	Boiling Point °C.	Color	Solubility in Water
YbF₃		1377	2377	c	sl. sol.
Yttrium					
Y	5.57	1475	3230	gy-bl	evol. H₂
Y₂O₃	4.84	2410		c	v. sl. sol.
Y(OH)₃		d.		y	v. sl. sol.
YCl₃·H₂O		an. 700	1507	c	6 aq. 43(25°)
Y(NO₃)₃·6H₂O	2.68			c	57.4(22.5°)
Y₂(SO₄)₃·8H₂O	2.56			c	aq. 6.7(25°)
Zinc					
Zn	7.14	419.5	907	gy	not sol.
ZnO	5.47	1975		w	0.0042(18°)
Zn(OH)₂	3.05	d. 125		c	0.00042
Zn(C₂H₃O₂)₂·2H₂O	1.73	237		c	23.7(20°)
ZnBr₂	4.22	394	697	c	82.5(25°)
ZnClO₃	4.44	d. 300		c	0.001(25°)
ZnCl₂	2.91	275	756	c	78.6(20°)
ZnCl₂·2NH₃		210.8	d. 271	c	giv. Zn(NH₃)₄⁺⁺
Zn(ClO₄)₂·6H₂O	2.15	60		c	v. sol.
Zn(CN)₂		d. 800		c	sol.
Zn₂Fe(CN)₆·3H₂O			d.	c	v. sl. sol.
ZnF₂	4.84	872	1502	c	1.6(18°)
ZnI₂	4.66	446	624	c	83.1(22°)
Zn(IO₃)₂	4.98	d.		c	0.87 in "cold" H₂O
Zn(NO₃)₂·6H₂O	2.06	36.4		c	55.9(25°)
ZnC₂O₄·2H₂O	2.56	d. 100		c	0.0007(25°)
Zn₃P₂	4.55	> 420	1100	gy	not sol. giv. PH₃ with H⁺
Zn₃(PO₄)₂	4.0	900		c	v. sl. sol.
Zn₂P₂O₇				c	v. sl. sol.
ZnS	4.08	1645	s. 1185	c	0.0007(18°)
ZnSO₄	3.74	d. 740		c	
ZnSO₄·7H₂O	1.97		d. 280	c	36.7(25°)
ZnO·SiO₂	3.52	1437		c	v. sl. sol.
ZnTe	5.54	1238.5		r	v. sl. sol.
Zirconium					
Zr	6.4	1852	3580	gy	not sol.
ZrO₂	5.49	2677		w	v. sl. sol.
Zr(OH)₄	3.25	2 aq. 550		w	0.02
ZrCl₄		437 P	331	c	sol. hydr.
ZrF₄	4.43	sub		c	1.3
Zr(NH₄)₃F₇				c	sl. sol.
Zr(NO₃)₄·5H₂O		d. 100		c	sol.
Zr(SO₄)₂·4H₂O				c	v. sol.
ZrO₂SiO₂	4.5	2500		c	v. sl. sol.

Index

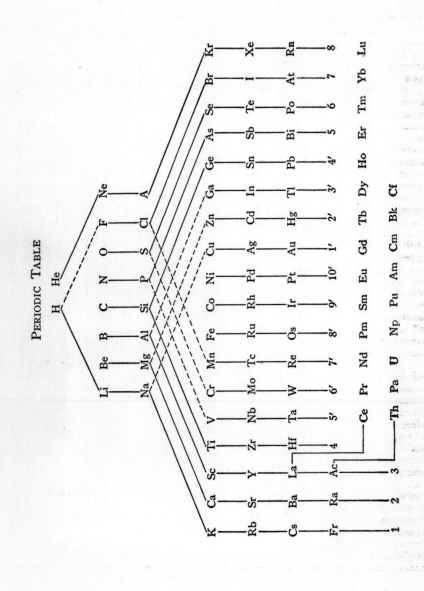

PERIODIC TABLE